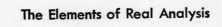

The Elements of Real Analysis

The Elements
of Real Analysis

Robert G. Bartle

Department of Mathematics, University of Illinois

John Wiley & Sons, Inc., New York · London · Sydney

Library of Congress Catalog Card Number: 64–20061
Printed in the United States of America

To my parents

Preface

There was a time when an undergraduate student of mathematics was expected to develop technique in solving problems that involved considerable computation; however, he was not expected to master theoretical subtleties such as uniform convergence or uniform continuity. The student was expected to be able to use the Implicit Function Theorem, but was not expected to know its hypotheses. The situation has changed. Now it is generally agreed that it is important for all students — whether future mathematicians, physicists, engineers, or economists — to grasp the basic theoretical nature of the subject. For, having done so, they will understand both the power and the limitation of the general theory and they will be better equipped to devise specific techniques to attack particular problems as they arise.

This text has developed from my experience in teaching courses in elementary real analysis at the University of Illinois since 1955. My audience has ranged from well-prepared freshman students to graduate students; the majority in these classes are usually not mathematics majors. Generally they have taken at least the equivalent of three semesters of non-rigorous calculus, including multiple integrals, vector calculus, line integrals, infinite series, and the like.

It would be desirable to have the students take a semester either in linear or modern algebra before this analysis course, for such a background facilitates the study of rigorous analysis. However, since the students I encounter do not all have this background, I purposely delay the study of analysis and first explore the notion of an ordered field to provide practice in giving proofs. Thus the first six sections of this text are mostly preparatory in nature; they can be covered in about three weeks in a normal class and more rapidly in a well-prepared one.

It has been my experience that it is possible to discuss Sections 1–13, 15–17.1, 19, and most of 22 in one semester. The entire text provides about the right amount of material for two semesters at this level. Most of the topics generally associated with courses in "advanced calculus" are treated here in a reasonably sophisticated way. The main exception is line and surface integrals and the various formulations of Stokes's Theorem. This topic is not discussed, since an intuitive and informal development is properly a part of calculus, and a rigorous treatment is advanced in nature.

The arrangement of this text is indicated by the adjoining diagram. A solid line in this diagram indicates the dependence on the preceding section; a dotted line indicates that there is a dependence on one or two results in the preceding section. All definitions, theorems, corollaries,

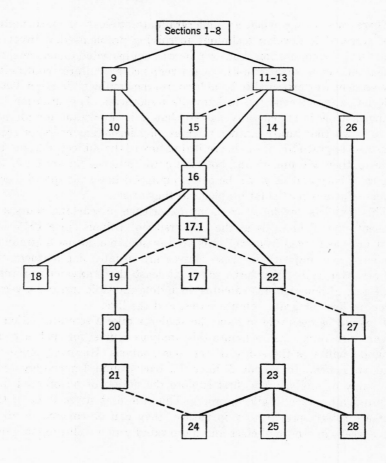

and lemmas are numbered consecutively and according to the section number. Similarly, the exercises and projects are labeled according to section number. I have given names to some of the more important theorems whenever I could think of one I felt was reasonably descriptive. The proofs, in order to be set off from the rest of the text, start with the heading PROOF and end with Q.E.D. This deviates somewhat from the classical tradition, since the conclusion is not always stated explicitly at the end of the proof.

In writing this text I have drawn from my classroom experience and have been influenced by many sources which I cannot enumerate. I have benefited by many conversations with students and colleagues and I am indebted to all of them. In particular, I am deeply grateful to Professors K.W. Anderson, W. G. Bade, and A. L. Peressini for their critical reading of this text in its various manuscript forms; I valued their comments even when I chose to disregard them. I have enjoyed unusually good secretarial help and am very grateful to Jelane Huber and Barbara Beadles, who typed the earlier version, and to Mari Hollos and Julie Sutter, who typed the later versions of the manuscript. Finally, I am appreciative of the staff at John Wiley and Sons for their assistance and cooperation.

ROBERT G. BARTLE

Urbana, Illinois
May 5, 1964

Chapter Summaries

The Elements of Real Analysis

Introduction: A Glimpse at Set Theory

The idea of a set is basic to all of mathematics, and all mathematical objects and constructions ultimately go back to set theory. In view of the fundamental importance of set theory, we shall present here a brief resumé of the set-theoretic notions that will be used frequently in this text. However, since the aim of this book is to present the *elements* (rather than the *foundations*) of real analysis, we adopt a rather pragmatic and naïve point of view. We shall be content with an informal discussion and shall regard the word "set" as understood and synonymous with the words "class," "collection," "aggregate," and "ensemble." No attempt will be made to define these terms or to present a list of axioms for set theory. A reader who is sophisticated enough to be troubled by our informal development should consult the references on set theory that are given at the end of this text. There he can see how this material can be put on an axiomatic basis. He will find this axiomatization to be an interesting development in the foundations of mathematics. Since we regard it to be outside the subject area of the present book, we shall not go through the details here.

Section 1 The Algebra of Sets

If A denotes a set of any description, and if x is an element of this set A, it is often convenient to write

$$x \in A$$

as an abbreviation for the statement that x is an **element** of A, or that x is a **member** of the set A, or that the set A **contains** the element x, or that x is in A. We shall not examine the nature of this property of being an element of a set any further. For most practical purposes it is possible to employ the naïve meaning of "membership," and an axiomatic characterization of this relation is not necessary.

If A is a set and x is an element which does *not* belong to A, we shall often write

$$x \notin A.$$

In accordance with our naïve conception of a set, we shall require that exactly one of the two possibilities

$$x \in A, \quad x \notin A,$$

holds for an element x and a set A.

If A and B are two sets and x is an element, then there are, in principle, four possibilities (see Figure 1.1):

$$(1) \quad x \in A \quad \text{and} \quad x \in B;$$
$$(2) \quad x \in A \quad \text{and} \quad x \notin B;$$
$$(3) \quad x \notin A \quad \text{and} \quad x \in B;$$
$$(4) \quad x \notin A \quad \text{and} \quad x \notin B.$$

If the second case cannot occur, that is, if every element of A is also an element of B, then we shall say that A is **contained** in B, or that B **contains** A, or that A is a **subset** of B and write

$$A \subseteq B \quad \text{or} \quad B \supseteq A.$$

Similarly, if the third possibility mentioned above cannot occur, that is, if every element of B is an element of A, then we say that B is a subset of A, and so on, and write $B \subseteq A$. If $A \subseteq B$ and there exists an element in B which is not in A, we say that A is a **proper subset** of B.

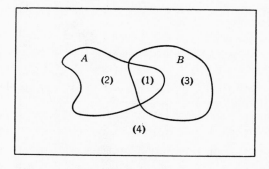

Figure 1.1

It should be noted that the statement that $A \subseteq B$ does not automatically preclude the possibility that A exhausts all of B. When this is true the sets A and B are "equal" in the sense we now define.

1.1 DEFINITION. Two sets are **equal** if they contain the same elements. If the sets A and B are equal, we write $A = B$.

Thus in order to show that the sets A and B are equal we must show that the possibilities (2) and (3) mentioned above cannot occur. Equivalently, we must show that both $A \subseteq B$ and $B \subseteq A$.

The word "property" is not easy to define precisely. However, we shall not hesitate to use it in the usual (informal) fashion. If P denotes a property that is meaningful for a collection of elements, then we agree to write

$$\{x : P(x)\}$$

for the set of all elements x for which the property P holds. We usually read this as "the set of all x such that $P(x)$." It is often worthwhile to specify which elements we are testing for the property P. Hence we shall often write

$$\{x \in S : P(x)\}$$

for the subset of S for which the property P holds.

EXAMPLES. (a) If $N = \{1, 2, 3, \ldots\}$ denotes the set of natural numbers, then the set

$$\{x \in N : x^2 - 3x + 2 = 0\}$$

consists of those natural numbers satisfying the stated equation. Now the only solutions of the quadratic equation $x^2 - 3x + 2 = 0$ are $x = 1$ and $x = 2$. Hence instead of writing the above expression, since we have detailed information concerning all of the elements in the set under examination, we shall ordinarily denote this set by $\{1, 2\}$, thereby listing the elements of the set.

(b) Sometimes a formula can be used to abbreviate the description of a set. For example, the set consisting of all even natural numbers could be denoted by $\{2x : x \in N\}$, instead of the more cumbersome $\{y \in N : y = 2x, x \in N\}$.

(c) The set denoted by $\{x \in N : 6 < x < 9\}$ can be written explicitly as $\{7, 8\}$, thereby exhibiting the elements of the set. Of course, there are many other possible descriptions of this set. For example:

$$\{x \in N : 40 < x^2 < 80\},$$
$$\{x \in N : x^2 - 15x + 56 = 0\},$$
$$\{7 + x : x = 0 \quad \text{or} \quad x = 1\}.$$

(d) In addition to the set of **natural numbers**, consisting of the elements denoted by 1, 2, 3, . . . and which we shall systematically denote by N, there are a few other sets for which we introduce a standard notation. The set of **integers** is

$$Z = \{0, 1, -1, 2, -2, 3, -3, \ldots\}.$$

The set of **rational numbers** is

$$Q = \{m/n : m, n \in Z \quad \text{and} \quad n \neq 0\}.$$

We shall treat the sets N, Z, and Q as if they are very well understood and shall not re-examine their properties in much detail. Of basic importance for our later study is the set R of all real numbers. Although we expect that the reader has had some familiarity with this set, we shall examine its properties more closely in Sections 4–6. A particular subset of R that will be useful is the **unit interval**

$$I = \{x \in R : 0 \leq x \leq 1\}.$$

Finally, we denote the set of **complex numbers** by C. A more detailed definition of C and a brief description of some of its properties will be given in Section 10.

Set Operations

We now introduce some methods of constructing new sets from old ones.

1.2 DEFINITION. If A and B are sets, then their **intersection** is the set of all elements that belong to both A and B. We shall denote the intersection of the sets A, B by the symbol $A \cap B$, which is read "A intersect B" or "A cap B."

1.3 DEFINITION. If A and B are sets, then their **union** is the set of all elements which belong either to A or to B or to both A and B. We shall denote the union of the sets A, B by the symbol $A \cup B$, which is read "A union B" or "A cup B." (See Figure 1.2.)

We could also define $A \cap B$ and $A \cup B$ by

$$A \cap B = \{x : x \in A \quad \text{and} \quad x \in B\},$$
$$A \cup B = \{x : x \in A \quad \text{or} \quad x \in B\}.$$

In connection with the latter, it is important to realize that the word "or" is being used in the inclusive sense that is customary in mathematics and logic. In legal terminology this inclusive sense is sometimes indicated by "and/or."

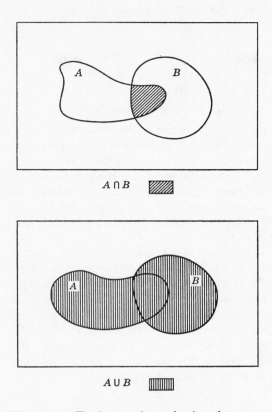

Figure 1.2.   The intersection and union of two sets.

We have tacitly assumed that the intersection and the union of two sets is again a set. Among other things this requires that there must exist a set which has no elements at all (for if A and B have no common elements, their intersection has no elements).

1.4   DEFINITION.   The set which has no elements is called the **empty** or the **void set** and will be denoted by the symbol $\emptyset$. If A and B are sets with no common elements (that is, if $A \cap B = \emptyset$), then we say that A and B are **disjoint** or that they are **non-intersecting.**

The next result gives some of the algebraic properties of the operations on sets that we have just defined. Since the proofs of these assertions are routine, we shall leave most of them to the reader as exercises.

1.5 THEOREM. *Let A, B, C, be any sets, then*

(a) $A \cap A = A$, $A \cup A = A$;

(b) $A \cap B = B \cap A$, $A \cup B = B \cup A$;

(c) $(A \cap B) \cap C = A \cap (B \cap C)$, $(A \cup B) \cup C = A \cup (B \cup C)$;

(d) $A \cap (B \cup C) = (A \cap B) \cup (A \cap C)$,
$$A \cup (B \cap C) = (A \cup B) \cap (A \cup C).$$

These equalities are sometimes referred to as the *idempotent*, the *commutative*, the *associative*, and the *distributive properties*, respectively, of the operations of intersection and union of sets.

In order to give a sample proof, we shall prove the first equation in (d). Let x be an element of $A \cap (B \cup C)$, then $x \in A$ and $x \in B \cup C$. This means that $x \in A$, and either $x \in B$ or $x \in C$. Hence we either have (i) $x \in A$ and $x \in B$, or we have (ii) $x \in A$ and $x \in C$. Therefore, $x \in A \cap B$ or $x \in A \cap C$, so $x \in (A \cap B) \cup (A \cap C)$. This shows that $A \cap (B \cup C)$ is a subset of $(A \cap B) \cup (A \cap C)$. Conversely, let y be an element of $(A \cap B) \cup (A \cap C)$. Then, either (iii) $y \in A \cap B$, or (iv) $y \in A \cap C$. It follows that $y \in A$, and either $y \in B$ or $y \in C$. Therefore, $y \in A$ and $y \in B \cup C$ so that $y \in A \cap (B \cup C)$. Hence $(A \cap B) \cup (A \cap C)$ is a subset of $A \cap (B \cup C)$. In view of Definition 1.1, we conclude that the sets $A \cap (B \cup C)$ and $(A \cap B) \cup (A \cap C)$ are equal.

As an indication of an alternate method, we note that there are, in principle, a total of $8 (= 2^3)$ possibilities for an element x relative to three sets A, B, C (see Figure 1.3); namely:

(1) $x \in A, x \in B, x \in C$;

(2) $x \in A, x \in B, x \notin C$;

(3) $x \in A, x \notin B, x \in C$;

(4) $x \in A, x \notin B, x \notin C$;

(5) $x \notin A, x \in B, x \in C$;

(6) $x \notin A, x \in B, x \notin C$;

(7) $x \notin A, x \notin B, x \in C$;

(8) $x \notin A, x \notin B, x \notin C$.

The proof consists in showing that both sides of the first equation in (d) contain those and only those elements x belonging to the cases (1), (2), or (3).

In view of the relations in Theorem 1.5(c), we usually drop the parentheses and write merely

$$A \cap B \cap C, \quad A \cup B \cup C.$$

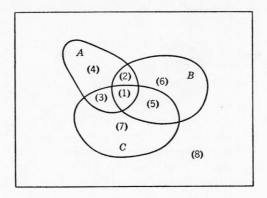

Figure 1.3

By using mathematical induction, it is possible to show that if $\{A_1, A_2, \ldots, A_n\}$ is a collection of sets, then there is a uniquely defined set A consisting of all elements which belong to at least one of the sets $A_j, j = 1, 2, \ldots, n$, and there exists a uniquely defined set B consisting of all elements which belong to all the sets $A_j, j = 1, 2, \ldots, n$. Dropping the use of parentheses, we write

$$A = A_1 \cup A_2 \cup \ldots \cup A_n,$$
$$B = A_1 \cap A_2 \cap \ldots \cap A_n.$$

Sometimes, in order to save space, we mimic the notation used in calculus for sums and employ a more condensed notation, such as

$$A = \bigcup_{j=1}^{n} A_j = \bigcup \{A_j : j = 1, 2, \ldots, n\},$$

$$B = \bigcap_{j=1}^{n} A_j = \bigcap \{A_j : j = 1, 2, \ldots, n\}.$$

Similarly, if for each j in a set J there is a set A_j, then $\bigcup \{A_j : j \in J\}$ denotes the set of all elements which belong to at least one of the sets A_j. In the same way, $\bigcap \{A_j : j \in J\}$ denotes the set of all elements which belong to all of the sets A_j for $j \in J$.

We now introduce another method of constructing a new set from two given ones.

1.6 DEFINITION. If A and B are sets, then the **complement of B relative to A** is the set of all elements of A which do not belong to B. We shall denote this set by $A \backslash B$ (read "A minus B"), although the

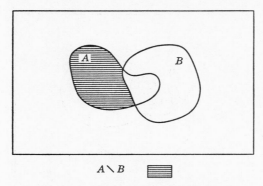

$$A \setminus B \quad \boxed{\equiv\equiv}$$

Figure 1.4.   The relative complement.

related notations $A - B$ and $A \sim B$ are sometimes used by other authors. (See Figure 1.4.)

In the notation introduced above, we have

$$A \setminus B = \{x \in A : x \notin B\}.$$

Sometimes the set A is thoroughly understood and does not need to be mentioned explicitly. In this situation we refer simply to the *complement* of B and denote $A \setminus B$ by $\mathfrak{C}(B)$.

Returning to Figure 1.1, we note that the elements x which satisfy (1) belong to $A \cap B$; those which satisfy (2) belong to $A \setminus B$; and those which satisfy (3) belong to $B \setminus A$. We shall now show that A is the union of the sets $A \cap B$ and $A \setminus B$.

1.7 THEOREM.   *The sets $A \cap B$ and $A \setminus B$ are non-intersecting and $A = (A \cap B) \cup (A \setminus B)$.*

PROOF.   Suppose $x \in A \cap B$ and $x \in A \setminus B$. The latter asserts that $x \in A$ and $x \notin B$ which contradicts the relation $x \in A \cap B$. Hence the sets are disjoint.

If $x \in A$, then either $x \in B$ or $x \notin B$. In the former case, $x \in A$ and $x \in B$ so that $x \in A \cap B$. In the latter situation, $x \in A$ and $x \notin B$ so that $x \in A \setminus B$. This shows that A is a subset of $(A \cap B) \cup (A \setminus B)$. Conversely, if $y \in (A \cap B) \cup (A \setminus B)$, then either (i) $y \in A \cap B$ or (ii) $y \in A \setminus B$. In either case $y \in A$, showing that $(A \cap B) \cup (A \setminus B)$ is a subset of A.

                                                          Q.E.D.

We shall now state the *De Morgan*† *laws* for three sets; a more general formulation will be given in the exercises.

† AUGUSTUS DE MORGAN (1806–1873) taught at University College, London. He was a mathematician and logician and helped prepare the way for modern mathematical logic.

1.8 THEOREM. *If A, B, C, are any sets, then*

$$A \backslash (B \cup C) = (A \backslash B) \cap (A \backslash C),$$
$$A \backslash (B \cap C) = (A \backslash B) \cup (A \backslash C).$$

PROOF. We shall carry out a demonstration of the first relation, leaving the second one to the reader. To establish the equality of the sets, we show that every element in $A \backslash (B \cup C)$ is contained in both $(A \backslash B)$ and $(A \backslash C)$ and conversely.

If x is in $A \backslash (B \cup C)$, then x is in A but x is not in $B \cup C$. Hence x is in A, but x is neither in B nor in C. (Why?) Therefore, x is in A but not B, and x is in A but not C. That is, $x \in A \backslash B$ and $x \in A \backslash C$, showing that $x \in (A \backslash B) \cap (A \backslash C)$.

Conversely, if $x \in (A \backslash B) \cap (A \backslash C)$, then $x \in (A \backslash B)$ and $x \in (A \backslash C)$. Thus $x \in A$ and both $x \notin B$ and $x \notin C$. It follows that $x \in A$ and $x \notin (B \cup C)$, so that $x \in A \backslash (B \cup C)$.

Since the sets $(A \backslash B) \cap (A \backslash C)$ and $A \backslash (B \cup C)$ contain the same elements, they are equal.

Q.E.D.

Cartesian Product

We now define the Cartesian† product of two sets.

1.9 DEFINITION. If A and B are two non-void sets, then the **Cartesian product** $A \times B$ of A and B is the set of all ordered pairs (a, b) with $a \in A$ and $b \in B$. (See Figure 1.5.)

(The definition just given is somewhat informal as we have not defined what is meant by an "ordered pair." We shall not examine the matter except to mention that the ordered pair (a, b) could be defined to be

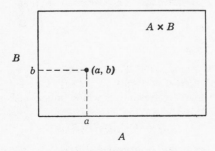

Figure 1.5

† RENÉ DESCARTES (1596–1650), the creator of analytic geometry, was a French gentleman, soldier, mathematician, and one of the greatest philosophers of all time.

the set whose sole elements are $\{a\}$, $\{a, b\}$. It can then be shown that the ordered pairs (a, b) and (a', b') are equal if and only if $a = a'$ and $b = b'$. This is the fundamental property of ordered pairs.)

Thus if $A = \{1, 2, 3\}$ and $B = \{4, 5\}$, then the set $A \times B$ is the set whose elements are the ordered pairs

$$(1, 4), (1, 5), (2, 4), (2, 5), (3, 4), (3, 5).$$

We shall often visualize the set $A \times B$ as the set of six points in the plane with the coordinates which we have just listed.

We shall often draw a diagram, such as Figure 1.5, to indicate the Cartesian product of two sets A, B. However, it should be realized that this diagram may be somewhat of a simplification. For example, if $A = \{x \in \mathbf{R} : 1 \le x \le 2\}$ and $B = \{x \in \mathbf{R} : 0 \le x \le 1 \text{ or } 2 \le x \le 3\}$, then instead of a rectangle, we should have a drawing like Figure 1.6.

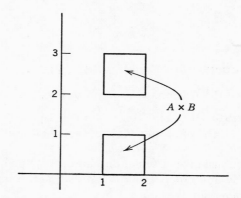

Figure 1.6.   The Cartesian product.

Exercises

1.A. Establish statement (d) of Theorem 1.5.

1.B. Prove that $A \subseteq B$ if and only if $A \cap B = A$.

1.C. Show that the set D of elements which belong either to A or B but not to both is given by

$$D = (A \backslash B) \cup (B \backslash A).$$

This set D is often called the **symmetric difference** of A and B.

1.D. Show that the symmetric difference D of A and B is also given by $D = (A \cup B) \backslash (A \cap B)$.

1.E. If $B \subseteq A$, show that $B = A \backslash (A \backslash B)$.

1.F. If A and B are any sets, show that $A \cap B = A \backslash (A \backslash B)$.

1.G. If $\{A_1, A_2, \ldots, A_n\}$ is a collection of sets, and if E is any set, show that

$$E \cap \bigcup_{j=1}^{n} A_j = \bigcup_{j=1}^{n} (E \cap A_j), \qquad E \cup \bigcup_{j=1}^{n} A_j = \bigcup_{j=1}^{n} (E \cup A_j).$$

1.H. If $\{A_1, A_2, \ldots, A_n\}$ is a collection of sets, and if E is any set, show that

$$E \cap \bigcap_{j=1}^{n} A_j = \bigcap_{j=1}^{n} (E \cap A_j), \qquad E \cup \bigcap_{j=1}^{n} A_j = \bigcap_{j=1}^{n} (E \cup A_j).$$

1.I. Let E be a set and $\{A_1, A_2, \ldots, A_n\}$ be a collection of sets. Establish the De Morgan laws:

$$E \backslash \bigcap_{j=1}^{n} A_j = \bigcup_{j=1}^{n} (E \backslash A_j), \qquad E \backslash \bigcup_{j=1}^{n} A_j = \bigcap_{j=1}^{n} (E \backslash A_j).$$

Note that if $E \backslash A_j$ is denoted by $\mathcal{C}(A_j)$, these relations take the form

$$\mathcal{C}\left(\bigcap_{j=1}^{n} A_j\right) = \bigcup_{j=1}^{n} \mathcal{C}(A_j), \qquad \mathcal{C}\left(\bigcup_{j=1}^{n} A_j\right) = \bigcap_{j=1}^{n} \mathcal{C}(A_j).$$

1.J. Let J be any set and, for each $j \in J$, let A_j be contained in X. Show that

$$\mathcal{C}(\cap\{A_j : j \in J\}) = \cup\{\mathcal{C}(A_j) : j \in J\},$$
$$\mathcal{C}(\cup\{A_j : j \in J\}) = \cap\{\mathcal{C}(A_j) : j \in J\}.$$

1.K. If B_1 and B_2 are subsets of B and if $B = B_1 \cup B_2$, then

$$A \times B = (A \times B_1) \cup (A \times B_2).$$

Section 2 Functions

We now turn to a rather abstract discussion of the fundamental notion of a function or mapping. It will be seen that a function is a special kind of a set, although there are other visualizations which are often helpful and more suggestive. All of the later sections will be concerned with various types of functions, but they will usually be of less abstract nature than considered in the present introductory section.

To the mathematician of a century ago the word "function" ordinarily meant a definite formula, such as

$$f(x) = x^2 + 3x - 5,$$

which associates to each real number x another real number $f(x)$. The fact that certain formulas, such as

$$g(x) = \sqrt{x - 5},$$

do not give rise to real numbers for all real values of x was, of course, well-known but was not regarded as sufficient grounds to require an extension of the notion of function. Probably one could arouse controversy among those mathematicians as to whether the absolute value

$$h(x) = |x|$$

of a real number is an honest "function" or not. For, after all, the definition of $|x|$ is given "in pieces" by

$$|x| = \begin{cases} x, & \text{if } x \geq 0, \\ -x, & \text{if } x < 0. \end{cases}$$

As mathematics developed, it became increasingly clear that the requirement that a function be a formula was unduly restrictive and that a more general definition would be useful. It also became evident that it is important to make a clear distinction between the function itself and the values of the function. The reader probably finds himself in the position of the mathematician of a century ago in these two respects and due to no fault of his own. We propose to bring him up to date with the current usage, but we shall do so in two steps. Our first revised definition of a function would be:

A function f from a set A to a set B is a rule of correspondence that assigns to each x in a certain subset $\mathfrak{D}$ of A, a uniquely determined element $f(x)$ of B.

Certainly, the explicit formulas of the type mentioned above are included in this tentative definition. The proposed definition allows the possibility that the function might not be defined for certain elements of A and also allows the consideration of functions for which the sets A and B are not necessarily real numbers (but might even be desks and chairs—or blondes and brunettes).

However suggestive the proposed definition may be, it has a significant and fatal defect: it is not clear. It merely shifts the difficulty to that of interpreting the phrase "rule of correspondence." Doubtless the reader can think of phrases that will satisfy him better than the above one, but it is not likely that he can dispel the fog entirely. The most satisfactory solution seems to be to define "function" entirely in terms of sets and the notions introduced in the preceding section. This has the disadvantage of being more artificial and loses some of the intuitive content of the earlier description, but the gain in clarity outweighs these disadvantages.

The key idea is to think of the *graph* of the function: that is, a collection of ordered pairs. We notice that an arbitrary collection of ordered

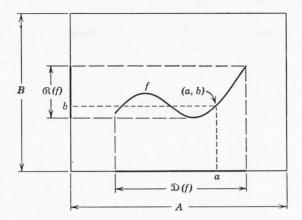

Figure 2.1. A function as a graph.

pairs cannot be the graph of a function, for, once the first member of the ordered pair is named, the second is uniquely determined.

After these preliminaries, we take the plunge and make our formal definition.

2.1   DEFINITION.   Let A and B be two sets which are not necessarily distinct. A **function from** A **to** B is a set f of ordered pairs in $A \times B$ with the property that if (a, b) and (a, b') are elements of f, then $b = b'$. The set of all elements of A that can occur as first members of elements in f is called the **domain** of f and will be denoted by $\mathfrak{D}(f)$. (See Figure 2.1.) Similarly, the set of all elements of B that can occur as second members of elements in f is called the **range** of f (or the **set of values** of f) and will be denoted by $\mathfrak{R}(f)$. In case $\mathfrak{D}(f) = A$, we often say that f is a **mapping** of A **into** B and write $f : A \rightarrow B$. If, in addition, the range $\mathfrak{R}(f)$ coincides with all of B, we sometimes say that f maps A **onto** B.

Since many of the functions that we shall consider in subsequent sections are not defined for all points in the set A, we shall employ the word "function" much more than "mapping."

If (a, b) is an element of a function f, then it is customary to write

$$b = f(a)$$

instead of $(a, b) \in f$, and we often refer to the element b as the **value** of f at the point a. Sometimes we say that b is the **image** under f of the point a.

Tabular Representation

One way of visualizing a function is as a graph. Another way which is important and widely used is as a *table*. Consider Table 2.1, which might be found in the sports page of the *Foosland Bugle-Gazette*.

TABLE 2.1

Player	Free Throws Made
Anderson	2
Bade	0
Bateman	5
Hochschild	1
Kakutani	4
Kovalevsky	8
Osborn	0
Peressini	2
Rosenberg	4

The domain of this free-throw function f consists of the nine players

$$\mathfrak{D}(f) = \{\text{Anderson, Bade, Bateman, Hochschild, Kakutani,}$$
$$\text{Kovalevsky, Osborn, Peressini, Rosenberg}\},$$

while the range of the function consists of the six numbers

$$\mathfrak{R}(f) = \{0, 1, 2, 4, 5, 8\}.$$

The actual elements of the function are the ordered pairs

(Anderson, 2), (Bade, 0), (Bateman, 5),
(Hochschild, 1), (Kakutani, 4), (Kovalevsky, 8),
(Osborn, 0), (Peressini, 2), (Rosenberg, 4).

In such tabular representations, we ordinarily write down only the domain of the function in the left-hand column (for there is no practical need to mention the members of the team that did not play). We could say that the value of this free-throw function f at Anderson is 2 and write $f(\text{Anderson}) = 2$, and so on. Of course, in a situation such as this we ordinarily leave everything in tabular form and do not employ such phrases.

We are all familiar with such use of tables to convey information. They are important examples of functions and are usually of a nature that would be difficult to express in terms of a formula.

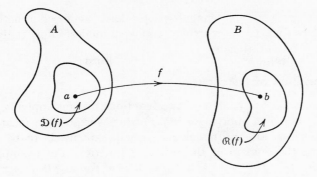

Figure 2.2.   A function as a transformation.

Transformations

There is another way of visualizing a function: as a *transformation* of part of the set A into part of B. In this phraseology, when $(a, b) \in f$, we think of f as taking the element a from the subset $\mathfrak{D}(f)$ of A and "transforming" or "mapping" it into an element $b = f(a)$ in the subset $\mathfrak{R}(f)$ of B. We often draw a diagram such as Figure 2.2. We frequently use this geometrical representation of a function even when the sets A and B are not subsets of the plane.

There is another way of visualizing a function: namely, as a *machine* which will accept elements of $\mathfrak{D}(f)$ as inputs and yield corresponding elements of $\mathfrak{R}(f)$ as outputs. (See Figure 2.3.) If we take an element x from $\mathfrak{D}(f)$ and drop it into f, then out comes the corresponding value $f(x)$. If we drop a different element y of $\mathfrak{D}(f)$ into f, we get $f(y)$ (which may or may not differ from $f(x)$). If we try to insert something which does not belong to $\mathfrak{D}(f)$ into f, we find that it is not accepted, for f can operate only on elements belonging to $\mathfrak{D}(f)$.

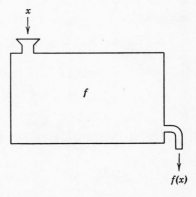

Figure 2.3.   A function as a machine.

This last visualization makes clear the distinction between f and $f(x)$: the first is the machine, the second is the output of the machine when we put x into it. Certainly it is useful to distinguish between a machine and its outputs. Only a fool would confuse a sausage-grinder with sausage; however, enough people have confused functions with their values that it is worthwhile to make a modest effort to distinguish between them notationally.

Composition of Functions

We now want to "compose" two functions by first applying f to each x in $\mathfrak{D}(f)$ and then applying g to $f(x)$ whenever possible (that is, when $f(x)$ belongs to $\mathfrak{D}(g)$). In doing so, some care needs to be exercised concerning the domain of the resulting function. For example, if f is defined on R by $f(x) = x^3$ and if g is defined for $x \geq 0$ by $g(x) = \sqrt{x}$, then the composition $g \circ f$ can be defined only for $x \geq 0$, and for these real numbers it is to have the value $\sqrt{x^3}$.

2.2 DEFINITION. Let f be a function with domain $\mathfrak{D}(f)$ in A and range $\mathfrak{R}(f)$ in B and let g be a function with domain $\mathfrak{D}(g)$ in B and range $\mathfrak{R}(g)$ in C. (See Figure 2.4.) The **composition** $g \circ f$ (note the order!) is the function from A to C given by

$$g \circ f = \{(a, c) \in A \times C: \text{there exists an element } b \in B \text{ such that}$$
$$(a, b) \in f \quad \text{and} \quad (b, c) \in g\}.$$

The fact that $g \circ f$ is actually a function (and not an arbitrary subset of $A \times C$) is a consequence of the fact that f and g are functions (see Exercise 2.A).

2.3 THEOREM. *If f and g are functions, the composition $g \circ f$ is a function with*

$$\mathfrak{D}(g \circ f) = \{x \in \mathfrak{D}(f) : f(x) \in \mathfrak{D}(g)\},$$
$$\mathfrak{R}(g \circ f) = \{g(f(x)) : x \in \mathfrak{D}(g \circ f)\}.$$

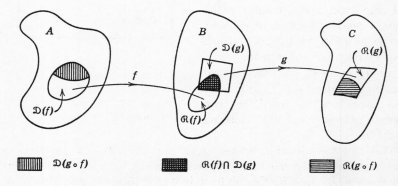

▦ $\mathfrak{D}(g \circ f)$	▦ $\mathfrak{R}(f) \cap \mathfrak{D}(g)$	▦ $\mathfrak{R}(g \circ f)$

Figure 2.4. Composition of functions.

2.4 EXAMPLES. (a) Let f, g be functions whose values at the real number x are the real numbers given by

$$f(x) = 2x, \qquad g(x) = 3x^2 - 1.$$

Since $\mathfrak{D}(g)$ is the set $\mathbf{R}$ of all real numbers and $\mathfrak{R}(f) \subseteq \mathfrak{D}(g)$, the domain $\mathfrak{D}(g \circ f)$ is also $\mathbf{R}$ and $g \circ f(x) = 3(2x)^2 - 1 = 12x^2 - 1$. On the other hand, $\mathfrak{D}(f \circ g) = \mathbf{R}$, but $f \circ g(x) = 2(3x^2 - 1) = 6x^2 - 2$.

(b) If h is the function with $\mathfrak{D}(h) = \{x \in \mathbf{R} : x \geq 1\}$ defined by

$$h(x) = \sqrt{x - 1},$$

and if f is as in part (a), then $\mathfrak{D}(h \circ f) = \{x \in \mathbf{R} : 2x \geq 1\} = \{x \in \mathbf{R} : x \geq \frac{1}{2}\}$ and $h \circ f(x) = \sqrt{2x - 1}$. Also $\mathfrak{D}(f \circ h) = \{x \in \mathbf{R} : x \geq 1\}$ and $f \circ h(x) = 2\sqrt{x - 1}$. If g is the function in part (a), then $\mathfrak{D}(h \circ g) = \{x \in \mathbf{R} : 3x^2 - 1 \geq 2\} = \{x \in \mathbf{R} : x \leq -\sqrt{\frac{2}{3}} \text{ or } x \geq \sqrt{\frac{2}{3}}\}$ and $h \circ g(x) = \sqrt{3x^2 - 2}$. Also $\mathfrak{D}(g \circ h) = \{x \in \mathbf{R} : x \geq 1\}$ and $g \circ h(x) = 3x - 4$. (Note that the formula expressing $g \circ h$ has meaning for values of x other than those in the domain of $g \circ h$.)

(c) Let F, G be the functions with domains $\mathfrak{D}(F) = \{x \in \mathbf{R} : x \geq 0\}$, $\mathfrak{D}(G) = \mathbf{R}$, such that the values of F and G at a point x in their domains are

$$F(x) = \sqrt{x}, \qquad G(x) = -x^2 - 1.$$

Then $\mathfrak{D}(G \circ F) = \{x \in \mathbf{R} : x \geq 0\}$ and $G \circ F(x) = -x - 1$, whereas $\mathfrak{D}(F \circ G) = \{x \in \mathfrak{D}(G) : G(x) \in \mathfrak{D}(F)\}$. This last set is void as $G(x) < 0$ for all $x \in \mathfrak{D}(G)$. Hence the function $F \circ G$ is not defined at any point, so $F \circ G$ is the "void function."

The Inverse Function

We now give a way of constructing a new function from a given one in case the original function does not take on the same value twice.

2.5 DEFINITION. Let f be a function with domain $\mathfrak{D}(f)$ in A and range $\mathfrak{R}(f)$ in B. We say that f is **one-one** if, whenever (a, b) and (a', b) are elements of f, then $a = a'$.

In other words, f is one-one if and only if the two relations $f(a) = b$, $f(a') = b$ imply that $a = a'$. Alternatively, f is one-one if and only if when a, a' are in $\mathfrak{D}(f)$ and $a \neq a'$, then $f(a) \neq f(a')$.

We claim that if f is a one-one function from A to B, then the set of ordered pairs in $B \times A$ obtained by interchanging the first and second members of ordered pairs in f yields a function g which is also one-one.

We omit the proof of this assertion, leaving it as an exercise; it is a good test for the reader. The connections between f and g are:

$$\mathfrak{D}(g) = \mathfrak{R}(f), \qquad \mathfrak{R}(g) = \mathfrak{D}(f),$$

$$(a, b) \in f \quad \text{if and only if} \quad (b, a) \in g.$$

This last statement can be written in the more usual form:

$$b = f(a) \quad \text{if and only if} \quad a = g(b).$$

2.6   DEFINITION.   Let f be a one-one function with domain $\mathfrak{D}(f)$ in A and range $\mathfrak{R}(f)$ in B. If $g = \{(b, a) \in B \times A : (a, b) \in f\}$, then g is a one-one function with domain $\mathfrak{D}(g) = \mathfrak{R}(f)$ in B and with range $\mathfrak{R}(g) = \mathfrak{D}(f)$ in A. The function g is called the function **inverse** to f and we ordinarily denote g by f^{-1}.

2.7   EXAMPLES.   (a) Let F be the function with domain $\mathfrak{D}(F) = \mathbf{R}$, the set of all real numbers, and range in $\mathbf{R}$ such that the value of F at the real number x is $F(x) = x^2$. In other words, F is the function $\{(x, x^2) : x \in \mathbf{R}\}$. It is readily seen that F is not one-one; in fact, the ordered pairs $(2, 4)$, $(-2, 4)$ both belong to F. Since F is not one-one, it does not have an inverse.

(b) Let f be the function with domain $\mathfrak{D}(f) = \{x \in \mathbf{R} : x \geq 0\}$ and $\mathfrak{R}(f) = \mathbf{R}$ whose value at x in $\mathfrak{D}(f)$ is $f(x) = x^2$. In terms of ordered pairs, $f = \{(x, x^2) : x \in \mathbf{R}, x \geq 0\}$. Unlike the function F in part (a), f is one-one, for if $x^2 = y^2$ with x, y in $\mathfrak{D}(f)$, then $x = y$. Therefore, f has an inverse function g with $\mathfrak{D}(g) = \mathfrak{R}(f) = \{x \in \mathbf{R} : x \geq 0\}$ and $\mathfrak{R}(g) = \mathfrak{D}(f) = \{x \in \mathbf{R} : x \geq 0\}$. Furthermore, $y = x^2 = f(x)$ if and only if $x = g(y)$. This inverse function g is ordinarily called the **positive square root function** and is denoted by

$$g(y) = \sqrt{y}, \qquad y \in \mathbf{R}, y \geq 0.$$

(c) If f_1 is the function $\{(x, x^2) : x \in \mathbf{R}, x \leq 0\}$, then as in (b), f_1 is one-one and has domain $\mathfrak{D}(f_1) = \{x \in \mathbf{R} : x \leq 0\}$ and range $\mathfrak{R}(f_1) = \{x \in \mathbf{R} : x \geq 0\}$. The function g_1 inverse to f is called the **negative square root function** and is denoted by

$$g_1(y) = -\sqrt{y}, \qquad y \in \mathbf{R}, y \geq 0,$$

so that $g_1(y) \leq 0$.

(d) The sine function F introduced in trigonometry with $\mathfrak{D}(F) = \mathbf{R}$ and $\mathfrak{R}(F) = \{y \in \mathbf{R} : -1 \leq y \leq +1\}$ is well known not to be one-one; for example, $\sin 0 = \sin 2\pi = 0$. However, if f is the function with $\mathfrak{D}(f) = \{x \in \mathbf{R} : -\pi/2 \leq x \leq +\pi/2\}$ and $\mathfrak{R}(f) = \{y \in \mathbf{R} : -1 \leq$

$y \leq +1\}$ defined by $f(x) = \sin x$, $x \in \mathfrak{D}(f)$, then f is one-one. It, therefore, has an inverse function g with $\mathfrak{D}(g) = \mathfrak{R}(f)$ and $\mathfrak{R}(g) = \mathfrak{D}(f)$. Also, $y = \sin x$ with $x \in \mathfrak{D}(f)$ if and only if $x = g(y)$. The function g is called the (principal branch) of the **inverse sine function** and is often denoted by

$$g(y) = \text{Arc sin } y \quad \text{or } g(y) = \text{Sin}^{-1} y.$$

The inverse function can be interpreted from the mapping point of view. (See Figure 2.5.) If f is a one-one function, it does not map distinct elements of $\mathfrak{D}(f)$ into the same element of $\mathfrak{R}(f)$. Thus, each element b

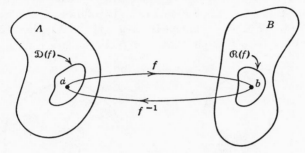

Figure 2.5.   The inverse function.

of $\mathfrak{R}(f)$ is the image under f of a unique element a in $\mathfrak{D}(f)$. The inverse function f^{-1} maps the element b into this unique element a.

Direct and Inverse Images

Once again, let f be an arbitrary function with domain $\mathfrak{D}(f)$ in A and range $\mathfrak{R}(f)$ in B. We do not assume that f is one-one.

2.8   DEFINITION.   If E is a subset of A, then the **direct image** of E under f is the subset of $\mathfrak{R}(f)$ given by

$$\{f(x) : x \in E \cap \mathfrak{D}(f)\}.$$

For the sake of brevity, we sometimes denote the direct image of a set E under f by the notation $f(E)$. (See Figure 2.6 on the next page.)

It will be observed that if $E \cap \mathfrak{D}(f) = \emptyset$, then $f(E) = \emptyset$. If E consists of the single point p in $\mathfrak{D}(f)$, then the set $f(E)$ consists of the single point $f(p)$. Certain properties of sets are preserved under the direct image, as we now show.

2.9 THEOREM. *Let f be a function with domain in A and range in B and let E, F be subsets of A.*

(a) *If $E \subseteq F$, then $f(E) \subseteq f(F)$.*
(b) $f(E \cap F) \subseteq f(E) \cap f(F)$.
(c) $f(E \cup F) = f(E) \cup f(F)$.
(d) $f(E \setminus F) \subseteq f(E)$.

PROOF.   (a) If $x \in E$, then $x \in F$ and hence $f(x) \in f(F)$. Since this is true for all $x \in E$, we infer that $f(E) \subseteq f(F)$.

(b) Since $E \cap F \subseteq E$, it follows from part (a) that $f(E \cap F) \subseteq F(E)$; likewise, $f(E \cap F) \subseteq f(F)$. Therefore, we conclude that $f(E \cap F) \subseteq f(E) \cap f(F)$.

(c) Since $E \subseteq E \cup F$ and $F \subseteq E \cup F$, it follows from part (a) that $f(E) \cup f(F) \subseteq f(E \cup F)$. Conversely, if $y \in f(E \cup F)$, then there exists an element $x \in E \cup F$ such that $y = f(x)$. Since $x \in E$ or $x \in F$, it

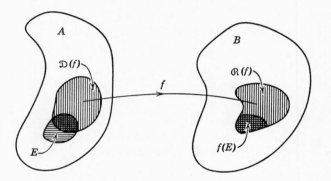

Figure 2.6.   Direct images.

follows that either $y = f(x) \in f(E)$ or $y \in f(F)$. Therefore, we conclude that $f(E \cup F) \subseteq f(E) \cup f(F)$, which completes the proof of part (c).

(d) Part (d) follows immediately from (a).

Q.E.D.

It will be seen in Exercise 2.J that it is not possible to replace the inclusion sign in (b) by equality, in general.

We now introduce the notion of the inverse image of a set under a function. Note that it is not required that the function be one-one.

2.10 DEFINITION.   If H is a subset of B, then the **inverse image of** H under f is the subset of $\mathfrak{D}(f)$ given by

$$\{x : f(x) \in H\}.$$

For the sake of brevity, we sometimes denote the inverse image of a set H under f by the symbol $f^{-1}(H)$. (See Figure 2.7.)

Once again, we emphasize that f need not be one-one so that the inverse function f^{-1} need not exist. (However, if f^{-1} does exist, then $f^{-1}(H)$ is the direct image of H under f^{-1}.) It will probably come as a surprise to the reader to learn that the inverse image is better behaved than the direct image. This is shown in the next result.

2.11   THEOREM.   *Let f be a function with domain in A and range in B and let G, H be subsets of B.*
  (a) *If $G \subseteq H$, then $f^{-1}(G) \subseteq f^{-1}(H)$.*
  (b) $f^{-1}(G \cap H) = f^{-1}(G) \cap f^{-1}(H)$.
  (c) $f^{-1}(G \cup H) = f^{-1}(G) \cup f^{-1}(H)$.
  (d) $f^{-1}(G \setminus H) = f^{-1}(G) \setminus f^{-1}(H)$.

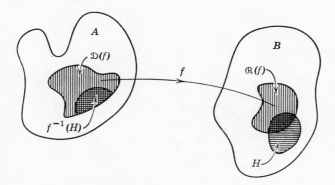

Figure 2.7.   Inverse images.

PROOF.   (a) Suppose that $x \in f^{-1}(G)$; then, by definition, $f(x) \in G \subseteq H$. Hence $x \in f^{-1}(H)$.

  (b) Since $G \cap H$ is a subset of G and H, it follows from part (a) that

$$f^{-1}(G \cap H) \subseteq f^{-1}(G) \cap f^{-1}(H).$$

Conversely, if $x \in f^{-1}(G) \cap f^{-1}(H)$, then $f(x) \in G$ and $f(x) \in H$. Therefore, $f(x) \in G \cap H$ and $x \in f^{-1}(G \cap H)$.

  (c) Since G and H are subsets of $G \cup H$, it follows from part (a) that

$$f^{-1}(G \cup H) \supseteq f^{-1}(G) \cup f^{-1}(H).$$

Conversely, if $x \in f^{-1}(G \cup H)$, then $f(x) \in G \cup H$. It follows that either $f(x) \in G$, whence $x \in f^{-1}(G)$, or $f(x) \in H$, in which case $x \in f^{-1}(H)$. Hence

$$f^{-1}(G \cup H) \subseteq f^{-1}(G) \cup f^{-1}(H).$$

(d) If $x \in f^{-1}(G \setminus H)$, then $f(x) \in G \setminus H$. Therefore, $x \in f^{-1}(G)$ and $x \notin f^{-1}(H)$, whence it follows that

$$f^{-1}(G \setminus H) \subseteq f^{-1}(G) \setminus f^{-1}(H).$$

Conversely, if $w \in f^{-1}(G) \setminus f^{-1}(H)$, then $f(w) \in G$ and $f(w) \notin H$. Hence $f(w) \in G \setminus H$ and it follows that

$$f^{-1}(G) \setminus f^{-1}(H) \subseteq f^{-1}(G \setminus H).$$

Q.E.D.

Exercises

2.A. Prove that Definition 2.2 actually yields a function and not just a subset.

2.B. Let $A = B = \mathbf{R}$ and consider the subset $C = \{(x, y) : x^2 + y^2 = 1\}$ of $A \times B$. Is this set a function with domain in $\mathbf{R}$ and range in $\mathbf{R}$?

2.C. Consider the subset of $\mathbf{R} \times \mathbf{R}$ defined by $D = \{(x, y) : |x| + |y| = 1\}$. Describe this set in words. Is it a function?

2.D. Give an example of two functions f, g on $\mathbf{R}$ to $\mathbf{R}$ such that $f \neq g$, but such that $f \circ g = g \circ f$.

2.E. Prove that if f is a one-one function from A to B, then $f^{-1} = \{(b, a) : (a, b) \in f\}$ is a function.

2.F. Suppose f is a one-one function. Show that $f^{-1} \circ f(x) = x$ for all x in $\mathfrak{D}(f)$ and $f \circ f^{-1}(y) = y$ for all y in $\mathfrak{R}(f)$.

2.G. Let f and g be functions and suppose that $g \circ f(x) = x$ for all x in $\mathfrak{D}(f)$. Show that f is one-one and that $\mathfrak{R}(f) \subseteq \mathfrak{D}(g)$.

2.H. Let f, g be functions such that

$$g \circ f(x) = x, \text{ for all } x \text{ in } \mathfrak{D}(f),$$

$$f \circ g(y) = y, \text{ for all } y \text{ in } \mathfrak{D}(g).$$

Prove that $g = f^{-1}$.

2.I. Show that the direct image $f(E) = \emptyset$ if and only if $E \cap \mathfrak{D}(f) = \emptyset$.

2.J. Let f be the function on $\mathbf{R}$ to $\mathbf{R}$ given by $f(x) = x^2$, and let $E = \{x \in \mathbf{R} : -1 \leq x \leq 0\}$ and $F = \{x \in \mathbf{R} : 0 \leq x \leq 1\}$. Then $E \cap F = \{0\}$ and $f(E \cap F) = \{0\}$ while $f(E) = f(F) = \{y \in \mathbf{R} : 0 \leq y \leq 1\}$. Hence $f(E \cap F)$ is a proper subset of $f(E) \cap f(F)$.

2.K. If f, E, F are as in Exercise 2.J, then $E \setminus F = \{x \in \mathbf{R} : -1 \leq x < 0\}$ and $f(E) \setminus f(F) = \emptyset$. Hence, it does not follow that

$$f(E \setminus F) \subseteq f(E) \setminus f(F).$$

2.L. Show that if f is a one-one mapping of $\mathfrak{D}(f)$ into $\mathfrak{R}(f)$ and if H is a subset of $\mathfrak{R}(f)$, then the inverse image of H under f coincides with the direct image of H under the inverse function f^{-1}.

2.M. If f and g are as in Definition 2.2, then $\mathfrak{D}(g \circ f) = f^{-1}(\mathfrak{D}(g))$.

Section 3   Finite and Infinite Sets

The purpose of this section is very restricted: it is to introduce the terms "finite," "countable," and "infinite." It provides a basis for the study of cardinal numbers, but it does not pursue this study. Although the theories of cardinal and ordinal numbers are fascinating in their own right, it turns out that very little exposure to these topics is really essential for the material in this text. A reader wishing to learn about these topics would do well to read the books of P. R. Halmos and W. Sierpinski which are cited in the References.

We shall assume familiarity with the set of *natural numbers*. We shall denote this set by the symbol N; the elements of N are denoted by the familiar symbols

$$1, 2, 3, \ldots.$$

The set N has the property of being ordered in a very well-known way: we all have an intuitive idea of what is meant by saying that a natural number n is less than or equal to a natural number m. We now borrow this notion, realizing that complete precision requires more analysis than we have given. We assume that, relative to this ordering, *every non-empty subset of N has a smallest element*. This is an important property of N; we sometimes say that N is *well-ordered*, meaning that N has this property. This Well-Ordering Property is equivalent to *mathematical induction*. We shall feel free to make use of arguments based on mathematical induction, which we suppose to be familiar to the reader.

By an **initial segment** of N is meant a set of natural numbers which precede or equal some fixed element of N. Thus an initial segment S of N determines and is determined by an element n of N as follows:

An element x of N belongs to S if and only if $x \leq n$.

For example, the subset $\{1, 2\}$ is the initial segment of N determined by the natural number 2; the subset $\{1, 2, 3, 4\}$ is the initial segment of N determined by the natural number 4; but the subset $\{1, 3, 5\}$ of N is not an initial segment of N, since it contains 3 but not 2, and 5 but not 4.

3.1 DEFINITION. A set B is **finite** if it is empty or if there is a one-one function with domain B and range in an initial segment of N. If there is no such function, the set is **infinite**. If there is a one-one function with domain B and range equal to all of N, then the set B is **denumerable** (or **enumerable**). If a set is either finite or denumerable, it is said to be **countable**.

When there is a one-one function with domain B and range C, we sometimes say that B can be put into one-one *correspondence* with C. By using this terminology, we rephrase Definition 3.1 and say that a set B is finite if it is empty or can be put into one-one correspondence with a subset of an initial segment of N. We say that B is denumerable if it can be put into one-one correspondence with all of N.

It will be noted that, by definition, a set B is either finite or infinite. However, it may be that, owing to the description of the set, it may not be a trivial matter to decide whether the given set B is finite or infinite. In other words, it may not be easy to define a one-one function on B to a subset of an initial segment of N, for it often requires some familiarity with B and considerable ingenuity in order to define such a function.

The subsets of N denoted by $\{1, 3, 5\}$, $\{2, 4, 6, 8, 10\}$, $\{2, 3, \ldots, 100\}$, are finite since, although they are not initial segments of N, they are contained in initial segments of N and hence can be put into one-one correspondence with subsets of initial segments of N. The set E of even natural numbers

$$E = \{2, 4, 6, 8, \ldots\}$$

and the set O of odd natural numbers

$$O = \{1, 3, 5, 7, \ldots\}$$

are not initial segments of N, and they cannot be put into one-one correspondence with subsets of initial segments of N. (Why?) Hence both of the sets E and O are infinite, but since they can be put into one-one correspondence with all of N (how?), they are both denumerable.

Even though the set Z of all integers

$$Z = \{\ldots, -2, -1, 0, 1, 2, \ldots\},$$

contains the set N, it may be seen that Z is a denumerable set.

We now state without proof some theorems which probably seem obvious to the reader. At first reading it is probably best to accept them without further examination. On a later reading, however, the reader will do well to attempt to provide proofs for these statements. In doing so, he will find the inductive property of the set N of natural numbers to be useful.†

3.1 THEOREM. *Any subset of a finite set is finite. Any subset of a countable set is countable.*

3.2 THEOREM. *The union of a finite collection of finite sets is a finite set. The union of a countable collection of countable sets is a countable set.*

† See the books of Halmos and Hamilton-Landin which are cited in the References.

It is a consequence of the second part of Theorem 3.2 that the set Q of all rational numbers forms a countable set. (We recall that a rational number is a fraction m/n, where m and n are integers and $n \neq 0$.) To see that Q is a countable set we form the sets

$$A_0 = \{0\},$$

$$A_1 = \{\tfrac{1}{1}, \ -\tfrac{1}{1}, \tfrac{2}{1}, \ -\tfrac{2}{1}, \tfrac{3}{1}, \ -\tfrac{3}{1}, \ldots\},$$

$$A_2 = \{\tfrac{1}{2}, \ -\tfrac{1}{2}, \tfrac{2}{2}, \ -\tfrac{2}{2}, \tfrac{3}{2}, \ -\tfrac{3}{2}, \ldots\},$$

$$\ldots\ldots\ldots\ldots\ldots\ldots\ldots\ldots\ldots\ldots\ldots$$

$$A_n = \left\{ \frac{1}{n}, \ -\frac{1}{n}, \frac{2}{n}, \ -\frac{2}{n}, \frac{3}{n}, \ -\frac{3}{n}, \cdots \right\},$$

$$\ldots\ldots\ldots\ldots\ldots\ldots\ldots\ldots\ldots\ldots\ldots$$

Note that each of the sets A_n is countable and that their union is all of Q. Hence Theorem 3.2 asserts that Q is countable. In fact, we can enumerate Q by the diagonal procedure:

$$0, \tfrac{1}{1}, \ -\tfrac{1}{1}, \tfrac{1}{2}, \tfrac{2}{1}, \ -\tfrac{1}{2}, \tfrac{1}{3}, \ldots..$$

By using this argument, the reader should be able to construct a proof of Theorem 3.2.

Despite the fact that the set of rational numbers is countable, the entire set R of real numbers is not countable. In fact, the set I of real numbers x satisfying $0 \leq x \leq 1$ is not countable. To demonstrate this, we shall use the elegant argument of G. Cantor.[†] We assume it is known that every real number x with $0 \leq x \leq 1$ has a decimal representation in the form $x = 0.a_1a_2a_3\ldots$, where each a_k denotes one of the digits 0, 1, 2, 3, 4, 5, 6, 7, 8, 9. It is to be realized that certain real numbers have two representations in this form; for example, the rational number $\tfrac{1}{10}$ has the two representations

$$0.1000\ldots \quad \text{and} \quad 0.0999\ldots.$$

We could decide in favor of one of these two representations, but it is not necessary to do so. Since there are infinitely many rational numbers in the interval $0 \leq x \leq 1$, the set I cannot be finite. (Why?) We shall now show that it is not denumerable. Suppose that there is an enumeration $x_1, x_2, x_3, \ldots$ of real numbers satisfying $0 \leq x \leq 1$ given by

[†] GEORG CANTOR (1845–1918) was born in St. Petersburg, studied in Berlin with Weierstrass, and taught at Halle. He is best known for his work on set theory, which he developed during the years 1874–1895.

$$x_1 = 0.a_1a_2a_3\ldots$$
$$x_2 = 0.b_1b_2b_3\ldots$$
$$x_3 = 0.c_1c_2c_3\ldots$$
$$\cdots\cdots\cdots\cdots$$

Now let y_1 be a digit different from 0, a_1, and 9; let y_2 be a digit different from 0, b_2, and 9; let y_3 be a digit different from 0, c_3, and 9, etc. Consider the number y with decimal representation

$$y = 0.y_1y_2y_3\ldots;$$

clearly y satisfies $0 \le y \le 1$. The number y is not one of the numbers with two decimal representations, since $y_n \ne 0, 9$. At the same time $y \ne x_n$ for any n since the nth digit in the decimal representations for y and x_n are different. Therefore, any denumerable collection of real numbers in this interval will omit at least one real number belonging to this interval. Therefore, this interval is not a countable set.

We have seen that any set that can be put into one-one correspondence with an initial segment of N is called a finite set and all other sets are said to be infinite. Suppose that a set A is infinite; we *suppose* (rather than prove) that there is a one-one correspondence with a subset of A and all of N. In other words, we *assume that every infinite set contains a denumerable subset*. The proof of this assertion is based on the so-called "Axiom of Choice," which is one of the axioms of set theory. After the reader has digested the contents of this book, he may turn to an axiomatic treatment of the foundations which we have been discussing in a somewhat informal fashion. However, for the moment he would do well to take the above statement as a temporary axiom. It can be replaced later by a more far-reaching axiom of set theory.

Exercises

3.A. Exhibit a one-one correspondence between the set E of even natural numbers and all of N. Exhibit a one-one correspondence between the set O of odd natural numbers and all of N.

3.B. Exhibit a one-one correspondence between all of N and a proper subset of N.

3.C. Show that every infinite set can be put into one-one correspondence with a proper subset of itself. (Hint: every infinite set has a denumerable subset.)

3.D. Show that a finite set does not have any infinite subset.

3.E. Give an example of a denumerable collection of finite sets whose union is not finite.

3.F. Show that if A can be put into one-one correspondence with B and B with C, then A can be put into one-one correspondence with C.

I

The Real Numbers

In this chapter we shall discuss the properties of the real number system. Although it would be possible to construct this system from a more primitive set (such as the set N of natural numbers or the set Q or rational numbers), we shall not do so. Instead, we shall exhibit a list of properties that are associated with the real number system and show how other properties can be deduced from the ones assumed.

For the sake of clarity we prefer not to state all the properties of the real number system at once. Instead, we shall introduce first, in Section 4, the "algebraic properties" based on the two operations of addition and multiplication and discuss briefly some of their consequences. Next, we introduce the "order properties." In Section 6, we make the final step by adding the "completeness property." There are several reasons for this somewhat piecemeal procedure. First, there are a number of properties to be considered, and it is well to take a few at a time. Also, there are systems other than the real numbers which are of interest and which possess some, but not all, of the properties of the real number system, and it is worthwhile to make their acquaintance. Furthermore, the proofs required in the preliminary algebraic stages are more natural at first than some of the proofs of the topological results. Finally, since there are several other interesting methods of adding the "completeness property," we wish to have it isolated from the other assumptions.

Part of the purpose of Sections 4 and 5 is to provide examples of proofs of elementary theorems which are derived from explicitly stated assumptions. It is our experience that students who have not had much exposure to rigorous proofs can grasp the arguments presented in these sections readily and can then proceed into Section 6. However, students who are familiar with the axiomatic method and the technique of proofs can go very quickly into Section 6.

Section 4   Fields

As we have mentioned, in this section we shall examine the "algebraic" structure of the real number system. Briefly expressed, the real numbers form a "field" in the sense of abstract algebra. In this section we shall introduce the notion of a field and examine those properties that will be of particular importance for later study.

In formulating the next definition, we shall follow a convention that is familiar to the reader from elementary courses and which is also used in modern algebra. By a **binary operation** in a set F we mean a function B with domain $F \times F$ and range in F. Instead of using the notation $B(a, b)$ to denote the value of the binary operation B at the point (a, b) in $F \times F$, we shall employ symbols such as $a + b$ or $a \cdot b$. Although this notation is at variance with the general notation used for functions, it is much more suggestive and is almost universally employed in such a situation.

4.1 DEFINITION. A set F is called a **field** if there are two binary operations (denoted by $+$ and $\cdot$ and called **addition** and **multiplication**, respectively) satisfying the properties

(A1) $a + b = b + a$, for all a, b in F;

(A2) $(a + b) + c = a + (b + c)$, for all a, b, c in F;

(A3)   there exists a unique element θ in F such that $\theta + a = a$ and $a + \theta = a$, for all a in F;

(A4)   for each element a in F there is an element $\bar{a}$ in F such that $a + \bar{a} = \theta$ and $\bar{a} + a = \theta$;

(M1) $a \cdot b = b \cdot a$, for all a, b in F;

(M2) $(a \cdot b) \cdot c = a \cdot (b \cdot c)$, for all a, b, c in F;

(M3)   there exists a unique element $e \neq \theta$ in F such that $e \cdot a = a$, $a \cdot e = a$, for all a in F;

(M4)   for each element $a \neq \theta$ in F there is an element a' in F such that $a \cdot a' = e$, and $a' \cdot a = e$;

(D) $a \cdot (b + c) = (a \cdot b) + (a \cdot c)$ and $(b + c) \cdot a = (b \cdot a) + (c \cdot a)$, for all a, b, c in F.

We generally refer to the element θ as the **zero element** of F and the element e as the **identity** or **unit element** of F.

Before we discuss some of the consequences of these assumptions, we shall give some examples of fields. The first three examples are familiar systems, but are somewhat loosely defined. The next two examples are probably unfamiliar; but, since they have so few elements, it is possible to check directly that they satisfy all the stated properties. Hence they show that systems with the required properties do exist. The final example is familiar in quality, but will be seen to be substantially different in character from the real and rational fields.

4.2 EXAMPLES. (a) Consider the system R of real numbers, as understood from algebra and with the usual operations of addition and multiplication. Here θ is the zero element 0, e is the real number 1, $\bar{a} = (-1)a$, and $a' = 1/a$ for $a \neq 0$.

(b) Let Q denote the system of rational numbers; that is, real numbers of the form m/n where m, n are integers and $n \neq 0$. Again $\theta = 0$ and $e = 1$.

(c) Let C denote the system of complex numbers; that is, ordered pairs (x, y) of real numbers with the operations defined by

$$(x_1, y_1) + (x_2, y_2) = (x_1 + x_2, y_1 + y_2),$$

$$(x_1, y_1) \cdot (x_2, y_2) = (x_1 x_2 - y_1 y_2, x_1 y_2 + y_1 x_2).$$

Here it may be seen that $\theta = (0, 0)$, $e = (1, 0)$, and

$$\overline{(x, y)} = (-x, -y), \qquad (x, y)' = \left(\frac{x}{x^2 + y^2}, \frac{-y}{x^2 + y^2} \right).$$

(d) Let F_2 consist of two distinct elements θ, e and define addition and multiplication as in Tables 4.1 and 4.2.

TABLE 4.1

+	θ	e
θ	θ	e
e	e	θ

TABLE 4.2

$\cdot$	θ	e
θ	θ	θ
e	θ	e

For example, the first column after the vertical bar in Table 4.1 indicates that $\theta + \theta = \theta$, and $e + \theta = e$. We leave it to the reader to check that the properties required in Definition 4.1 are satisfied and that θ and e have the properties required. In particular, $\bar{\theta} = \theta$, $\bar{e} = e$, $e' = e$. (What about θ'?)

(e) Let F_3 consist of three distinct elements θ, e, t where we define addition and multiplication as in Tables 4.3 and 4.4. Check to see that

TABLE 4.3

+	θ	e	t
θ	θ	e	t
e	e	t	θ
t	t	θ	e

TABLE 4.4

$\cdot$	θ	e	t
θ	θ	θ	θ
e	θ	e	t
t	θ	t	e

the system F_3 forms a field under the indicated operations. In particular,
$\bar{\theta} = \theta$, $\bar{e} = t$, $\bar{t} = e$, $e' = e$, $t' = t$.

(f) Let $Q(t)$ denote the system of all rational functions with rational
numbers as coefficients. Hence an element of $Q(t)$ is a function f of
the form

$$f(t) = \frac{p(t)}{q(t)},$$

where p and q are polynomials in t with rational coefficients and q is not
the zero polynomial. The operations of addition and multiplication are
the usual ones employed when dealing with rational functions.

Properties of Fields

In (A3) it was supposed that there is a unique element θ in F such that
$a = \theta + a$ for all a in F. We now show that if t is an element such that
for some element b in F we have $b = t + b$, then necessarily $t = \theta$.

4.3 THEOREM. *If t and b are elements of F such that $t + b = b$, then*
$t = \theta$. *Similarly, if w and $b \neq \theta$ are elements of F such that $w \cdot b = b$, then*
$w = e$.

PROOF. By hypothesis $b = t + b$. Add $\bar{b}$ to both sides and use (A4),
(A2), (A4), (A3) to obtain

$$\theta = b + \bar{b} = (t + b) + \bar{b} = t + (b + \bar{b}) = t + \theta = t,$$

so that $t = \theta$. The proof of the second assertion is similar.

Q.E.D.

Theorem 4.3 shows that the hypothesis that θ and e are unique, which
was made in (A3) and (M3), was not essential and can be proved from
the remaining assumptions. We now prove that the elements $\bar{a}$ and a'
(when $a \neq \theta$) are unique.

4.4 THEOREM. *If a and b are elements of F and $a + b = \theta$, then*
$b = \bar{a}$. *Similarly, if $a \neq \theta$ and b are elements of F and $a \cdot b = e$, then $b = a'$.*

PROOF. If $a + b = \theta$, add $\bar{a}$ to both sides to obtain $\bar{a} + (a + b) =$
$\bar{a} + \theta$. Now use (A2) on the left and (A3) on the right to obtain $(\bar{a} + a)$
$+ b = \bar{a}$. By using (A4) and (A3) on the left side, we obtain $b = \bar{a}$.
The second assertion is proved similarly.

Q.E.D.

Properties (A4) and (M4) guarantee the possibility of solving the
equations

$$a + x = \theta, \qquad a \cdot x = e \ (a \neq \theta),$$

for x, and Theorem 4.4 yields the uniqueness of the solutions. We now show that the right-hand sides of these equations can be arbitrary elements of F and are not required to be θ, e, respectively.

4.5 Theorem. (a) *Let a, b be arbitrary elements of F. Then the equation $a + x = b$ has the unique solution $x = \bar{a} + b$.*

(b) *Let $a \neq \theta$ and b be arbitrary elements of F. Then the equation $a \cdot x = b$ has the unique solution $x = a' \cdot b$.*

proof. Observe that $a + (\bar{a} + b) = (a + \bar{a}) + b = \theta + b = b$ so that $x = \bar{a} + b$ is a solution of the equation $a + x = b$. To show the uniqueness, let x_1 be any solution of this equation and add $\bar{a}$ to both sides of $a + x_1 = b$ to obtain

$$\bar{a} + (a + x_1) = \bar{a} + b.$$

Employing (A3), (A4), (A2) and this relation, we get

$$x_1 = \theta + x_1 = (\bar{a} + a) + x_1 = \bar{a} + (a + x_1) = \bar{a} + b.$$

The proof of part (b) of the theorem is similar.

Q.E.D.

We now establish some results which are familiar "laws of algebra," but are written in a slightly disguised form.

4.6 Theorem. *If a and b are any elements of F, then*
(a) $a \cdot \theta = \theta$;
(b) $\bar{a} = a \cdot \bar{e}$, $\overline{a + b} = \bar{a} + \bar{b}$;
(c) $\bar{\bar{a}} = a$, $\bar{e} \cdot \bar{e} = e$.

proof. (a) From (M3), we know that $a \cdot e = a$. Hence

$$a + a \cdot \theta = a \cdot e + a \cdot \theta = a \cdot (e + \theta) = a \cdot e = a.$$

Applying Theorem 4.3, we infer that $a \cdot \theta = \theta$.

(b) It is seen that

$$a + a \cdot \bar{e} = a \cdot e + a \cdot \bar{e} = a \cdot (e + \bar{e}) = a \cdot \theta = \theta.$$

It follows from Theorem 4.4 that $a \cdot \bar{e} = \bar{a}$. Hence

$$\overline{a + b} = (a + b) \cdot \bar{e} = (a \cdot \bar{e}) + (b \cdot \bar{e}) = \bar{a} + \bar{b},$$

proving the second assertion in (b).

(c) By definition of $\bar{a}$, we have $\bar{a} + a = \theta$. According to the uniqueness assertion of Theorem 4.4, it follows that $a = \bar{\bar{a}}$. If $a = \bar{e}$, then by part (b), we have $e = \bar{\bar{e}} = \bar{a} = a \cdot \bar{e} = \bar{e} \cdot \bar{e}$.

Q.E.D.

4.7 Theorem. (a) *If a is an element of F and $a \neq \theta$, then $a = a''$.*
(b) *If $a \cdot b = \theta$, then either $a = \theta$ or $b = \theta$.*
(c) *$\bar{a} \cdot \bar{b} = a \cdot b$ for any a, b in F.*

PROOF. (a) If $a \neq \theta$, then $a' \neq \theta$, for otherwise, $e = a \cdot a' = a \cdot \theta = \theta$ contrary to (M3). Therefore, since $a' \cdot a = e$, it follows from Theorem 4.4 that $a = a''$.

(b) Suppose $a \neq \theta$ and $a \cdot b = \theta$. On multiplying by a', we obtain

$$b = e \cdot b = (a' \cdot a) \cdot b = a' \cdot (a \cdot b) = a' \cdot \theta = \theta.$$

A similar argument holds if $b \neq \theta$.

(c) From Theorem 4.6, we have $\bar{a} = a \cdot \bar{e}$, and $\bar{b} = b \cdot \bar{e}$; hence

$$\bar{a} \cdot \bar{b} = (a \cdot \bar{e}) \cdot (b \cdot \bar{e}) = (a \cdot \bar{e}) \cdot (\bar{e} \cdot b)$$
$$= a \cdot (\bar{e} \cdot \bar{e}) \cdot b = a \cdot e \cdot b = a \cdot b. \qquad \text{Q.E.D.}$$

Until now we have been excessively formal in our notation; although we have used $+$ and $\cdot$ to denote the operations of addition and multiplication, we have denoted the neutral elements under these operations by θ and e. Now that the basic properties of these elements have been explored without notational bias, we revert to the usual procedure of denoting the neutral element θ by 0 and denoting the identity element e by 1.

In a similar vein we shall denote the element $\bar{a} = \bar{e} \cdot a$ by the notation $(-1)a$ or simply $-a$. Also, the element a' is generally denoted by a^{-1} or by $1/a$. Similarly, $b + \bar{a}$ is represented by $b - a$ and $b \cdot a'$ is represented by the fraction b/a, or by $b \cdot a^{-1}$. Moreover, we generally drop the use of the dot to denote multiplication and merely use juxtaposition; thus we write ab in place of $a \cdot b$. As in elementary algebra, we write a^2 for aa, a^3 for $aaa = a(a^2)$; in general, we employ the abbreviation a^n for the product of a taken n times. It follows by use of mathematical induction that if $m, n \in N$, then

$$a^{m+n} = a^m a^n,$$

for any element a.

Once again, we agree to write 1 for e. Furthermore, we write 2 for $1 + 1 = e + e$, 3 for $2 + 1 = 1 + 1 + 1$, and so forth. We saw in Examples 4.2(d) and 4.2(e) that it is possible to have $2 = 1 + 1 = 0$ or $3 = 0$. However, for the fields considered in mathematical analysis, it is the case that if n is a natural number, then the sum of $1(= e)$ taken n times is different from 0. In algebra, fields with this property are said to have **characteristic zero**. We shall deal exclusively with such fields; in fact, we are primarily interested in "ordered" fields and it will be seen in Section 5 that such fields necessarily have characteristic zero.

It has been observed in the preceding paragraph that if F is a field with characteristic zero, then F contains a subset which is in one-one correspondence with the set N of natural numbers. In fact, the notation introduced in the last paragraph has the effect of using the same symbol to denote a natural number n and the sum of $1(=e)$, taken n times. This notation is extraordinarily useful and almost universally employed. In fact, we usually go further and regard the set N as being a subset of F. In the same way we regard not only the set Z of integers, but even the field Q of rational numbers, as being imbedded in any field F with characteristic zero. Thus the element of F which is identified with the rational number m/n, where m, n are positive integers, is

$$(me) \cdot (ne)',$$

and the element of F which is identified with $-m/n$ is

$$(m\bar{e}) \cdot (ne)'.$$

With this understanding, we can say that *the field of rational numbers is contained in any field of characteristic zero.*

Therefore, if F is a field with characteristic zero, it makes sense to refer to the **rational elements** of F. All of the elements of F which are not rational elements are called **irrational elements**. We shall use this terminology freely in later sections.

Exercises

4.A. Why must a field contain at least two elements?

4.B. Verify that the system C of complex numbers, as defined in Example 4.2(c), forms a field.

4.C. Does the collection of polynomials with rational coefficients form a field?

4.D. Restate Theorem 4.6 employing the usual notation; that is, using 0, 1, $-a$, a^{-1} instead of $\theta, e, \bar{a}, a'$.

4.E. Restate Theorem 4.7 employing the usual notation.

4.F. If $F_4 = \{0, 1, a, b\}$ consists of four distinct elements, show that F_4 forms a field with the operations given by Tables 4.5 and 4.6.

TABLE 4.5

+	0	1	a	b
0	0	1	a	b
1	1	0	b	a
a	a	b	0	1
b	b	a	1	0

TABLE 4.6

·	0	1	a	b
0	0	0	0	0
1	0	1	a	b
a	0	a	b	1
b	0	b	1	a

Show that, with these operations, if $x \neq 0$, then $x^3 = 1$ and if y is any element, then $y^4 = y$ and $2y = 0$.

4.G. Let $G_4 = \{0, 1, a, b\}$ consist of four distinct elements. Determine whether G_4 forms a field with the operations given by Tables 4.7 and 4.8.

TABLE 4.7				
+	0	1	a	b
0	0	1	a	b
1	1	a	b	0
a	a	b	0	1
b	b	0	1	a

TABLE 4.8				
·	0	1	a	b
0	0	0	0	0
1	0	1	a	b
a	0	a	0	a
b	0	b	a	1

Show that either $x^2 = 0$ or $x^2 = 1$ and that if y is any element, then $y^4 = y^2$ and $4y = 0$. Show that there exist non-zero elements x, y in G_4 such that $xy = 0$.

Section 5   Ordered Fields

Throughout this section the letter F denotes a field as defined in the preceding section. As promised, we shall use the more conventional notations 0, 1, $-a$, a^{-1}, and so forth (instead of θ, e, $\bar{a}$, a', etc.). The purpose of this section is to introduce the notion of "order," for it is the ordered field of real numbers that will provide a basis for the later sections. First, however, it is of some interest to introduce the general concept of order and positivity.

5.1 DEFINITION. A non-empty subset P of elements of a field F is called a **positive class** if it satisfies the following three properties:

(i) If a, b belong to P, then their sum $a + b$ belongs to P.
(ii) If a, b belong to P, then their product ab belongs to P.
(iii) If a belongs to F, then precisely one of the following relations holds: $a \in P$, $a = 0$, $-a \in P$.

Condition (iii) is sometimes called the **property of trichotomy**. It implies that if P is a positive class in a field F, then the set $N = \{-a: a \in P\}$ has no elements in common with P. The set N is called the **negative class** (corresponding to P) and it is clear that the entire field F is the union of the three disjoint sets P, $\{0\}$, N.

Before continuing, we wish to consider some simple examples.

5.2 EXAMPLES. (a) Consider the field **Q** of rational numbers; that is, quotients of the form p/q where p and q are integers and $q \neq 0$. Let P denote the subset consisting of quotients of the form p/q where both p and q are natural numbers. It is readily checked that P forms a positive class for the field of rational numbers.

(b) Let **R** be the field of real numbers (which has not been formally defined, but may be regarded as familiar). Let P be the subset in **R** consisting of all elements x in **R** for which $x > 0$ (or, in geometrical terms, those x which lie to the right of the origin). This subset P forms a positive class in **R**.

(c) Let $\mathbf{Q}(t)$ be the field of rational functions with rational numbers as coefficients. Hence an element of $\mathbf{Q}(t)$ is a quotient p/q, where p and q are polynomials with rational coefficients and not all of the coefficients of q are zero. Let P be the subset of $\mathbf{Q}(t)$ consisting of all quotients p/q such that the coefficient of the highest power of t in the product $p(t)q(t)$ is a positive rational number (in the sense of Example (a)). This set P forms a positive class in $\mathbf{Q}(t)$, as may be demonstrated.

(d) Let F be the field consisting of the two elements 0, 1. If $P_1 = \{0\}$, then the subset P_1 satisfies properties (i), (ii) of Definition 5.1 but not property (iii). Further, the subset $P_2 = \{1\}$ satisfies (ii) but not (i) or (iii). Hence neither P_1 nor P_2 forms a positive class for this field. (It will be seen from Theorem 5.5, that there is no positive class for this field.)

5.3   DEFINITION.   If P is a positive class of elements in a field F, we say that F is ordered by P and that F is an ordered field. If a belongs to P, we say that a is a positive element of F and write $a > 0$. If a is either in P or is 0, we say that a is non-negative and write $a \geq 0$. If the difference $a - b$ belongs to P, we write $a > b$ and if $a - b$ either belongs to P or equals 0, we write $a \geq b$.

As usual, it is often convenient to turn the signs around and write $0 < a$, $0 \leq a$, $b < a$, and $b \leq a$, respectively. In addition, if both $a < b$ and $b < c$, then we write $a < b < c$ or $c > b > a$; if $a \leq b$ and $b < c$, then we write $a \leq b < c$ or $c > b \geq a$.

Properties of Ordered Fields

We shall now establish the basic properties possessed by an ordered field F. These are the more or less familiar "laws" for inequalities which the student has met in earlier courses. We shall make much use of these properties in later sections.

5.4   THEOREM.   (a) *If $a > b$ and $b > c$, then $a > c$.*

(b) *If a and b belong to F, then exactly one of the following relations holds: $a > b$, $a = b$, $a < b$.*

(c) *If $a \geq b$ and $b \geq a$, then $a = b$.*

PROOF.   (a) If $a - b$ and $b - c$ belong to P, then from 5.1(i) we infer that $a - c = (a - b) + (b - c)$ also belongs to P.

(b) By 5.1(iii) exactly one of the following possibilities holds: $a - b$ belongs to P, $a - b = 0$, or $b - a = -(a - b)$ belongs to P.

(c) If $a \neq b$, then from part (b) we must have either $a - b$ in P or $b - a$ in P. Hence either $a > b$ or $b > a$; in either case a portion of the hypothesis is contradicted.

Q.E.D.

5.5   THEOREM.   *Let F be an ordered field.*

(a) *If $a \neq 0$, then $a^2 > 0$.*

(b) $1 > 0$.

(c) *If n is a natural number, then $n > 0$.*

PROOF.   (a) Either a or $-a$ belongs to P. If $a \in P$, then from property 5.1(ii) the element $a^2 = a \cdot a$ also belongs to P. If $-a \in P$, then from Theorem 4.7(c), $a^2 = (-a)(-a)$ and so a^2 belongs to P.

(b) Since $1 = (1)^2$, part (b) follows from (a).

(c) We use mathematical induction. The assertion with $n = 1$ has just been proved. Supposing the assertion true for the natural number k (that is, supposing $k \in P$), then since $1 \in P$, it follows from 5.1(i) that $k + 1 \in P$.

Q.E.D.

In the terminology introduced at the end of the preceding section, Theorem 5.5(c) asserts that *an ordered field has characteristic zero.* Hence any ordered field contains the rational numbers in the sense described at the end of Section 4.

We now establish the basic manipulative properties of inequalities, which are familiar to the reader from elementary algebra.

5.6   THEOREM.   *Let a, b, c, d denote elements in F.*

(a) *If $a > b$, then $a + c > b + c$.*

(b) *If $a > b$ and $c > d$, then $a + c > b + d$.*

(c) *If $a > b$ and $c > 0$, then $ac > bc$.*

(c′) *If $a > b$ and $c < 0$, then $ac < bc$.*

(d) *If $a > 0$, then $a^{-1} > 0$.*

(d′) *If $a < 0$, then $a^{-1} < 0$.*

PROOF.   (a) Observe that $(a + c) - (b + c) = a - b$.

(b) If $a - b$ and $c - d$ belong to P, then by property 5.1(i) we conclude that $(a + c) - (b + d) = (a - b) + (c - d)$ also belongs to P.

(c) If $a - b$ and c belong to P, then by property 5.1(ii) we infer that $ac - bc = (a - b)c$ also belongs to P.

(c′) If $a - b$ and $-c$ belong to P, then $bc - ac = (a - b)(-c)$ also belongs to P.

(d) If $a > 0$, then by 5.1(iii) we have $a \neq 0$ so that the inverse element a^{-1} exists. If $a^{-1} = 0$, then $1 = aa^{-1} = a0 = 0$, a contradiction.

If $a^{-1} < 0$, then property (c′) with $c = a^{-1}$ implies that $aa^{-1} < 0$ from which it follows that $1 < 0$, contradicting Theorem 5.5(b). Invoking 5.1(iii) we conclude that $a^{-1} > 0$, since the other two possibilities have been excluded.

(d′) This part can be proved by an argument analogous to that used in (d). Alternatively, we can observe that $(-a)^{-1} = -a^{-1}$ and use [(d) directly.

Q.E.D.

We now show that the arithmetic mean (= average) of two elements of an ordered field lies between the two elements. Recall that it is conventional to write $c/2$ or $\dfrac{c}{2}$ for $c2^{-1}$, and so forth.

5.7 COROLLARY. *If* $a > b$, *then* $a > \dfrac{a + b}{2} > b$.

PROOF. Since $a > b$, it follows from Theorem 5.6(a) with $c = a$ that $2a = a + a > a + b$, and from Theorem 5.6(c) with $c = b$ that $a + b > b + b = 2b$. By Theorem 5.5(c) we know that $2 > 0$ and from 5.6(d) that $2^{-1} > 0$. After applying Theorem 5.6(c) with $c = 2^{-1}$ to the above relations, we obtain

$$a > (a + b)2^{-1}, \qquad (a + b)2^{-1} > b$$

Hence $a > (a + b)/2 > b$.

Q.E.D.

The corollary just proved with $b = 0$ implies that given any positive number a, there is a smaller positive number, namely $a/2$. Expressed differently, *in an ordered field there is no smallest positive number*.

It follows from Theorem 5.6(c) with $b = 0$ that if $a > 0$ and $c > 0$, then $ac > 0$. Similarly, from 5.6(c′) with $a = 0$ it follows that if $b < 0$ and $c < 0$, then $bc > 0$. We now establish the converse statement.

5.8 THEOREM. *If* $ab > 0$, *then we either have* $a > 0$ *and* $b > 0$ *or we have* $a < 0$ *and* $b < 0$.

PROOF. If $ab > 0$, then neither of the elements a, b can equal 0. (Why?) If $a > 0$, then from Theorem 5.6(d) we infer that $a^{-1} > 0$ and from Theorem 5.6(c) that

$$b = (a^{-1}a)b = a^{-1}(ab) > 0.$$

On the other hand, if $a < 0$, we employ Theorem 5.6(d′) and (c′) to conclude that

$$b = (a^{-1}a)b = a^{-1}(ab) < 0.$$

Q.E.D.

Absolute Value

The trichotomy property 5.1(iii) assures that if $a \neq 0$, then either a or $-a$ is a positive element. The absolute value of an element a is defined to be the positive one of the pair $\{a, -a\}$; for completeness, the absolute value of 0 is defined to be 0.

5.9 DEFINITION. If F is a field with positive class P, we define the absolute value function by

$$|a| = \begin{cases} a, & \text{if} & a \geq 0, \\ -a, & \text{if} & a < 0. \end{cases}$$

Thus the domain of the absolute value function is all of F, its range is $P \cup \{0\}$, and it maps the elements a, $-a$ into the same element. We now obtain the basic properties of the absolute value function.

5.10 THEOREM. (a) $|a| = 0$ *if and only if* $a = 0$.

(b) $|-a| = |a|$ *for all a in F.*

(c) $|ab| = |a|\,|b|$ *for all a, b in F.*

(d) *If* $c \geq 0$, *then* $|a| \leq c$ *if and only if* $-c \leq a \leq c$.

(e) $-|a| \leq a \leq |a|$ *for all a in F.*

PROOF. (a) By definition, $|0| = 0$. If $a \neq 0$, then $-a \neq 0$ so that $|a| \neq 0$.

(b) If $a > 0$, then $|a| = a = |-a|$; if $a < 0$, then $|a| = -a = |-a|$; and if $a = 0$, then $|0| = 0 = |-0|$.

(c) If $a > 0$ and $b > 0$, then $ab > 0$ so that $|ab| = ab = |a|\,|b|$. If $a < 0$ and $b > 0$, then $ab < 0$ so that $|ab| = -(ab) = (-a)b = |a|\,|b|$. The other cases are handled similarly.

(d) If $|a| \leq c$, then both $a \leq c$ and $-a \leq c$. From the latter and Theorem 5.6(c') we have $-c \leq a$ so that $-c \leq a \leq c$. Conversely, if this latter relation holds, then we have both $a \leq c$ and $-a \leq c$, whence $|a| \leq c$.

(e) Since $|a| \geq 0$, this part follows from (d).

Q.E.D.

The next result is commonly called the **Triangle Inequality** and will be used frequently in the sequel.

5.11 THEOREM. *Let a, b be any elements of an ordered field F, then*

$$||a| - |b|| \leq |a \pm b| \leq |a| + |b|.$$

PROOF. According to Theorem 5.10(e), we obtain $-|a| \leq a \leq |a|$ and since $|b| = |-b|$, we also have $-|b| \leq \pm b \leq |b|$. Employing 5.6(b) we infer that

$$-(|a| + |b|) = -|a| - |b| \leq a \pm b \leq |a| + |b|.$$

From Theorem 5.10(d) it follows that $|a \pm b| \leq |a| + |b|$.

Since $|a| = |(a - b) + b| \leq |a - b| + |b|$, then $|a| - |b| \leq |a - b|$. Similarly, $|b| - |a| \leq |a - b|$, whence it follows that $||a| - |b|| \leq |a - b|$. Replacing b by $-b$, we obtain $||a| - |b|| \leq |a + b|$ as well.

Q.E.D.

5.12 COROLLARY. *Let $x_1, x_2, \ldots, x_n$ be elements of an ordered field F, then $|x_1 + x_2 + \cdots + x_n| \leq |x_1| + |x_2| + \cdots + |x_n|$.*

PROOF. If $n = 2$, the conclusion follows from 5.11. If $n > 2$, we use mathematical induction.

Q.E.D.

Intervals

If F is an ordered field and a, b are elements of F with $a \leq b$, then the set of all x in F satisfying $a < x < b$ is called the open interval determined by a, b and is denoted by (a, b). The set of all x in F satisfying $a \leq x \leq b$ is called the closed interval determined by a, b and is denoted by $[a, b]$. In analogous fashion, the sets $\{x \in F : a \leq x < b\}$ and $\{x \in F : a < x \leq b\}$ are said to be either half-open or half-closed and are denoted by $[a, b)$ and $(a, b]$, respectively.

Archimedean Ordered Fields

We have seen in Theorem 5.5 that if F is an ordered field and if n is a natural number, then $n = n \cdot 1 > 0$. Our experience with the number system leads us to expect that each element in F is exceeded by some natural number. Alternatively, we expect that each positive element is contained in some interval $[n, n + 1]$, where n takes on one of the values $0, 1, 2, \ldots$.

It may come as a surprise to learn that it is not possible to establish either of these expected properties for an arbitrary ordered field. In fact, there exist ordered fields which have positive elements which exceed any natural number; such positive elements evidently cannot be enclosed between consecutive natural numbers. As an example of such a field, we cite $Q(t)$, mentioned in Example 5.2(c). It is to be shown in Exercise 5.K that if p is a polynomial with degree at least one and positive leading coefficient and if $n \in N$, than $n < p$. Thus we see that an ordered field need not have the property that each positive element is exceeded by some natural number. However, in the following we shall consider only ordered fields with this additional property.

5.13 DEFINITION. An ordered field F is said to be an **Archimedean field**† if for each x in F there is a natural number n such that $x < n$.

(In somewhat more precise terms, we should state that the positive class P of F is Archimedean if for each x in F there is a natural number n such that $n - x$ belongs to P.) It is easy to see (cf. Exercise 5.J) that the rational numbers form an Archimedean field under the usual order.

5.14 THEOREM. *Let F be an Archimedean field.*

(a) *If $y > 0$ and $z > 0$, there is a natural number n such that $ny > z$.*

(b) *If $z > 0$, there is a natural number n such that $0 < 1/n < z$.*

(c) *If $y > 0$, there is a natural number n such that $n - 1 \leq y < n$.*

PROOF. (a) If $y > 0$ and $z > 0$, then $x = z/y$ is also positive. Let n be a natural number such that $n > x = z/y$. Then $ny > z$.

(b) If $z > 0$, then $1/z > 0$. Hence there exists a natural number n such that $n > 1/z$. It then follows that $0 < 1/n < z$.

(c) If $y > 0$, it follows from the Archimedean property that there exist natural numbers m such that $y < m$. Let n be the smallest such natural number, hence $n \geq 1$. By definition of n, we have $n - 1 \leq y < n$.

Q.E.D.

It should be observed that, in the proof of 5.14(c), we employed the Well-ordering Property of the set N, which asserts that every non-void subset of N has a smallest element.

We noted after Corollary 5.7 that there is no smallest positive element in an ordered field; for, given $z > 0$, the element $z/2$ is smaller than z but still positive. In view of Theorem 5.14(b), it is seen that if z is a given positive element, there is a rational element of the form $1/n$ such that $1/n < z$. This property is sometimes expressed by saying that "in an Archimedean field there are arbitrarily small positive rational elements." It is important that this phrase should *not* be interpreted as saying:

(i) "There is a smallest positive rational element;" or

(ii) "There is a positive rational element r such that $r < z$ for any positive z in F."

The reader should convince himself that both of these statements are false.

The rational field Q forms an Archimedean field, as observed above; hence the hypothesis that a field F is Archimedean does not imply that there need be any irrational elements in F. However, we shall now show that if F is an Archimedean field with at least one irrational element,

---

† This term is named for ARCHIMEDES (287–212 B.C.), who has been called "the greatest intellect of antiquity," and was one of the founders of the scientific method.

then there are arbitrarily small irrational elements. We first note that if ξ is an irrational element of F, then either ξ or $-\xi$ is a positive irrational element of F.

5.15 THEOREM. *Let F be an Archimedean field containing a positive irrational element ξ. If z is a positive element of F, then there is a natural number m such that the positive irrational element ξ/m satisfies $0 < \xi/m < z$.*

PROOF. Since $\xi > 0$, $z > 0$ it follows from Theorem 5.6(d) and 5.6(c) that $\xi/z > 0$. Since F is Archimedean, there exists a natural number m such that $0 < \xi/z < m$. By using Theorem 5.6 again, we obtain the conclusion.

Q.E.D.

We now show that in any Archimedean field F the rational elements are "dense" in the sense that between any two elements of F there is a rational element of F. Once again, we shall use the Well-ordering Property of **N**.

5.16 THEOREM. *If y, z are elements of an Archimedean field F and if $y < z$, then there is a rational element r of F such that $y < r < z$.*

PROOF. It is no loss of generality to assume that $0 < y < z$. (Why?) Since $y > 0$ and $z - y > 0$, it follows from Theorem 5.14(b) that there is a natural number m such that $0 < 1/m < y$ and $0 < 1/m < z - y$. From Theorem 5.14(a) there is a natural number k such that $k/m = k(1/m) > y$ and we let n be the smallest such natural number. Therefore, $(n - 1)/m \le y < n/m$, and we shall now show that $n/m < z$. If this latter relation does not hold, then $z \le n/m$ and we have

$$\frac{n - 1}{m} \le y < z < \frac{n}{m}.$$

It follows from this (as in Exercise 5.D) that $z - y \le 1/m$, contradicting the fact that $1/m < z - y$.

Q.E.D.

If F is an Archimedean field with at least one irrational element ξ, then the irrational elements of F are also dense in the sense that between any two elements of F there is an irrational element of F.

5.17 THEOREM. *If the Archimedean field F contains an irrational element ξ and if $y < z$, then there is a rational number r such that the irrational element $r\xi$ satisfies $y < r\xi < z$.*

The proof of the result is very close to that of Theorem 5.16 except that it is based on Theorem 5.15 rather than 5.14(b). We leave it as an exercise for the reader.

Nested Intervals

The next result provides a theoretical basis for the binary (= base 2) expansion of the fractional part of an element in an Archimedean field. A similar result can be obtained for any base.

5.18   THEOREM.   *Let x be an element of an Archimedean field F. For each integer $n = 0, 1, 2, \ldots$, there is a closed interval*

$$I_n = \left[a_n, a_n + \frac{1}{2^n} \right]$$

containing the point x, where a_n is a rational element and

$$I_{n+1} \subseteq I_n \text{ for } n = 0, 1, 2, \ldots.$$

PROOF.   It is no loss of generality (why?) to assume that $x \geq 0$, as we shall do. Then there is an integer n_0 such that x belongs to the interval

$$I_0 = [n_0, n_0 + 1].$$

Let $a_0 = n_0$ so that x is in $I_0 = [a_0, a_0 + 1]$ and consider the two closed intervals obtained by bisecting I_0, namely, the intervals

$$[a_0, a_0 + \tfrac{1}{2}], \qquad [a_0 + \tfrac{1}{2}, a_0 + 1].$$

If the point x belongs to the first of these two intervals, we put $a_1 = a_0$; otherwise, we put $a_1 = a_0 + \tfrac{1}{2}$. Therefore, the point x belongs to the interval $I_1 = [a_1, a_1 + \tfrac{1}{2}]$. We then bisect the interval I_1 to obtain the two intervals

$$\left[a_1, a_1 + \frac{1}{2^2} \right], \qquad \left[a_1 + \frac{1}{2^2}, a_1 + \frac{1}{2} \right].$$

If the point x belongs to the first of these two intervals, we put $a_2 = a_1$; otherwise, we put

$$a_2 = a_1 + \frac{1}{2^2}.$$

Therefore, the point x belongs to the interval

$$I_2 = \left[a_2, a_2 + \frac{1}{2^2} \right].$$

By continuing in this manner, we obtain intervals I_n for $n = 0, 1, 2, \ldots$ each containing x. (See Figure 5.1.) Moreover, the end points of these intervals are rational elements of F and $I_{n+1} \subseteq I_n$ for each n.

Q.E.D.

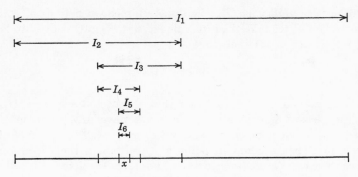

Figure 5.1.   Nested intervals.

We shall often say that a sequence of closed intervals I_n, $n \in \mathbf{N}$, is nested in case the chain

$$I_1 \supseteq I_2 \supseteq I_3 \supseteq \ldots \supseteq I_n \supseteq I_{n+1} \supseteq \ldots$$

of inclusions holds. We can then summarize the content of Theorem 5.18 informally by saying that every element of an Archimedean field F is the common point of a nested sequence of non-empty closed intervals in F.

It is an important consequence of Theorem 5.18 that *to every element of an Archimedean field F, there corresponds a point on the line*. For having chosen an origin and a unit length on the line, we can lay off the integral points. Once we have bracketed an element between two integral points, we bisect repeatedly. Thus we associate a unique point on the line to each element in the Archimedean field F. It must not be supposed, however, that *every* point of the line is necessarily the correspondent of an element in F. In fact, if the field F is the field $\mathbf{Q}$ of rational numbers, then we know that not every point of the line is needed to represent all the elements of $\mathbf{Q}$.

We conclude these remarks about Theorem 5.18 by observing that it does *not* assert that if (I_n) is any nested sequence of non-empty closed intervals, then there is a point x in F which belongs to each interval. For, let ξ be any irrational element of an Archimedean field F. According to Theorem 5.18 there is a nested sequence (J_n) of closed intervals

$$J_n = \left[a_n, a_n + \frac{1}{2^n} \right]$$

with rational end points which contain ξ as a common point (and it is easy to see it is the only common point). We now look at the corresponding sequence of intervals (K_n) in the Archimedean field Q of rational numbers; that is, we take the intervals K_n, $n \in N$, in Q defined to be the set of elements x in Q such that

$$a_n \leq x \leq a_n + \frac{1}{2^n} \cdot$$

The reader should convince himself that the nested sequence (K_n) of non-empty closed intervals in Q does not have any common point, since ξ is not an element of Q. Thus not every nested sequence of closed intervals in Q has a common point in Q, although the corresponding sequence will have a common point in a larger Archimedean field. The essential distinction between the real number system R and any other Archimedean field F is that *every* nested sequence of closed intervals in R has a common point. It is this property that assures that there are no "gaps" in the real number system.

Exercises

5.A. No ordered field contains only a finite number of elements.

5.B. In an ordered field, if $a^2 + b^2 = 0$, then $a = b = 0$.

5.C. Show that it is not possible to make the complex numbers into an ordered field.

5.D. If $0 \leq x \leq b$ and $0 \leq y \leq b$, then $|x - y| \leq b$. More generally, if $a \leq x \leq b$ and $a \leq y \leq b$, then $|x - y| \leq b - a$.

5.E. If $1 + a > 0$ and $n \in N$, then $(1 + a)^n \geq 1 + na$. (Hint: use mathematical induction.) This inequality is sometimes called Bernoulli's Inequality.†

5.F. Suppose $c > 1$. If $n \in N$, then $c^n \geq c$. More generally, if $m, n \in N$ and $m \geq n$, then $c^m \geq c^n$. (Hint: $c = 1 + a$ with $a > 0$.)

5.G. Suppose $0 < c < 1$. If $n \in N$ then $0 < c^n < c$. More generally, if $m, n \in N$ and $m \geq n$, then $c^m \leq c^n$.

5.H. If $n \in N$, then $n < 2^n$.

5.I. If a, b are positive real numbers and $n \in N$, then $a^n < b^n$ if and only if $a < b$.

5.J. Show that the rational numbers form an Archimedean field with the order given in Example 5.2(a).

5.K. Show that the ordered field $Q(t)$ is not Archimedean with the order given in Example 5.2(c).

5.L. Show that an ordered field is Archimedean if and only if for each element $z > 0$ there is a natural number n such that

$$0 < \frac{1}{2^n} < z.$$

† JACOB BERNOULLI (1654–1705) was a member of a Swiss family that produced several mathematicians who played an important role in the development of calculus.

5.M. Show that statements (i) and (ii) after Theorem 5.14 do not hold in an Archimedean field.

5.N. Give the details of the proof of Theorem 5.17.

5.O. Explain how Theorem 5.18 provides a basis for the binary expansion of the fractional part of an element in an Archimedean field.

5.P. Modify Theorem 5.18 to provide a basis for the decimal expansion of a fraction.

5.Q. Prove that the intervals in Theorem 5.18 have x as the only common point.

Section 6   The Real Number System

We have come to the point where we shall introduce a formal description of the real number system R. Since we are more concerned in this text with the study of real functions than the development of the number system, we choose to introduce R as an Archimedean field which has one additional property.

The reader will recall from Section 5 that if F is an ordered field and if a, b belong to F and $a \leq b$, then the closed interval determined by a, b, which we shall denote by $[a, b]$, consists of all elements x in F satisfying $a \leq x \leq b$. It will also be recalled from Theorem 5.18 that if x is any element of an Archimedean field F, then there is a nested sequence (I_n) of non-empty closed intervals whose only common point is x. However, it was seen at the end of Section 5, that a nested sequence of closed intervals does not always have a common point in certain Archimedean fields (such as Q). It is this property that we now use to characterize the real number system among general Archimedean fields.

6.1 DEFINITION. An Archimedean field R is said to be **complete** if each sequence of non-empty closed intervals $I_n = [a_n, b_n]$, $n \in \mathrm{N}$, of R which is nested in the sense that

$$I_1 \supseteq I_2 \supseteq \cdots \supseteq I_n \supseteq \cdots,$$

has an element which belongs to all of the intervals I_n.

6.2 ASSUMPTION. In the remainder of this book, we shall assume that there exists a complete ordered field which we shall call the **real number system** and shall denote by R. An element of R will be called a **real number**.

We have introduced R axiomatically, in that we assume that it is a set which satisfies a certain list of properties. This approach raises the question as to whether such a set exists and to what extent it is uniquely determined. Since we shall not settle these questions, we have frankly identified as an assumption that there is a complete ordered field. However a few words supporting the reasonableness of this assumption are in order.

The existence of a set which is a complete ordered field can be demonstrated by actual construction. If one feels sufficiently familiar with the rational field Q, one can define real numbers to be special subsets of Q and define addition, multiplication, and order relations between these subsets in such a way as to obtain a complete ordered field. There are two standard procedures that are used in doing this: one is Dedekind's method of "cuts" which is discussed in the books of W. Rudin and E. Landau that are cited in the References. The second way is Cantor's method of "Cauchy sequences" which is discussed in the book of N. T. Hamilton and J. Landin.

In the last paragraph we have asserted that it is possible to construct a model of R from Q (in at least two different ways). It is also possible to construct a model of R from the set N of natural numbers and this is often taken as the starting point by those who, like Kronecker,† regard the natural numbers as given by God. However, since even the set of natural numbers has its subtleties (such as the Well-ordering Property), we feel that the most satisfactory procedure is to go through the process of first constructing the set N from primitive set theoretic concepts, then developing the set Z of integers, next constructing the field Q of rationals, and finally the set R. This procedure is not particularly difficult to follow and it is edifying; however, it is rather lengthy. Since it is presented in detail in the book of N. T. Hamilton and J. Landin, it will not be given here.

From the remarks already made, it is clear that complete ordered fields can be constructed in different ways. Thus we cannot say that there is a unique complete ordered field. However, it is true that all of the methods of construction suggested above lead to complete ordered fields that are "isomorphic." (This means that if R_1 and R_2 are complete ordered fields obtained by these constructions, then there exists a one-one mapping φ of R_1 onto R_2 such that (i) φ sends a rational element of R_1 into the corresponding rational element of R_2, (ii) φ sends $a + b$ into $\varphi(a) + \varphi(b)$, (iii) φ sends ab into $\varphi(a)\varphi(b)$, and (iv) φ sends a positive

---

† LEOPOLD KRONECKER (1823–1891) studied with Dirichlet in Berlin and Kummer in Bonn. After making a fortune before he was thirty, he returned to mathematics. He is known for his work in algebra and number theory and for his personal opposition to the ideas of Cantor on set theory.

element of R_1 into a positive element of R_2.) Within naïve set theory, we can provide an argument showing that any two complete ordered fields are isomorphic in the sense described. Whether this argument can be formalized within a given system of logic depends on the rules of inference employed in the system. Thus the question of the extent to which the real number system can be regarded as being uniquely determined is a rather delicate logical and philosophical issue. However, for our purposes this uniqueness (or lack of it) is not important, for we can choose any particular complete ordered field as our model for the real number system.

Suprema and Infima

We now introduce the notion of an upper bound of a set of real numbers. This idea will be of utmost importance in later sections.

6.3   DEFINITION.   Let S be a subset of **R**. An element u of **R** is said to be an **upper bound** of S if $s \leq u$ for all s in S. Similarly, an element w of **R** is said to be a **lower bound** of S if $w \leq s$ for all s in S.

It should be observed that a subset S of **R** may not have an upper bound; but if it has one, then it has infinitely many. For example, if $S_1 = \{x \in \mathbf{R} : x \geq 0\}$, then S_1 has no upper bound. Similarly, the set $S_2 = \{1, 2, 3, \ldots\}$ has no upper bound. The situation is different for the interval $S_3 = \{x \in \mathbf{R} : 0 < x < 1\}$ which has 1 as an upper bound; in fact, any real number $u \geq 1$ is also an upper bound of S_3. Again, the set $S_4 = \{x \in \mathbf{R} : 0 \leq x \leq 1\}$ has the same upper bounds as S_3. However, the reader may note that S_4 actually contains one of its upper bounds. Note that any real number is an upper bound for the empty set.

As a matter of terminology, when a set S has an upper bound, we shall say that it is **bounded above**; when a set has a lower bound, we shall say that it is **bounded below**. If S is bounded both above and below, we say that it is **bounded**. If S lacks either an upper or a lower bound, we say that it is **unbounded**. For example, both S_1 and S_2 are unbounded but are bounded below, whereas both S_3 and S_4 are bounded.

6.4   DEFINITION.   Let S be a subset of **R** which is bounded above. An upper bound of S is said to be a **supremum** (or a **least upper bound**) of S if it is less than any other upper bound of S. Similarly, if S is bounded below, then a lower bound of S is said to be an **infimum** (or a **greatest lower bound**) of S if it is greater than any other lower bound of S. (See Figure 6.1 on the next page.)

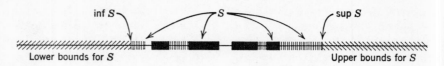

Figure 6.1   Suprema and infima.

Expressed differently, a real number u is a supremum of a subset S if it satisfies the following conditions:

(i) $s \leq u$ for all s in S;
(ii) if $s \leq v$ for all s in S, then $u \leq v$.

The first condition makes u an upper bound of S and the second makes it less than, or equal to, any upper bound of S.

It is apparent that there can be only one supremum for a given set. For, suppose $u_1 \neq u_2$ are both suprema of S; then they are both upper bounds of S. Since u_1 is a supremum of S and u_2 is an upper bound of S we must have $u_1 \leq u_2$. A similar argument gives $u_2 \leq u_1$, showing that $u_1 = u_2$, a contradiction. Hence a set S can have at most one supremum; a similar argument shows that it can have at most one infimum. When these numbers exist, we sometimes denote them by

$$\sup S, \qquad \inf S.$$

It is often convenient to have another characterization of the supremum of a set.

6.5   Lemma. *A number u is the supremum of a non-empty set S of real numbers if and only if it has the following two properties:*

(i) *There are no elements s of S with $u < s$.*
(ii) *If $v < u$, then there is an element s in S such that $v < s$.*

proof. Suppose u satisfies (i) and (ii). The first condition implies that u is an upper bound of S. If u is not the supremum of S, let v be an upper bound of S such that $v < u$. Property (ii) then contradicts the possibility of v being an upper bound.

Conversely, let u be the supremum of S. Since u is an upper bound of S, then (i) holds. If $v < u$, then v is not an upper bound of S. Therefore, there exists at least one element of S exceeding v, establishing (ii).

                                                              Q.E.D.

The reader should convince himself that the number $x = 1$ is the supremum of both of the sets S_3 and S_4 which were defined after Definition 6.3. It is to be noted that one of these sets contains its supremum, whereas the other does not. Thus *when we say that a set has a supremum we are making no statement as to whether the set contains the supremum as an element or not.*

Since the supremum of a set S is a special upper bound, it is plain that only sets which are bounded above can have a supremum. The empty set is bounded above by any real number; hence it does not have a supremum. However, it is a deep and fundamental property of the real number system that every non-empty subset of **R** which is bounded above does have a supremum. We now establish this result.

6.6 SUPREMUM PRINCIPLE. *Every non-empty subset of real numbers which has an upper bound also has a supremum.*

PROOF.   Let a be some real number which is not an upper bound of a non-empty set S and let b be an upper bound of S. Then $a < b$, and we let I_1 be the closed interval $[a, b]$. If the point $(a + b)/2$ of I_1 is an upper bound of S, we let $I_2 = [a, (a + b)/2]$; otherwise, we let $I_2 = [(a + b)/2, b]$. In either case, we relabel the left and right end point of I_2 to be a_2 and b_2, respectively. If the midpoint $(a_2 + b_2)/2$ of I_2 is an upper bound of S, we let $I_3 = [a_2, (a_2 + b_2)/2]$; otherwise, we let $I_3 = [(a_2 + b_2)/2, b_2]$. We then relabel the end points, bisect the interval, and so on. In this way we obtain a nested sequence (I_n) of non-empty closed intervals such that the length of I_n is $(b - a)/2^{n-1}$, the left end point a_n of I_n is not an upper bound of S, but the right end point b_n of I_n is an upper bound of the set S. According to the completeness (cf. Definition 6.1) of the real numbers, there is a real number x which belongs to all of the intervals I_n. We shall now show, using Lemma 6.5, that x is the supremum of S.

Suppose there exists an element s in S such that $x < s$. Then $s - x > 0$ and there exists a natural number n such that

$$\text{length } (I_n) = b_n - a_n = \frac{b - a}{2^{n-1}} < s - x.$$

Since x belongs to I_n, we have $a_n \leq x \leq b_n < s$, which contradicts the fact that b_n is an upper bound of S. Hence x is an upper bound of S.

Now suppose that $v < x$; since $x - v > 0$, there exists a natural number m such that

$$\text{length } (I_m) = b_m - a_m = \frac{b - a}{2^{m-1}} < x - v.$$

Since $x \in I_m$, then $v < a_m \leq x \leq b_m$. By construction, a_m is not an upper bound of S, so there exists an element s' in S such that $v < a_m < s'$. According to Lemma 6.5, the point x is the supremum of S.

Q.E.D.

6.7 COROLLARY. *Every non-empty set of real numbers which has a lower bound also has an infimum.*

PROOF. Let S be bounded below. In order to show that S has an infimum, we can proceed in two different ways. The first method is to use the idea of the proof of Theorem 6.6, replacing upper bounds by lower bounds, $>$ by $<$, etc. The reader is advised to carry out this proof without reference to the details given above. The second method of proof is to replace the set S with its "reflection"

$$S_1 = \{-s : s \in S\}.$$

Thus a real number is in S_1 if and only if its negative is in S. Since S is bounded below (say by w), then S_1 is bounded above (by $-w$). Invoking Theorem 6.6, we infer that S_1 has a supremum u. From this we show that $-u$ is the infimum of S. The details of this argument are left as an exercise.

Q.E.D.

The reader should note where the completeness of the real number system was used in the proof of the Supremum Principle. It is a fact of some interest and importance that if F is an ordered field in which every non-empty set which has an upper bound also has a supremum, then the ordering is necessarily Archimedean and the completeness property stated in Definition 6.1 also holds (see Exercises 6.J, 6.K). Hence we could characterize the real number system as an ordered field in which the Supremum Principle holds, and this means of introducing the real number system is often used. We chose the approach used here because it seems more intuitive to us and brings out all the needed properties in a reasonably natural way.

Dedekind Cuts

In order to establish the connection between the preceding considerations and Dedekind's† method of completing the rational numbers to obtain the real number system, we shall include the next theorem. First, however, it is convenient to introduce a definition.

6.8 DEFINITION. Let F be an ordered field. An ordered pair of non-void subsets A, B of F is said to form a cut in F if $A \cap B = \emptyset$, $A \cup B = F$, and if whenever $a \in A$ and $b \in B$, then $a < b$.

† RICHARD DEDEKIND (1831–1916) was a student of Gauss. He contributed to number theory, but he is best known for his work on the foundations of the real number system.

A typical example of a cut in F is obtained for a fixed element ξ in F by defining

$$A = \{x \in F : x \leq \xi\}, \qquad B = \{x \in F : x > \xi\}.$$

Both A and B are non-void and they form a cut in F. Alternatively, we could take

$$A_1 = \{x \in F : x < \xi\}, \qquad B_1 = \{x \in F : x \geq \xi\}.$$

We can also define cuts in other ways (see Exercise 6.L) and, in a general Archimedean field F, a cut is not necessarily "determined" by an element in the sense that ξ determines the cuts A, B or A_1, B_1. However,

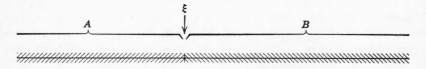

Figure 6.2.   A Dedekind cut.

it is an important property of the real number system that every cut in **R** is determined by some real number. We shall now establish this property.

6.9   CUT PRINCIPLE.   *If the pair A, B forms a cut in* **R**, *then there exists a real number ξ such that every element a in A satisfies $a \leq \xi$ and every element b in B satisfies $b \geq \xi$.*

PROOF.   By hypothesis the sets A, B are non-void. If $b \in B$, then it is an upper bound for the non-void set A. According to the Supremum Principle, the set A has a supremum which we denote by ξ. We shall now show that ξ has the properties stated. Since ξ is an upper bound of A, we have $a \leq \xi$ for all a in A. If b is an element of B, then from the definition of a cut, $a < b$ for all a in A so that b is an upper bound of A. Therefore (why?), we infer that $\xi \leq b$, as was to be proved.

Q.E.D.

The Cantor Set

We shall conclude this section by introducing a subset of the unit interval I which is of considerable interest and is frequently useful in constructing examples and counter-examples in real analysis. We shall denote this set by **F** and refer to it as the *Cantor set*, although it is also sometimes called *Cantor's ternary set* or the *Cantor discontinuum*.

One way of describing F is as the set of real numbers in I which have a ternary (= base 3) expansion using only the digits 0, 2. However, we choose to define it in different terms. In a sense that will be made more precise, F consists of those points in I that remain after "middle third" intervals have been successively removed.

To be more explicit: if we remove the open middle third of I, we obtain the set

$$F_1 = [0, \tfrac{1}{3}] \cup [\tfrac{2}{3}, 1].$$

If we remove the open middle third of each of the two closed intervals in F_1, we obtain the set

$$F_2 = [0, \tfrac{1}{9}] \cup [\tfrac{2}{9}, \tfrac{1}{3}] \cup [\tfrac{2}{3}, \tfrac{7}{9}] \cup [\tfrac{8}{9}, 1].$$

Hence F_2 is the union of $4 (= 2^2)$ closed intervals all of which are of the form $[k/3^2, (k + 1)/3^2]$. We now obtain the set F_3 by removing the open middle third of each of these sets. In general, if F_n has been con-

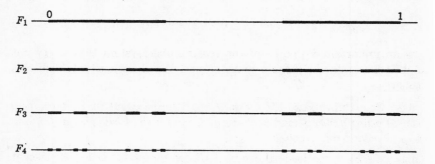

Figure 6.3.   The Cantor set.

structed and consists of the union of 2^n closed intervals of the form $[k/3^n, (k + 1)/3^n]$, then we obtain F_{n+1} by removing the open middle third of each of these intervals. The Cantor set is what remains after this process has been carried out for each n in N.

6.10   DEFINITION.   The **Cantor set** F is the intersection of the sets $F_n, n \in$ N, obtained by successive removal of open middle thirds.

At first glance, it may appear that every point is ultimately removed by this process. However, this is evidently not the case since the points $0, \tfrac{1}{3}, \tfrac{2}{3}, 1$ belong to all the sets $F_n, n \in$ N, and hence to the Cantor set F. In fact, it is easily seen that there are an infinite number of points in F, even though F is relatively thin in some other respects. In fact, it is not difficult to show that there are a non-denumberable number of elements of F and that the points of F can be put into one-one corre-spondence with the points of I. Hence the set F contains a large number of elements.

We now give two senses in which F is "thin." First we observe that F does not contain any non-void interval. For if x belongs to F and (a, b) is an open interval containing x, then (a, b) contains some middle thirds that were removed to obtain F. (Why?) Hence (a, b) is not a subset of the Cantor set, but contains infinitely many points in its complement $\mathfrak{C}(F)$.

A second sense in which F is thin refers to "length." While it is not possible to define length for arbitrary subsets of R, it is easy to convince oneself that F cannot have positive length. For, the length of F_1 is $\frac{2}{3}$, that of F_2 is $\frac{4}{9}$, and, in general, the length of F_n is $(\frac{2}{3})^n$. Since F is a sub-set of F_n, it cannot have length exceeding that of F_n. Since this must be true for each n in N, we conclude that F, although uncountable, cannot have positive length.

As strange as the Cantor set may seem, it is relatively well behaved in many respects. It provides us with a bit of insight into how compli-cated subsets of R can be and how little our intuition guides us. It also serves as a test for the concepts that we will introduce in later sections and whose import are not fully grasped in terms of intervals and other very elementary subsets.

Exercises

6.A. Show that the open intervals $J_n = (0, 1/n)$, $n \in$ N, do not have a common point.

6.B. Show that the unbounded sets

$$K_n = \{x \in \mathrm{R} : x \geq n\}, \ n \in \mathrm{N},$$

do not have a common point.

6.C. Prove that a non-empty finite set of real numbers has a supremum and an infimum. (Hint: use induction.)

6.D. If a subset S of real numbers contains an upper bound, then this upper bound is the supremum of S.

6.E. Give an example of a set of rational numbers which is bounded but which does not have a rational supremum.

6.F. Give an example of a set of irrational numbers which has a rational supremum.

6.G. Prove that the union of two bounded sets is bounded.

6.H. Give an example of a countable collection of bounded sets whose union is bounded and an example where the union is unbounded.

6.I. Carry out the two proofs of Corollary 6.7 that were suggested.

6.J. Prove that if F is an ordered field in which every non-empty set which has an upper bound also has a supremum, then F is an Archimedean field.

6.K. If (I_n) is a nested sequence of closed intervals, $I_n = [a_n, b_n]$, $n \in \mathbf{N}$, show that the numbers

$$a = \sup \{a_n\}, \qquad b = \inf \{b_n\},$$

belong to all of the I_n. In fact, show that the intersection of the I_n, $n \in \mathbf{N}$, consists of the interval $[a, b]$. Conclude, therefore, that in an ordered field in which every non-empty set which has an upper bound also has a supremum, the Completeness Property of Definition 6.1 also holds.

6.L. Let $A = \{x \in \mathbf{Q} : x \leq 0 \text{ or } x^2 < 2\}$ and $B = \{x \in \mathbf{Q} : x > 0 \text{ and } x^2 > 2\}$. Prove that the pair A, B forms a cut in $\mathbf{Q}$. Show that there does not exist a rational number c which is both an upper bound for A and a lower bound for B. Hence there is no rational number determining this cut.

6.M. Show that every element in the Cantor set $\mathbf{F}$ has a ternary ($=$ base 3) expansion using the digits 0, 2.

6.N. Show that the Cantor set $\mathbf{F}$ is a non-denumerable subset of $\mathbf{I}$. [Hint: if the denumberable collection of "right-hand" end points of $\mathbf{F}$ is deleted, then what remains can be put into one-one correspondence with *all* of the non-denumberable subset $[0, 1)$ of $\mathbf{R}$.]

6.O. Show that every open interval (a, b) containing a point of $\mathbf{F}$ also contains an entire "middle third" set, which belongs to $\mathcal{C}(\mathbf{F})$. Hence the Cantor set $\mathbf{F}$ does not contain any non-void open interval.

6.P. By removing sets with ever decreasing length, show that we can construct a "Cantor-like" set which has positive length. How large can we make the length?

6.Q. Show that $\mathbf{F}$ is not the union of a countable collection of closed intervals.

6.R. If S is a bounded set of real numbers and if S_0 is a non-empty subset of S, then

$$\inf S \leq \inf S_0 \leq \sup S_0 \leq \sup S.$$

(Sometimes it is more convenient to express this relation in another form. Let f be defined on a non-empty set D and have bounded range in $\mathbf{R}$. If D_0 is a non-empty subset of D, then

$$\inf \{f(x) : x \in D\} \leq \inf \{f(x) : x \in D_0\}$$

$$\leq \sup \{f(x) : x \in D_0\} \leq \sup \{f(x) : x \in D\}.)$$

6.S. Let X and Y be non-empty sets and let f be defined on $X \times Y$ to a bounded subset of $\mathbf{R}$. Let

$$f_1(x) = \sup \{f(x, y) : y \in Y\},$$
$$f_2(y) = \sup \{f(x, y) : x \in X\}.$$

Establish the Principle of Iterated Suprema:

$$\sup \{f(x, y) : x \in X, y \in Y\} = \sup \{f_1(x) : x \in X\}$$
$$= \sup \{f_2(y) : y \in Y\}.$$

(We sometimes express this in symbols by

$$\sup_{x,\,y} f(x, y) = \sup_x \sup_y f(x, y) = \sup_y \sup_x f(x, y).)$$

6.T. Let f and f_1 be as in the preceding exercise and let

$$g_2(y) = \inf \{f(x, y) : x \in X\}.$$

Prove that

$$\sup \{g_2(y) : y \in Y\} \leq \inf \{f_1(x) : x \in X\}.$$

Show that strict inequality can hold. (We sometimes express this inequality by

$$\sup_y \inf_x f(x, y) \leq \inf_x \sup_y f(x, y).)$$

6.U. Let X be a non-empty set and let f and g be functions on X to bounded subsets of $\mathbf{R}$. Show that

$$\inf \{f(x) : x \in X\} + \inf \{g(x) : x \in X\} \leq \inf \{f(x) + g(x) : x \in X\}$$
$$\leq \inf \{f(x) : x \in X\} + \sup \{g(x) : x \in X\} \leq \sup \{f(x) + g(x) : x \in X\}$$
$$\leq \sup \{f(x) : x \in X\} + \sup \{g(x) : x \in X\}.$$

Give examples to show that each inequality can be strict.

Projects

6.α. If a and b are positive real numbers and if $n \in \mathbf{N}$, we have defined a^n and b^n. It follows by mathematical induction that if $m, n \in \mathbf{N}$, then

(i) $a^m a^n = a^{m+n}$;

(ii) $(a^m)^n = a^{mn}$;

(iii) $(ab)^n = a^n b^n$;

(iv) $a < b$ if and only if $a^n < b^n$.

We shall adopt the convention that $a^0 = 1$ and $a^{-n} = 1/a^n$. Thus we have defined a^x for x in $\mathbf{Z}$ and it is readily checked that properties (i)–(iii) remain valid.

We wish to define a^x for rational numbers x in such a way that (i)–(iii) hold. The following steps can be used as an outline. Throughout we shall assume that a and b are real numbers exceeding 1.

(a) If r is a rational number given by $r = m/n$, where m and n are integers and $n > 0$ and define $S_r(a) = \{x \in \mathbf{R} : 0 \leq x^n \leq a^m\}$. Show that $S_r(a)$ is a bounded non-empty subset of $\mathbf{R}$ and define $a^r = \sup S_r(a)$.

(b) Prove that $z = a^r$ is the unique positive root of the equation $z^n = a^m$. (Hint: there is a constant K such that if ϵ satisfies $0 < \epsilon < 1$, $(1 + \epsilon)^n < 1 + K\epsilon$. Hence if $x^n < a^m < y^n$, there exists an $\epsilon > 0$ such that

$$x^n (1 + \epsilon)^n < a^m < y^n/(1 + \epsilon)^n.)$$

(c) Show that the value of a^r given in part (a) does not depend on the representation of r in the form m/n. Also show that if r is an integer, then the new definition of a^r gives the same value as the old one.

(d) Show that if $r, s \in Q$, then $a^r a^s = a^{r+s}$ and $(a^r)^s = a^{rs}$.

(e) Show that $a^r b^r = (ab)^r$.

(f) If $r \in Q$, then $a < b$ if and only if $a^r < b^r$.

(g) If $r, s \in Q$, then $r < s$ if and only if $a^r < a^s$.

(h) If c is a real number satisfying $0 < c < 1$, we define $c^r = (1/c)^{-r}$. Show that parts (d) and (e) hold and that a result similar to (g), but with the inequality reversed, holds.

6.β. Now that a^x has been defined for rational numbers x, we wish to define it for real x. In doing so, make free use of the results of the preceding project. As before, let a and b be a real numbers exceeding 1. If $u \in R$, let

$$T_u(a) = \{a^r : r \in Q, r \leq u\}.$$

Show that $T_u(a)$ is a bounded non-empty subset of R and define

$$a^u = \sup T_u(a).$$

Prove that this definition yields the same result as the previous one when u is rational. Establish the properties that correspond to the statements given in parts (d)–(g) of the preceding project. The very important function which has been defined on R in this project is called the **exponential function** (to the base a). Some alternative definitions will be given in later sections. Sometimes it is convenient to denote this function by the symbol

$$\exp_a,$$

and denote its value at the real number u by

$$\exp_a(u)$$

instead of the more familiar a^u.

6.γ. Making use of the properties of the exponential function that were established in the preceding project, show that $\exp_a$ is a one-one function with domain R and range $\{y \in R : y > 0\}$. Under our standing assumption that $a > 1$, this exponential function is strictly increasing in the sense that if $x < u$, then $\exp_a(x) < \exp_a(u)$. Therefore, the inverse function exists with domain $\{v \in R : v > 0\}$ and range R. We call this inverse function the **logarithm** (to the base a) and denote it by

$$\log_a.$$

Show that $\log_a$ is a strictly increasing function and that

$$\exp_a(\log_a(v)) = v \text{ for } v > 0,$$
$$\log_a(\exp_a(u)) = u \text{ for } u \in R.$$

Also show that $\log_a(1) = 0$, $\log_a(a) = 1$, and that

$$\log_a(v) < 0 \text{ for } v < 1,$$
$$\log_a(v) > 0 \text{ for } v > 1.$$

Prove that if $v, w > 0$, then

$$\log_a(vw) = \log_a(v) + \log_a(w).$$

Moreover, if $v > 0$ and $x \in \mathbf{R}$, then

$$\log_a(v^x) = x \log_a(v).$$

II

The Topology of Cartesian Spaces

The sections of Chapter I were devoted to developing the algebraic properties, the order properties, and the completeness property of the real number system. Considerable use of these properties will be made in this and later chapters.

Although it would be possible to turn immediately to a discussion of sequences of real numbers and continuous real functions, we prefer to delay the study of these topics a bit longer. Indeed, we shall inject here a brief discussion of the Cartesian spaces R^p and make a rudimentary study of the topology of these spaces. Once this has been done, we will be well prepared for a reasonably sophisticated attack on the analytic notions of convergence and continuity and will not need to interrupt our study of these notions to develop the topological properties that are required for an adequate understanding of analysis.

As mentioned in the Preface, we have elected to keep our discussion at the level of the finite dimensional Cartesian spaces R^p. We chose to do this for several reasons. One reason is that it seems to be easier to grasp the ideas and to remember them by drawing diagrams in the plane. Moreover, in much of analysis (to say nothing of its application to geometry, physics, engineering, economics, etc.) it is often essential to consider functions that depend on more than one quantity. Fortunately, our intuition for R^2 and R^3 usually carries over without much change to the space R^p, and therefore it is no more difficult to consider this case. Finally, the experience gained from a study of the spaces R^p can be immediately transferred to a more general topological setting whenever we want.

Section 7 Cartesian Spaces

The reader will recall from Definition 1.9 that the Cartesian product $A \times B$ of two non-void sets A and B consists of the set of all ordered pairs (a, b) with a in A and b in B. Similarly, the Cartesian product $A \times B \times C$ of three non-void sets A, B, C consists of the set of all ordered triples (a, b, c) with a in A, b in B, and c in C. In the same manner, if $A_1, A_2, \ldots, A_p$ are p non-void sets, then their Cartesian product $A_1 \times A_2 \times \cdots \times A_p$ consists of all ordered "p-tuples" $(a_1, a_2, \ldots, a_p)$ with a_i in A_i for $i = 1, 2, \ldots, p$. In the case where the sets are all the same (that is, $A_1 = A_2 = \cdots = A_p$), we shall denote the Cartesian product $A_1 \times A_2 \times \cdots \times A_p$ by the more compact symbol A^p. In particular, we employ this notation when $A = \mathbf{R}$.

7.1 DEFINITION. If p is a natural number, then the p-fold Cartesian product of the real number system $\mathbf{R}$ is called p-dimensional real Cartesian space.

Just as we sometimes refer to $\mathbf{R} = \mathbf{R}^1$ as the real line, we shall sometimes refer to $\mathbf{R}^2$ as the real plane.

For the sake of brevity, we shall denote the p-tuple $(\xi_1, \xi_2, \ldots, \xi_p)$ by the single letter x and use similar notations for other p-tuples. The real numbers $\xi_1, \xi_2, \ldots, \xi_p$ will be called the first, second, . . ., pth coordinates (or components) respectively, of x. Sometimes we refer to x as a vector or sometimes merely as a point or element of $\mathbf{R}^p$. Particular mention should be made of the zero vector or origin which is the element θ of $\mathbf{R}^p$, all of whose coordinates are the real number zero.

The Algebra of Vectors

We shall now introduce two algebraic operations in $\mathbf{R}^p$. It is suggested that the reader interpret the geometrical meaning of these operations in $\mathbf{R}^2$.

7.2 DEFINITION. If c is a real number and $x = (\xi_1, \xi_2, \ldots, \xi_p)$ is an element of $\mathbf{R}^p$, then we define cx to be the element of $\mathbf{R}^p$ given by

$$(7.1) \qquad cx = (c\xi_1, c\xi_2, \ldots, c\xi_p).$$

If $y = (\eta_1, \eta_2, \ldots, \eta_p)$, then we define $x + y$ to be the element of $\mathbf{R}^p$ given by

$$(7.2) \qquad x + y = (\xi_1 + \eta_1, \xi_2 + \eta_2, \ldots, \xi_p + \eta_p).$$

The vector cx, given by (7.1), is called the product or multiple of x by the real number c. Similarly, the vector denoted by $x + y$, given by formula (7.2), is called the sum of the elements x and y. It should be noted that the plus sign on the right side of equation (7.2) is the ordinary addition of real numbers, while the plus sign on the left side of this equation is being defined by this formula. When $p > 1$, we shall denote the zero element of $\mathbf{R}^p$ by θ instead of 0.

7.3   Theorem.   *Let x, y, z be any elements of $\mathbf{R}^p$ and let b, c be any real numbers. Then*

(A1) $x + y = y + x$;

(A2) $(x + y) + z = x + (y + z)$;

(A3) $\theta + x = x$ *and* $x + \theta = x$;

(A4)   *for each x in $\mathbf{R}^p$, the element $u = (-1)x$ satisfies $x + u = \theta$, and $u + x = \theta$;*

(M1) $1x = x$;

(M2) $b(cx) = (bc)x$;

(D) $c(x + y) = cx + cy$ *and* $(b + c)x = bx + cx$.

PARTIAL PROOF.   Most of this will be left as an exercise for the reader; we shall present only samples.

For (A1) we note that, by definition,

$$x + y = (\xi_1 + \eta_1, \xi_2 + \eta_2, \ldots, \xi_p + \eta_p).$$

Since the real numbers form a field, it follows from property (A1) of Definition 4.1 that $\xi_i + \eta_i = \eta_i + \xi_i$, for $i = 1, 2, \ldots, p$, whence $x + y = y + x$.

For (A4), note that $u = (-1)x = (-\xi_1, -\xi_2, \ldots, -\xi_p)$; hence

$$x + u = (\xi_1 - \xi_1, \xi_2 - \xi_2, \ldots, \xi_p - \xi_p) = (0, 0, \ldots, 0) = \theta.$$

To prove (M2), we observe that

$$b(cx) = b(c\xi_1, c\xi_2, \ldots, c\xi_p) = (b(c\xi_1), b(c\xi_2), \ldots, b(c\xi_p)).$$

Using property (M2) of Definition 4.1, we have $b(c\xi_i) = (bc)\xi_i$ for $i = 1, 2, \ldots, p$, from which the present (M2) follows.

The proofs of the remaining assertions are left as exercises.

Q.E.D.

As would be expected, we shall denote the elements $(-1)x$ and $x + (-1)y$ by the simpler notations $-x, x - y$, respectively.

The Inner Product

The reader will note that the product defined by equation (7.1) is a function with domain $\mathbf{R} \times \mathbf{R}^p$ and range $\mathbf{R}^p$. We shall now define a function with domain $\mathbf{R}^p \times \mathbf{R}^p$ and range $\mathbf{R}$ that will be useful.

7.4 DEFINITION. If x and y are elements of $\mathbf{R}^p$, we define the inner product, sometimes called the dot or scalar product, of $x = (\xi_1, \xi_2, \ldots, \xi_p)$ and $y = (\eta_1, \eta_2, \ldots, \eta_p)$ to be the real number

$$x \cdot y = \xi_1 \eta_1 + \xi_2 \eta_2 + \cdots + \xi_p \eta_p.$$

The norm (or the length) of x is defined to be the real number

$$|x| = \sqrt{x \cdot x} = (\xi_1{}^2 + \cdots + \xi_p{}^2)^{1/2}.$$

7.5 INNER PRODUCT PROPERTIES. *If x, y, z belong to $\mathbf{R}^p$ and c is a real number, then*

(i) $x \cdot x \geq 0$;

(ii) $x \cdot x = 0$ *if and only if* $x = \theta$;

(iii) $x \cdot y = y \cdot x$;

(iv) $x \cdot (y + z) = x \cdot y + x \cdot z$ *and* $(x + y) \cdot z = x \cdot z + y \cdot z$;

(v) $(cx) \cdot y = c(x \cdot y) = x \cdot (cy)$.

PARTIAL PROOF. For example, the first equality in (iv) states that

$$x \cdot (y + z) = \xi_1(\eta_1 + \zeta_1) + \xi_2(\eta_2 + \zeta_2) + \cdots + \xi_p(\eta_p + \zeta_p)$$
$$= (\xi_1 \eta_1 + \xi_2 \eta_2 + \cdots + \xi_p \eta_p) + (\xi_1 \zeta_1 + \xi_2 \zeta_2 + \cdots + \xi_p \zeta_p)$$
$$= x \cdot y + x \cdot z.$$

The other assertions are proved by similar calculations.

Q.E.D.

We now obtain an equality which was proved by A. Cauchy[†]. Since useful generalizations of this result were established independently by V. Bunyakovskiĭ[‡] and H. A. Schwarz,[§] we shall refer to this result as the C.-B.-S. Inequality.

7.6 C.-B.-S. INEQUALITY. *If x and y are elements of $\mathbf{R}^p$, then*

$$x \cdot y \leq |x|\,|y|.$$

Moreover, if x and y are non-zero, then the equality holds if and only if there is some positive real number c such that $x = cy$.

[†] AUGUSTIN-LOUIS CAUCHY (1789–1857) was the founder of modern analysis but also made profound contributions to other mathematical areas. He served as an engineer under Napoleon, followed Charles X into self-imposed exile, and was excluded from his position at the Collège de France during the years of the July monarchy because he would not take a loyalty oath. Despite his political and religious activities, he found time to write 789 mathematical papers.

[‡] VICTOR BUNYAKOVSKIĬ (1804–1889), a professor at St. Petersburg, established a generalization of the Cauchy Inequality for integrals in 1859. His contribution was overlooked by western writers and was later discovered independently by Schwarz.

[§] HERMANN AMANDUS SCHWARZ (1843–1921) was a student and successor of Weierstrass at Berlin. He made numerous contributions, especially to complex analysis.

PROOF. If a, b are real numbers and $z = ax - by$, then by 7.5(i) we have $z \cdot z \geq 0$. Using (iii), (iv), and (v) of 7.5, we obtain

(7.3) $$0 \leq z \cdot z = a^2 \, x \cdot x - 2ab \, x \cdot y + b^2 \, y \cdot y.$$

Now select $a = |y|$ and $b = |x|$. This yields

(7.4) $$0 \leq |y|^2 \, |x|^2 - 2|y| \, |x| \, (x \cdot y) + |x|^2 \, |y|^2$$
$$= 2|x| \, |y| \, \{ |x| \, |y| - (x \cdot y) \}.$$

Hence it follows that $x \cdot y \leq |x| \, |y|$.

If $x = cy$ with $c > 0$, then it is readily seen that $|x| = c|y|$. Hence it follows that

$$x \cdot y = (cy) \cdot y = c(y \cdot y) = c|y|^2 = (c|y|)|y| = |x| \, |y|,$$

proving that $x \cdot y = |x| \, |y|$.

Conversely, if $x \cdot y = |x| \, |y|$, then from equations (7.3) and (7.4) it follows that when $a = |y|$, $b = |x|$, then the element $z = ax - by$ has the property that $z \cdot z = 0$. In view of Theorem 7.5 (ii) we infer that $z = \theta$, whence $|y|x = |x|y$. Since x and y are not the zero vector θ, then $c = |x|/|y|$ is a positive real number and $x = cy$.

Q.E.D.

7.7   COROLLARY.   *If x, y are elements of $\mathbf{R}^p$, then*

(7.5) $$|x \cdot y| \leq |x| \, |y|.$$

Moreover, if x and y are non-zero, then the equality holds in (7.5) if and only if there is some real number c such that $x = cy$.

This corollary (which is also referred to as the C.-B.-S. Inequality) is easily proved using Theorems 7.5 and 7.6. We leave the details to the reader as an exercise.

If u and v are unit vectors; that is, if $|u| = |v| = 1$, then $|u \cdot v| \leq 1$. In this case the geometrical interpretation of $u \cdot v$ is as the cosine of the angle between u and v. In the space $\mathbf{R}^2$ or $\mathbf{R}^3$, where one can define what is meant by the angle ψ between two vectors x, y, it can be proved that $x \cdot y = |x| \, |y| \cos (\psi)$ and this formula is often used to define the product $x \cdot y$ rather than using Definition 7.4.

We shall now derive the main properties of the length, or norm.

7.8   NORM PROPERTIES.   *Let x, y belong to $\mathbf{R}^p$ and let c be a real number, then*

(i) $|x| \geq 0$;

(ii) $|x| = 0$ *if and only if $x = \theta$;*

(iii) $|cx| = |c| \, |x|$;

(iv) $||x| - |y|| \leq |x \pm y| \leq |x| + |y|$.

PROOF. Property (i) is a restatement of 7.5(i) and property (ii) is a restatement of 7.5(ii).

To show (iii), notice that

$$|cx|^2 = \sum_{i=1}^{p} |c\xi_i|^2 = |c|^2 \sum_{i=1}^{p} |\xi_i|^2 = |c|^2 |x|^2.$$

To prove (iv), we first observe that

$$|x + y|^2 = (x + y) \cdot (x + y) = x \cdot x + 2x \cdot y + y \cdot y.$$

According to Corollary 7.7, $|x \cdot y| \leq |x|\,|y|$, so that

$$|x + y|^2 \leq |x|^2 + 2|x|\,|y| + |y|^2 = (|x| + |y|)^2,$$

which yields the second part of (iv). In addition, we have the inequalities

$$|x| \leq |x + y - y| \leq |x + y| + |y|, \quad |y| \leq |x + y| + |x|.$$

Therefore it is seen that both $|x| - |y|$ and $|y| - |x|$, and hence $||x| - |y||$, are at most equal to $|x + y|$. Consequently, we have

$$||x| - |y|| \leq |x + y| \leq |x| + |y|.$$

Replace y by $-y$ and use the fact that $|y| = |-y|$ to obtain (iv).

Q.E.D.

The real number $|x|$ can be thought of as being either the length of x or as the distance from x to θ. More generally, we often interpret the real number $|x - y|$ as the distance from x to y. With this interpretation, property 7.8(i) implies that the distance from x to y is a non-negative real number. Property 7.8(ii) asserts that the distance from x to y is zero if and only if $x = y$. Property 7.8(iii), with $c = -1$, implies that $|x - y| = |y - x|$ which means that the distance from x to y is equal

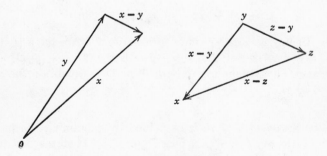

Figure 7.1

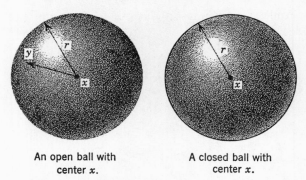

An open ball with   A closed ball with
center x.   center x.

Figure 7.2

to the distance from y to x. Finally, the important property 7.8(iv), which is often called the **Triangle Inequality**, implies that

$$|x - y| \leq |x - z| + |z - y|,$$

which means that the distance from x to y is no greater than the sum of the distance from x to z and the distance from z to y.

7.9   Definition.   Let $x \in \mathbf{R}^p$ and let $r > 0$. Then the set $\{y \in \mathbf{R}^p: |x - y| < r\}$ is called the **open ball** with center x and radius r and the set $\{y \in \mathbf{R}^p: |x - y| \leq r\}$ is called the **closed ball** with center x and radius r. The set $\{y \in \mathbf{R}^p: |x - y| = r\}$ is called the **sphere** in $\mathbf{R}^p$ with center x and radius r. (See Figure 7.2.)

Note that the open ball with center x and radius r consists of all points in $\mathbf{R}^p$ whose distance from x is less than r.

7.10   Parallelogram Identity.   *If x and y are any two vectors in* $\mathbf{R}^p$, *then*

$$(7.6) \qquad |x + y|^2 + |x - y|^2 = 2\{|x|^2 + |y|^2\}.$$

proof.   Using the inner product properties 7.5, we have $|x \pm y|^2 = (x \pm y) \cdot (x \pm y) = x \cdot x \pm 2\, x \cdot y + y \cdot y = |x|^2 \pm 2\, x \cdot y + |y|^2$. Upon adding the relations corresponding to both $+$ and $-$, we obtain the relation in (7.6).

Q.E.D.

The name attached to 7.10 is explained by examining the parallelogram with vertices θ, x, $x + y$, y (see Figure 7.3). It states that the sum of the squares of the lengths of the four sides of this parallelogram equals the sum of the squares of the lengths of the diagonals.

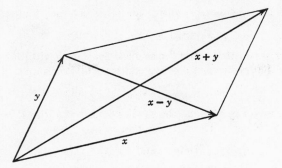

Figure 7.3. The Parallelogram Identity.

It is convenient to have relations between the norm or length of a vector and the absolute value of its components.

7.11   Theorem.   *If* $x = (\xi_1, \xi_2, \ldots, \xi_p)$ *is any element in* $\mathbf{R}^p$, *then*

(7.7) $|\xi_j| \leq |x| \leq \sqrt{p}\, \sup \{|\xi_1|, |\xi_2|, \ldots |\xi_p|\}.$

proof.   Since $|x|^2 = \xi_1{}^2 + \xi_2{}^2 + \cdots + \xi_p{}^2$, it is plain that $|\xi_j| \leq |x|$. Similarly, if $M = \sup \{|\xi_1|, \ldots, |\xi_p|\}$, then $|x|^2 \leq pM^2$, so $|x| \leq \sqrt{p}\, M$.

Q.E.D.

The inequality (7.7) asserts, in a quantitative fashion, that if the length of x is small, then the lengths of its components are small, and conversely.

Exercises

7.A. Prove that if w, z belong to $\mathbf{R}^p$ and if $w + z = z$, then $w = \theta$. (Hence the zero element in $\mathbf{R}^p$ is unique.)

7.B. If $x = (\xi_1, \xi_2, \ldots, \xi_p)$, define $|x|_1$ by

$$|x|_1 = |\xi_1| + |\xi_2| + \ldots + |\xi_p|.$$

Prove that the function $f(x) = |x|_1$ satisfies all of the properties of Theorem 7.8, but that it does not satisfy the Parallelogram Identity.

7.C. If $x = (\xi_1, \xi_2, \ldots, \xi_p)$, define $|x|_\infty$ by

$$|x|_\infty = \sup \{|\xi_1|, |\xi_2|, \ldots, |\xi_p|\}.$$

Prove that the function $g(x) = |x|_\infty$ satisfies all of the properties of Theorem 7.8, but that it does not satisfy the Parallelogram Identity.

7.D. In the space $\mathbf{R}^2$ describe the sets

$$S_1 = \{x \in \mathbf{R}^2 : |x|_1 < 1\},$$
$$S_2 = \{x \in \mathbf{R}^2 : |x| < 1\},$$
$$S_\infty = \{x \in \mathbf{R}^2 : |x|_\infty < 1\}.$$

7.E. Show that there exist positive constants a, b such that

$$a|x|_1 \leq |x| \leq b|x|_1 \qquad \text{for all } x \in \mathbf{R}^p.$$

Find the largest constant a and the smallest constant b with this property.

7.F. Show that there exist positive constants a, b such that

$$a|x|_1 \leq |x|_\infty \leq b|x|_1 \qquad \text{for all } x \in \mathbf{R}^p.$$

Find the largest constant a and the smallest constant b with this property.

7.G. If x, y belong to $\mathbf{R}^p$, is it true that

$$|x \cdot y| \leq |x|_1 |y|_1 \quad \text{and} \quad |x \cdot y| \leq |x|_\infty |y|_\infty ?$$

7.H. If x, y belong to $\mathbf{R}^p$, then is it true that the relation

$$|x + y| = |x| + |y|$$

holds if and only if $x = cy$ or $y = cx$ with $c \geq 0$?

7.I. Let x, y belong to $\mathbf{R}^p$, then is it true that the relation

$$|x + y|_\infty = |x|_\infty + |y|_\infty$$

holds if and only if $x = cy$ or $y = cx$ with $c \geq 0$?

7.J. If x, y belongs to $\mathbf{R}^p$, then

$$|x + y|^2 = |x|^2 + |y|^2$$

holds if and only if $x \cdot y = 0$. In this case, one says that x and y are **orthogonal** or **perpendicular**.

7.K. A subset K of $\mathbf{R}^p$ is said to be **convex** if, whenever x, y belong to K and t is a real number such that $0 \leq t \leq 1$, then the point

$$tx + (1 - t)y$$

also belongs to K. Interpret this condition geometrically and show that the subsets

$$K_1 = \{x \in \mathbf{R}^2 : |x| \leq 1\},$$
$$K_2 = \{(\xi, \eta) \in \mathbf{R}^2 : 0 < \xi < \eta\},$$
$$K_3 = \{(\xi, \eta) \in \mathbf{R}^2 : 0 \leq \eta \leq \xi \leq 1\},$$

are convex. Show that the subset

$$K_4 = \{x \in \mathbf{R}^2 : |x| = 1\}$$

is not convex.

7.L. The intersection of any collection of convex subsets of $\mathbf{R}^p$ is convex. The union of two convex subsets of $\mathbf{R}^p$ may not be convex.

7.M. If K is a subset of $\mathbf{R}^p$, a point z in K is said to be an **extreme point** of K if there do not exist points x, y in K with $x \neq z$ and $y \neq z$ and a real number t with $0 < t < 1$ such that $z = tx + (1 - t)y$. Find the extreme points of the sets K_1, K_2, K_3 in Exercise 7.K.

7.N. If M is a set, then a real-valued function d on $M \times M$ is called a **metric** on M if it satisfies:

(i) $d(x, y) \geq 0$ for all x, y in M;

(ii) $d(x, y) = 0$ if and only if $x = y$;

(iii) $d(x, y) = d(y, x)$ for all x, y in M;

(iv) $d(x, y) \leq d(x, z) + d(z, y)$ for all x, y, z in M.

It has been observed that the Norm Properties 7.8 imply that if the function d_2 is defined by $d_2(x, y) = |x - y|$, then d_2 is a metric on $\mathbf{R}^p$.

Use Exercise 7.B and show that if d_1 is defined by $d_1(x, y) = |x - y|_1$ for x, y in $\mathbf{R}^p$, then d_1 is a metric on $\mathbf{R}^p$. Similarly, if d_∞ is defined by $d_\infty(x, y) = |x - y|_\infty$, then d_∞ is a metric on $\mathbf{R}^p$. (Therefore, the same set can have more than one metric.)

7.O. Suppose that d is a metric on a set M. By employing Definition 7.9 as a model, use the metric to define an open ball with center x and radius r. Interpret the sets S_1, S_2, and S_∞ in Exercise 7.D as open balls with center θ in $\mathbf{R}^2$ relative to three different metrics. Interpret Exercise 7.E as saying that a ball with center θ, relative to the metric d_2, contains and is contained in balls with center θ, relative to the metric d_1. Make similar interpretations of Exercise 7.F and Theorem 7.11.

7.P. Let M be any set and let d be defined on $M \times M$ by the requirement that

$$d(x, y) = \begin{cases} 0, & \text{if } x = y, \\ 1, & \text{if } x \neq y. \end{cases}$$

Show that d gives a metric on M in the sense defined in Exercise 7.N. If x is any point in M, then the open ball with center x and radius 1 (relative to the metric d) consists of precisely one point. However, the open ball with center x and radius 2 (relative to d) consists of all of M. This metric d, is sometimes called the **discrete metric** on the set M.

Projects

7.α. In this project we develop a few important inequalities.

(a) Let a and b be positive real numbers. Show that

$$ab \leq (a^2 + b^2)/2,$$

and that the equality holds if and only if $a = b$. (Hint: consider $(a - b)^2$.)

(b) Let a_1 and a_2 be positive real numbers. Show that

$$\sqrt{a_1 a_2} \leq (a_1 + a_2)/2$$

and that the equality holds if and only if $a_1 = a_2$.

(c) Let $a_1, a_2, \ldots, a_m$ be $m = 2^n$ positive real numbers. Show that

$$(*) \qquad (a_1 a_2 \ldots a_m)^{1/m} \leq (a_1 + a_2 + \ldots + a_m)/m$$

and that the equality holds if and only if $a_1 = \ldots = a_m$.

(d) Show that the inequality (*) between the geometric mean and the arithmetic mean holds even when m is not a power of 2. (Hint: if $2^{n-1} < m < 2^n$, let $b_j = a_j$ for $j = 1, \ldots, m$ and let

$$b_j = (a_1 + a_2 + \ldots + a_m)/m$$

for $j = m + 1, \ldots, 2^n$. Now apply part (c) to the numbers $b_1, b_2, \ldots, b_{2^n}$.)

(e) Let $a_1, a_2, \ldots, a_n$ and $b_1, b_2, \ldots, b_n$ be two sets of real numbers. Prove Lagrange's Identity†

$$\left\{ \sum_{j=1}^{n} a_j b_j \right\}^2 = \left\{ \sum_{j=1}^{n} a_j{}^2 \right\} \left\{ \sum_{k=1}^{n} b_k{}^2 \right\} - (\tfrac{1}{2}) \sum_{j,k=1}^{n} (a_j b_k - a_k b_j)^2.$$

(Hint: experiment with the cases $n = 2$ and $n = 3$ first.)

(f) Use part (e) to establish Cauchy's Inequality

$$\left\{ \sum_{j=1}^{n} a_j b_j \right\}^2 \le \left\{ \sum_{j=1}^{n} a_j{}^2 \right\} \left\{ \sum_{k=1}^{n} b_k{}^2 \right\}.$$

Show that the equality holds if and only if the ordered sets $\{a_1, a_2, \ldots, a_n\}$ and $\{b_1, b_2, \ldots, b_n\}$ are proportional.

(g) Use part (f) and establish the Triangle Inequality

$$\left\{ \sum_{j=1}^{n} (a_j + b_j)^2 \right\}^{1/2} \le \left\{ \sum_{j=1}^{n} a_j{}^2 \right\}^{1/2} + \left\{ \sum_{j=1}^{n} b_j{}^2 \right\}^{1/2}.$$

7.β. In this project, let $\{a_1, a_2, \ldots, a_n\}$, and so forth be sets of n non-negative real numbers and let $r \ge 1$.

(a) It can be proved (for example, by using the Mean Value Theorem) that if a and b are non-negative and $0 < \alpha < 1$, then

$$a^\alpha b^{1-\alpha} \le \alpha a + (1 - \alpha) b$$

and that the equality holds if and only if $a = b$. Assuming this, let $r > 1$ and let s satisfy

$$\frac{1}{r} + \frac{1}{s} = 1,$$

(so that $s > 1$ and $r + s = rs$). Show that if A and B are non-negative, then

$$AB \le \frac{A^r}{r} + \frac{B^s}{s},$$

and that the equality holds if and only if $A = B$.

(b) Let $\{a_1, \ldots, a_n\}$ and $\{b_1, \ldots, b_n\}$ be non-negative real numbers. If $r, s > 1$ and $(1/r) + (1/s) = 1$, establish Hölder's Inequality‡

† JOSEPH-LOUIS LAGRANGE (1736–1813) was born in Turin, where he became professor at the age of nineteen. He later went to Berlin for twenty years as successor to Euler and then to Paris. He is best known for his work on the calculus of variations and analytical mechanics.

‡ OTTO HÖLDER (1859–1937) studied at Göttingen and taught at Leipzig. He worked in both algebra and analysis.

$$\sum_{j=1}^{n} a_j b_j \leq \left\{\sum_{j=1}^{n} a_j{}^r\right\}^{1/r} \left\{\sum_{j=1}^{n} b_j{}^s\right\}^{1/s}.$$

(Hint: Let $A = \{\sum a_j{}^r\}^{1/r}$ and $B = \{\sum b_j{}^s\}^{1/s}$ and apply part (a) to a_j/A and b_j/B.)

(c) Using Hölder's Inequality, establish the Minkowski Inequality†

$$\left\{\sum_{j=1}^{n} (a_j + b_j)^r\right\}^{1/r} \leq \left\{\sum_{j=1}^{n} a_j{}^r\right\}^{1/r} + \left\{\sum_{j=1}^{n} b_j{}^r\right\}^{1/r}.$$

(Hint: $(a + b)^r = (a + b)(a + b)^{r/s} = a(a + b)^{r/s} + b(a + b)^{r/s}$.)

(d) Using Hölder's Inequality, prove that

$$(1/n) \sum_{j=1}^{n} a_j \leq \left\{(1/n) \sum_{j=1}^{n} a_j{}^r\right\}^{1/r}.$$

(e) If $a_1 \leq a_2$ and $b_1 \leq b_2$, then $(a_1 - a_2)(b_1 - b_2) \geq 0$ and hence

$$a_1 b_1 + a_2 b_2 \geq a_1 b_2 + a_2 b_1.$$

Show that if $a_1 \leq a_2 \leq \cdots \leq a_n$ and $b_1 \leq b_2 \leq \cdots \leq b_n$, then

$$n \sum_{j=1}^{n} a_j b_j \geq \left\{\sum_{j=1}^{n} a_j\right\} \left\{\sum_{j=1}^{n} b_j\right\}.$$

(f) Suppose that $0 \leq a_1 \leq a_2 \leq \cdots \leq a_n$ and $0 \leq b_1 \leq b_2 \leq \cdots \leq b_n$ and $r \geq 1$. Establish the Chebyshev Inequality‡

$$\left\{(1/n) \sum_{j=1}^{n} a_j{}^r\right\}^{1/r} \left\{(1/n) \sum_{j=1}^{n} b_j{}^r\right\}^{1/r} \leq \left\{(1/n) \sum_{j=1}^{n} (a_j b_j)^r\right\}^{1/r}.$$

Show that this inequality must be reversed if $\{a_j\}$ is increasing and $\{b_j\}$ is decreasing.

Section 8 Elementary Topological Concepts

Many of the deepest properties of real analysis depend on certain topological notions and results. In this section we shall introduce these basic concepts and derive some of the most crucial topological properties of the space R^p. These results will be frequently used in the following sections.

† HERMANN MINKOWSKI (1864–1909) was professor at Königsberg and Göttingen. He is best known for his work on convex sets and the "geometry of numbers."

‡ PAFNUTI L. CHEBYSHEV (1821–1894) was a professor at St. Petersburg. He made many contributions to mathematics, but his most important work was in number theory, probability, and approximation theory.

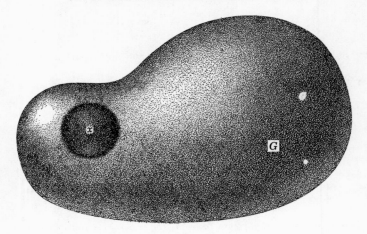

Figure 8.1.   An open set.

8.1   DEFINITION.   A set G in $\mathbf{R}^p$ is said to be **open in $\mathbf{R}^p$** (or merely open) if, for each point x in G, there is a positive real number r such that every point y in $\mathbf{R}^p$ satisfying $|x - y| < r$ also belongs to the set G. (See Figure 8.1.)

By using Definition 7.9, we can rephrase this definition by saying that a set G is open if every point in G is the center of some open ball entirely contained in G.

8.2   EXAMPLES.   (a) The entire set $\mathbf{R}^p$ is open, since we can take $r = 1$ for any x.

(b) The set $G = \{x \in \mathbf{R} : 0 < x < 1\}$ is open in $\mathbf{R} = \mathbf{R}^1$. The set $F = \{x \in \mathbf{R} : 0 \le x \le 1\}$ is not open in $\mathbf{R}$. (Why?)

(c) The sets $G = \{(\xi, \eta) \in \mathbf{R}^2 : \xi^2 + \eta^2 < 1\}$ and $H = \{(\xi, \eta) : 0 < \xi^2 + \eta^2 < 1\}$ are open, but the set $F = \{(\xi, \eta) : \xi^2 + \eta^2 \le 1\}$ is not open in $\mathbf{R}^2$. (Why?)

(d) The set $G = \{(\xi, \eta) \in \mathbf{R}^2 : 0 < \xi < 1, \eta = 0\}$ is not open in $\mathbf{R}^2$. [Compare this with (b).] The set $H = \{(\xi, \eta) \in \mathbf{R}^2 : 0 < \xi < 1\}$ is open, but the set $K = \{(\xi, \eta) \in \mathbf{R}^2 : 0 \le \xi < 1\}$ is not open in $\mathbf{R}^2$.

(e) The set $G = \{(\xi, \eta, \zeta) \in \mathbf{R}^3 : \zeta > 0\}$ is open in $\mathbf{R}^3$ as is the set $H = \{(\xi, \eta, \zeta) \in \mathbf{R}^3 : \xi > 0, \eta > 0, \zeta > 0\}$. On the other hand, the set $F = \{(\xi, \eta, \zeta) \in \mathbf{R}^3 : \xi = \eta = \zeta\}$ is not open.

(f) The empty set $\emptyset$ is open in $\mathbf{R}^p$, since it contains no points at all, and hence the requirement in Definition 8.1 is trivially satisfied.

(g) If B is the open ball with center z and radius $a > 0$ and if $x \in B$, then the ball with center x and radius $a - |z - x|$ is contained in B. Thus B is open in $\mathbf{R}^p$.

We now state the basic properties of open sets in $\mathbf{R}^p$. In courses on topology this next result is summarized by saying that the open sets, as defined in Definition 8.1, form a topology for $\mathbf{R}^p$.

8.3 OPEN SET PROPERTIES. (a) *The empty set Ø and the entire space* $\mathbf{R}^p$ *are open in* $\mathbf{R}^p$.

(b) *The intersection of any two open sets is open in* $\mathbf{R}^p$.

(c) *The union of any collection of open sets is open in* $\mathbf{R}^p$.

PROOF. We have already commented on the open character of the sets Ø and $\mathbf{R}^p$.

To prove (b), let G_1, G_2 be open and let $G_3 = G_1 \cap G_2$. To show that G_3 is open, let $x \in G_3$. Since x belongs to the open set G_1, there exists $r_1 > 0$ such that if $|x - z| < r_1$, then $z \in G_1$. Similarly, there exists $r_2 > 0$ such that if $|x - w| < r_2$, then $w \in G_2$. Choosing r_3 to be the minimum of r_1 and r_2, we conclude that if $y \in \mathbf{R}^p$ is such that $|x - y| < r_3$, then y belongs to both G_1 and G_2. Hence such elements y belong to $G_3 = G_1 \cap G_2$, showing that G_3 is open in $\mathbf{R}^p$.

To prove (c), let $\{G_\alpha, G_\beta, \ldots\}$ be a collection of sets which are open and let G be their union. To show that G is open, let $x \in G$. By definition of the union, it follows that for some set, say for G_λ, we have $x \in G_\lambda$. Since G_λ is open, there exists a ball with center x which is entirely contained in G_λ. Since $G_\lambda \subseteq G$, this ball is entirely contained in G, showing that G is open in $\mathbf{R}^p$.

Q.E.D.

By induction, it follows from property (b) above that the intersection of any *finite* collection of sets which are open is also open in $\mathbf{R}^p$. That the intersection of an infinite collection of open sets may not be open can be seen from the example

$$(8.1) \qquad G_n = \left\{ x \in \mathbf{R} : -\frac{1}{n} < x < 1 + \frac{1}{n} \right\}, \quad n \in \mathbf{N}.$$

The intersection of the sets G_n is the set $F = \{x \in \mathbf{R} : 0 \leq x \leq 1\}$, which is not open.

Closed Sets

We now introduce the important notion of a closed set in $\mathbf{R}^p$.

8.4 DEFINITION. A set F in $\mathbf{R}^p$ is said to be closed in $\mathbf{R}^p$ (or merely closed) in case its complement $\mathcal{C}(F) = \mathbf{R}^p \backslash F$ is open in $\mathbf{R}^p$.

8.5 EXAMPLES. (a) The entire set $\mathbf{R}^p$ is closed in $\mathbf{R}^p$, since its complement is the empty set (which was seen in 8.2(f) to be open in $\mathbf{R}^p$).

(b) The empty set $\emptyset$ is closed in $\mathbf{R}^p$, since its complement in $\mathbf{R}^p$ is all of $\mathbf{R}^p$ (which was seen in 8.2(a) to be open in $\mathbf{R}^p$).

(c) The set $F = \{x \in \mathbf{R} : 0 \le x \le 1\}$ is closed in $\mathbf{R}$. One way of seeing this is by noting that the complement of F in $\mathbf{R}$ is the union of the two sets $\{x \in \mathbf{R} : x < 0\}$, $\{x \in \mathbf{R} : x > 1\}$, each of which is open. Similarly, the set $\{x \in \mathbf{R} : 0 \le x\}$ is closed.

(d) The set $F = \{(\xi, \eta) \in \mathbf{R}^2 : \xi^2 + \eta^2 \le 1\}$ is closed, since its complement in $\mathbf{R}^2$ is the set

$$\{(\xi, \eta) \in \mathbf{R}^2 : \xi^2 + \eta^2 > 1\},$$

which is seen to be open.

(e) The set $H = \{(\xi, \eta, \zeta) \in \mathbf{R}^3 : \xi \ge 0\}$ is closed in $\mathbf{R}^3$, as is the set $F = \{(\xi, \eta, \zeta) \in \mathbf{R}^3 : \xi = \eta = \zeta\}$.

(f) The closed ball B with center x in $\mathbf{R}^p$ and radius $r > 0$ is a closed set of $\mathbf{R}^p$. For, if $z \notin B$, then the open ball B_z with center z and radius $|z - x| - r$ is contained in $\mathcal{C}(B)$. Therefore, $\mathcal{C}(B)$ is open and B is closed in $\mathbf{R}^p$.

In ordinary parlance, when applied to doors, windows, and minds, the words "open" and "closed" are antonyms. However, when applied to subsets of $\mathbf{R}^p$, these words are not antonyms. For example, we noted above that the sets $\emptyset$, $\mathbf{R}^p$ are *both* open and closed in $\mathbf{R}^p$. (The reader will probably be relieved to learn that there are no other subsets of $\mathbf{R}^p$ which have both properties.) In addition, there are many subsets of $\mathbf{R}^p$ which are *neither* open nor closed; in fact, most subsets of $\mathbf{R}^p$ have this neutral character. As a simple example, we cite the set

(8.2) $$A = \{x \in \mathbf{R} : 0 \le x < 1\}.$$

This set A fails to be open in $\mathbf{R}$, since it contains the point 0. Similarly, it fails to be closed in $\mathbf{R}$, because its complement in $\mathbf{R}$ is the set $\{x \in \mathbf{R} : x < 0 \text{ or } x \ge 1\}$, which is not open since it contains the point 1. The reader should construct other examples of sets which are neither open nor closed in $\mathbf{R}^p$.

We now state the fundamental properties of closed sets. The proof of this result follows directly from Theorem 8.3 by using DeMorgan's laws (Theorem 1.8 and Exercise 1.I).

8.6 CLOSED SET PROPERTIES.   (a) *The empty set $\emptyset$ and the entire space $\mathbf{R}^p$ are closed in $\mathbf{R}^p$.*

(b) *The union of any two closed sets is closed in $\mathbf{R}^p$.*

(c) *The intersection of any collection of closed sets is closed in $\mathbf{R}^p$.*

Neighborhoods

We now introduce some additional topological notions that will be useful later and which will permit us to characterize open and closed sets in other terms.

8.7   DEFINITION.   If x is a point in $\mathbf{R}^p$, then any set which contains an open set containing x is called a **neighborhood** of x in $\mathbf{R}^p$. A point x is said to be an **interior point** of a set A in case A is a neighborhood of the point x. A point x is said to be a **cluster point** of a set A (or a **point of accumulation** of A) in case every neighborhood of x contains at least one point of A distinct from x.

Before we proceed any further, it will be useful to consider some reformulations and examples of these new concepts.

8.8   EXAMPLES.   (a) A set N is a neighborhood of a point x if and only if there exists an open ball with center x contained in N.

(b) A point x is an interior point of a set A if and only if there exists an open ball with center x contained in A.

(c) A point x is a cluster point of a set A if and only if for every natural number n there exists an element x_n belonging to A such that $0 < |x - x_n| < 1/n$.

(d) Every point of the unit interval $\mathbf{I}$ of $\mathbf{R}$ is a cluster point of $\mathbf{I}$. Every point in the open interval $(0, 1)$ is an interior point of $\mathbf{I}$ in $\mathbf{R}$, but 0 and 1 are not interior points of $\mathbf{I}$.

(e) Let A be the open interval $(0, 1)$ in $\mathbf{R}$. Then every point of A is both a cluster and an interior point of A. However, the points $x = 0$ and $x = 1$ are also cluster points of A. (Hence, a cluster point of a set does not need to belong to the set.)

(f) Let $B = \mathbf{I} \cap \mathbf{Q}$ be the set of all rational points in the unit interval. Every point of $\mathbf{I}$ is a cluster point of B in $\mathbf{R}$, but there are no interior points of B.

(g) A finite subset of $\mathbf{R}^p$ has no cluster points. (Why?) A finite subset of $\mathbf{R}^p$ has no interior points. (Why?)

We now characterize open sets in terms of neighborhoods and interior points.

8.9   THEOREM.   *Let B be a subset of $\mathbf{R}^p$, then the following statements are equivalent:*

(a) *B is open.*

(b) *Every point of B is an interior point of B.*

(c) *B is a neighborhood of each of its points.*

PROOF.   If (a) holds and $x \in B$ then B, which is open, is a neighborhood of x and x is an interior point of B.

It is immediate from the definitions that (b) implies (c).

Finally, if B is a neighborhood of each point y in B, then B contains an open set $G(y)$ containing y. Hence $B = \bigcup \{G(y):y \in B\}$, and it follows from Theorem 8.3(c) that B is open in $\mathbf{R}^p$.

Q.E.D.

8.10 THEOREM. *A set F is closed in $\mathbf{R}^p$ if and only if it contains every cluster point of F.*

PROOF. Suppose that F is closed and that x is a cluster point of F. If x does not belong to F, the complementary set $\mathcal{C}(F) = \mathbf{R}^p \backslash F$ is a neighborhood of x and so must contain at least one point in F. This is a contradiction, since $\mathcal{C}(F)$ contains no points of F. Therefore, the cluster point x must belong to F.

Conversely, suppose that a set F contains all of its cluster points. We shall prove that F is closed by proving that $\mathcal{C}(F)$ is open. To do this, let y belong to $\mathcal{C}(F)$; according to our hypothesis, y is not a cluster point of F so there exists a neighborhood V of y which contains no points of F. It follows that V is contained in $\mathcal{C}(F)$ so that $\mathcal{C}(F)$ is a neighborhood of y. Since y was any point of $\mathcal{C}(F)$, we infer from Theorem 8.9 that $\mathcal{C}(F)$ is open.

Q.E.D.

Intervals

We recall from Section 5 that if $a \leq b$, then the **open interval in R**, denoted by (a, b), is the set defined by

$$(a, b) = \{x \in \mathbf{R} : a < x < b\}.$$

It is readily seen that such a set is open in R. Similarly, the **closed interval $[a, b]$** in R is the set

$$[a, b] = \{x \in \mathbf{R} : a \leq x \leq b\},$$

which may be verified to be closed in R. The Cartesian product of two intervals is usually called a **rectangle** and the Cartesian product of three intervals is often called a **parallelepiped**. For simplicity, we shall employ the term **interval** regardless of the dimension of the space.

8.11 DEFINITION. An **open interval** J in $\mathbf{R}^p$ is the Cartesian product of p open intervals of real numbers. Hence J has the form

$$J = \{x = (\xi_1, \ldots, \xi_p) \in \mathbf{R}^p : a_i < \xi_i < b_i, \quad \text{for} \quad i = 1, 2, \ldots, p\}.$$

Similarly, a **closed interval** I in $\mathbf{R}^p$ is the Cartesian product of p closed intervals of real numbers. Hence I has the form

$$I = \{x = (\xi_1, \ldots, \xi_p) \in \mathbf{R}^p : a_i \leq \xi_i \leq b_i, \quad \text{for} \quad i = 1, 2, \ldots, p\}.$$

A subset of R^p is **bounded** if it is contained in some interval.

As an exercise, show that an open interval in R^p is an open set and a closed interval is a closed set. Also, a subset of R^p is bounded if and only if it is contained in some ball. It will be observed that this terminology for bounded sets is consistent with that introduced in Section 6 for the case $p = 1$.

The Nested Intervals and Bolzano-Weierstrass Theorems

The reader will recall from Section 6 that the crucial completeness property of the real number system hinged on the fact that every nested sequence of non-empty closed intervals in R has a common point. We shall now prove that this property carries over to the space R^p.

8.12 NESTED INTERVALS THEOREM. *Let (I_k) be a sequence of non-empty closed intervals in R^p which is nested in the sense that $I_1 \supseteq I_2 \supseteq \cdots \supseteq I_k \supseteq \cdots$. Then there exists a point in R^p which belongs to all of the intervals.*

PROOF. Suppose that I_k is the interval

$$I_k = \{ (\xi_1, \ldots, \xi_p) : a_{k1} \leq \xi_1 \leq b_{k1}, \ldots, a_{kp} \leq \xi_p \leq b_{kp} \}.$$

It is easy to see that the intervals $\{[a_{k1}, b_{k1}] : k \in N\}$ form a nested sequence of non-empty closed intervals of real numbers and hence by the completeness of the real number system R, there is a real number η_1 which belongs to all of these intervals. Applying this argument to each coordinate, we obtain a point $y = (\eta_1, \ldots, \eta_p)$ of R^p such that if j satisfies $j = 1, 2, \ldots, p$, then η_j belongs to all the intervals $\{[a_{kj}, b_{kj}] : k \in N\}$. Hence the point y belongs to all of the intervals (I_k).

Q.E.D.

The next result will be of fundamental importance in the sequel. It should be noted (cf. Exercise 8.U) that the conclusion may fail if either hypothesis is removed.†

---

† BERNARD BOLZANO (1781–1848) was professor of the philosophy of religion at Prague, but he had deep thoughts about mathematics. Like Cauchy, he was a pioneer in introducing a higher standard of rigor in mathematical analysis. His treatise on the paradoxes of the infinite appeared after his death.

KARL WEIERSTRASS (1815–1897) was for many years a professor at Berlin and exercised a profound influence on the development of analysis. Always insisting on rigorous proof he developed, but did not publish, an introduction to the real number system. He also made important contributions to real and complex analysis, differential equations, and the calculus of variations.

8.13 BOLZANO-WEIERSTRASS THEOREM. *Every bounded infinite sub-set of R^p has a cluster point.*

PROOF. If B is a bounded set with an infinite number of elements, let I_1 be a closed interval containing B. We divide I_1 into 2^p closed intervals by bisecting each of its sides. Since I_1 contains infinitely many points of B, at least one part obtained in this subdivision will also contain infinitely many points of B. (For if each of the 2^p parts contained only a finite number of points of the set B, then B must be a finite set, contrary to hypothesis.) Let I_2 be one of these parts in the subdivision of I_1 which contains infinitely many elements of B. Now divide I_2 into 2^p closed intervals by bisecting each of its sides. Again, one of these subintervals of I_2 must contain an infinite number of points of B, for otherwise I_2 could contain only a finite number, contrary to its construction. Let I_3 be a subinterval of I_2 containing infinitely many points of B. Continuing this process, we obtain a nested sequence (I_k) of non-

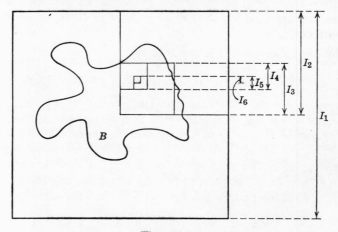

Figure 8.2

empty closed intervals of R^p. According to the Nested Intervals Theorem, there is a point y which belongs to all of the intervals I_k, $k = 1, 2, \ldots$. We shall now show that y is a cluster point of B and this will complete the proof of the assertion.

First, we note that if $I_1 = [a_1, b_1] \times \cdots \times [a_p, b_p]$ with $a_k < b_k$, and if $l(I_1) = \sup \{b_1 - a_1, \ldots, b_p - a_p\}$, then $l(I_1) > 0$ is the length of the largest side of I_1. According to the above construction of the sequence (I_k), we have

$$0 < l(I_k) = \frac{1}{2^{k-1}} l(I_1)$$

for $k \in \mathbf{N}$. Suppose that V is any neighborhood of the common point y and suppose that all points z in $\mathbf{R}^p$ with $|y - z| < r$ belong to V. We now choose k so large that $I_k \subseteq V$; such a choice is possible since if w is any other point of I_k, then it follows from Theorem 7.11 that

$$|y - w| \leq \sqrt{p}\, l(I_k) = \frac{\sqrt{p}}{2^{k-1}}\, l(I_1).$$

According to the Archimedean property of $\mathbf{R}$, it follows that if k is sufficiently large, then

$$\frac{\sqrt{p}}{2^{k-1}}\, l(I_1) < r.$$

For such a value of k we have $I_k \subseteq V$. Since I_k contains infinitely many elements of B, it follows that V contains at least one element of B different from y. Therefore, y is a cluster point of B.

Q.E.D.

Connected Sets

We shall now introduce the notion of connectedness and make limited use of this concept in the following. However, further study in courses in topology will reveal the central role of this property in certain parts of topology.

8.14 DEFINITION. A subset D of $\mathbf{R}^p$ is said to be disconnected if there exist two open sets A, B such that $A \cap D$ and $B \cap D$ are disjoint non-empty sets whose union is D. In this case the pair A, B is said to form a disconnection of D. A subset C of $\mathbf{R}^p$ which is not disconnected is said to be connected. (See Figure 8.3 on the next page.)

8.15 EXAMPLES. (a) The set $\mathbf{N}$ of natural numbers is disconnected in $\mathbf{R}$, since we can take $A = \{x \in \mathbf{R} : x < \frac{3}{2}\}$ and $B = \{x \in \mathbf{R} : x > \frac{3}{2}\}$.

(b) The set $H = \{1/n : n \in \mathbf{N}\}$ is also disconnected in $\mathbf{R}$ as a similar construction shows.

(c) The set S consisting of positive rational numbers is disconnected in $\mathbf{R}$, for we can take $A = \{x \in \mathbf{R} : x < \sqrt{2}\}$, $B = \{x \in \mathbf{R} : x > \sqrt{2}\}$.

(d) If $0 < c < 1$, then the sets $A = \{x \in \mathbf{R} : -1 < x \leq c\}$, $B = \{x \in \mathbf{R} : c < x < 2\}$ split the unit interval $I = \{x \in \mathbf{R} : 0 \leq x \leq 1\}$ into two non-empty disjoint subsets whose union is I, but since A is not open, it does not show that I is disconnected. In fact, we shall show below that I is connected.

Thus far, we have not established the existence of a connected set. The reader should realize that it is more difficult to show that a set is

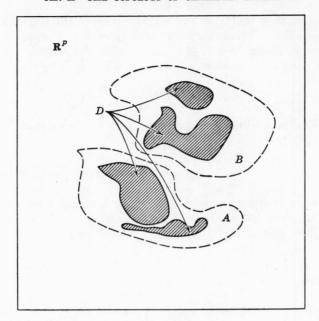

Figure 8.3.   A disconnected set.

connected than to show that a set is disconnected. For in order to show that a set is disconnected we need to produce only *one* disconnection, whereas to show that a set is connected we need to show that no disconnection can exist.

8.16 Theorem. *The closed unit interval* $\mathbf{I} = [0, 1]$ *is a connected subset of* $\mathbf{R}$.

proof. We proceed by contradiction and suppose that A, B are open sets forming a disconnection of $\mathbf{I}$. Thus $A \cap \mathbf{I}$ and $B \cap \mathbf{I}$ are nonempty bounded disjoint sets whose union is $\mathbf{I}$. For the sake of definiteness, we suppose that 1 belongs to B. Applying the Supremum Principle 6.6, we let $c = \sup A \cap \mathbf{I}$ so that $c > 0$ and $c \in A \cup B$. If $c \in A$, then $c < 1$; since A is open there are points in $A \cap \mathbf{I}$ which exceed c, contrary to its definition. If $c \in B$, then since B is open there is a point $c_1 < c$ such that the interval $[c_1, c]$ is contained in $B \cap \mathbf{I}$; hence $[c_1, c] \cap A = \varnothing$. This also contradicts the definition of c as $\sup A \cap \mathbf{I}$. Hence the hypothesis that $\mathbf{I}$ is disconnected leads to a contradiction.

Q.E.D.

The proof just given can also be used to prove that the open interval $(0, 1)$ is connected in $\mathbf{R}$.

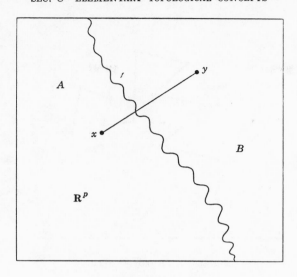

Figure 8.4

8.17   THEOREM. *The entire space* $\mathbf{R}^p$ *is connected.*

PROOF.   If not, then there exist two disjoint non-empty open sets A, B whose union is $\mathbf{R}^p$. (See Figure 8.4.) Let $x \in A$ and $y \in B$ and consider the line segment S joining x and y; namely,

$$S = \{x + t(y - x) : t \in \mathbf{I}\}.$$

Let $A_1 = \{t \in \mathbf{R} : x + t(y - x) \in A\}$ and   let $B_1 = \{t \in \mathbf{R} : x + t(y - x) \in B\}$. It is easily seen that A_1 and B_1 are disjoint non-empty open subsets of $\mathbf{R}$ and provide a disconnection for $\mathbf{I}$, contradicting Theorem 8.16.

Q.E.D.

8.18   COROLLARY. *The only subsets of* $\mathbf{R}^p$ *which are both open and closed are* $\emptyset$ *and* $\mathbf{R}^p$.

PROOF.   For if A is both open and closed in $\mathbf{R}^p$, then $B = \mathbf{R}^p \backslash A$ is also. If A is not empty and not all of $\mathbf{R}^p$, then the pair A, B forms a disconnection for $\mathbf{R}^p$, contradicting the theorem.

Q.E.D.

In certain areas of analysis, connected open sets play an especially important role. By using the definition it is easy to establish the next result.

8.19   LEMMA. *An open subset of* $\mathbf{R}^p$ *is connected if and only if it cannot be expressed as the union of two disjoint non-empty open sets.*

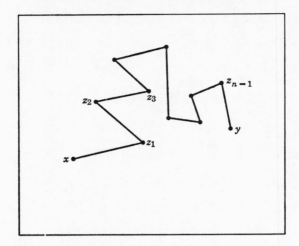

Figure 8.5. A polygonal curve.

It is sometimes useful to have another characterization of open connected sets. In order to give such a characterization, we shall introduce some terminology. If x and y are two points in $\mathbf{R}^p$, then a **polygonal curve** joining x and y is a set P obtained as the union of a finite number of ordered line segments $(L_1, L_2, \ldots, L_n)$ in $\mathbf{R}^p$ such that the line segment L_1 has end points x, z_1; the line segment L_2 has end points z_1, z_2; $\ldots$; and the line segment L_n has end points z_{n-1}, y. (See Figure 8.5.)

8.20 Theorem. *Let G be an open set in $\mathbf{R}^p$. Then G is connected if and only if any pair of points x, y in G can be joined by a polygonal curve lying entirely in G.*

proof. Assume that G is not connected and that A, B is a disconnection for G. Let $x \in A \cap G$ and $y \in B \cap G$ and let $P = (L_1, L_2, \ldots, L_n)$ be a polygonal curve lying entirely in G and joining x and y. Let k be the smallest natural number such that the end point z_{k-1} of L_k belongs to $A \cap G$ and the end point z_k belongs to $B \cap G$ (see Figure 8.6). If we define A_1 and B_1 by

$$A_1 = \{t \in \mathbf{R} : z_{k-1} + t(z_k - z_{k-1}) \in A \cap G\},$$
$$B_1 = \{t \in \mathbf{R} : z_{k-1} + t(z_k - z_{k-1}) \in B \cap G\},$$

then it is easily seen that A_1 and B_1 are disjoint non-empty open subsets of $\mathbf{R}$. Hence the pair A_1, B_1 form a disconnection for the unit interval $\mathbf{I}$, contradicting Theorem 8.16. Therefore, if G is not connected, there exist two points in G which cannot be joined by a polygonal curve in G.

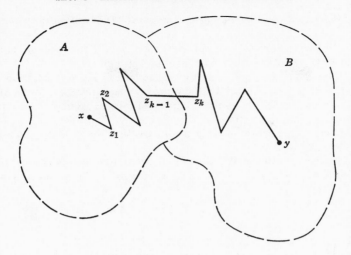

Figure 8.6

Next, suppose that G is a connected open set in $\mathbf{R}^p$ and that x belongs to G. Let G_1 be the subset of G consisting of all points in G which can be joined to x by a polygonal curve which lies entirely in G; let G_2 consist of all the points in G which cannot be joined to x by a polygonal curve lying in G. It is clear that $G_1 \cap G_2 = \emptyset$. The set G_1 is not empty since it contains the point x. We shall now show that G_1 is open in $\mathbf{R}^p$. If y belongs to G_1, it follows from the fact that G is open that for some positive real number r, then $|w - y| < r$ implies that $w \in G$. By definition of G_1, the point y can be joined to x by a polygonal curve and by adding a segment from y to w, we infer that w belongs to G_1. Hence G_1 is an open subset of $\mathbf{R}^p$. Similarly, the subset G_2 is open in $\mathbf{R}^p$. If G_2 is not empty, then the sets G_1, G_2 form a disconnection of G, contrary to the hypothesis that G is connected. Therefore, $G_2 = \emptyset$ and every point of G can be joined to x by a polygonal curve lying entirely in G.

Q.E.D.

Exercises

8.A. Justify the assertion about the sets G, F made in Example 8.2(b).

8.B. Justify the assertions made in Example 8.2(c).

8.C. Prove that the intersection of a finite collection of open sets is open in $\mathbf{R}^p$. (Hint: use Theorem 8.3(b) and induction.)

8.D. Verify in detail that the sets G_n, defined in equation (8.1), are open and that their intersection is not open. (Compare with Exercise 8.A.)

8.E. Show in detail that the set in equation (8.2) is neither open nor closed in $\mathbf{R}$.

8.F. Give an example of a subset of $\mathbf{R}^2$ which is neither open nor closed.

8.G. Write out the details of the proof of Theorem 8.6.

8.H. The union of a collection of closed subsets of $\mathbf{R}^p$ may fail to be closed.

8.I. Every open subset of $\mathbf{R}^p$ is the union of a countable collection of sets which are closed. (Hint: the set of points all of whose coordinates are rational is countable.)

8.J. Every closed subset in $\mathbf{R}^p$ is the intersection of a countable collection of sets which are open.

8.K. If A is a subset of $\mathbf{R}^p$, let A^- denote the intersection of all closed sets which contain A. The set A^- is called the **closure** of A. Prove that A^- is a closed set and that

$$A \subseteq A^-, \qquad (A^-)^- = A^-,$$

$$(A \cup B)^- = A^- \cup B^-, \qquad \emptyset^- = \emptyset.$$

Observe that A^- is the smallest closed set containing A.

8.L. If A, B are any subsets of $\mathbf{R}^p$, then is

$$(A \cap B)^- = A^- \cap B^- ?$$

8.M. If A is a subset of $\mathbf{R}^p$, let A° denote the union of all open sets which are contained in A. The set A° is called the **interior** of A. Prove that A° is an open set and that

$$A^\circ \subseteq A, \qquad (A^\circ)^\circ = A^\circ,$$

$$(A \cap B)^\circ = A^\circ \cap B^\circ, \qquad (\mathbf{R}^p)^\circ = \mathbf{R}^p.$$

Observe that A° is the largest open set contained in A.

8.N. Can there be a subset A of $\mathbf{R}^p$ such that $A^\circ = \emptyset$ and $A^- = \mathbf{R}^p$?

8.O. Show that an open interval in $\mathbf{R}^p$, as in Definition 8.11, is an open set. Prove that a closed interval in $\mathbf{R}^p$ is a closed set.

8.P. An open subset G of $\mathbf{R}$ is the union of a countable collection of open intervals. (Hint: The set of points in G with rational coordinates is countable.) The same result holds in $\mathbf{R}^p$, $p > 1$.

8.Q. If A and B are open sets in $\mathbf{R}$, show that their Cartesian product $A \times B$ is open in $\mathbf{R}^2$.

8.R. Let A, B be subsets of $\mathbf{R}$. The Cartesian product $A \times B$ is closed in $\mathbf{R}^2$ if and only if A and B are closed in $\mathbf{R}$.

8.S. If A is any subset of $\mathbf{R}^p$, then there exists a countable subset C of A such that if $x \in A$ and $\epsilon > 0$, then there is an element z in C such that $|x - z| < \epsilon$. Hence every element of A is either in C or is a cluster point of C.

8.T. If A is a subset of $\mathbf{R}^p$, then x is a cluster point of A if and only if every neighborhood of x contains infinitely many points in A.

8.U. A finite subset of $\mathbf{R}^p$ has no cluster points. An unbounded subset of $\mathbf{R}^p$ may not have any cluster point.

8.V. If A is a subset of $\mathbf{R}^p$, then a point x in $\mathbf{R}^p$ is said to be a **boundary point** of A if every neighborhood of x contains a point of A and a point of $\mathcal{C}(A)$. Show that a set is open if and only if it contains none of its boundary points. Show that a set is closed if and only if it contains all of its boundary points.

8.W. Interpret the concepts that were introduced in this section for the Cantor set of Definition 6.10.

(a) Show that the Cantor set $\mathbf{F}$ is closed in $\mathbf{R}$.

(b) Every point of $\mathbf{F}$ is a cluster point of both $\mathbf{F}$ and $\mathcal{C}(\mathbf{F})$.

(c) No non-void open set is contained in $\mathbf{F}$.

(d) The complement of $\mathbf{F}$ can be expressed as the union of a countable collection of open intervals.

(e) The set $\mathbf{F}$ cannot be expressed as the union of a countable collection of closed intervals.

(f) Show that $\mathbf{F}$ is disconnected; in fact, for every two distinct points x, y in $\mathbf{F}$, there is a disconnection A, B of $\mathbf{F}$ such that $x \in A$ and $y \in B$.

8.X. If C_1, C_2 are connected subsets of $\mathbf{R}$, then the product $C_1 \times C_2$ is a connected subset of $\mathbf{R}^2$.

8.Y. Show that the set

$$A = \{(x, y) \in \mathbf{R}^2 : 0 < y \leq x^2, x \neq 0\} \cup \{(0, 0)\}$$

is connected in $\mathbf{R}^2$, but it is not true that every pair of points in A can be joined by a polygonal curve lying entirely in A.

8.Z. Show that the set

$$S = \{(x, y) \in \mathbf{R}^2 : y = \sin(1/x), x \neq 0\}$$
$$\cup \{(0, y) : -1 \leq y \leq 1\},$$

is connected in $\mathbf{R}^2$, but it is not possible, in general, to join two points of S by a polygonal curve lying in S. In fact, it is not possible, in general, to join two points of S by a curve which lies entirely in S.

Projects

8.α. Let M be a set and d be a metric on M as defined in Exercise 7.N. Reexamine the definitions and theorems of Section 8, in order to determine which carry over for sets that have a metric. It will be seen, for example, that the notions of open, closed, and bounded set carry over. The Bolzano-Weierstrass fails for suitable M and d, however. Whenever possible, either show that the theorem extends or give a counterexample to show that it may fail.

8.β. Let $\mathfrak{I}$ be a family of subsets of a set X which (i) contains $\emptyset$ and X, (ii) contains the intersection of any finite family of sets in $\mathfrak{I}$, and (iii) contains the union of any family of sets in $\mathfrak{I}$. We call $\mathfrak{I}$ a **topology** for X, and refer to the sets in $\mathfrak{I}$ as the **open sets**. Reexamine the definitions and theorems of Section 8, trying to determine which carry over for sets X which have a topology $\mathfrak{I}$.

Section 9   The Theorems of Heine-Borel and Baire

The Nested Intervals Theorem 8.12 and the Bolzano-Weierstrass Theorem 8.13 are intimately related to the very important notion of compactness, which we shall discuss in the present section. Although it is possible to obtain most of the results of the later sections without knowing the Heine-Borel Theorem, we cannot go much farther in analysis without requiring this theorem, so it is false economy to avoid exposure to this deep result.

9.1 DEFINITION.   A set K is said to be compact if, whenever it is contained in the union of a collection $\mathcal{G} = \{G_\alpha\}$ of open sets, then it is also contained in the union of some *finite* number of the sets in $\mathcal{G}$.

A collection $\mathcal{G}$ of open sets whose union contains K is often called a **covering** of K. Thus the requirement that K be compact is that every covering $\mathcal{G}$ of K can be replaced by a finite covering of K, using only sets in $\mathcal{G}$. We note that in order to apply this definition to prove that a set K is compact, we need to examine *all* collections of open sets whose union contains K and show that K is contained in the union of some finite subcollection of each such collection. On the other hand, to show that a set H is not compact, it is sufficient to exhibit only *one* covering which cannot be replaced by a finite subcollection which still covers H.

9.2 EXAMPLES.   (a) Let $K = \{x_1, x_2, \ldots, x_m\}$ be a finite subset of $\mathbf{R}^p$. It is clear that if $\mathcal{G} = \{G_\alpha\}$ is a collection of open sets in $\mathbf{R}^p$, and if every point of K belongs to some subset of $\mathcal{G}$, then at most m carefully selected subsets of $\mathcal{G}$ will also have the property that their union contains K. Hence K is a compact subset of $\mathbf{R}^p$.

(b) In $\mathbf{R}$ we consider the subset $H = \{x \in \mathbf{R} : x \geq 0\}$. Let $G_n = (-1, n)$, $n \in \mathbf{N}$, so that $\mathcal{G} = \{G_n : n \in \mathbf{N}\}$ is a collection of open subsets of $\mathbf{R}$ whose union contains H. If $\{G_{n_1}, G_{n_2}, \ldots, G_{n_k}\}$ is a finite subcollection of $\mathcal{G}$, let $M = \sup \{n_1, n_2, \ldots, n_k\}$ so that $G_{n_j} \subseteq G_M$, for $j = 1, 2, \ldots, k$. It follows that G_M is the union of $\{G_{n_1}, G_{n_2}, \ldots, G_{n_k}\}$. However, the real number M does not belong to G_M and hence does not belong to

$$\bigcup_{j=1}^{k} G_{n_j}.$$

Therefore, no finite union of the sets G_n can contain H, and H is not compact.

(c) Let $H = (0, 1)$ in $\mathbf{R}$. If $G_n = (1/n, 1 - 1/n)$ for $n > 2$, then the collection $\mathcal{G} = \{G_n : n > 2\}$ of open sets is a covering of H. If $\{G_{n_1}, \ldots, G_{n_k}\}$ is a finite subcollection of $\mathcal{G}$, let $M = \sup \{n_1, \ldots, n_k\}$ so that $G_{n_j} \subseteq G_M$, for $j = 1, 2, \ldots, k$. It follows that G_M is the union of the sets $\{G_{n_1}, \ldots, G_{n_k}\}$. However, the real number $1/M$ belongs to H but does not belong to G_M. Therefore, no finite subcollection of $\mathcal{G}$ can form a covering of H, so that H is not compact.

(d) Consider the set $I = [0, 1]$; we shall show that I is compact. Let $\mathcal{G} = \{G_\alpha\}$ be a collection of open subsets of $\mathbf{R}$ whose union contains I. The real number $x = 0$ belongs to some open set in the collection $\mathcal{G}$ and so do numbers x satisfying $0 \leq x < \epsilon$, for some $\epsilon > 0$. Let x^* be the supremum of those points x in I such that the interval $[0, x]$ is contained in the union of a finite number of sets in $\mathcal{G}$. Since x^* belongs to I, it follows that x^* is an element of some open set in $\mathcal{G}$. Hence for some $\epsilon > 0$, the interval $[x^* - \epsilon, x^* + \epsilon]$ is contained in a set G_0 in the collection $\mathcal{G}$. But (by the definition of x^*) the interval $[0, x^* - \epsilon]$ is contained in the union of a finite number of sets in $\mathcal{G}$. Hence by adding the single set G_0 to the finite number already needed to cover $[0, x^* - \epsilon]$, we infer that the set $[0, x^* + \epsilon]$ is contained in the union of a finite number of sets in $\mathcal{G}$. This gives a contradiction unless $x^* = 1$.

It is usually not an easy matter to prove that a set is compact, using the definition only. We now present a remarkable and important theorem which completely characterizes compact subsets of $\mathbf{R}^p$. In fact, part of the importance of the Heine-Borel Theorem[†] is due to the simplicity of the conditions for compactness in $\mathbf{R}^p$.

9.3 HEINE-BOREL THEOREM. *A subset of $\mathbf{R}^p$ is compact if and only if it is closed and bounded.*

PROOF. First we show that if K is compact in $\mathbf{R}^p$, then K is closed. Let x belong to $\mathcal{C}(K)$ and for each natural number m, let G_m be the set defined by

$$G_m = \{y \in \mathbf{R}^p : |y - x| > 1/m\}.$$

It is readily seen that each set G_m, $m \in \mathbf{N}$, is open in $\mathbf{R}^p$. Also, the union of all the sets G_m, $m \in \mathbf{N}$, consists of all points of $\mathbf{R}^p$ except x. Since $x \notin K$, each point of K belongs to some set G_m. In view of the compact-

---

[†] EDUARD HEINE (1821–1881) studied at Berlin under Weierstrass and later taught at Bonn and Halle. In 1872 he proved that a continuous function on a closed interval is uniformly continuous.

(F. E. J.) ÉMILE BOREL (1871–1938), a student of Hermite's, was professor at Paris and one of the most influential mathematicians of his day. He made numerous and deep contributions to analysis and probability. In 1895 he proved that if a countable collection of open intervals cover a closed interval, then they have a finite subcovering.

ness of K, it follows that there exists a natural number M such that K is contained in the union of the sets

$$G_1, G_2, \ldots, G_M.$$

Since the sets G_m increase with m, then K is contained in G_M. Hence the neighborhood $\{z \in \mathbf{R}^p : |z - x| < 1/M\}$ does not intersect K, showing that $\complement(K)$ is open. Therefore, K is closed in $\mathbf{R}^p$. (See Figure 9.1, where the closed balls complementary to the G_m are depicted.)

Next we show that if K is compact in $\mathbf{R}^p$, then K is bounded (that is, K is contained in some set $\{x \in \mathbf{R}^p : |x| < r\}$ for sufficiently large r). In fact, for each natural number m, let H_m be the open set defined by

$$H_m = \{x \in \mathbf{R}^p : |x| < m\}.$$

The entire space $\mathbf{R}^p$, and hence K, is contained in the union of the increasing sets $H_m, m \in \mathbf{N}$. Since K is compact, there exists a natural number M such that $K \subseteq H_M$. This proves that K is bounded.

To complete the proof of this theorem we need to show that if K is a closed and bounded set which is contained in the union of a collection

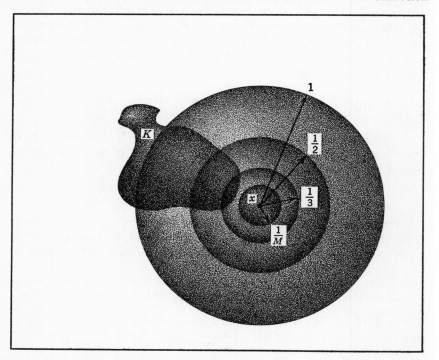

Figure 9.1.   A compact set is closed.

$\mathcal{G} = \{G_\alpha\}$ of open sets in $\mathbf{R}^p$, then it is contained in the union of some finite number of sets in $\mathcal{G}$. Since the set K is bounded, we may enclose it in a closed interval I_1 in $\mathbf{R}^p$. For example, we may take $I_1 = \{(\xi_1, \ldots, \xi_p) : |\xi_k| \leq r, k = 1, \ldots, p\}$ for suitably large $r > 0$. For the purpose of obtaining a contradiction, we shall assume that K is not contained in the union of any finite number of the sets in $\mathcal{G}$. Therefore, at least one of the 2^p closed intervals obtained by bisecting the sides of I_1 contains points of K and is such that the part of K in it is not contained in the union of any finite number of the sets in $\mathcal{G}$. (For, if each of the 2^p parts of K were contained in the union of a finite number of sets in $\mathcal{G}$, then K would be contained in the union of a finite number of sets in $\mathcal{G}$, contrary to hypothesis.) Let I_2 be any one of the subintervals in this subdivision of I_1 which is such that the non-empty set $K \cap I_2$ is not contained in the union of any finite number of sets in $\mathcal{G}$. We continue this process by bisecting the sides of I_2 to obtain 2^p closed subintervals of I_2 and letting I_3 be one of these subintervals such that the non-empty set $K \cap I_3$ is not contained in the union of a finite number of sets in $\mathcal{G}$, and so on.

In this way we obtain a nested sequence (I_n) of non-empty intervals (see Figure 9.2); according to the Nested Intervals Theorem there is a point y common to the I_n. Since each I_n contains points in K, the common element y is a cluster point of K. Since K is closed, then y belongs to K and is contained in some open set G_λ in $\mathcal{G}$. Therefore, there exists a number $\epsilon > 0$ such that all points w with $|y - w| < \epsilon$ belong to G_λ. On the other hand, the intervals I_k, $k \geq 2$, are obtained by successive

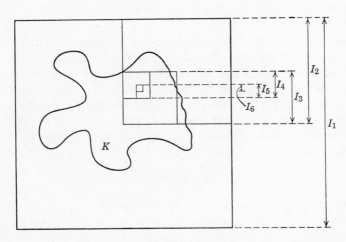

Figure 9.2

bisection of the sides of the interval $I_1 = \{ (\xi_1, \ldots, \xi_p) : |\xi_j| \le r \}$ so the length of the side of I_k is $r/2^{k-2}$. It follows from Theorem 7.11 that if $w \in I_k$, then

$$|y - w| \le \frac{r \sqrt{p}}{2^{k-1}} \, .$$

Hence, if k is chosen so large that

$$\frac{r \sqrt{p}}{2^{k-1}} < \epsilon,$$

then all points in I_k are contained in the single set G_λ. But this contradicts the construction of I_k as a set such that $K \cap I_k$ is not contained in the union of a finite number of sets in $\mathcal{G}$. This contradiction shows that the assumption that the closed bounded set K requires an infinite number of sets in $\mathcal{G}$ to enclose it is untenable.

Q.E.D.

As a consequence of the Heine-Borel Theorem, we obtain the next result, which is due to G. Cantor. It is a strengthening of our basic completeness property, since general closed sets are considered here and not just closed intervals.

9.4 CANTOR INTERSECTION THEOREM. *Let F_1 be a non-empty closed, bounded subset of $\mathbf{R}^p$ and let*

$$F_1 \supseteq F_2 \supseteq \cdots \supseteq F_n \supseteq \cdots$$

be a sequence of non-empty closed sets. Then there exists a point belonging to all of the sets $\{F_k : k \in \mathbf{N}\}$.

PROOF. Since F_1 is closed and bounded, it follows from the Heine-Borel Theorem that it is compact. For each natural number k, let G_k be the complement of F_k in $\mathbf{R}^p$. Since F_k is assumed to be closed, G_k is open in $\mathbf{R}^p$. If, contrary to the theorem, there is no point belonging to all of the sets F_k, $k \in \mathbf{N}$, then the union of the sets G_k, $k \in \mathbf{N}$, contains the compact set F_1. Therefore, the set F_1 is contained in the union of a finite number of the sets G_k; say, in $G_1, G_2, \ldots, G_K$. Since the G_k increase, we have

$$\bigcup_{k=1}^{K} G_k = G_K.$$

Since $F_1 \subseteq G_K$, it follows that $F_1 \cap F_K = \emptyset$. By hypothesis $F_1 \supseteq F_K$, so $F_1 \cap F_K = F_K$. Our assumption leads to the conclusion that $F_K = \emptyset$, which contradicts the hypothesis and establishes the theorem.

Q.E.D.

9.5   LEBESGUE COVERING THEOREM. *Suppose* $\mathcal{G} = \{G_\alpha\}$ *is a covering of a compact subset* K *of* $\mathbf{R}^p$. *There exists a positive number* λ *such that if* x, y *belong to* K *and* $|x - y| < \lambda$, *then there is a set in* $\mathcal{G}$ *containing both* x *and* y.

PROOF.   For each point u in K, there is an open set $G_{\alpha(u)}$ in $\mathcal{G}$ containing u. Let $\delta(u) > 0$ be such that if $|v - u| < 2\delta(u)$, then v belongs to $G_{\alpha(u)}$. Consider the open set $S(u) = \{v \in \mathbf{R}^p : |v - u| < \delta(u)\}$ and the collection $\mathcal{S} = \{S(u) : u \in K\}$ of open sets. Since S is a covering of the compact set K, then K is contained in the union of a finite number of sets in $\mathcal{S}$, say in

$$S(u_1), \ldots, S(u_n).$$

We now define λ to be the positive real number

$$\lambda = \inf \{\delta(u_1), \ldots, \delta(u_n)\}.$$

If x, y belong to K and $|x - y| < \lambda$, then x belongs to $S(u_j)$ for some j with $1 \leq j \leq n$, so $|x - u_j| < \delta(u_j)$. Since $|x - y| < \lambda$, we have $|y - u_j| \leq |y - x| + |x - u_j| < 2\delta(u_j)$. According to the definition of $\delta(u_j)$, we infer that both x and y belong to the set $G_{\alpha(u_j)}$.

Q.E.D.

We remark that a positive number λ having the property stated in the theorem is sometimes called a **Lebesgue**† number for the covering $\mathcal{G}$.

Although we shall make use of arguments based on compactness in later sections, it seems appropriate to insert here two results which appear intuitively clear, but whose proof seems to require use of some type of compactness argument.

9.6   NEAREST POINT THEOREM. *Let* F *be a non-void closed subset of* $\mathbf{R}^p$ *and let* x *be a point outside of* F. *Then there exists at least one point* y *belonging to* F *such that* $|z - x| \geq |y - x|$ *for all* $z \in F$.

PROOF.   Since F is closed and $x \notin F$, then (cf. Exercise 9.H) the distance from x to F, which is defined to be $d = \inf \{|x - z| : z \in F\}$ satisfies $d > 0$. Let $F_k = \{z \in F : |x - z| \leq d + 1/k\}$ for $k \in \mathbf{N}$. According to Example 8.5(f) these sets are closed in $\mathbf{R}^p$ and it is clear that F_1 is bounded and that $F_1 \supseteq F_2 \supseteq \cdots \supseteq F_k \supseteq \cdots$.

Furthermore, by the definition of d and F_k, it is seen that F_k is non-empty. It follows from the Cantor Intersection Theorem 9.4 that there

---

† HENRI LEBESGUE (1875–1941) is best known for his pioneering work on the modern theory of the integral which is named for him and which is basic to present-day analysis.

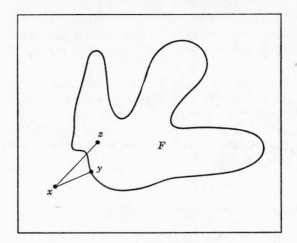

Figure 9.3

is a point y belonging to all F_k, $k \in \mathbf{N}$. It is readily seen that $|x - y| = d$, so that y satisfies the conclusion. (See Figure 9.3.)

Q.E.D.

A variant of the next theorem is of considerable importance in the theory of analytic functions. We shall state the result only for $p = 2$ and use intuitive ideas as to what it means for a set to be surrounded by a closed curve (that is, a curve which has no end points).

9.7   Circumscribing Contour Theorem. *Let F be a closed and bounded set in $\mathbf{R}^2$ and let G be an open set which contains F. Then there exists a closed curve C, lying entirely in G and made up of arcs of a finite number of circles, such that F is surrounded by C.*

PROOF.   If x belongs to $F \subseteq G$, there exists a positive number $\delta(x)$ such that if $|y - x| < \delta(x)$, then y also belongs to G. Let $G(x) = \{y \in \mathbf{R}^2 : |y - x| < \frac{1}{2}\delta(x)\}$ for each x in F. Since the collection $\mathcal{G} = \{G(x) : x \in F\}$ constitutes a covering of the compact set F, the union of a finite number of the sets in $\mathcal{G}$, say $G(x_1), \ldots, G(x_k)$, contains the compact set F. By using arcs from the circles with centers x_j and radii $(\frac{1}{2})\,\delta(x_j)$, we obtain the desired curve C.(See Figure 9.4) The detailed construction of the curve will not be given here.

Q.E.D.

As the final main result of this section, we present a form of what is sometimes called the "Baire† Category Theorem." One way of inter-

---

† René Louis Baire (1874–1932) was a professor at Dijon. He worked in set theory and real analysis.

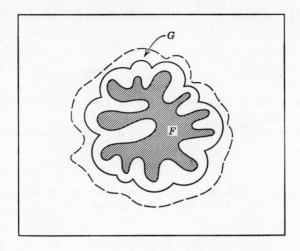

Figure 9.4

preting Baire's theorem is from the consideration of the "fatness" of a subset. A non-empty open subset of $\mathbf{R}^p$ is "fat" in the sense that it contains a neighborhood of each of its points. A closed set, however, need not be "fat" at all. Baire's theorem says that if a non-empty open set is contained in the union of a *countable* number of closed sets, then at least one of the closed sets must be "fat" enough to contain some non-empty open set.

9.8 BAIRE'S THEOREM.   *If $\{H_k : k \in \mathbf{N}\}$ is a countable family of closed subsets of $\mathbf{R}^p$ whose union contains a non-void open set, then at least one of the sets H_k contains a non-void open set.*

PROOF.   Suppose that no set H_k, $k \in \mathbf{N}$, contains a non-void open set but that G_0 is a non-void open set contained in the union of H_k, $k \in \mathbf{N}$. If x_1 belongs to $G_0 \backslash H_1$, there is a non-void open ball $G_1 = \{x \in \mathbf{R}^p : |x - x_1| < r_1\}$ such that the set $F_1 = \{x \in \mathbf{R}^p : |x - x_1| \leq r_1\}$ is contained in G_0 and such that $F_1 \cap H_1 = \emptyset$. In the same way, if x_2 belongs to $G_1 \backslash H_2$, there is a non-void open ball $G_2 = \{x \in \mathbf{R}^p : |x - x_2| < r_2\}$ contained in G_1 with $F_2 = \{x \in \mathbf{R}^p : |x - x_2| \leq r_2\}$ such that $F_2 \cap H_2 = \emptyset$. To continue, for each natural number k we obtain a point $x_k \in G_{k-1} \backslash H_k$ and a non-void open set $G_k = \{x \in \mathbf{R}^p : |x - x_k| < r_k\}$ contained in G_{k-1} with $F_k = \{x \in \mathbf{R}^p : |x - x_k| \leq r_k\}$ such that $F_k \cap H_k = \emptyset$. Evidently, the family $\{F_k : k \in \mathbf{N}\}$ of closed sets is nested; according to the Cantor Intersection Theorem, there exists a point w which belongs to all the sets F_k, $k \geq 1$. Since $F_k \cap H_k = \emptyset$ for each k in $\mathbf{N}$, the point w cannot belong to G_0, because G_0 is contained in the union of $\{H_k : k \in \mathbf{N}\}$. On the other hand $F_k \subseteq G_0$, $k \in \mathbf{N}$, so we must have $w \in G_0$. This contradiction proves that at least one of the sets H_k, $k \in \mathbf{N}$, must contain a non-void open set.

Q.E.D.

We shall conclude this section with a pair of easy applications of Baire's Theorem.

A line in $\mathbf{R}^2$ is a set L of points (x, y) in $\mathbf{R}^2$ which satisfy an equation of the form

$$ax + by + c = 0,$$

where a, b, c are real numbers and a and b are not both zero. Any line L is a closed subset of $\mathbf{R}^2$ which does not contain any non-void open set (cf. Exercise 9.N).

9.9 COROLLARY. *The space $\mathbf{R}^2$ is not the union of a countable number of lines.*

PROOF. Suppose that there is a countable family $\{L_k : k \in \mathbf{N}\}$ of lines whose union is $\mathbf{R}^2$. Since $\mathbf{R}^2$ is a non-void open set in $\mathbf{R}^2$, it follows from Baire's theorem that at least one of the closed sets L_k must contain a non-void open set. But, we have already observed that a line does not contain any non-void open sets.

Q.E.D.

In order to give a final application of Baire's Theorem, we note that a subset of $\mathbf{R}$ consisting of a single point is closed in $\mathbf{R}$. As we have seen in Section 3, the subset $\mathbf{Q}$ of $\mathbf{R}$ consisting of rational numbers is countable; it follows that $\mathbf{Q}$ is the union of a countable number of closed sets, none of which contains a non-empty open set. We now show that it follows from Baire's Theorem that the set of irrational numbers in $\mathbf{R}$ cannot have this same property.

9.10 COROLLARY. *The set of irrational numbers in $\mathbf{R}$ is not the union of a countable family of closed sets, none of which contains a non-empty open set.*

PROOF. Suppose, on the contrary, that the set $\mathbf{R}\backslash\mathbf{Q}$ is the union of such a countable collection of closed sets. As we have seen, $\mathbf{Q}$ is contained in the union of another countable collection of closed sets. Therefore, we conclude that $\mathbf{R}$ is also the union of a countable collection of closed sets, none of which contains a non-void open set. However, this contradicts Baire's Theorem.

Q.E.D.

Exercises

9.A. Show directly from the definition (i.e., without using the Heine-Borel Theorem) that the open ball given by $\{(x, y) : x^2 + y^2 < 1\}$ is not compact in $\mathbf{R}^2$.

9.B. Show directly that the entire space $\mathbf{R}^2$ is not compact.

9.C. Prove directly that if K is compact in $\mathbf{R}^p$ and F is a closed subset of K, then F is compact in $\mathbf{R}^p$.

9.D. Prove that if K is a compact subset of $\mathbf{R}$, then K is compact when regarded as a subset of $\mathbf{R}^2$.

9.E. By modifying the argument in Example 9.2(d), prove that the interval $J = \{(x, y) : 0 \le x \le 1, 0 \le y \le 1\}$ is compact in $\mathbf{R}^2$.

9.F. Locate the places where the hypotheses that the set K is bounded and that it is closed were used in the proof of the Heine-Borel Theorem.

9.G. Prove the Cantor Intersection Theorem by selecting a point x_n from F_n and then applying the Bolzano-Weierstrass Theorem 8.13 to the set $\{x_n : n \in \mathbf{N}\}$.

9.H. If F is closed in $\mathbf{R}^p$ and if

$$d(x, F) = \inf \{|x - z| : z \in F\} = 0,$$

then x belongs to F.

9.I. Does the Nearest Point Theorem in $\mathbf{R}$ imply that there is a positive real number nearest zero?

9.J. If F is a non-empty closed set in $\mathbf{R}^p$ and if $x \notin F$, is there a *unique* point of F that is nearest to x?

9.K. If K is a compact subset of $\mathbf{R}^p$ and x is a point of $\mathbf{R}^p$, then the set $K_x = \{x + y : y \in K\}$ is also compact. (This set K_x is sometimes called the **translation** of the set K by x.)

9.L. The intersection of two open sets is compact if and only if it is empty. Can the intersection of an infinite collection of open sets be a non-empty compact set?

9.M. If F is a compact subset of $\mathbf{R}^2$ and G is an open set which contains F, then there exists a closed polygonal curve C lying entirely in G which surrounds F.

9.N. Prove that a line in $\mathbf{R}^2$ is a closed subset of $\mathbf{R}^2$ and contains no non-void open sets.

9.O. If the set A does not contain a non-void open set, can the closure A^- (see Exercise 8.K) contain a non-void open subset of $\mathbf{R}^p$?

9.P. If a set B contains a non-void closed set, must the interior B° (see Exercise 8.M) contain a non-void closed subset of $\mathbf{R}^p$?

9.Q. The set of rational numbers $\mathbf{Q}$ is not the intersection of a countable collection of open sets.

9.R. A closed set F does not contain any non-void open set of $\mathbf{R}^p$, if and only if every point in $\mathbf{R}^p$ is a cluster point of its complement.

9.S. A set D is said to be **dense** in $\mathbf{R}^p$, if every point in $\mathbf{R}^p$ is a cluster point of D. Prove that D is dense in $\mathbf{R}^p$, if and only if its closure D^- (see Exercise 8.K) coincides with $\mathbf{R}^p$.

9.T. Give an example of an open subset of $\mathbf{R}^p$ which is dense in $\mathbf{R}^p$. Can you give an example of a closed subset of $\mathbf{R}^p$ which is dense in $\mathbf{R}^p$?

9.U. If D_1 and D_2 are open sets which are dense in $\mathbf{R}^p$, then $D_1 \cup D_2$ and $D_1 \cap D_2$ are also dense open sets in $\mathbf{R}^p$.

9.V. If D_1 and D_2 are dense subsets of $\mathbf{R}^p$, are $D_1 \cup D_2$ and $D_1 \cap D_2$ also dense subsets of $\mathbf{R}^p$?

9.W. If $\{D_n : n \in \mathbf{N}\}$ is a countable collection of dense open subsets of $\mathbf{R}^p$, then their intersection is a dense subset of $\mathbf{R}^p$.

Section 10   The Complex Number System

Once the real number system is at hand, it is a simple matter to create the complex number system. We shall indicate in this section how the complex field can be constructed.

As seen before, the real number system is a field which satisfies certain additional properties. In Section 7, we constructed the Cartesian space $\mathbf{R}^p$ and introduced some algebraic operations in the p-fold Cartesian product of R. However, we did *not* make $\mathbf{R}^p$ into a field. It may come as a surprise that it is not possible to define a multiplication which makes $\mathbf{R}^p$, $p \geq 3$, into a field. Nevertheless, it is possible to define a multiplication operation in $\mathbf{R} \times \mathbf{R}$ which makes this set into a field. We now introduce the desired operations.

10.1 DEFINITION. The complex number system $\mathbf{C}$ consists of all ordered pairs (x, y) of real numbers with the operation of **addition** defined by

$$(x, y) + (x', y') = (x + x', y + y'),$$

and the operation of **multiplication** defined by

$$(x, y) \cdot (x', y') = (xx' - yy', xy' + x'y).$$

Thus the complex number system $\mathbf{C}$ has the same elements as the two-dimensional space $\mathbf{R}^2$. It has the same addition operation, but it possesses a multiplication as R does not. Therefore, considered merely as sets, $\mathbf{C}$ and $\mathbf{R}^2$ are equal since they have the same elements; however, from the standpoint of algebra, they are not the same since they possess different operations.

An element of $\mathbf{C}$ is called a **complex number** and is often denoted by a single letter such as z. If $z = (x, y)$, then we refer to the real number x as the **real part** of z and to y as the **imaginary part** of z, in symbols,

$$x = \operatorname{Re} z, \qquad y = \operatorname{Im} z.$$

The complex number $\bar{z} = (x, -y)$ is called the **conjugate** of $z = (x, y)$.

10.2 Theorem. *The complex number system* **C** *forms a field with the operations defined in Definition 10.1.*

PARTIAL PROOF. We shall leave most of the details to the reader and mention only that the zero element of **C** is the complex number $(0, 0)$ and the identity element is $(1, 0)$. Furthermore, if $z = (x, y) \neq (0, 0)$, then the inverse to z is given by

$$z' = \left(\frac{x}{x^2 + y^2}, \frac{-y}{x^2 + y^2} \right).$$

Q.E.D.

Sometimes it is convenient to adopt part of the notation of Section 7 and write

$$az = a(x, y) = (ax, ay),$$

when a is a real number and $z = (x, y)$ is in **C**. With this notation, it is clear that each element in **C** has a unique representation in the form of a sum of a product of a real number with $(1, 0)$ and of the product of a real number with $(0, 1)$. Thus we can write

$$z = (x, y) = x(1, 0) + y(0, 1).$$

Since the element $(1, 0)$ is the identity element of **C**, it is natural to denote it by 1 (or to suppress it entirely when it is a factor). For the sake of brevity it is convenient to introduce a symbol for $(0, 1)$ and i is the conventional choice. With this notation, we write

$$z = (x, y) = x + iy.$$

In addition, we have $\bar{z} = (x, -y) = x - iy$ and

$$x = \operatorname{Re} z = \frac{z + \bar{z}}{2}, \quad y = \operatorname{Im} z = \frac{z - \bar{z}}{2i}$$

By Definition 10.1, $(0, 1)(0, 1) = (-1, 0)$ which can be written as $i^2 = -1$. Thus in **C** the quadratic equation

$$z^2 + 1 = 0,$$

has a solution. The historical reason for the development of the complex number system was to obtain a system of "numbers" in which every quadratic equation has a solution. It was realized that not every equation with real coefficients has a real solution, and so complex numbers were invented to remedy this defect. It is a well-known fact that not only do the complex numbers suffice to produce solutions for every quadratic equation with real coefficients, but they also suffice to guarantee solutions for any polynomial equation of arbitrary degree and with coefficients which may be complex numbers. This result is called the Fundamental Theorem of Algebra and was proved first by the great Gauss† in 1799.

Although C cannot be given the order properties discussed in Section 5, it is easy to endow it with the metric and topological structure of Sections 7 and 8. For, if $z = (x, y)$ belongs to C, we define the *absolute value* of z to be

$$|z| = (x^2 + y^2)^{1/2}.$$

It is readily seen that the absolute value just defined has the properties:
   (i) $|z| \geq 0$;
   (ii) $|z| = 0$ if and only if $z = 0$;
   (iii) $|wz| = |w|\,|z|$;
   (iv) $||w| - |z|| \leq |w \pm z| \leq |w| + |z|$.

It will be observed that the absolute value of the complex number $z = (x, y)$ is precisely the same as the length or norm of the element (x, y) in R^2. Therefore, all of the topological properties of the Cartesian spaces that were introduced and studied in Sections 8 and 9 are meaningful and valid for C. In particular, the notions of open and closed sets in C are exactly as for the Cartesian space R^2. Furthermore, the Nested Intervals Theorem 8.12, the Bolzano-Weierstrass Theorem 8.13, and the Connectedness Theorem 8.20 hold in C exactly as in R^2. In addition, the Heine-Borel Theorem 9.3 and the Baire Theorem 9.8, together with their consequences, also hold in C.

The reader should keep these remarks in mind throughout the remaining section of this book. It will be seen that *all of the succeeding material which applies to Cartesian spaces of dimension exceeding one, applies equally well to the complex number system.* Thus most of the results to be obtained pertaining to sequences, continuous functions, derivatives, integrals, and infinite series are also valid for C without change either in statement or in proof. The only exceptions to this statement are those properties which are based on the order properties of R.

In this sense complex analysis is a special case of real analysis; however, there are a number of deep and important new features to the study of analytic functions that have no general counterpart in the realm of real analysis. Hence only the fairly superficial aspects of complex analysis are subsumed in what we shall do.

† CARL FRIEDRICH GAUSS (1777–1855), the prodigious son of a day laborer, was one of the greatest of all mathematicians, but is also remembered for his work in astronomy, physics, and geodesy. He became professor and director of the Observatory at Göttingen.

Exercises

10.A. Show that the complex number iz is obtained from z by a counter-clockwise rotation of $\pi/2$ radians ($= 90°$) around the origin.

10.B. If $c = (\cos \theta, \sin \theta) = \cos \theta + i \sin \theta$, then the number cz is obtained from z by a counter-clockwise rotation of θ radians around the origin.

10.C. Describe the geometrical relation between the complex numbers z and $az + b$, where $a \neq 0$. Show that the mapping defined for $z \in \mathbf{C}$, by $f(z) = az + b$, sends circles into circles and lines into lines.

10.D. Describe the geometrical relations among the complex numbers z, $\bar{z}$ and $1/z$ for $z \neq 0$. Show that the mapping defined by $g(z) = \bar{z}$ sends circles into circles and lines into lines. Which circles and lines are left fixed under g?

10.E. Show that the **inversion mapping,** defined by $h(z) = 1/z$, sends circles and lines into circles and lines. Which circles are sent into lines? Which lines are sent into circles? Examine the images under h of the vertical lines given by the equation Re $z = $ constant; of the horizontal lines Im $z = $ constant; of the circles $|z| = $ constant.

10.F. Investigate the geometrical character of the mapping defined by $g(z) = z^2$. Determine if the mapping g is one-one and if it maps $\mathbf{C}$ onto all of $\mathbf{C}$. Examine the inverse images under g of the lines

$$\text{Re } z = \text{constant}, \qquad \text{Im } z = \text{constant},$$

and the circles $|z| = $ constant.

III

Convergence

The material in the preceding two chapters should provide an adequate understanding of the real number system and the Cartesian spaces. Now that these algebraic and topological foundations have been laid, we are prepared to pursue questions of a more analytic nature. We shall begin with the study of convergence of sequences, to be followed in later chapters by continuity, differentiation, integration, and series. Some of the results in this chapter may be familiar to the reader from earlier courses in analysis, but the presentation given here is intended to be entirely rigorous and to present certain more profound results which have not been discussed in earlier courses.

In Section 11 we shall introduce the notion of convergence of a sequence of elements in R^p and establish some elementary but useful results about convergent sequences. Section 12 is primarily concerned with obtaining the Monotone Convergence Theorem and the Cauchy Criterion. Next, in Section 13, we consider the convergence and uniform convergence of sequences of functions. The last section of this chapter deals briefly with the limit superior of a sequence in R; the Landau symbols O, o; Cesàro summation of a sequence in R^p; and double and iterated limits. This final section can be omitted without loss of continuity.

Section 11 Introduction to Sequences

Although the theory of convergence can be presented on a very abstract level, we prefer to discuss the convergence of sequences in a Cartesian space R^p, paying special attention to the case of the real line. The reader should interpret the ideas by drawing diagrams in R and R^2.

11.1 DEFINITION. A **sequence in R^p** is a function whose domain is the set $N = \{1, 2, \ldots\}$ of natural numbers and whose range is contained in R^p.

In other words, a sequence assigns to each natural number $n = 1, 2,$ ..., a uniquely determined element of $\mathbf{R}^p$. Traditionally, the element of $\mathbf{R}^p$ which is assigned to a natural number n is denoted by a symbol such as x_n and, although this notation is at variance with that employed for most functions, we shall adhere to the conventional symbolism. To be consistent with earlier notation, if $X : \mathbf{N} \to \mathbf{R}^p$ is a sequence, the value of X at $n \in \mathbf{N}$ should be symbolized by $X(n)$, rather than by x_n. While we accept the traditional notation, we also wish to distinguish between the function X and its values $X(n) = x_n$. Hence when the elements of the sequence (that is, the values of the function) are denoted by x_n, we shall denote the function by the notation $X = (x_n)$ or by $X = (x_n : n \in \mathbf{N})$. We use the parentheses to indicate that the ordering in the range of X, induced by that in $\mathbf{N}$, is a matter of importance. Thus we are distinguishing notationally between the sequence $X = (x_n : n \in \mathbf{N})$ and the set $\{x_n : n \in \mathbf{N}\}$ of values of this sequence.

In defining sequences we often list in order the elements of the sequence, stopping when the rule of formation seems evident. Thus we may write

$$(2, 4, 6, 8, \ldots)$$

for the sequence of even integers. A more satisfactory method is to specify a formula for the general term of the sequence, such as

$$(2n : n \in \mathbf{N}).$$

In practice it is often more convenient to specify the value x_1 and a method of obtaining x_{n+1}, $n \geq 1$, when x_n is known. Still more generally, we may specify x_1 and a rule for obtaining x_{n+1} from $x_1, x_2, \ldots, x_n$. We shall refer to either of these methods as *inductive* definitions of the sequence. In this way we might define the sequence of even natural numbers by the definition

$$x_1 = 2, \qquad x_{n+1} = x_n + 2, n \geq 1.$$

or by the (apparently more complicated) definition

$$x_1 = 2, \qquad x_{n+1} = x_n + x_1, n \geq 1.$$

Clearly, many other methods of defining this sequence are possible.

We now introduce some methods of constructing new sequences from given ones.

11.2 DEFINITION. If $X = (x_n)$ and $Y = (y_n)$ are sequences in $\mathbf{R}^p$, then we define their sum to be the sequence $X + Y = (x_n + y_n)$ in $\mathbf{R}^p$, their difference to be the sequence $X - Y = (x_n - y_n)$, and their

inner product to be the sequence $X \cdot Y = (x_n \cdot y_n)$ in R which is obtained
by taking the inner product of corresponding terms. Similarly, if
$X = (x_n)$ is a sequence in R and if $Y = (y_n)$ is a sequence in $\mathbf{R}^p$, we
define the **product** of X and Y to be the sequence in $\mathbf{R}^p$ denoted by
$XY = (x_n y_n)$. Finally, if $Y = (y_n)$ is a sequence in R with $y_n \neq 0$, we
can define the **quotient** of a sequence $X = (x_n)$ in $\mathbf{R}^p$ by Y to be the
sequence $X/Y = (x_n/y_n)$.

For example, if X, Y are the sequences in R given by

$$X = (2, 4, 6, \ldots, 2n, \ldots), \qquad Y = \left(1, \frac{1}{2}, \frac{1}{3}, \ldots, \frac{1}{n}, \ldots\right),$$

then we have

$$X + Y = \left(3, \frac{9}{2}, \frac{19}{3}, \ldots, \frac{2n^2 + 1}{n}, \ldots\right),$$

$$X - Y = \left(1, \frac{7}{2}, \frac{17}{3}, \ldots, \frac{2n^2 - 1}{n}, \ldots\right),$$

$$XY = (2, 2, 2, \ldots, 2, \ldots),$$

$$\frac{X}{Y} = (2, 8, 18, \ldots, 2n^2, \ldots).$$

Similarly, if Z denotes the sequence in R given by

$$Z = \left(1, 0, 1, \ldots, \frac{1 - (-1)^n}{2}, \ldots\right),$$

then we have defined $X + Z$, $X - Z$ and XZ; but X/Z is not defined,
since some of the elements in Z are zero.

We now come to the notion of the limit of a sequence.

11.3 DEFINITION. Let $X = (x_n)$ be a sequence in $\mathbf{R}^p$. An element
x of $\mathbf{R}^p$ is said to be a **limit** of X if, for each neighborhood V of x there is
a natural number K_V such that if $n \geq K_V$, then x_n belongs to V. If x is
a limit of X, we also say that X **converges** to x. If a sequence has a limit,
we say that the sequence is **convergent**. If a sequence has no limit then
we say that it is **divergent**.

The notation K_V is used to suggest that the choice of K will depend
on V. It is clear that a small neighborhood V will usually require a large
value of K_V in order to guarantee that $x_n \in V$ for $n \geq K_V$.

We have defined the limit of a sequence $X = (x_n)$ in terms of neighborhoods. It is often convenient to use the norm in $\mathbf{R}^p$ to give an equivalent definition, which we now state as a theorem.

11.4   THEOREM. *Let* $X = (x_n)$ *be a sequence in* $\mathbf{R}^p$. *An element* x *of* $\mathbf{R}^p$ *is a limit of* X *if and only if for each positive real number* ϵ *there is a natural number* $K(\epsilon)$ *such that if* $n \geq K(\epsilon)$, *then* $|x_n - x| < \epsilon$.

PROOF. Suppose that x is a limit of the sequence X according to Definition 11.3. Let ϵ be a positive real number and consider the open ball $V(\epsilon) = \{y \in \mathbf{R}^p : |y - x| < \epsilon\}$, which is a neighborhood of x. By Definition 11.3 there is a natural number $K_{V(\epsilon)}$ such that if $n \geq K_{V(\epsilon)}$, then $x_n \in V(\epsilon)$. Hence if $n \geq K_{V(\epsilon)}$, then $|x_n - x| < \epsilon$. This shows that the stated ϵ property holds when x is a limit of X.

Conversely, suppose that the property in the theorem holds for all $\epsilon > 0$; we must show that Definition 11.3 is satisfied. To do this, let V be any neighborhood of x; then there is a positive real number ϵ such that the open ball $V(\epsilon)$ with center x and radius ϵ is contained in V. According to the ϵ property in the theorem, there is a natural number $K(\epsilon)$ such that if $n \geq K(\epsilon)$, then $|x_n - x| < \epsilon$. Stated differently, if $n \geq K(\epsilon)$, then $x_n \in V(\epsilon)$; hence $x_n \in V$ and the requirement in Definition 11.3 is satisfied.   Q.E.D.

11.5   UNIQUENESS OF LIMITS. *A sequence in* $\mathbf{R}^p$ *can have at most one limit.*

PROOF. Suppose, on the contrary that x', x'' are limits of $X = (x_n)$ and that $x' \neq x''$. Let V', V'' be disjoint neighborhoods of x', x'', respectively, and let K', K'' be natural numbers such that if $n \geq K'$ then $x_n \in V'$ and if $n \geq K''$ then $x_n \in V''$. Let $K = \sup \{K', K''\}$ so that both $x_K \in V'$ and $x_K \in V''$. We infer that x_K belongs to $V' \cap V''$, contrary to the supposition that V' and V'' are disjoint.

                                                      Q.E.D.

When a sequence $X = (x_n)$ in $\mathbf{R}^p$ has a limit x, we often write

$$x = \lim X, \quad \text{or} \quad x = \lim_n (x_n),$$

or sometimes use the symbolism $x_n \to x$.

11.6   LEMMA. *A convergent sequence in* $\mathbf{R}^p$ *is bounded.*

PROOF. Let $x = \lim (x_n)$ and let $\epsilon = 1$. By Theorem 11.4 there exists a natural number $K = K(1)$ such that if $n \geq K$, then $|x_n - x| \leq 1$. By using the Triangle Inequality, we infer that if $n \geq K$, then $|x_n| \leq |x| + 1$. If we set $M = \sup \{|x_1|, |x_2|, \ldots, |x_{K-1}|, |x| + 1\}$, then $|x_n| \leq M$ for all $n \in \mathbf{N}$.

                                                      Q.E.D.

It might be suspected that the theory of convergence of sequences in $\mathbf{R}^p$ is more complicated than in $\mathbf{R}$, but this is not the case (except for notational matters). In fact, the next result is important in that it shows that questions of convergence in $\mathbf{R}^p$ can be reduced to the identical questions in $\mathbf{R}$ for the coordinate sequences. Before stating this result, we recall that a typical element x in $\mathbf{R}^p$ is represented in coordinate fashion by "p-tuple"

$$x = (\xi_1, \xi_2, \ldots, \xi_p).$$

Hence each element in a sequence (x_n) in $\mathbf{R}^p$ has a similar representation; thus $x_n = (\xi_{1n}, \xi_{2n}, \ldots, \xi_{pn})$. In this way, the sequence (x_n) generates p sequences of real numbers; namely,

$$(\xi_{1n}), (\xi_{2n}), \ldots, (\xi_{pn}).$$

We shall now show that the convergence of the sequence (x_n) is faithfully reflected by the convergence of these p sequences of coordinates.

11.7 **THEOREM.** *A sequence (x_n) in $\mathbf{R}^p$ with*

$$x_n = (\xi_{1n}, \xi_{2n}, \ldots, \xi_{pn}), \; n \in \mathbf{N},$$

converges to an element $y = (\eta_1, \eta_2, \ldots, \eta_p)$ if and only if the corresponding p sequences of real numbers

(11.1) $(\xi_{1n}), (\xi_{2n}), \ldots, (\xi_{pn}),$

converge to $\eta_1, \eta_2, \ldots, \eta_p$ respectively.

PROOF. If $x_n \to y$, then $|x_n - y| < \epsilon$ for $n \geq K(\epsilon)$. In view of Theorem 7.11, we have

$$|\xi_{jn} - \eta_j| \leq |x_n - y| < \epsilon, \qquad n \geq K(\epsilon), j = 1, \ldots, p.$$

Hence each of the p coordinate sequences must converge to the corresponding real number.

Conversely, suppose that the sequences in (11.1) converge to η_j, $j = 1, 2, \ldots, p$. Given $\epsilon > 0$, there is a natural number $M(\epsilon)$ such that if $n \geq M(\epsilon)$, then

$$|\xi_{jn} - \eta_j| < \epsilon/\sqrt{p} \quad \text{for} \quad j = 1, 2, \ldots, p.$$

From this it follows that, when $n \geq M(\epsilon)$, then

$$|x_n - y|^2 = \sum_{j=1}^{p} |\xi_{jn} - \eta_j|^2 \leq \epsilon^2,$$

so that the sequence (x_n) converges to y.

                                                                Q.E.D.

We shall now present some examples. For the sake of simplicity in the calculations, we consider examples in $\mathbf{R}$.

11.8 EXAMPLES. (a) Let (x_n) be the sequence in $\mathbf{R}$ whose nth element is $x_n = 1/n$. We shall show that $\lim (1/n) = 0$. To do this, let ϵ be a positive real number; according to Theorem 5.14 there exists a natural number $K(\epsilon)$, whose value depends on ϵ, such that $1/K(\epsilon) < \epsilon$. Then, if $n \geq K(\epsilon)$ we have

$$0 < x_n = \frac{1}{n} \leq \frac{1}{K(\epsilon)} < \epsilon,$$

whence it follows that $|x_n - 0| < \epsilon$ for $n \geq K(\epsilon)$. This proves that $\lim (1/n) = 0$.

(b) Let $a > 0$ and consider the sequence $\left(\dfrac{1}{1 + na}\right)$ in $\mathbf{R}$. We shall show that $\lim \left(\dfrac{1}{1 + na}\right) = 0$. To this end, we infer from Theorem 5.14 that there exists a natural number $K(\epsilon)$ such that $1/K(\epsilon) < a\epsilon$. Then, if $n > K(\epsilon)$, we have $1 < an\epsilon$ and hence $1 < an\epsilon + \epsilon = \epsilon(an + 1)$. We conclude, therefore, that if $n \geq K(\epsilon)$, then

$$0 < \frac{1}{1 + an} < \epsilon,$$

showing that $\lim (1/(1 + an)) = 0$.

(c) Let b be a real number satisfying $0 < b < 1$ and consider the sequence (b^n). We shall show that $\lim (b^n) = 0$. To do this, we note that we can write b in the form

$$b = \frac{1}{1 + a},$$

where a is a positive real number. Furthermore, using the Binomial Theorem, we have Bernoulli's Inequality $(1 + a)^n > 1 + na$ for $n > 1$. Hence

$$0 < b^n = \frac{1}{(1 + a)^n} < \frac{1}{1 + na} \quad \text{for} \quad n > 1.$$

Since the term on the right side can be dominated by ϵ for $n \geq K(\epsilon)$, then so can b^n. From this we infer that $b^n \to 0$ whenever $0 < b < 1$.

(d) Let c be a positive real number and consider the sequence $(c^{1/n})$. It will be seen that $\lim (c^{1/n}) = 1$. We shall carry out the details only for the case $0 < c < 1$, leaving the similar but slightly easier case where $1 \leq c$ as an exercise for the reader. We note that if $\epsilon > 0$, then since $0 < c$, there exists a natural number $K(\epsilon)$ such that if $n \geq K(\epsilon)$ then

$1/(1 + \epsilon n) < c$. By using Bernoulli's Inequality again we conclude that, for $n \geq K(\epsilon)$, then

$$\frac{1}{(1 + \epsilon)^n} < \frac{1}{1 + \epsilon n} < c < 1.$$

We infer that $1/(1 + \epsilon) < c^{1/n} < 1$, whence it follows that

$$\frac{-\epsilon}{1 + \epsilon} = \frac{1}{1 + \epsilon} - 1 < c^{1/n} - 1 < 0,$$

so that

$$|c^{1/n} - 1| < \frac{\epsilon}{1 + \epsilon} < \epsilon,$$

whenever $n \geq K(\epsilon)$. This establishes the fact that $c^{1/n} \to 1$, when $0 < c < 1$.

11.9   DEFINITION.   If $X = (x_n)$ is a sequence in $\mathbf{R}^p$ and if $r_1 < r_2 < \cdots < r_n < \cdots$ is a strictly increasing sequence of natural numbers, then the sequence X' in $\mathbf{R}^p$ given by

$$(x_{r_1}, x_{r_2}, \ldots, x_{r_n}, \ldots),$$

is called a **subsequence** of X.

It may be helpful to connect the notion of a subsequence with that of the composition of two functions. Let g be a function with domain $\mathbf{N}$ and range in $\mathbf{N}$ and let g be **strictly increasing** in the sense that if $n < m$, then $g(n) < g(m)$. Then g defines a subsequence of $X = (x_n)$ by the formula

$$X \circ g = (x_{g(n)} : n \in \mathbf{N}).$$

Conversely, every subsequence of X has the form $X \circ g$ for some strictly increasing function g with $\mathfrak{D}(g) = \mathbf{N}$ and $\mathfrak{R}(g) \subseteq \mathbf{N}$.

It is clear that a given sequence has many different subsequences. Although the next result is very elementary, it is of sufficient importance that it must be made explicit.

11.10   LEMMA.   *If a sequence X in $\mathbf{R}^p$ converges to an element x, then any subsequence of X also converges to x.*

PROOF.   Let V be a neighborhood of the limit element x; by definition, there exists a natural number K_V such that if $n \geq K_V$, then x_n belongs to V. Now let X' be a subsequence of X; say

$$X' = (x_{r_1}, x_{r_2}, \ldots, x_{r_n}, \ldots).$$

Since $r_n \geq n$, then $r_n \geq K_V$ and hence x_{r_n} belongs to V. This proves that X' also converges to x.

Q.E.D.

11.11 COROLLARY. *If* $X = (x_n)$ *is a sequence which converges to an element* x *of* $\mathbf{R}^p$ *and if* m *is any natural number, then the sequence* $X' = (x_{m+1}, x_{m+2}, \ldots)$ *also converges to* x.

PROOF. Since X' is a subsequence of X, the result follows directly from the preceding lemma.

Q.E.D.

The preceding results have been mostly directed towards proving that a sequence converges to a given point. It is also important to know precisely what it means to say that a sequence X does *not* converge to x. The next result is elementary but not trivial and its verification is an important part of everyone's education. Therefore, we leave its detailed proof to the reader.

11.12 THEOREM. *If* $X = (x_n)$ *is a sequence in* $\mathbf{R}^p$, *then the following statements are equivalent:*

(a) X *does not converge to* x.

(b) *There exists a neighborhood* V *of* x *such that if* n *is any natural number, then there is a natural number* $m = m(n) \geq n$ *such that* x_m *does not belong to* V.

(c) *There exists a neighborhood* V *of* x *and a subsequence* X' *of* X *such that none of the elements of* X' *belong to* V.

11.13 EXAMPLES. (a) Let X be the sequence in R consisting of the natural numbers

$$X = (1, 2, \ldots, n, \ldots).$$

Let x be any real number and consider the neighborhood V of x consisting of the open interval $(x - 1, x + 1)$. According to Theorem 5.14 there exists a natural number k_0 such that $x + 1 < k_0$; hence, if $n \geq k_0$, it follows that $x_n = n$ does not belong to V. Therefore the subsequence

$$X' = (k_0, k_0 + 1, \ldots)$$

of X has no points in V, showing that X does not converge to x.

(b) Let $Y = (y_n)$ be the sequence in R consisting of $Y = (-1, 1, \ldots, (-1)^n, \ldots)$. We leave it to the reader to show that no point y, except possibly $y = \pm 1$, can be a limit of Y. We shall show that the point $y = -1$ is not a limit of Y; the consideration for $y = +1$ is entirely similar. Let V be the neighborhood of $y = -1$ consisting of the open interval $(-2, 0)$. Then, if n is even, the element $y_n = (-1)^n = +1$

does not belong to V. Therefore, the subsequence Y' of Y corresponding to $r_n = 2n$, $n \in \mathbf{N}$, avoids the neighborhood V, showing that $y = -1$ is not a limit of Y.

(c) Let $Z = (z_n)$ be a sequence in $\mathbf{R}$ with $z_n \geq 0$, for $n \geq 1$. We conclude that no number $z < 0$ can be a limit for Z. In fact, the open set $V = \{x \in \mathbf{R} : x < 0\}$ is a neighborhood of z containing none of the elements of Z. This shows (why?) that z cannot be the limit of Z. Hence if Z has a limit, this limit must be non-negative.

The next theorem enables one to use the algebraic operations of Definitions 11.2 to form new sequences whose convergence can be predicted from the convergence of the given sequences.

11.14   THEOREM.   (a) *Let X and Y be sequences in $\mathbf{R}^p$ which converge to x and y, respectively. Then the sequences $X + Y$, $X - Y$, and $X \cdot Y$ converge to $x + y$, $x - y$ and $x \cdot y$, respectively.*

(b) *Let $X = (x_n)$ be a sequence in $\mathbf{R}^p$ which converges to x and let $A = (a_n)$ be a sequence in $\mathbf{R}$ which converges to a. Then the sequence $(a_n x_n)$ in $\mathbf{R}^p$ converges to ax.*

(c) *Let $X = (x_n)$ be a sequence in $\mathbf{R}^p$ which converges to x and let $B = (b_n)$ be a sequence of non-zero real numbers which converges to a non-zero number b. Then the sequence $(b_n^{-1} x_n)$ in $\mathbf{R}^p$ converges to $b^{-1}x$.*

PROOF.   (a) To show that $(x_n + y_n) \to x + y$, we need to appraise the magnitude of $|(x_n + y_n) - (x + y)|$. To do this, we use the Triangle Inequality to obtain

$$(11.2) \qquad |(x_n + y_n) - (x + y)| = |(x_n - x) + (y_n - y)|$$
$$\leq |x_n - x| + |y_n - y|.$$

By hypothesis, if $\epsilon > 0$ we can choose K_1 such that if $n \geq K_1$, then $|x_n - x| < \epsilon/2$ and we choose K_2 such that if $n \geq K_2$, then $|y_n - y| < \epsilon/2$. Hence if $K_0 = \sup \{K_1, K_2\}$ and $n \geq K_0$, then we conclude from (11.2) that

$$|(x_n + y_n) - (x + y)| < \epsilon/2 + \epsilon/2 = \epsilon.$$

Since this can be done for arbitrary $\epsilon > 0$, we infer that $X + Y$ converges to $x + y$. Precisely the same argument can be used to show that $X - Y$ converges to $x - y$.

To prove that $X \cdot Y$ converges to $x \cdot y$, we make the estimate

$$|x_n \cdot y_n - x \cdot y| = |(x_n \cdot y_n - x_n \cdot y) + (x_n \cdot y - x \cdot y)|$$
$$\leq |x_n \cdot (y_n - y)| + |(x_n - x) \cdot y|.$$

Using the C.-B.-S. Inequality, we obtain

$$(11.3) \qquad |x_n \cdot y_n - x \cdot y| \leq |x_n||y_n - y| + |x_n - x||y|.$$

According to Lemma 11.6, there exists a positive real number M which is an upper bound for $\{|x_n|, |y|\}$. In addition, from the convergence of X, Y, we conclude that if $\epsilon > 0$ is given, then there exist natural numbers K_1, K_2 such that if $n \geq K_1$, then $|y_n - y| < \epsilon/2M$ and if $n \geq K_2$ then $|x_n - x| < \epsilon/2M$. Now choose $K = \sup\{K_1, K_2\}$; then, if $n \geq K$, we infer from (11.3) that

$$|x_n \cdot y_n - x \cdot y| \leq M|y_n - y| + M|x_n - x|$$

$$< M\left(\frac{\epsilon}{2M} + \frac{\epsilon}{2M}\right) = \epsilon.$$

This proves that $X \cdot Y$ converges to $x \cdot y$.

Part (b) is proved in the same way.

To prove (c), we estimate as follows:

$$\left|\frac{1}{b_n} x_n - \frac{1}{b} x\right| = \left|\left(\frac{1}{b_n} x_n - \frac{1}{b} x_n\right) + \left(\frac{1}{b} x_n - \frac{1}{b} x\right)\right|$$

$$\leq \left|\frac{1}{b_n} - \frac{1}{b}\right| |x_n| + \frac{1}{|b|} |x_n - x|$$

$$= \frac{|b - b_n|}{|b_n b|} |x_n| + \frac{1}{|b|} |x_n - x|.$$

Now let M be a positive real number such that

$$\frac{1}{M} < |b| \quad \text{and} \quad |x| < M.$$

It follows that there exists a natural number K_0 such that if $n \geq K_0$, then

$$\frac{1}{M} < |b_n| \quad \text{and} \quad |x_n| < M.$$

Hence if $n \geq K_0$, the above estimate yields

$$\left|\frac{1}{b_n} x_n - \frac{1}{b} x\right| \leq M^3 |b_n - b| + M|x_n - x|.$$

Therefore, if ϵ is a preassigned positive real number, there are natural numbers K_1, K_2 such that if $n \geq K_1$, then $|b_n - b| < \epsilon/2M^3$ and if $n \geq K_2$, then $|x_n - x| < \epsilon/2M$. Letting $K = \sup\{K_0, K_1, K_2\}$ we conclude that if $n \geq K$, then

$$\left|\frac{1}{b_n} x_n - \frac{1}{b} x\right| < M^3 \frac{\epsilon}{2M^3} + M \frac{\epsilon}{2M} = \epsilon,$$

which proves that (x_n/b_n) converges to x/b.

Q.E.D.

11.15 APPLICATIONS. Again we restrict our attention to sequences in R.

(a) Let $X = (x_n)$ be the sequence in R defined by

$$x_n = \frac{2n + 1}{n + 5}, \qquad n \in \mathbf{N}.$$

We note that we can write x_n in the form

$$x_n = \frac{2 + 1/n}{1 + 5/n};$$

thus X can be regarded as the quotient of $Y = (2 + 1/n)$ and $Z = (1 + 5/n)$. Since the latter sequence consists of non-zero terms and has limit 1 (why?), the preceding theorem applies to allow us to conclude that

$$\lim X = \frac{\lim Y}{\lim Z} = \frac{2}{1} = 2.$$

(b) If $X = (x_n)$ is a sequence in R which converges to x and if p is a polynomial, then the sequence defined by $(p(x_n) : n \in \mathbf{N})$ converges to $p(x)$. (Hint: use Theorem 11.14 and induction.)

(c) Let $X = (x_n)$ be a sequence in R which converges to x and let r be a rational function; that is, $r(y) = p(y)/q(y)$, where p and q are polynomials. Suppose that $q(x_n)$ and $q(x)$ are non-zero, then the sequence $(r(x_n) : n \in \mathbf{N})$ converges to $r(x)$. (Hint: use part (b) and Theorem 11.14.)

We conclude this section with a result which is often useful. It is sometimes described by saying that one "passes to the limit in an inequality."

11.16 LEMMA. *Suppose that $X = (x_n)$ is a convergent sequence in $\mathbf{R}^p$ with limit x. If there exists an element c in $\mathbf{R}^p$ and a number $r > 0$ such that*

$$|x_n - c| \le r$$

for n sufficiently large, then $|x - c| \le r$.

PROOF. The set $V = \{y \in \mathbf{R}^p : |y - c| > r\}$ is an open subset of $\mathbf{R}^p$. If $x \in V$, then V is a neighborhood of x and so $x_n \in V$ for sufficiently large values of n, contrary to the hypothesis. Therefore $x \notin V$ and hence $|x - c| \le r$.

Q.E.D.

It is important to note that we have assumed the existence of the limit in this result, for the remaining hypotheses are not sufficient to enable us to prove its existence.

Exercises

11.A. If (x_n) and (y_n) are convergent sequences of real numbers and if $x_n \leq y_n$ for all $n \in \mathbf{N}$, then $\lim(x_n) \leq \lim(y_n)$.

11.B. If $X = (x_n)$ and $Y = (y_n)$ are sequences of real numbers which both converge to c and if $Z = (z_n)$ is a sequence such that $x_n \leq z_n \leq y_n$ for $n \in \mathbf{N}$, then Z also converges to c.

11.C. For x_n given by the following formulas, either establish the convergence or the divergence of the sequence $X = (x_n)$:

(a) $x_n = \dfrac{n}{n+1}$,

(b) $x_n = \dfrac{(-1)^n n}{n+1}$,

(c) $x_n = \dfrac{2n}{3n^2+1}$,

(d) $x_n = \dfrac{2n^2+3}{3n^2+1}$,

(e) $x_n = n^2 - n$,

(f) $x_n = \sin(n)$.

11.D. If X and Y are sequences in $\mathbf{R}^p$ and if $X + Y$ converges, do X and Y converge and have $\lim (X + Y) = \lim X + \lim Y$?

11.E. If X and Y are sequences in $\mathbf{R}^p$ and if $X \cdot Y$ converges, do X and Y converge and have $\lim X \cdot Y = (\lim X) \cdot (\lim Y)$?

11.F. If X is a sequence in $\mathbf{R}^p$, does X converge to an element x if and only if the real sequence $Y = (|x_n|)$ converges to $|x|$?

11.G. If $X = (x_n)$ is a non-negative sequence which converges to x, then $(\sqrt{x_n})$ converges to $\sqrt{x}$. (Hint: $\sqrt{x_n} - \sqrt{x} = (x_n - x)/(\sqrt{x_n} + \sqrt{x})$ when $x \neq 0$.)

11.H. If $X = (x_n)$ is a sequence of real numbers such that $Y = (x_n{}^2)$ converges to 0, then does X converge to 0?

11.I. If $x_n = \sqrt{n+1} - \sqrt{n}$, do the sequences $X = (x_n)$ and $Y = (\sqrt{n}\, x_n)$ converge?

11.J. If $X = (x_n)$ is a sequence of positive numbers and if $\lim (x_{n+1}/x_n)$ exists and equals a number less than 1, then $\lim X = 0$. (Hint: show that for some r with $0 < r < 1$ and some $A > 0$, then $0 < x_n < Ar^n$ for sufficiently large n.)

11.K. If, in Exercise 11.J. the sequence (x_{n+1}/x_n) converges to a number greater than 1, then the sequence X does not converge.

11.L. Give an example of a sequence $X = (x_n)$ of positive numbers with $\lim (x_{n+1}/x_n) = 1$ and such that $\lim X = 0$. Also give an example of a divergent sequence X such that $\lim (x_{n+1}/x_n) = 1$.

11.M. Let c be a positive real number. Examine the convergence of the sequence $X = (x_n)$ with $x_n = n/c^n$.

11.N. Let $c > 0$ and examine the convergence of $X = (c^n/n!)$.

11.O. Examine the convergence of $X = (n^2/2^n)$.

11.P. Let $x_n = n^{1/n}$ for $n \in \mathbf{N}$, and let $h_n = x_n - 1 > 0$. If $n \geq 2$, it follows from the Binomial Theorem that

$$n = (1 + h_n)^n > \tfrac{1}{2} n(n-1) h_n{}^2.$$

Use this to show that $\lim (n^{1/n}) = 1$.

11.Q. If $X = (x_n)$ is a sequence of positive numbers and if $\lim (x_n^{1/n})$ exists and equals a number less than 1, then $\lim X = 0$. (Hint: show that for some r with $0 < r < 1$ and some $A > 0$, then $0 < x_n < Ar^n$ for large n.)

11.R. If, in Exercise 11.Q, $\lim (x_n^{1/n}) > 1$, then the sequence X is divergent.

11.S. Give an example of a sequence $X = (x_n)$ of positive numbers with $\lim (x_n^{1/n}) = 1$ and such that $\lim X = 0$. Also, give an example of a divergent sequence X such that $\lim (x_n^{1/n}) = 1$.

11.T. Re-examine the convergence of Exercises 11.M, N, O in the light of Exercises 11.P, Q, R.

11.U. If $0 < b \le a$ and if $x_n = (a^n + b^n)^{1/n}$, then $\lim (x_n) = a$.

11.V. If $x = \lim (x_n)$ and if $|x_n - c| < \epsilon$ for all $n \in \mathbf{N}$, then is it true that $|x - c| < \epsilon$?

Projects

11.α. Let d be a metric on a set M in the sense of Exercise 7.N. If $X = (x_n)$ is a sequence in M, then an element x in M is said to be a **limit** of X if, for each positive number ϵ there exists a natural number $K(\epsilon)$ such that if $n \ge K(\epsilon)$, then $d(x_n, x) < \epsilon$. Use this definition and show that Theorems 11.5, 11.6, 11.10, 11.11, 11.12 can be extended to metric spaces. Show that the metrics d_1, d_2, d_∞ in $\mathbf{R}^p$ give rise to the same convergent sequences. Show that if d is the discrete metric on a set, then the only sequences which converge relative to d are those sequences which are constant after some point.

11.β. Let s denote the collection of all sequences in $\mathbf{R}$, let m denote the collection of all bounded sequences in $\mathbf{R}$, let c denote the collection of all convergent sequences in $\mathbf{R}$, and let c_0 denote the collection of all sequences in $\mathbf{R}$ which converge to zero.

(a) With the definition of sum given in Definition 11.2 and the definition of product of a sequence and real number given by $a(x_n) = (ax_n)$, show that each of these collections has the properties of Theorem 7.3. In each case the zero element is the sequence $\theta = (0, 0, \ldots, 0, \ldots)$. (We sometimes say that these collections are **linear spaces** or **vector spaces**.)

(b) If $X = (x_n)$ belongs to one of the collections m, c, c_0, define the **norm** of X by $|X| = \sup\{|x_n| : n \in N\}$. Show that this norm function has the properties of Theorem 7.8. (For this reason, we sometimes say that these collections are **normed linear spaces**.)

(c) If X and Y belong to one of these three collections, then the product XY also belongs to it and $|XY| \le |X| |Y|$. Give an example to show that equality may hold and one to show that it may fail.

(d) Suppose that $X = (x_n)$ and $Y = (y_n)$ belong to m, c, or c_0, and define $d(X, Y) = \sup \{|x_n - y_n| : n \in \mathbf{N}\}$. Show that d yields a metric on each of these collections.

(e) Show that, if a sequence (X_n) converges to Y relative to the metric d defined in (d), then each coordinate sequence converges to the corresponding coordinate of Y.

(f) Give an example of a sequence (X_n) in c_0 where each coordinate sequence converges to 0, but where $d(X_n, \theta)$ does not converge to 0.

Section 12   Criteria for the Convergence of Sequences

Until now the main method available for showing that a sequence is convergent is to identify it as a subsequence or an algebraic combination of convergent sequences. When this can be done, we are able to calculate the limit using the results of the preceding section. However, when this cannot be done, we have to fall back on Definition 11.3 or Theorem 11.4 in order to establish the existence of the limit. The use of these latter tools has the noteworthy disadvantage that we must already know (or at least suspect) the correct value of the limit and we merely verify that our suspicion is correct.

There are many cases, however, where there is no obvious candidate for the limit of a given sequence, even though a preliminary analysis has led to the belief that convergence does take place. In this section we give some results which are deeper than those in the preceding section and which can be used to establish the convergence of a sequence when no particular element presents itself as a candidate for the limit. In fact we do not even determine the exact value of the limit of the sequence. The first result in this direction is very important. Although it can be generalized to $\mathbf{R}^p$, it is convenient to restrict its statement to the case of sequences in $\mathbf{R}$.

12.1 MONOTONE CONVERGENCE THEOREM. *Let* $X = (x_n)$ *be a sequence of real numbers which is monotone increasing in the sense that*

$$x_1 \leq x_2 \leq \cdots \leq x_n \leq x_{n+1} \leq \cdots$$

Then the sequence X *converges if and only if it is bounded, in which case* $\lim (x_n) = \sup \{x_n\}$.

PROOF.   It was seen in Lemma 11.6 that a convergent sequence is bounded. If $x = \lim (x_n)$ and $\epsilon > 0$, then there exists a natural number $K(\epsilon)$ such that if $n \geq K(\epsilon)$, then

$$x - \epsilon \leq x_n \leq x + \epsilon.$$

Since X is monotone, this relation yields

$$x - \epsilon \leq \sup \{x_n\} \leq x + \epsilon,$$

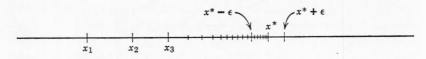

Figure 12.1

whence it follows that $|x - \sup\{x_n\}| \leq \epsilon$. Since this holds for all $\epsilon > 0$, we infer that $\lim(x_n) = x = \sup\{x_n\}$.

Conversely, suppose that $X = (x_n)$ is a bounded monotone increasing sequence of real numbers. According to the Supremum Principle 6.6, the supremum $x^* = \sup\{x_n\}$ exists; we shall show that it is the limit of X. Since x^* is an upper bound of the elements in X, then $x_n \leq x^*$ for $n \in \mathbb{N}$. Since x^* is the supremum of X, if $\epsilon > 0$ the number $x^* - \epsilon$ is not an upper bound of X and exists a natural number K such that

$$x^* - \epsilon < x_K.$$

In view of the monotone character of X, if $n \geq K$, then

$$x^* - \epsilon < x_n \leq x^*,$$

whence it follows that $|x_n - x^*| < \epsilon$. Recapitulating, the number $x^* = \sup\{x_n\}$ has the property that, given $\epsilon > 0$ there is a natural number K (depending on ϵ) such that $|x_n - x^*| < \epsilon$ whenever $n \geq K$. This shows that $x^* = \lim X$.

Q.E.D.

12.2   Corollary.   *Let $X = (x_n)$ be a sequence of real numbers which is monotone decreasing in the sense that*

$$x_1 \geq x_2 \geq \cdots \geq x_n \geq x_{n+1} \geq \cdots.$$

Then the sequence X converges if and only if it is bounded, in which case $\lim(x_n) = \inf\{x_n\}$.

PROOF.   Let $y_n = -x_n$ for $n \in \mathbb{N}$. Then the sequence $Y = (y_n)$ is readily seen to be a monotone increasing sequence. Moreover, Y is bounded if and only if X is bounded. Therefore, the conclusion follows from the theorem.

Q.E.D.

12.3   Examples.   (a) Let $X = (x_n)$ be the sequence in $\mathbb{R}$ defined by $x_n = 1/n$. It is seen from Theorem 5.5 that $1 < 2 < \cdots < n < \cdots$, and it follows from Theorem 5.6 that $x_1 > x_2 > \cdots > x_n > \cdots$. Also we see that $x_n > 0$ for all natural numbers n. It therefore follows from Corollary 12.2 that the sequence $X = (1/n)$ converges. (Of course, we know that the limit of X is 0; but the existence of the limit follows even if we are not able to evaluate inf $\{x_n\}$.) Once the convergence of X is assured, we can evaluate its limit by using Lemma 11.10 and Theorem 11.14. In fact, if $X' = (1/2, 1/4, \ldots, 1/2n, \ldots)$, then it follows that

$$\lim X = \lim X' = \tfrac{1}{2} \lim X.$$

We conclude, therefore, that $\lim X = 0$.

(b) Let $Y = (y_n)$ be the sequence in R defined inductively by

$$y_1 = 1, \qquad y_{n+1} = (2y_n + 3)/4 \qquad \text{for } n \in \mathbf{N}.$$

Direct calculation shows that $y_1 < y_2 < 2$. If $y_{n-1} < y_n < 2$, then

$$2y_{n-1} + 3 < 2y_n + 3 < 2 \cdot 2 + 3,$$

from which it follows that $y_n < y_{n+1} < 2$. By induction, the sequence Y is monotone increasing and bounded above by the number 2. It follows from the Monotone Convergence Theorem that the sequence Y converges to a limit which is no greater than 2. In this case it might not be so easy to evaluate $y = \lim Y$ by calculating sup $\{y_n\}$. However, once we know that the limit exists, there is another way to calculate its value. According to Lemma 11.10, we have $y = \lim (y_n) = \lim (y_{n+1})$. Using Theorem 11.14, the limit y must satisfy the relation

$$y = (2y + 3)/4.$$

Therefore, we conclude that $y = \tfrac{3}{2}$.

(c) Let $Z = (z_n)$ be the sequence in R defined by

$$z_1 = 1, \qquad z_{n+1} = \sqrt{2z_n} \qquad \text{for } n \in \mathbf{N}.$$

It is clear that $z_1 < z_2 < 2$. If $z_n < z_{n+1} < 2$, then $2z_n < 2z_{n+1} < 4$ and $z_{n+1} = \sqrt{2z_n} < z_{n+2} = \sqrt{2z_{n+1}} < 2 = \sqrt{4}$. (Why?) This shows that Z is a monotone increasing sequence which is bounded above by 2; hence Z converges to a number z. It may be shown directly that $2 = \sup \{z_n\}$ so that the limit $z = 2$. Alternatively, we can use the method of the preceding example. Knowing that the sequence has a limit z, we conclude from the relation $z_{n+1} = \sqrt{2z_n}$ that z must satisfy $z = \sqrt{2z}$. To find the roots of this last equation, we square to obtain $z^2 = 2z$, which has roots 0, 2. Evidently 0 cannot be the limit; hence this limit must equal 2.

(d) Let $U = (u_n)$ be the sequence of real numbers defined by $(1 + 1/n)^n$ for $n \in \mathbf{N}$. Applying the Binomial Theorem, we can write

$$u_n = 1 + \frac{n}{1}\frac{1}{n} + \frac{n(n-1)}{2!}\frac{1}{n^2} + \frac{n(n-1)(n-2)}{3!}\frac{1}{n^3} + \cdots$$
$$+ \frac{n(n-1)\cdots 2 \cdot 1}{n!}\frac{1}{n^n}.$$

Dividing the powers of n into the numerators of the binomial coefficients, we have

$$u_n = 1 + 1 + \frac{1}{2!}\left(1 - \frac{1}{n}\right) + \frac{1}{3!}\left(1 - \frac{1}{n}\right)\left(1 - \frac{2}{n}\right)$$
$$+ \cdots + \frac{1}{n!}\left(1 - \frac{1}{n}\right)\left(1 - \frac{2}{n}\right) \cdots \left(1 - \frac{n-1}{n}\right).$$

Expressing u_{n+1} in the same way, we have

$$u_{n+1} = 1 + 1 + \frac{1}{2!}\left(1 - \frac{1}{n+1}\right) + \frac{1}{3!}\left(1 - \frac{1}{n+1}\right)\left(1 - \frac{2}{n+1}\right)$$
$$+ \cdots + \frac{1}{n!}\left(1 - \frac{1}{n+1}\right)\left(1 - \frac{2}{n+1}\right) \cdots \left(1 - \frac{n-1}{n+1}\right)$$
$$+ \frac{1}{(n+1)!}\left(1 - \frac{1}{n+1}\right)\left(1 - \frac{2}{n+1}\right) \cdots \left(1 - \frac{n}{n+1}\right).$$

Note that the expression for u_n contains $n + 1$ terms and that for u_{n+1} contains $n + 2$ terms. An elementary examination shows that each term in u_n is no greater than the corresponding term in u_{n+1} and the latter has one more positive term. Therefore, we have

$$u_1 < u_2 < \cdots < u_n < u_{n+1} < \cdots.$$

To show that the sequence is bounded, we observe that if $p = 1, 2, \ldots, n$, then $(1 - p/n) < 1$. Moreover, $2^{p-1} \le p!$ (why?) so that $1/p! \le 1/2^{p-1}$. From the above expression for u_n, these estimates yield

$$2 < u_n < 1 + 1 + \frac{1}{2} + \frac{1}{2^2} + \cdots + \frac{1}{2^{n-1}} < 3, \quad n > 2.$$

It follows that the monotone sequence U is bounded above by 3. The Monotone Convergence Theorem implies that the sequence U converges to a real number which is at most 3. As is probably well-known to the reader, the limit of U is the fundamental number e. By refining our estimates we can find closer rational approximations to the value of e, but we cannot evaluate it exactly in this way since it is irrational — although it is possible to calculate as many decimal places as desired. (This illustrates that a result such as Theorem 12.1, which only establishes the existence of the limit of a sequence, can be of great use even when the exact value cannot be easily obtained.)

The Monotone Convergence Theorem is extraordinarily useful and important, but it has the drawback that it applies only to sequences which are monotone. It behooves us, therefore, to find a condition which will imply convergence in R or R^p without using the monotone property. This desired condition is the Cauchy Criterion, which will be introduced below. However, we shall first give a form of the Bolzano-Weierstrass Theorem 8.13 that is particularly applicable for sequences.

12.4   BOLZANO-WEIERSTRASS THEOREM. *A bounded sequence in R^p has a convergent subsequence.*

PROOF. Let $X = (x_n)$ be a bounded sequence in R^p. If there are only a finite number of distinct values in the sequence X, then at least one of these values must occur infinitely often. If we define a subsequence of X by selecting this element each time it appears, we obtain a convergent subsequence of X.

On the other hand, if the sequence X contains an infinite number of distinct values in R^p, then since these points are bounded, the Bolzano-Weierstrass Theorem 8.13 for sets implies that there is at least one cluster point, say x^*. Let x_{n_1} be an element of X such that

$$|x_{n_1} - x^*| < 1.$$

Consider the neighborhood $V_2 = \{y : |y - x^*| < \frac{1}{2}\}$. Since the point x^* is a cluster point of the set $S_1 = \{x_m : m \geq 1\}$, it is also a cluster point of the set $S_2 = \{x_m : m > n_1\}$ obtained by deleting a finite number of elements of S_1. (Why?) Therefore, there is an element x_{n_2} of S_2 (whence $n_2 > n_1$) belonging to V_2. Now let V_3 be the neighborhood $V_3 = \{y : |y - x^*| < \frac{1}{3}\}$ and let $S_3 = \{x_m : m > n_2\}$. Since x^* is a cluster point of S_3 there must be an element x_{n_3} of S_3 (whence $n_3 > n_2$) belonging to V_3. By continuing in this way we obtain a subsequence

$$X' = (x_{n_1}, x_{n_2}, \ldots)$$

of X with

$$|x_{n_r} - x^*| < 1/r,$$

so that $\lim X' = x^*$.

Q.E.D.

12.5   COROLLARY. *If $X = (x_n)$ is a sequence in R^p and x^* is a cluster point of the set $\{x_n : n \in N\}$, then there is a subsequence X' of X which converges to x^*.*

In fact, this is what the second part of the proof of 12.4 established.

We now introduce the important notion of a Cauchy sequence in R^p. It will turn out later that a sequence in R^p is convergent if and only if it is a Cauchy sequence.

12.6   DEFINITION. A sequence $X = (x_n)$ in R^p is said to be a **Cauchy sequence** in case for every positive real number ϵ there is a natural number $M(\epsilon)$ such that if $m, n \geq M(\epsilon)$, then $|x_m - x_n| < \epsilon$.

In order to help motivate the notion of a Cauchy sequence, we shall show that every convergent sequence in R^p is a Cauchy sequence.

12.7 LEMMA. *If $X = (x_n)$ is a convergent sequence in R^p, then X is a Cauchy sequence.*

PROOF. If $x = \lim X$; then given $\epsilon > 0$ there is a natural number $K(\epsilon/2)$ such that if $n \geq K(\epsilon/2)$, then $|x_n - x| < \epsilon/2$. Thus if $M(\epsilon) = K(\epsilon/2)$ and $m, n \geq M(\epsilon)$, then

$$|x_m - x_n| \leq |x_m - x| + |x - x_n| < \epsilon/2 + \epsilon/2 = \epsilon.$$

Hence the convergent sequence X is a Cauchy sequence.

Q.E.D.

In order to apply the Bolzano-Weierstrass Theorem, we shall require the following result.

12.8 LEMMA. *A Cauchy sequence in R^p is bounded.*

PROOF. Let $X = (x_n)$ be a Cauchy sequence and let $\epsilon = 1$. If $m = M(1)$ and $n \geq M(1)$, then $|x_m - x_n| < 1$. From the Triangle Inequality this implies that $|x_n| < |x_m| + 1$ for $n \geq M(1)$. Therefore, if $B = \sup \{|x_1|, \ldots, |x_{m-1}|, |x_m| + 1\}$, then we have

$$|x_n| \leq B \quad \text{for} \quad n \in N.$$

Thus the Cauchy sequence X is bounded.

Q.E.D.

12.9 LEMMA. *If a subsequence X' of a Cauchy sequence X in R^p converges to an element x, then the entire sequence X converges to x.*

PROOF. Since $X = (x_n)$ is a Cauchy sequence, given $\epsilon > 0$ there is a natural number $M(\epsilon)$ such that if $m, n \geq M(\epsilon)$, then

$$(*) \qquad\qquad |x_m - x_n| < \epsilon.$$

If the sequence $X' = (x_{n_j})$ converges to x, there is a natural number $K \geq M(\epsilon)$, belonging to the set $\{n_1, n_2, \ldots\}$ and such that

$$|x - x_K| < \epsilon.$$

Now let n be any natural number such that $n \geq M(\epsilon)$. It follows that $(*)$ holds for this value of n and for $m = K$. Thus

$$|x - x_n| \leq |x - x_K| + |x_K - x_n| < 2\epsilon,$$

when $n \geq M(\epsilon)$. Therefore, the sequence X converges to the element x, which is the limit of the subsequence X'.

Q.E.D.

Since we have taken these preliminary steps, we are now prepared to obtain the important Cauchy Criterion. Our proof is deceptively short, but the alert reader will note that the work has already been done and we are merely putting the pieces together.

12.10 CAUCHY CONVERGENCE CRITERION. *A sequence in* $\mathbf{R}^p$ *is convergent if and only if it is a Cauchy sequence.*

PROOF.   It was seen in Lemma 12.7 that a convergent sequence must be a Cauchy sequence.

Conversely, suppose that X is a Cauchy sequence in $\mathbf{R}^p$. It follows from Lemma 12.8 that the sequence X is bounded in $\mathbf{R}^p$. According to the Bolzano-Weierstrass Theorem 12.4, the bounded sequence X has a convergent subsequence X'. By Lemma 12.9 the entire sequence X converges to the limit of X'.

Q.E.D.

12.11 EXAMPLES.   (a) Let $X = (x_n)$ be the sequence in $\mathbf{R}$ defined by

$$x_1 = 1,\ x_2 = 2,\ \ldots,\ x_n = (x_{n-2} + x_{n-1})/2 \quad \text{for} \quad n > 2.$$

It can be shown by induction that

$$1 \leq x_n \leq 2 \quad \text{for} \quad n \in \mathbf{N},$$

but the sequence X is neither monotone decreasing nor increasing. (Actually the terms with odd subscript form an increasing sequence and those with even subscript form a decreasing sequence.) Since the terms in the sequence are formed by averaging, it is readily seen that

$$|x_n - x_{n+1}| = \frac{1}{2^{n-1}} \quad \text{for} \quad n \in \mathbf{N}.$$

Thus if $m > n$, we employ the Triangle Inequality to obtain

$$|x_n - x_m| \leq |x_n - x_{n+1}| + \cdots + |x_{m-1} - x_m|$$

$$= \frac{1}{2^{n-1}} + \cdots + \frac{1}{2^{m-2}} = \frac{1}{2^{n-1}}\left(1 + \frac{1}{2} + \cdots + \frac{1}{2^{m-n-1}}\right) < \frac{1}{2^{n-2}}.$$

Given $\epsilon > 0$, if n is chosen so large that $1/2^n < \epsilon/4$ and if $m \geq n$, it follows that

$$|x_n - x_m| < \epsilon.$$

Therefore, X is a Cauchy sequence in $\mathbf{R}$ and, by the Cauchy Criterion, the sequence X converges to a number x. To evaluate the limit we note that on taking the limit the rule of definition yields the valid, but uninformative, result

$$x = \tfrac{1}{2}\,(x + x) = x.$$

However, since the sequence X converges, so does the subsequence with odd indices. By induction we can establish that

$$x_1 = 1, \; x_3 = 1 + \frac{1}{2}, \; x_5 = 1 + \frac{1}{2} + \frac{1}{2^3}, \cdots,$$

$$x_{2n+1} = 1 + \frac{1}{2} + \frac{1}{2^3} + \cdots + \frac{1}{2^{2n-1}}, \cdots$$

It follows that

$$x_{2n+1} = 1 + \frac{1}{2}\left(1 + \frac{1}{4} + \cdots + \frac{1}{4^{n-1}}\right)$$

$$= 1 + \frac{1}{2} \cdot \frac{1 - 1/4^n}{1 - 1/4} = 1 + \frac{2}{3}\left(1 - \frac{1}{4^n}\right).$$

Therefore, the subsequence with odd indices converges to $\frac{5}{3}$; hence the entire sequence has the same limit.

(b) Let $X = (x_n)$ be the real sequence given by

$$x_1 = \frac{1}{1!}, \; x_2 = \frac{1}{1!} - \frac{1}{2!}, \; \cdots, \; x_n = \frac{1}{1!} - \frac{1}{2!} + \cdots + \frac{(-1)^{n+1}}{n!}, \cdots$$

Since this sequence is not monotone, a direct application of the Monotone Convergence Theorem is not possible. Observe that if $m > n$, then

$$x_n - x_m = \frac{(-1)^{n+2}}{(n+1)!} + \frac{(-1)^{n+3}}{(n+2)!} + \cdots + \frac{(-1)^m}{m!}.$$

Recalling that $2^{r-1} \leq r!$, we find that

$$|x_n - x_m| \leq \frac{1}{(n+1)!} + \frac{1}{(n+2)!} + \cdots + \frac{1}{m!}$$

$$\leq \frac{1}{2^n} + \frac{1}{2^{n+1}} + \cdots + \frac{1}{2^{m-1}} < \frac{1}{2^{n-1}}.$$

Therefore the sequence is a Cauchy sequence in $\mathbf{R}$.

(c) If $X = (x_n)$ is the sequence in $\mathbf{R}$ defined by

$$x_n = \frac{1}{1} + \frac{1}{2} + \cdots + \frac{1}{n} \qquad \text{for } n \in \mathbf{N},$$

and if $m > n$, then

$$x_m - x_n = \frac{1}{n+1} + \frac{1}{n+2} + \cdots + \frac{1}{m}.$$

Since each of these $m - n$ terms exceeds $1/m$, this difference exceeds $(m - n)/m = 1 - n/m$. In particular, if $m = 2n$, we have

$$x_{2n} - x_n > \tfrac{1}{2}$$

This shows that X is not a Cauchy sequence, whence we conclude that X is divergent. (We have just proved that the "harmonic series" is divergent.)

Exercises

12.A. Give the details of the proof of Corollary 12.2.

12.B. Let x_1 be any real number satisfying $x_1 > 1$ and let $x_2 = 2 - 1/x_1$, ..., $x_{n+1} = 2 - 1/x_n$, ... Using induction, show that the sequence $X = (x_n)$ is monotone and bounded. What is the limit of this sequence?

12.C. Let $x_1 = 1$, $x_2 = \sqrt{2 + x_1}$, ..., $x_{n+1} = \sqrt{2 + x_n}$, ... Show that the sequence (x_n) is monotone increasing and bounded. What is the limit of this sequence?

12.D. If a satisfies $0 < a < 1$, show that the real sequence $X = (a^n)$ converges. Since $Y = (a^{2n})$ is a subsequence of X, it is also convergent and

$$\lim X = \lim Y = (\lim X)^2.$$

Use this to show that $\lim X = 0$.

12.E. Show that a sequence of real numbers has either a monotone increasing subsequence or a monotone decreasing subsequence. Give an example of a sequence with both a monotone increasing subsequence and a monotone decreasing subsequence.

12.F. Use Exercise 12.E. to prove the Bolzano-Weierstrass Theorem for sequences in $\mathbf{R}$.

12.G. Give an example of a sequence in $\mathbf{R}^p$ which has no convergent subsequence.

12.H. Consider the convergence of the sequence $X = (x_n)$, where

$$x_n = \frac{1}{n + 1} + \frac{1}{n + 2} + \cdots + \frac{1}{2n} \qquad \text{for } n \in \mathbf{N}.$$

12.I. Let $X = (x_n)$ and $Y = (y_n)$ be sequences in $\mathbf{R}^p$ and let $Z = (z_n)$ be the "shuffled" sequence in $\mathbf{R}^p$ defined by

$$z_1 = x_1, z_2 = y_1, z_3 = x_2, z_4 = y_2, \ldots$$

$$z_{2n} = y_n, z_{2n+1} = x_{n+1}, \ldots$$

Is it true that Z is convergent if and only if X and Y are convergent and $\lim X = \lim Y$?

12.J. Show directly that the sequences

(a) $\left(\dfrac{1}{n}\right)$,   (b) $\left(\dfrac{n + 1}{n}\right)$,   (c) $\left(1 + \dfrac{1}{1!} + \cdots + \dfrac{1}{n!}\right)$,

are Cauchy sequences in $\mathbf{R}$.

12.K. Show directly that the sequences

(a) $((-1)^n)$,　(b) $\left(n + \dfrac{(-1)^n}{n}\right)$,　(c) (n^2),

are not Cauchy sequences in $\mathbf{R}$.

12.L. If $X = (x_n)$ is a sequence of positive real numbers, if

$$\lim\left(\frac{x_{n+1}}{x_n}\right) = L,$$

and if $\epsilon > 0$, then there exist positive numbers A, B and a number K such that

$$A(L - \epsilon)^n \leq x_n \leq B(L + \epsilon)^n \qquad \text{for} \quad n \geq K.$$

Use Example 11.8(d) and prove that $\lim (x_n{}^{1/n}) = L$.

12.M. Apply Example 12.3(d) and the preceding exercise to the sequence $(n^n/n!)$ to show that

$$\lim\left(\frac{n}{(n!)^{1/n}}\right) = e.$$

12.N. If $X = (x_n)$ is a sequence in $\mathbf{R}$ and $x > 0$, then is it true that $\lim X = x$ if and only if

$$\lim\left(\frac{x_n - x}{x_n + x}\right) = 0 ?$$

12.O. If $x_n = (1 + 1/n)^{n+1}$, show that $\lim (x_n) = e$.

12.P. If $x_n = (1 + 1/2n)^n$ and $y_n = (1 + 2/n)^n$, show that (x_n) and (y_n) are convergent.

12.Q. Let $0 < a_1 < b_1$ and define

$$a_2 = \sqrt{a_1 b_1}, \ b_2 = (a_1 + b_1)/2, \ldots,$$
$$a_{n+1} = \sqrt{a_n b_n}, \ b_{n+1} = (a_n + b_n)/2, \ldots.$$

Prove that $a_2 < b_2$ and, by induction, that $a_n < b_n$. Show that the sequences (a_n) and (b_n) converge to the same limit.

12.R. If $X = (x_n)$ is not a Cauchy sequence in $\mathbf{R}^p$, then does there exist an unbounded subsequence of X?

12.S. If x_n belongs to a subset A of $\mathbf{R}^p$, and $x_n \neq x$ for all $n \in \mathbf{N}$ and if $x = \lim(x_n)$, then x is a cluster point of A.

12.T. If x is a cluster point of a subset A of $\mathbf{R}^p$, then does there exist a sequence (x_n) of elements of A which converges to x?

12.U. Prove the Cantor Intersection Theorem 9.4 by taking a point x_n in F_n and applying the Bolzano-Weierstrass Theorem 12.4.

12.V. Prove the Nearest Point Theorem 9.6 by applying the Bolzano-Weierstrass Theorem 12.4.

12.W. Prove that if K_1 and K_2 are compact subsets of $\mathbf{R}^p$, then there exist points x_1 in K_1 and x_2 in K_2 such that if $z_1 \in K_1$ and $z_2 \in K_2$, then $|z_1 - z_2| \geq |x_1 - x_2|$.

12.X. If K_1 and K_2 are compact subsets of $\mathbf{R}^p$, then the set $K = \{x + y : x \in K_1, y \in K_2\}$ is compact.

Projects

12.α. Let F be an Archimedean field in the sense of Section 5.

(a) Show that if F has the property that every bounded monotone increasing sequence in F is convergent, then F is complete in the sense of Definition 6.1.

(b) Show that if F has the property that every bounded sequence in F has a subsequence which converges to an element of F, then F is complete.

(c) Show that if F has the property that every Cauchy sequence in F has a limit in F, then F is complete.

(In view of these results, we could have taken any of these three properties as our fundamental completeness property for the real number system.)

12.β. In this project, let m, c, and c_0 designate the collections of real sequences that were introduced in Project 11.β and let d denote the metric defined in part (d) of that project.

(a) If $r \in I$ and $r = 0.r_1 r_2 \ldots r_n \ldots$ is its decimal expansion, consider the element $X_r = (r_n)$ in m. Conclude that there is an uncountable subset A of m such that if X_r and X_s are distinct elements of A, then $d(X_r, X_s) \geq 1$.

(b) Suppose that B is a subset of c with the property that if X and Y are distinct elements of B, then $d(X, Y) \geq 1$. Prove that B is a countable set.

(c) If $j \in N$, let $Z_j = (z_{nj} : n \in N)$ be the sequence whose first j elements are 1 and whose remaining elements are 0. Observe that Z_j belongs to each of the metric spaces m, c, and c_0 and that $d(Z_j, Z_k) = 1$ for $j \neq k$. Show that the sequence $(Z_j : j \in N)$ is monotone in the sense that each coordinate sequence $(z_{nj} : j \in N)$ is monotone. Show that the sequence (Z_j) does not converge with respect to the metric d in any of the three spaces.

(d) Show that there is a sequence (X_j) in m, c, and c_0 which is bounded (in the sense that there exists a constant K such that $d(X_j, \theta) \leq K$ for all $j \in N$) but which possesses no convergent subsequence.

(e) (If d is a metric on a set M, we say that a sequence (X_j) in M is a **Cauchy sequence** if $d(X_j, X_k) < \epsilon$ whenever $j, k \geq K(\epsilon)$. We say that M is **complete** with respect to d in case every Cauchy sequence in M converges to an element of M.) Prove that the sets m, c, and c_0 are complete with respect to the metric d we have been considering.

(f) Let f be the collection of all real sequences which have only a finite number of non-zero elements and define d as before. Show that d is a metric on f, but that f is not complete with respect to d.

Section 13   Sequences of Functions

In the two preceding sections we considered the convergence of sequences of elements in R^p; in the present section we shall consider *sequences of functions*. After some preliminaries, we shall introduce the basic notion of *uniform convergence* of a sequence of functions.

Unless there is special mention to the contrary, we shall consider functions which have their common domain D in the Cartesian space R^p and their range in R^q. We shall use the same symbols to denote the algebraic operations and the distances in the spaces R^p and R^q.

If, for each natural number n there is a function f_n with domain D and range in R^q, we shall say that (f_n) is a *sequence of functions* on D to R^q. It should be understood that, for any point x in D such a sequence of functions gives a sequence of elements in R^q; namely, the sequence

(13.1) $(f_n(x))$

which is obtained by evaluating each of the functions at x. For certain points x in D the sequence (13.1) may converge and for other points x in D this sequence may diverge. For each of those points x for which the sequence (13.1) converges there is, by Theorem 11.5, a uniquely determined point of R^q. In general, the value of this limit, when it exists, will depend on the choice of the point x. In this way, there arises a function whose domain consists of all points x in $D \subseteq R^p$ for which the sequence (13.1) converges in R^q.

We shall now collect these introductory words in a formal definition of convergence of a sequence of functions.

13.1 DEFINITION.   Let (f_n) be a sequence of functions with common domain D in R^p and with range in R^q, let D_0 be a subset of D, and let f be a function with domain containing D_0 and range in R^q. We say that the sequence (f_n) **converges** on D_0 to f if, for each x in D_0 the sequence $(f_n(x))$ converges in R^q to $f(x)$. In this case we call the function f the limit on D_0 of the sequence (f_n). When such a function f exists we say that the sequence (f_n) **converges to** f on D_0, or simply that the sequence is **convergent** on D_0.

It follows from Theorem 11.5 that, except for possible restrictions of the domain D_0, the limit function is uniquely determined. Ordinarily, we choose D_0 to be the largest set possible; that is, the set of all x in D for which (13.1) converges. In order to symbolize that the sequence (f_n) converges on D_0 to f we sometimes write

$$f = \lim \, (f_n) \text{ on } D_0, \quad \text{or} \quad f_n \to f \text{ on } D_0.$$

We shall now consider some examples of this idea. For simplicity, we shall treat the special case $p = q = 1$.

13.2 EXAMPLES.   (a) For each natural number n, let f_n be defined for x in $D = R$ by $f_n(x) = x/n$. Let f be defined for all x in $D = R$ by $f(x) = 0$. (See Figure 13.1.) The statement that the sequence (f_n) converges on R to f is equivalent to the statement that for each real number

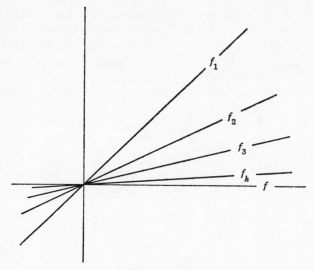

Figure 13.1

x the numerical sequence (x/n) converges to 0. To see that this is the case, we apply Example 12.3(a) and Theorem 11.14(b).

(b) Let $D = \{x \in R : 0 \le x \le 1\}$ and for each natural number n let f_n be defined by $f_n(x) = x^n$ for all x in D and let f be defined by

$$f(x) = 0, \quad 0 \le x < 1,$$
$$= 1, \quad x = 1.$$

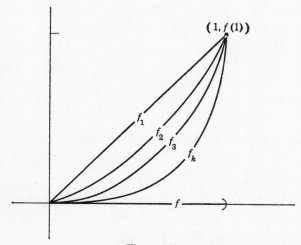

Figure 13.2

(See Figure 13.2.) It is clear that when $x = 1$, then $f_n(x) = f_n(1) = 1^n = 1$ so that $f_n(1) \to f(1)$. We have shown in Example 11.8(c), that if $0 \leq x < 1$, then $f_n(x) = x^n \to 0$. Therefore, we conclude that (f_n) converges on D to f. (It is not hard to prove that if $x > 1$ then $(f_n(x))$ does not converge at all.)

(c) Let $D = R$ and for each natural number n, let f_n be the function defined for x in D by

$$f_n(x) = \frac{x^2 + nx}{n},$$

and let $f(x) = x$. (See Figure 13.3.) Since $f_n(x) = (x^2/n) + x$, it follows from Example 12.3(a) and Theorem 11.14 that $(f_n(x))$ converges to $f(x)$ for all $x \in R$.

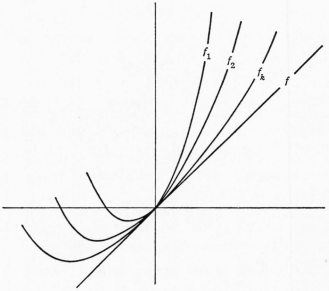

Figure 13.3

(d) Let $D = R$ and, for each natural number n, let f_n be defined to be $f_n(x) = (1/n) \sin (nx + n)$. (See Figure 13.4.) (A rigorous definition of the sine function is not needed here; in fact, all we require is that $|\sin y| \leq 1$ for any real number y.) If f is defined to be the zero function $f(x) = 0$, $x \in R$, then $f = \lim (f_n)$ on R. Indeed, for any real number x, we have

$$|f_n(x) - f(x)| = \frac{1}{n} |\sin (nx + n)| \leq \frac{1}{n}.$$

Figure 13.4

If $\epsilon > 0$, there exists a natural number $K(\epsilon)$ such that if $n \geq K(\epsilon)$, then $1/n < \epsilon$. Hence for such n we conclude that

$$|f_n(x) - f(x)| < \epsilon$$

no matter what the value of x. Therefore, we infer that the sequence (f_n) converges to f. (Note that by choosing n sufficiently large, we can make the differences $|f_n(x) - f(x)|$ arbitrarily small for all values of x simultaneously!)

Partly to reinforce Definition 13.1 and partly to prepare the way for the important notion of uniform convergence, we formulate the following restatement of Definition 13.1.

13.3   LEMMA.   *A sequence (f_n) of functions on $D \subseteq \mathbf{R}^p$ to $\mathbf{R}^q$ converges to a function f on a set $D_0 \subseteq D$ if and only if for each $\epsilon > 0$ and each x in D_0 there is a natural number $K(\epsilon, x)$ such that if $n \geq K(\epsilon, x)$, then*

(13.2) $$|f_n(x) - f(x)| < \epsilon.$$

Since this is just a reformulation of Definition 13.1, we shall not go through the details of the proof, but leave them to the reader as an exercise. We wish only to point out that the value of n required in inequality (13.2) will depend, in general, on *both* $\epsilon > 0$ and $x \in D_0$. An alert reader will have already noted that, in Examples 13.2(a–c) the value of n required to obtain (13.2) does depend on both $\epsilon > 0$ and $x \in D_0$. However, in Example 13.2(d) the inequality (13.2) can be satisfied for all x in D_0 provided n is chosen sufficiently large but dependent on ϵ alone.

It is precisely this rather subtle difference which distinguishes between the notions of "ordinary" convergence of a sequence of functions (in the sense of Definition 13.1) and "uniform" convergence, which we now define.

13.4 DEFINITION. A sequence (f_n) of functions on $D \subseteq \mathbf{R}^p$ to $\mathbf{R}^q$ converges uniformly on a subset D_0 of D to a function f in case for each $\epsilon > 0$ there is a natural number $K(\epsilon)$ (depending on ϵ but not on $x \in D_0$) such that if $n \geq K(\epsilon)$, and $x \in D_0$, then

(13.3) $$|f_n(x) - f(x)| < \epsilon.$$

In this case we say that the sequence is **uniformly convergent on** D_0. (See Figure 13.5.)

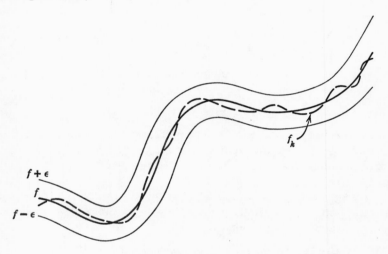

Figure 13.5

It follows immediately that if the sequence (f_n) is uniformly convergent on D_0 to f, then this sequence of functions also converges to f in the sense of Definition 13.1. That the converse is not true is seen by a careful examination of Examples 13.2(a–c); other examples will be given below. Before we proceed, it is useful to state a necessary and sufficient condition for the sequence (f_n) to *fail* to converge uniformly on D_0 to f.

13.5 LEMMA. *A sequence (f_n) does not converge uniformly on D_0 to f if and only if for some $\epsilon_0 > 0$ there is a subsequence (f_{n_k}) of (f_n) and a sequence (x_k) in D_0 such that*

(13.4) $$|f_{n_k}(x_k) - f(x_k)| \geq \epsilon_0 \quad for \quad k \in \mathbf{N}.$$

The proof of this result merely requires that the reader negate Definition 13.4. It will be left to the reader as an essential exercise. The preceding lemma is useful to show that Examples 13.2 (a–c) do not converge uniformly on the given sets D_0.

13.6 EXAMPLES. (a) We consider Example 13.2(a). If $n_k = k$ and $x_k = k$, then $f_k(x_k) = 1$ so that

$$|f_k(x_k) - f(x_k)| = |1 - 0| = 1.$$

This shows that the sequence (f_n) does not converge uniformly on **R** to f.

(b) We consider Example 13.2(b). If $n_k = k$ and $x_k = (\frac{1}{2})^{1/k}$, then

$$|f_k(x_k) - f(x_k)| = |f_k(x_k)| = \tfrac{1}{2}.$$

Therefore, we infer that the sequence (f_n) does not converge uniformly on $\{x \in \mathbf{R} : 0 \le x \le 1\}$ to f.

(c) We consider Example 13.2(c). If $n_k = k$ and $x_k = k$, then

$$|f_k(x_k) - f(x_k)| = k,$$

showing that (f_k) does not converge uniformly on **R** to f.

(d) We consider Example 13.2(d). Then, since

$$|f_n(x) - f(x)| \le 1/n$$

for all x in **R**, the sequence (f_n) converges uniformly on **R** to f. However, if we restrict our attention to $D = [0, 1]$ and shuffle (f_n) with (g_n), where $g_n(x) = x^n$, the resulting sequence (h_n) converges on D to the zero function. That the convergence of (h_n) is not uniform can be seen by looking at the subsequence $(g_n) = (h_{2n})$ of (h_n).

In order to establish uniform convergence it is often convenient to make use of the notion of the *norm* of a function.

13.7 DEFINITION. If f is a bounded function defined on a subset D of $\mathbf{R}^p$ and with values in $\mathbf{R}^q$, the *D-norm* of f is the real number given by

$$(13.5) \qquad\qquad \|f\|_D = \sup \{|f(x)| : x \in D\}.$$

When the subset D is understood, we can safely omit the subscript on the left side of (13.5) and denote the D-norm of f by $\|f\|$.

13.8 LEMMA. *If f and g are bounded functions defined on $D \subseteq \mathbf{R}^p$ to $\mathbf{R}^q$, then the D-norm satisfies:*

(a) $\|f\| = 0$ *if and only if $f(x) = \theta$ for all $x \in D$.*

(b) $\|cf\| = |c| \, \|f\|$ *for any real number c.*

(c) $| \, \|f\| - \|g\| \, | \le \|f \pm g\| \le \|f\| + \|g\|.$

PROOF. (a) If $f(x) = \theta$ for all $x \in D$, then $|f(x)| = |\theta| = 0$ for all $x \in D$ so that $\|f\| = \sup \{|f(x)| : x \in D\} = 0$. Conversely, if there exists an element $x_0 \in D$ with $f(x_0) \neq \theta$, then $|f(x_0)| > 0$ and hence $||f|| \geq |f(x_0)| > 0$.

(b) This follows since $|cf(x)| = |c| \, |f(x)|$.

(c) According to the Triangle Inequality 7.8(iv),

$$|f(x) \pm g(x)| \leq |f(x)| + |g(x)|,$$

and by Definition 13.7 the right-hand side is dominated, for each $x \in D$, by $||f|| + ||g||$. Therefore, this last number is an upper bound for the set $\{|f(x) \pm g(x)| : x \in D\}$, so we conclude that

$$||f \pm g|| \leq ||f|| + ||g||.$$

The other part of this inequality is proved as in Theorem 7.8.

Q.E.D.

The reader will have noted that the set of bounded functions on D to $\mathbf{R}^q$ admits a function which possesses some of the same properties as the distance function in $\mathbf{R}^q$. The fact that the D-norm, as defined in Definition 13.7, satisfies the Norm Properties 7.8 is sometimes summarized by saying that the set of bounded functions on $D \subseteq \mathbf{R}^p$ to $\mathbf{R}^q$ is a **normed linear space.** Although such ideas are of considerable interest and importance, we shall not pursue this line of thought any further, but content ourselves with the connection between the D-norm and uniform convergence on the set D.

13.9 LEMMA. *A sequence* (f_n) *of bounded functions on* $D \subseteq \mathbf{R}^p$ *to* $\mathbf{R}^q$ *converges uniformly on* D *to a function* f *if and only if*

$$||f_n - f|| \to 0.$$

PROOF.   If the sequence (f_n) converges to f uniformly on D, then for $\epsilon > 0$ there is a natural number $K(\epsilon)$ such that if $n \geq K(\epsilon)$ and $x \in D$, then $|f_n(x) - f(x)| < \epsilon$. This implies that if $n \geq K(\epsilon)$, then

$$||f_n - f|| = \sup \{|f_n(x) - f(x)| : x \in D\} \leq \epsilon.$$

Hence $||f_n - f||$ converges to zero.

Conversely, if $||f_n - f||$ converges to zero, then for $\epsilon > 0$ and $x \in D$ we have

$$|f_n(x) - f(x)| \leq ||f_n - f|| < \epsilon,$$

provided that $n \geq K(\epsilon)$. Therefore, if $x \in D$ and $n \geq K(\epsilon)$, then

$$|f_n(x) - f(x)| < \epsilon.$$

This shows that the sequence (f_n) converges uniformly on D to the function f.

Q.E.D.

We now illustrate the use of this lemma as a tool in examining a sequence of functions for uniform convergence. We observe first that the norm has been defined only for bounded functions; hence we can employ it (directly, at least) only when the sequence consists of bounded functions.

13.10 EXAMPLES.   (a) We cannot apply Lemma 13.9 to the example considered in 13.2(a) and 13.6(a) for the reason that the functions f_n, defined to be $f_n(x) = x/n$, are not bounded on R, which was given as the domain. For the purpose of illustration, we change the domain to obtain a bounded sequence on the new domain. For convenience, let us take $D = [0, 1]$. Although the sequence (x/n) did not converge uniformly to the zero function on the domain R (as was seen in Example 13.6(a)), the convergence is uniform on $D = [0, 1]$. To see this, we calculate the D-norm of $f_n - f$. In fact,

$$\|f_n - f\| = \sup\left\{\left|\frac{x}{n} - 0\right| : 0 \leq x \leq 1\right\} = \frac{1}{n},$$

and hence $\|f_n - f\| = 1/n \to 0$.

(b) We now consider the sequence discussed in Examples 13.2(b) and 13.6(b) without changing the domain. Here $D = \{x \in \mathbf{R} : x > 0\}$ and $f_n(x) = x^n$. The set D_0 on which convergence takes place is $D_0 = [0, 1]$ and the limit function f is equal to 0 for $0 \leq x < 1$ and equal to 1 for $x = 1$. Calculating the D_0-norm of the difference $f_n - f$, we have

$$\|f_n - f\| = \sup\begin{cases} x^n, & 0 \leq x < 1 \\ 0, & x = 1 \end{cases} = 1 \quad \text{for} \quad n \in \mathbf{N}.$$

Since this D_0-norm does not converge to zero, we infer that the sequence (f_n) does not converge uniformly on $D_0 = [0, 1]$ to f. This bears out our earlier considerations.

(c) We consider Example 13.2(c). Once again we cannot apply Lemma 13.9, since the functions are not bounded. Again, we choose a smaller domain, taking $D = [0, a]$ with $a > 0$. Since

$$|f_n(x) - f(x)| = \left|\frac{x^2 + nx}{n} - x\right| = \frac{x^2}{n},$$

the D-norm of $f_n - f$ is

$$\|f_n - f\| = \sup\{|f_n(x) - f(x)| : 0 \leq x \leq a\} = \frac{a^2}{n}.$$

Hence the sequence converges uniformly to f on the interval $[0, a]$. (Why does this not contradict the result obtained in Exercises 13.6(c)?)

(d) Referring to Example 13.2(d), we consider the function $f_n(x) = (1/n) \sin (nx + n)$ on $D = \mathbf{R}$. Here the limit function $f(x) = 0$ for all $x \in D$. In order to establish the uniform convergence of this sequence, note that

$$||f_n - f|| = \sup \{(1/n) |\sin (nx + n)| : x \in \mathbf{R}\}$$

But since $|\sin y| \leq 1$, we conclude that $||f_n - f|| = 1/n$. Hence (f_n) converges uniformly on $\mathbf{R}$, as was established in Example 13.6(d).

One of the more useful aspects of the norm is that it facilitates the formulation of a Cauchy Criterion for the uniform convergence of a sequence of bounded functions.

13.11 Cauchy Criterion for Uniform Convergence. *Let (f_n) be a sequence of bounded functions on D in $\mathbf{R}^p$ with values in $\mathbf{R}^q$. Then there is a function to which (f_n) is uniformly convergent on D if and only if for each $\epsilon > 0$ there is a natural number $M(\epsilon)$ such that if $m, n \geq M(\epsilon)$, then the D-norm satisfies*

$$||f_m - f_n|| < \epsilon.$$

proof. Suppose that the sequence (f_n) converges uniformly on D to a function f. Then, for $\epsilon > 0$ there is a natural number $K(\epsilon)$ such that if $n \geq K(\epsilon)$, then the D-norm satisfies

$$||f_n - f|| < \epsilon/2.$$

Hence if both $m, n \geq K(\epsilon)$, we conclude that

$$||f_m - f_n|| \leq ||f_m - f|| + ||f - f_n|| < \epsilon.$$

Conversely, suppose the Cauchy Criterion is satisfied and that for $\epsilon > 0$ there is a natural number $M(\epsilon)$ such that the D-norm satisfies $||f_m - f_n|| < \epsilon$ when $m, n \geq M(\epsilon)$. Now for each $x \in D$ we have

$$(13.6) \qquad |f_m(x) - f_n(x)| \leq ||f_m - f_n|| < \epsilon \quad \text{for} \quad m, n \geq M(\epsilon).$$

Hence the sequence $(f_n(x))$ is a Cauchy sequence in $\mathbf{R}^q$ and so converges to some element of $\mathbf{R}^q$. We define f for x in D by

$$f(x) = \lim (f_n(x)).$$

From (13.6) we conclude that if m is a fixed natural number satisfying $m \geq M(\epsilon)$ and if n is any natural number with $n \geq M(\epsilon)$, then for all x in D we have

$$|f_m(x) - f_n(x)| < \epsilon.$$

Applying Lemma 11.16, it follows that for $m \geq M(\epsilon)$ and $x \in D$, then

$$|f_m(x) - f(x)| \leq \epsilon.$$

Therefore, the sequence (f_m) converges uniformly on D to the function f.

Q.E.D.

Exercises

In these exercises you may make use of the elementary properties of the trigonometric and exponential functions from earlier courses.

13.A. For each $n \in \mathbf{N}$, let f_n be defined for $x > 0$ by $f_n(x) = 1/(nx)$. For what values of x does $\lim (f_n(x))$ exist?

13.B. For each $n \in \mathbf{N}$, let g_n be defined for $x \geq 0$ by the formula

$$g_n(x) = nx, \qquad 0 \leq x \leq 1/n,$$

$$= \frac{1}{nx}, \qquad 1/n < x.$$

Show that $\lim (g_n(x)) = 0$ for all $x > 0$.

13.C. Show that $\lim ((\cos \pi x)^{2n})$ exists for all values of x. What is its limit?

13.D. Show that, if we define f_n on $\mathbf{R}$ by

$$f_n(x) = \frac{nx}{1 + n^2 x^2},$$

then (f_n) converges on $\mathbf{R}$.

13.E. Let h_n be defined on the interval $\mathbf{I} = [0, 1]$ by the formula

$$h_n(x) = 1 - nx, \qquad 0 \leq x \leq 1/n,$$

$$= 0, \qquad 1/n < x \leq 1.$$

Show that $\lim (h_n)$ exists on $\mathbf{I}$.

13.F. Let g_n be defined on $\mathbf{I}$ by

$$g_n(x) = nx, \qquad\qquad 0 \leq x \leq 1/n,$$

$$= \frac{n}{n-1}(1-x), \qquad 1/n < x \leq 1.$$

Show that $\lim (g_n)$ exists on $\mathbf{I}$.

13.G. Show that if f_n is defined on $\mathbf{R}$ by

$$f_n(x) = \frac{2}{\pi} \operatorname{Arc} \tan (nx),$$

then $f = \lim (f_n)$ exists on $\mathbf{R}$. In fact the limit is given by

$$f(x) = 1, \qquad x > 0,$$

$$= 0, \qquad x = 0,$$

$$= -1, \qquad x < 0.$$

13.H. Show that $\lim (e^{-nx})$ exists for $x \geq 0$. Also consider the existence of $\lim (xe^{-nx})$.

13.I. Suppose that (x_n) is a convergent sequence of points which lies, together with its limit x, in a set $D \subseteq \mathbf{R}^p$. Suppose that (f_n) converges on D to the function f. Is it true that $f(x) = \lim (f_n(x_n))$?

13.J. Consider the preceding exercise with the additional hypothesis that the convergence of the (f_n) is uniform on D.

13.K. Prove that the convergence in Exercise 13.A is not uniform on the entire set of convergence, but that it is uniform for $x \geq 1$.

13.L. Show that the convergence in Exercise 13.B is not uniform on the domain $x \geq 0$, but that it is uniform on the set $x \geq c$, where $c > 0$.

13.M. Is the convergence in Exercise 13.D uniform on $\mathbf{R}$?

13.N. Is the convergence in Exercise 13.E uniform on $\mathbf{I}$?

13.O. Is the convergence in Exercise 13.F uniform on $\mathbf{I}$? Is it uniform on $[c, 1]$ for $c > 0$?

13.P. Does the sequence (xe^{-nx}) converge uniformly for $x \geq 0$?

13.Q. Does the sequence (x^2e^{-nx}) converge uniformly for $x \geq 0$?

13.R. Let (f_n) be a sequence of functions which converges on D to a function f. If A and B are subsets of D and it is known that the convergence is uniform on A and also on B, show that the convergence is uniform on $A \cup B$.

13.S. Let M be the set of all bounded functions on a subset D of $\mathbf{R}^p$ with values in $\mathbf{R}^q$. If f, g belong to M, define $d(f, g) = \|f - g\|$. Show that d is a metric on M and that convergence relative to d is uniform convergence on D. Give an example of a sequence of elements of M which is bounded relative to d but which does not have a subsequence which converges relative to d.

Section 14   Some Extensions and Applications

The Limit Superior

In Section 6 we introduced the supremum of a set of real numbers and we have made much use of this notion since then. The reader will recall that we can describe the supremum of a set S of real numbers as the infimum of those real numbers which are exceeded by no element of S. In dealing with infinite sets it is often useful to relax things somewhat and to allow a finite number of larger elements. Thus if S is a bounded infinite set, it is reasonable to consider the infimum of those real numbers which are exceeded by only a finite number of elements of S.

For many purposes, however, it is important to consider a slight modification of this idea applied to sequences and not just sets of real numbers. Indeed, a sequence $X = (x_n)$ of real numbers does form a set $\{x_n\}$ of real numbers, but the sequence has somewhat more structure in that it is indexed by the set of natural numbers; hence there is a kind of ordering that is not present in arbitrary sets. As a result of this indexing, the same number may occur often in the sequence, while there is no such idea of "repetition" for a general set of real numbers. Once this difference is pointed out it is easy to make the appropriate modification.

14.1 DEFINITION. If $X = (x_n)$ is a sequence of real numbers which is bounded above, then the **limit superior** of $X = (x_n)$, which we denote by

$$\limsup X, \quad \limsup (x_n), \quad \text{or} \quad \overline{\lim} (x_n),$$

is the infimum of those real numbers v with the property that there are only a finite number of natural numbers n such that $v < x_n$. (See Figure 14.1.)

Figure 14.1

In a dual fashion, if the real sequence X is bounded below, then the **limit inferior** of $X = (x_n)$, which we denote by

$$\liminf X, \quad \liminf (x_n), \quad \text{or} \quad \underline{\lim} (x_n)$$

is the supremum of those real numbers w with the property that there are only a finite number of natural numbers m such that $x_m < w$.

14.2 LEMMA. *Let $X = (x_n)$ be a sequence of real numbers which is bounded. Then the limit superior of X exists and is uniquely determined.*

(Many authors use the notation $\limsup X = +\infty$ as an abbreviation of the statement that the sequence X is not bounded above. When it is realized that this is merely an abbreviation and is not a promotion of $+\infty$ into the real number system, no harm is done. However, we shall not employ this notational convention.)

There are other ways that one can define the limit superior of a sequence. The verification of the equivalence of these alternative definitions is an instructive exercise which the reader should write out in detail.

14.3 THEOREM. *If $X = (x_n)$ is a sequence of real numbers which is bounded above, then the following statements are equivalent:*

(a) $x^* = \limsup (x_n)$.

(b) *If $\epsilon > 0$, there are only a finite number of natural numbers n such that $x^* + \epsilon < x_n$ but there are an infinite number such that $x^* - \epsilon < x_n$.*

(c) If $v_m = \sup \{x_n : n \geq m\}$,   then $x^* = \inf \{v_m : m \geq 1\}$.

(d) If $v_m = \sup \{x_n : n \geq m\}$,   then $x^* = \lim (v_m)$.

(e) If V is the set of real numbers v such that there is a subsequence of X which converges to v, then $x^* = \sup V$.

Both characterizations (d) and (e) can be regarded as justification for the term "limit superior". There are corresponding characterizations for the limit inferior of a sequence in R which is bounded below, but we shall not write out a detailed statement of these characterizations.

We now establish the basic algebraic properties of the superior and inferior limits of a sequence. For simplicity we shall assume that the sequences are bounded, although some extensions are clearly possible.

14.4 THEOREM. Let $X = (x_n)$ and $Y = (y_n)$ be bounded sequences of real numbers. Then the following relations hold:

(a) $\lim \inf (x_n) \leq \lim \sup (x_n)$.

(b) If $c \geq 0$, then $\lim \inf (cx_n) = c \lim \inf (x_n)$ and $\lim \sup (cx_n) = c \lim \sup (x_n)$.

(b') If $c \leq 0$, then $\lim \inf (cx_n) = c \lim \sup (x_n)$ and $\lim \sup (cx_n) = c \lim \inf (x_n)$.

(c) $\lim \inf (x_n) + \lim \inf (y_n) \leq \lim \inf (x_n + y_n)$.

(d) $\lim \sup (x_n + y_n) \leq \lim \sup (x_n) + \lim \sup (y_n)$.

(e) If $x_n \leq y_n$ for all n, then $\lim \inf (x_n) \leq \lim \inf (y_n)$ and also $\lim \sup (x_n) \leq \lim \sup (y_n)$.

PROOF. (a) If $w < \lim \inf (x_n)$ and $v > \lim \sup (x_n)$, then there are infinitely many natural numbers n such that $w \leq x_n$, while there are only a finite number such that $v < x_n$. Therefore, we must have $w \leq v$, which proves (a).

(b) If $c \geq 0$, then multiplication by c preserves all inequalities of the form $w \leq x_n$, etc.

(b') If $c \leq 0$, then multiplication by c reverses inequalities and converts the limit superior into the limit inferior, and conversely.

Statement (c) is dual to (d) and can be derived directly from (d) or proved by using the same type of argument. To prove (d), let $v > \lim \sup (x_n)$ and $u > \lim \sup (y_n)$; by definition there are only a finite number of natural numbers n such that $x_n > v$ and a finite number such that $y_n > u$. Therefore there can be only a finite number of n such that $x_n + y_n > v + u$, showing that $\lim \sup (x_n + y_n) \leq v + u$. This proves statement (d).

We now prove the second assertion in (e). If $u > \lim \sup (y_n)$, then there can be only a finite number of natural numbers n such that $u < y_n$. Since $x_n \leq y_n$, then $\lim \sup (x_n) \leq u$, and so $\lim \sup (x_n) \leq \lim \sup (y_n)$.

                                                                Q.E.D.

Each of the alternative definitions given in Theorem 14.3 can be used to prove the parts of Theorem 14.4. It is suggested that some of these alternative proofs be written out as an exercise.

It might be asked whether the inequalities in Theorem 14.4 can be replaced by equalities. In general, the answer is no. For, if $X = ((-1)^n)$, then $\lim \inf X = -1$ and $\lim \sup X = +1$. If $Y = ((-1)^{n+1})$, then $X + Y = (0)$ so that

$$\lim \inf X + \lim \inf Y = -2 < 0 = \lim \inf (X + Y),$$

$$\lim \sup (X + Y) = 0 < 2 = \lim \sup X + \lim \sup Y.$$

We have seen that the inferior and superior limits exist for any bounded sequence, regardless of whether the sequence is convergent. We now show that the existence of $\lim X$ is equivalent to the equality of $\lim \inf X$ and $\lim \sup X$.

14.5   LEMMA. *Let X be a bounded sequence of real numbers. Then X is convergent if and only if $\lim \inf X = \lim \sup X$ in which case $\lim X$ is the common value.*

PROOF. If $x = \lim X$, then for each $\epsilon > 0$ there is a natural number $N(\epsilon)$ such that

$$x - \epsilon < x_n < x + \epsilon, \quad n \geq N(\epsilon).$$

The second inequality shows that $\lim \sup X \leq x + \epsilon$. In the same way, the first inequality shows that $x - \epsilon \leq \lim \inf X$. Hence $0 \leq \lim \sup X - \lim \inf X \leq 2\epsilon$, and from the arbitrary nature of $\epsilon > 0$, we have the stated equality.

Conversely, suppose that $x = \lim \inf X = \lim \sup X$. If $\epsilon > 0$, it follows from Theorem 14.3(b) that there exists a natural number $N_1(\epsilon)$ such that if $n \geq N_1(\epsilon)$, then $x_n < x + \epsilon$. Similarly, there exists a natural number $N_2(\epsilon)$ such that if $n \geq N_2(\epsilon)$, then $x - \epsilon < x_n$. Let $N(\epsilon) = \sup \{N_1(\epsilon), N_2(\epsilon)\}$; if $n \geq N(\epsilon)$, then $|x_n - x| < \epsilon$, showing that $x = \lim X$.

Q.E.D.

The Landau† Symbols O, o

It is frequently important to estimate the "order of magnitude" of a quantity or to compare two quantities relative to their orders of magnitude. In doing so, it is often convenient to discard terms which

† EDMUND (G. H.) LANDAU (1877–1938) was a professor at Göttingen. He is well-known for his research and his books on number theory and analysis. His books are noted for their rigor and brevity of style.

are of a lower order of magnitude since they make no essential contribution. As an example of what is meant, consider the real sequences defined by

$$x_n = 2n + 17, \quad y_n = n^2 - 5n \quad \text{for} \quad n \in \mathbf{N}.$$

In a sense, the term 17 plays no essential role in the order of magnitude of x_n; for when n is very large the dominant contribution comes from the term $2n$. We would like to say that, for large n the order of magnitude of (x_n) is the same as that of the sequence $(2n)$. In the same way it is seen that for large n the term n^2 in y_n dominates the term $-5n$ and so the order of magnitude of the sequences (y_n) and (n^2) are the same. Furthermore, although the first few terms of the sequence (x_n) are larger than the corresponding terms of (y_n), this latter sequence ultimately out-distances the former. In such a case we wish to say that, for large n the sequence (x_n) has lower order of magnitude than the sequence (y_n).

The discussion in the preceding paragraph was intended to be suggestive and to exhibit, in a qualitative fashion, the idea of the comparative order of magnitude of two sequences. We shall now make this idea more precise.

14.6 DEFINITION. Let $X = (x_n)$ be a sequence of $\mathbf{R}^p$ and let $Y = (y_n)$ be a non-zero sequence in $\mathbf{R}^q$. We say that they are **equivalent** and write

$$X \sim Y \quad \text{or} \quad (x_n) \sim (y_n),$$

in case

$$\lim \left(\frac{|x_n|}{|y_n|} \right) = 1.$$

We say that X is of **lower order of magnitude** than Y and write

$$X = o(Y) \quad \text{or} \quad x_n = o(y_n),$$

in case

$$\lim \left(\frac{|x_n|}{|y_n|} \right) = 0.$$

Finally, we say that X is **dominated** by Y and write

$$X = O(Y) \quad \text{or} \quad x_n = O(y_n),$$

in case there is a positive constant K such that $|x_n| \leq K |y_n|$ for all sufficiently large natural numbers n.

[In the important special case where $\mathbf{R}^p = \mathbf{R}^q = \mathbf{R}$, we often write $(x_n) \sim (y_n)$ only when the somewhat more restrictive relation $\lim (x_n/y_n) = 1$ holds.]

It is clear that if $X \sim Y$ or if $X = o(Y)$, then $X = O(Y)$. The relation of equivalence is symmetric in the sense that if $X \sim Y$, then $Y \sim X$. However, if $X = o(Y)$, then it is impossible that $Y = o(X)$. On the other hand, it is possible that both $X = O(Y)$ and $Y = O(X)$ without having $X \sim Y$. For example, if $X = (2)$ and $Y = (2 + (-1)^n)$, then

$$|x_n| \leq 2|y_n|, \quad |y_n| \leq 2|x_n|, \quad n \in \mathbf{N}.$$

Hence $X = O(Y)$ and $Y = O(X)$, but X and Y are not equivalent. Some additional properties of these relations will be considered in the exercises.

Cesàro Summation

We have already defined what is meant by the convergence of a sequence $X = (x_n)$ in $\mathbf{R}^p$ to an element x. However, it may be possible to attach x to the sequence X as a sort of "generalized limit," even though the sequence X does not converge to x in the sense of Definition 11.3. There are many ways in which one can generalize the idea of the limit of a sequence and to give very much of an account of some of them would take us far beyond the scope of this book. However, there is a method which is both elementary in nature and useful in applications to oscillatory sequences. Since it is of some importance and the proof of the main result is typical of many analytical arguments, we inject here a brief introduction to the theory of Cesàro† summability.

14.7 DEFINITION. If $X = (x_n)$ is a sequence of elements in $\mathbf{R}^p$, then the sequence $S = (\sigma_n)$ defined by

$$\sigma_1 = x_1, \; \sigma_2 = \frac{x_1 + x_2}{2}, \; \ldots, \; \sigma_n = \frac{x_1 + x_2 + \cdots + x_n}{n}, \; \ldots,$$

is called the **sequence of arithmetic means** of X.

In other words, the elements of S are found by averaging the terms in X. Since this average tends to smooth out occasional fluctuations in X, it is reasonable to expect that the sequence S has more chance of converging than the original sequence X. In case the sequence S of arithmetic means converges to an element y, we say that the sequence X is **Cesàro summable** to y, or that y is the $(C, 1)$-limit of the sequence X.

For example, let X be the non-convergent real sequence $X = (1, 0, 1, 0, \ldots)$; it is readily seen that if n is an even natural number,

† ERNESTO CESÀRO (1859–1906) studied in Rome and taught at Naples. He did work in geometry and algebra as well as analysis.

then $\sigma_n = \frac{1}{2}$ and if n is odd then $\sigma_n = (n + 1)/2n$. Since $\frac{1}{2} = \lim (\sigma_n)$, the sequence X is Cesàro summable to $\frac{1}{2}$, which is not the limit of X but seems like the most natural "generalized limit" we might try to attach to X.

It seems reasonable, in generalizing the notion of the limit of a sequence, to require that the generalized limit give the usual value of the limit whenever the sequence is convergent. We now show that the Cesàro method has this property.

14.8 Theorem. *If the sequence $X = (x_n)$ converges to x, then the sequence $S = (\sigma_n)$ of arithmetic means also converges to x.*

PROOF. We need to estimate the magnitude of

$$(14.2) \quad \sigma_n - x = \frac{x_1 + x_2 + \cdots + x_n}{n} - x$$

$$= \frac{1}{n} \{ (x_1 - x) + (x_2 - x) + \cdots + (x_n - x) \}.$$

Since $x = \lim (x_n)$, given $\epsilon > 0$ there is a natural number $N(\epsilon)$ such that if $m \geq N(\epsilon)$, then $|x_m - x| < \epsilon$. Also, since the sequence $X = (x_n)$ is convergent, there is a real number A such that $|x_k - x| < A$ for all k. If $n \geq N = N(\epsilon)$, we break the sum on the right side of (14.2) into a sum from $k = 1$ to $k = N$ plus a sum from $k = N + 1$ to $k = n$. We apply the estimate $|x_k - x| < \epsilon$ to the latter $n - N$ terms to obtain

$$|\sigma_n - x| \leq \frac{NA}{n} + \frac{n - N}{n} \epsilon \quad \text{for} \quad n \geq N(\epsilon).$$

If n is sufficiently large, then $NA/n < \epsilon$ and since $(n - N)/n < 1$, we find that

$$|\sigma_n - x| < 2\epsilon$$

for n sufficiently large. This proves that $x = \lim (\sigma_n)$.

Q.E.D.

We shall not pursue the theory of summability any further, but refer the reader to books on divergent series and summability. For example, see the books of E. Knopp, G. H. Hardy, and P. Dienes listed in the References. One of the most interesting and elementary applications of Cesàro summability is the celebrated theorem of Fejér† which asserts that a continuous function can be recovered from its Fourier series by

---

† Leopold Fejér (1880–1959) studied and taught at Budapest. He made interesting contributions to various areas of real and complex analysis.

the process of Cesàro summability, even though it cannot always be recovered from this series by ordinary convergence. (See Apostol or H. Bohr.)

Double and Iterated Sequences

We recall that a sequence in R^p is a function defined on the set N of natural numbers and with range in R^p. A double sequence in R^p is a function X with domain $N \times N$ consisting of all ordered pairs of natural numbers and range in R^p. In other words, at each ordered pair (m, n) of natural numbers the value of the double sequence X is an element of R^p which we shall typically denote by x_{mn}. Generally we shall use a symbolism such as $X = (x_{mn})$ to represent X, but sometimes it is convenient to list the elements in an array such as

(14.3)
$$X = \begin{bmatrix} x_{11} & x_{12} & \cdots & x_{1n} & \cdots \\ x_{21} & x_{22} & \cdots & x_{2n} & \cdots \\ \cdot & \cdot & \cdot & \cdot & \cdot & \cdot & \cdot & \cdot & \cdot & \cdot \\ x_{m1} & x_{m2} & \cdots & x_{mn} & \cdots \\ & \cdot & \cdot & \cdot & \cdot & \cdot & \cdot & \cdot & \cdot & \cdot \end{bmatrix}.$$

Observe that, in this array, the first index refers to the row in which the element x_{mn} appears and the second index refers to the column.

14.9 DEFINITION. If $X = (x_{mn})$ is a double sequence in R^p, then an element x is said to be a limit, or a double limit, of X if for each positive number ϵ there is a natural number $N(\epsilon)$ such that if $m, n \geq N(\epsilon)$ then

$$|x_{mn} - x| < \epsilon.$$

In this case we say that the double sequence converges to x and write

$$x = \lim_{mn} (x_{mn}), \quad \text{or} \quad x = \lim X.$$

Much of the elementary theory of limits of sequences carries over with little change to double sequences. In particular, the fact that the double limit is uniquely determined (when it exists) is proved in exactly the same manner as in Theorem 11.5. Similarly, one can define algebraic operations for double sequences and obtain results exactly parallel to those discussed in Theorem 11.14. There is also a Cauchy Criterion for the convergence of a double sequence which we will state, but whose proof we leave to the reader.

14.10 CAUCHY CRITERION. *If* $X = (x_{mn})$ *is a double sequence in* $\mathbf{R}^p$, *then* X *is convergent if and only if for each positive real number* ϵ *there is a natural number* $M(\epsilon)$ *such that if* $m, n, r, s \geq M(\epsilon)$, *then*

$$|x_{mn} - x_{rs}| < \epsilon.$$

We shall not pursue in any more detail that part of the theory of double sequences which is parallel to the theory of (single) sequences. Rather, we propose to look briefly at the relation between the limit as defined in 14.9 and the iterated limits.

To begin with, we note that a double sequence can be regarded, in at least two ways, as giving a *sequence of sequences*! On one hand, we can regard each row in the array given in (14.3) as a sequence in $\mathbf{R}^p$. Thus the first row in (14.3) yields the sequence $Y_1 = (x_{1n} : n \in \mathbf{N}) = (x_{11}, x_{12}, \ldots, x_{1n}, \ldots)$; the second row in (14.3) yields the sequence $Y_2 = (x_{2n} : n \in \mathbf{N})$; etc. It makes perfectly good sense to consider the limits of the row sequences $Y_1, Y_2, \ldots, Y_m, \ldots$ (when these limits exist). Supposing that these limits exist and denoting them by $y_1, y_2, \ldots, y_m, \ldots$, we obtain a sequence of elements in $\mathbf{R}^p$ which might well be examined for convergence. Thus we are considering the existence of $y = \lim (y_m)$. Since the elements y_m are given by $y_m = \lim Y_m$ where $Y_m = (x_{mn} : n \in \mathbf{N})$, we are led to denote the limit $y = \lim (y_m)$ (when it exists) by the expression

$$y = \lim_{m} \lim_{n} (x_{mn}).$$

We shall refer to y as an **iterated limit** of the double sequence (or more precisely as the **row iterated limit** of this double sequence).

What has been done for rows can equally well be done for columns. Thus we form the sequences

$$Z_1 = (x_{m1} : m \in \mathbf{N}), \quad Z_2 = (x_{m2} : m \in \mathbf{N}),$$

and so forth. Supposing that the limits $z_1 = \lim Z_1, z_2 = \lim Z_2, \ldots$, exist, we can then consider $z = \lim (z_n)$. When this latter limit exists, we denote it by

$$z = \lim_{n} \lim_{m} (x_{mn}),$$

and refer to z as an **iterated limit**, or the **column iterated limit** of the double sequence $X = (x_{mn})$.

The first question we might ask is: if the double limit of the sequence $X = (x_{mn})$ exists, then do the iterated limits exist? The answer to this question may come as a surprise to the reader; it is negative. To see this, let X be the double sequence in R which is given by $x_{mn} = (-1)^{m+n} \left(\dfrac{1}{m} + \dfrac{1}{n} \right)$, then it is readily seen that the double limit of this sequence exists and is 0. However, it is also readily verified that none of the sequences

$$Y_1 = (x_{1n} : n \in \mathbf{N}), \ldots, Y_m = (x_{mn} : n \in \mathbf{N}), \ldots$$

has a limit. Hence neither iterated limit can possibly exist, since none of the "inner" limits exists.

The next question is: if the double limit exists and if one of the iterated limits exists, then does this iterated limit equal the double limit? This time the answer is affirmative. In fact, we shall now establish a somewhat stronger result.

14.11. DOUBLE LIMIT THEOREM. *If the double limit*

$$x = \lim_{mn} (x_{mn})$$

exists, and if for each natural number m the limit $y_m = \lim_n (x_{mn})$ exists, then the iterated limit $\lim_m \lim_n (x_{mn})$ exists and equals x.

PROOF. By hypothesis, given $\epsilon > 0$ there is a natural number $N(\epsilon)$ such that if $m, n \geq N(\epsilon)$, then

$$|x_{mn} - x| < \epsilon.$$

Again by hypothesis, the limits $y_m = \lim_n (x_{mn})$ exist, and from the above inequality and Lemma 11.16 it follows that

$$|y_m - x| \leq \epsilon, \quad m \geq N(\epsilon).$$

Therefore, we conclude that $x = \lim (y_m)$.

Q.E.D.

The preceding result shows that if the double limit exists, then the only thing that can prevent the iterated limits from existing and being equal to the double limit is that the "inner" limits may not exist. More precisely, we have the following result.

14.12 COROLLARY. *Suppose the double limit exists and that the limits*

$$y_m = \lim_n (x_{mn}), \quad z_n = \lim_m (x_{mn})$$

exist for all natural numbers m, n. Then the iterated limits

$$\lim_m \lim_n (x_{mn}), \quad \lim_n \lim_m (x_{mn})$$

exist and equal the double limit.

We next inquire as to whether the existence and equality of the two iterated limits implies the existence of the double limit. The answer is no. This is seen by examining the double sequence X in $\mathbf{R}$ defined by

$$x_{mn} = \begin{cases} 1, & m \neq n, \\ 0, & m = n. \end{cases}$$

Here both iterated limits exist and are equal, but the double limit does not exist. However, under some additional conditions, we can establish the existence of the double limit from the existence of one of the iterated limits.

14.13 DEFINITION. For each natural number m, let $Y_m = (x_{mn})$ be a sequence in $\mathbf{R}^p$ which converges to y_m. We say that the sequences $\{Y_m : m \in \mathbf{N}\}$ are **uniformly convergent** if, for each $\epsilon > 0$ there is a natural number $N(\epsilon)$ such that if $n > N(\epsilon)$, then $|x_{mn} - y_m| < \epsilon$ for all natural numbers m.

The reader will do well to compare this definition with Definition 13.4 and observe that they are of the same character. Partly in order to motivate Theorem 14.15 to follow, we show that if each of the sequences Y_m is convergent, then the existence of the double limit implies that the sequences $\{Y_m : m \in \mathbf{N}\}$ are uniformly convergent.

14.14 LEMMA. *If the double limit of the double sequence* $X = (x_{mn})$ *exists and if, for each natural number* m, *the sequence* $Y_m = (x_{mn} : n \in \mathbf{N})$ *is convergent, then this collection is uniformly convergent.*

PROOF. Since the double limit exists, given $\epsilon > 0$ there is a natural number $N(\epsilon)$ such that if $m, n \geq N(\epsilon)$, then $|x_{mn} - x| < \epsilon$. By hypothesis, the sequence $Y_m = (x_{mn} : n \in \mathbf{N})$ converges to an element y_m and, applying Lemma 11.16, we find that if $m \geq N(\epsilon)$, then $|y_m - x| \leq \epsilon$. Thus if $m, n \geq N(\epsilon)$, we infer that

$$|x_{mn} - y_m| \leq |x_{mn} - x| + |x - y_m| < 2\epsilon.$$

In addition, for $m = 1, 2, \ldots, N(\epsilon) - 1$ the sequence Y_m converges to y_m; hence there is a natural number $K(\epsilon)$ such that if $n \geq K(\epsilon)$, then

$$|x_{mn} - y_m| < \epsilon, \quad m = 1, 2, \ldots, N(\epsilon) - 1.$$

Letting $M(\epsilon) = \sup \{N(\epsilon), K(\epsilon)\}$, we conclude that if $n \geq M(\epsilon)$, then for any value of m we have

$$|x_{mn} - y_m| < 2\epsilon.$$

This establishes the uniformity of the convergence of the sequences $\{Y_m : m \in \mathbf{N}\}$.

Q.E.D.

The preceding lemma shows that, under the hypothesis that the sequences Y_m converge, then the uniform convergence of this collection of sequences is a necessary condition for the existence of the double limit. We now establish a result in the reverse direction.

14.15 ITERATED LIMIT THEOREM. *Suppose that the single limits*

$$y_m = \lim_n (x_{mn}), \quad z_n = \lim_m (x_{mn}), \quad m, n \in \mathbf{N},$$

exist and that the convergence of one of these collections is uniform. Then both iterated limits and the double limit exist and all three are equal.

PROOF. Suppose that the convergence of the collection $\{Y_m : m \in \mathbf{N}\}$ is uniform. Hence given $\epsilon > 0$, there is a natural number $N(\epsilon)$ such that if $n \geq N(\epsilon)$, then

$$(14.4) \qquad\qquad |x_{mn} - y_m| < \epsilon$$

for all natural numbers m. To show that $\lim (y_m)$ exists, take a fixed number $q \geq N(\epsilon)$. Since $z_q = \lim (x_{rq} : r \in \mathbf{N})$ exists, we know that if $r, s \geq R(\epsilon, q)$, then

$$|y_r - y_s| \leq |y_r - x_{rq}| + |x_{rq} - x_{sq}| + |x_{sq} - y_s| < 3\epsilon.$$

Therefore, (y_r) is a Cauchy sequence and converges to an element y in $\mathbf{R}^p$. This establishes the existence of the iterated limit

$$y = \lim_m (y_m) = \lim_m \lim_n (x_{mn}).$$

We now show that the double limit exists. Since $y = \lim (y_m)$, given $\epsilon > 0$ there is an $M(\epsilon)$ such that if $m > M(\epsilon)$, then $|y_m - y| < \epsilon$. Letting $K(\epsilon) = \sup \{N(\epsilon), M(\epsilon)\}$, we again use (14.4) to conclude that if $m, n \geq K(\epsilon)$, then

$$|x_{mn} - y| \leq |x_{mn} - y_m| + |y_m - y| < 2\epsilon.$$

This proves that the double limit exists and equals y.

Finally, to show that the other iterated limit exists and equals y, we make use of Theorem 14.11 or its corollary.

Q.E.D.

It might be conjectured that, although the proof just given makes use of the existence of both collections of single limits and the uniformity of one of them, the conclusion may follow with the existence (and uniformity) of just one collection of single limits. We leave it to the reader to investigate the truth or falsity of this conjecture.

Exercises

14.A. Find the limit superior and the limit inferior (when they exist) of the following sequences:

(a) $((-1)^n)$, (b) $(1 + (-1)^n)$, (c) $((-1)^n n)$

(d) $\left((-1)^n + \dfrac{1}{n}\right)$, (e) $(\sin (n))$, (f) $(\text{Arc } \tan(n))$.

14.B. Show that if $\lim (x_n)$ exists, then $\limsup(x_n) = \lim (x_n)$.

14.C. Show that if $X = (x_n)$ is a bounded sequence in $\mathbf{R}$, then there exists a subsequence of X which converges to $\liminf X$.

14.D. Give the details of the proof of Theorem 14.3.

14.E. Formulate the theorem corresponding to Theorem 14.3 for the limit inferior.

14.F. Give the direct proof of the part (c) of Theorem 14.4 and a proof using the other parts of this theorem.

14.G. Prove part (d) of Theorem 14.4 by using property (b) in Theorem 14.3 as the definition of the limit superior. Do the same using property (d). Property (e).

14.H. If X is a sequence of positive elements, show that

$$\limsup (\sqrt[n]{x_n}) \le \limsup \left(\frac{x_{n+1}}{x_n}\right).$$

14.I. Establish the following relations:

(a) $(n^2 + 2) \sim (n^2 - 3)$, (b) $(n^2 + 2) = o(n^3)$,

(c) $((-1)^n n^2) = O(n^2)$, (d) $((-1)^n n^2) = o(n^3)$,

(e) $(\sqrt{n+1} - \sqrt{n}) \sim (1/2\sqrt{n})$, (f) $(\sin n) = O(1)$.

14.J. Let X, Y, and Z be sequences with non-zero elements. Show that:

(a) $X \sim X$.

(b) If $X \sim Y$, then $Y \sim X$.

(c) If $X \sim Y$ and $Y \sim Z$, then $X \sim Z$.

14.K. If $X_1 = O(Y)$ and $X_2 = O(Y)$, we conclude that $X_1 \pm X_2 = O(Y)$ and summarize this in the "equation"

(a) $O(Y) \pm O(Y) = O(Y)$. Give similar interpretations for and prove that

(b) $o(Y) \pm o(Y) = o(Y)$.

(c) If $c \ne 0$, then $o(cY) = o(Y)$ and $O(cY) = O(Y)$.

(d) $O(o(Y)) = o(Y)$, $o(O(Y)) = o(Y)$. If X is a sequence of real numbers, show that

(e) $O(X) \cdot O(Y) = O(XY)$, $o(X) \cdot o(Y) = o(XY)$.

14.L. Show that $X = o(Y)$ and $Y = o(X)$ cannot hold simultaneously. Give an example of sequences such that $X = O(Y)$ but $Y \ne O(X)$.

14.M. If X is a monotone sequence in $\mathbf{R}$, show that the sequence of arithmetic means is monotone.

14.N. If $X = (x_n)$ is a bounded sequence in $\mathbf{R}$ and (σ_n) is the sequence of arithmetic means, show that

$$\limsup (\sigma_n) \le \limsup (x_n).$$

14.O. If $X = (x_n)$ is a bounded sequence in $\mathbf{R}^p$ and (σ_n) is the sequence of arithmetic means, then

$$\lim \sup (|\sigma_n|) \leq \lim \sup (|x_n|).$$

Give an example where inequality holds.

14.P. If $X = (x_n)$ is a sequence of positive real numbers, then is (σ_n) monotone increasing?

14.Q. If a sequence $X = (x_n)$ in $\mathbf{R}^p$ is Cesàro summable, then $X = o(n)$. (Hint: $x_n = n\sigma_n - (n-1)\sigma_{n-1}$.)

14.R. Let X be a monotone sequence in $\mathbf{R}$. Is it true that X is Cesàro summable if and only if it is convergent?

14.S. Give a proof of Theorem 14.10.

14.T. Consider the existence of the double and the iterated limits of the double sequences (x_{mn}), where x_{mn} is given by

(a) $(-1)^{m+n}$,   (b) $\dfrac{1}{m+n}$,   (c) $\dfrac{1}{m} + \dfrac{1}{n}$,

(d) $\dfrac{m}{m+n}$,   (e) $(-1)^m \left(\dfrac{1}{m} + \dfrac{1}{n} \right)$,   (f) $\dfrac{mn}{m^2 + n^2}$.

14.U. Is a convergent double sequence bounded?

14.V. If $X = (x_{mn})$ is a convergent double sequence of real numbers, and if for each $m \in \mathbf{N}$,

$$y_m = \lim_{n} \sup (x_{mn})$$

exists, then we have

$$\lim_{mn} (x_{mn}) = \lim_{m} (y_m).$$

14.W. Which of the double sequences in Exercise 14.T are such that the collection $\{ Y_m = \lim (x_{mn}) : m \in \mathbf{N} \}$ is uniformly convergent?

14.X. Let $X = (x_{mn})$ be a bounded double sequence in $\mathbf{R}$ with the property that for each $m \in \mathbf{N}$ the sequence

$$Y_m = (x_{mn} : n \in \mathbf{N})$$

is monotone increasing and for each $n \in \mathbf{N}$ the sequence $Z_n = (x_{mn} : m \in \mathbf{N})$ is monotone increasing. Is it true that the iterated limits exist and are equal? Does the double limit need to exist?

14.Y. Discuss the problem posed in the final paragraph of this section.

IV

Continuous Functions

We now begin our study of the most important class of functions in analysis, namely the continuous functions. In this chapter, we shall blend the results of Chapters II and III and reap a rich harvest of theorems which have considerable depth and utility.

Section 15 examines continuity at a point and introduces the important class of linear functions. The fundamental Section 16 studies the consequences of continuity on compact and connected sets. The results obtained in this section, as well as Theorem 17.1, are used repeatedly throughout the rest of the book. The remainder of Section 17 treats some very interesting questions, but the results are not applied in later sections. The final section discusses various kinds of limit concepts.

It is not assumed that the reader has any previous familiarity with a rigorous treatment of continuous functions. However, in a few of the examples and exercises, we make reference to the exponential, the logarithm, and the trigonometric functions in order to give some non-trivial examples. All that is required here is a knowledge of the graphs of these functions.

Section 15 Local Properties of Continuous Functions

We shall suppose that f is a function with domain $\mathfrak{D}$ contained in $\mathbf{R}^p$ and with range contained in $\mathbf{R}^q$. We shall not require that $\mathfrak{D} = \mathbf{R}^p$ or that $p = q$. We shall define continuity in terms of neighborhoods and then mention a few alternative definitions as necessary and sufficient conditions.

15.1 DEFINITION. Let a be a point in the domain $\mathfrak{D}$ of the function f. We say that f is **continuous at** a if for every neighborhood V of $f(a)$

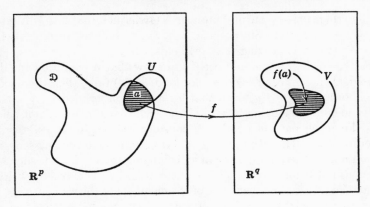

Figure 15.1

there is a neighborhood U of a (which depends on V) such that if x belongs to $\mathfrak{D} \cap U$, then $f(x)$ belongs to V. (See Figure 15.1.) If $\mathfrak{D}_1$ is a subset of $\mathfrak{D}$, we say that f is continuous on $\mathfrak{D}_1$ in case it is continuous at every point of $\mathfrak{D}_1$.

Sometimes it is said that a continuous function is one which "sends neighboring points into neighboring points." This intuitive phrase is to be avoided if it leads one to believe that the image of a neighborhood of a need be a neighborhood of $f(a)$.

We now give two equivalent statements which could have been used as the definition.

15.2. THEOREM. *Let a be a point in the domain $\mathfrak{D}$ of the function f. The following statements are equivalent:*

(a) *f is continuous at a.*

(b) *If ϵ is any positive real number, there exists a positive number $\delta(\epsilon)$ such that if $x \in \mathfrak{D}$ and $|x - a| < \delta(\epsilon)$, then $|f(x) - f(a)| < \epsilon$.*

(c) *If (x_n) is any sequence of elements of $\mathfrak{D}$ which converges to a, then the sequence $(f(x_n))$ converges to $f(a)$.*

PROOF. Suppose that (a) holds and that $\epsilon > 0$, then the ball $V_\epsilon = \{y \in \mathbf{R}^q : |y - f(a)| < \epsilon\}$ is a neighborhood of the point $f(a)$. By Definition 15.1 there is a neighborhood U of a such that if $x \in U \cap \mathfrak{D}$, then $f(x) \in V_\epsilon$. Since U is a neighborhood of a, there is a positive real number $\delta(\epsilon)$ such that the open ball with radius $\delta(\epsilon)$ and center a is contained in U. Therefore, condition (a) implies (b).

Suppose that (b) holds and let (x_n) be a sequence of elements in $\mathfrak{D}$ which converges to a. Let $\epsilon > 0$ and invoke condition (b) to obtain a $\delta(\epsilon) > 0$ with the property stated in (b). Because of the convergence of

(x_n) to a, there exists a natural number $N(\delta(\epsilon))$ such that if $n \geq N(\delta(\epsilon))$, then $|x_n - a| < \delta(\epsilon)$. Since each $x_n \in \mathcal{D}$, it follows from (b) that $|f(x_n) - f(a)| < \epsilon$, proving that (c) holds.

Finally, we shall argue indirectly and show that if condition (a) does not hold, then condition (c) does not hold. If (a) fails, then there exists a neighborhood V_0 of $f(a)$ such that for any neighborhood U of a, there is an element x_U belonging to $\mathcal{D} \cap U$ but such that $f(x_U)$ does not belong to V_0. For each natural number n consider the neighborhood U_n of a defined by $U_n = \{x \in \mathbf{R}^p : |x - a| < 1/n\}$; from the preceding sentence, for each n in $\mathbf{N}$ there is an element x_n belonging to $\mathcal{D} \cap U_n$ but such that $f(x_n)$ does not belong to V_0. The sequence (x_n) just constructed belongs to $\mathcal{D}$ and converges to a, yet none of the elements of the sequence $(f(x_n))$ belong to the neighborhood V_0 of $f(a)$. Hence we have constructed a sequence for which the condition (c) does not hold. This shows that part (c) implies (a).

Q.E.D.

The following useful discontinuity criterion is a consequence of what we have just done.

15.3 DISCONTINUITY CRITERION. *The function f is not continuous at a point a in* $\mathcal{D}$ *if and only if there is a sequence* (x_n) *of elements in* $\mathcal{D}$ *which converges to a but such that the sequence* $(f(x_n))$ *of images does not converge to* $f(a)$.

The next result is a simple reformulation of the definition. We recall from Definition 2.10 that the *inverse image* $f^{-1}(H)$ of a subset H of $\mathbf{R}^q$ under f is defined by

$$f^{-1}(H) = \{x \in \mathcal{D} : f(x) \in H\}.$$

15.4 THEOREM. *The function f is continuous at a point a in* $\mathcal{D}$ *if and only if for every neighborhood V of* $f(a)$ *there is a neighborhood* V_1 *of a such that*

$$(15.1) \qquad\qquad V_1 \cap \mathcal{D} = f^{-1}(V).$$

PROOF. If V_1 is a neighborhood of a satisfying this equation, then we can take $U = V_1$ and satisfy Definition 15.1. Conversely, if Definition 15.1 is satisfied, then we can take $V_1 = U \cup f^{-1}(V)$ to obtain equation (15.1).

Q.E.D.

Before we push the theory any further, we shall pause to give some examples. For simplicity, most of the examples are for the case where $\mathbf{R}^p = \mathbf{R}^q = \mathbf{R}$.

15.5 EXAMPLES. (a) Let $\mathfrak{D} = \mathbf{R}$ and let f be the "constant" function defined to be equal to the real number c for all real numbers x. Then f is continuous at every point of $\mathbf{R}$; in fact, we can take the neighborhood U of Definition 15.1 to be equal to $\mathbf{R}$ for any point a in $\mathfrak{D}$. Similarly, the function g defined by

$$g(x) = 1, \qquad 0 \le x \le 1,$$
$$= 2, \qquad 2 \le x \le 3,$$

is continuous at each point in its domain.

(b) Let $\mathfrak{D} = \mathbf{R}$ and let f be the "identity" function defined by $f(x) = x$, $x \in \mathbf{R}$. (See Figure 15.2.) If a is a given real number, let $\epsilon > 0$ and let $\delta(\epsilon) = \epsilon$. Then, if $|x - z| < \delta(\epsilon)$, we have $|f(x) - f(a)| = |x - a| < \epsilon$.

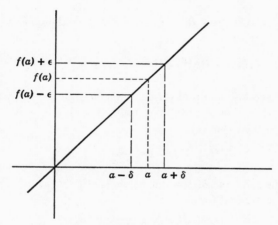

Figure 15.2

(c) Let $\mathfrak{D} = \mathbf{R}$ and let f be the "squaring" function defined by $f(x) = x^2$, $x \in \mathbf{R}$. Let a belong to $\mathbf{R}$ and let $\epsilon > 0$; then $|f(x) - f(a)| = |x^2 - a^2| = |x - a||x + a|$. We wish to make the above expression less than ϵ by making $|x - a|$ sufficiently small. If $a = 0$, then we choose $\delta(\epsilon) = \sqrt{\epsilon}$. If $a \ne 0$, then we want to obtain a bound for $|x + a|$ on a neighborhood of a. For example, if $|x - a| < |a|$, then $0 < |x| < 2|a|$ and $|x + a| \le |x| + |a| < 3|a|$. Hence

$$(15.2) \qquad |f(x) - f(a)| \le 3|a| \, |x - a|,$$

provided that $|x - a| < |a|$. Thus if we define $\delta(\epsilon) = \inf\left\{|a|, \dfrac{\epsilon}{3|a|}\right\}$, then when $|x - a| < \delta(\epsilon)$, the inequality (15.2) holds and we have $|f(x) - f(a)| < \epsilon$.

(d) We consider the same function as in (c) but use a slightly different technique. Instead of factoring $x^2 - a^2$, we write it as a polynomial in $x - a$. Thus

$$x^2 - a^2 = (x^2 - 2ax + a^2) + (2ax - 2a^2) = (x - a)^2 + 2a(x - a).$$

Using the Triangle Inequality, we obtain

$$|f(x) - f(a)| \le |x - a|^2 + 2|a|\,|x - a|.$$

If $\delta \le 1$ and $|x - a| < \delta$, then $|x - a|^2 < \delta^2 \le \delta$ and the term on the right side is dominated by $\delta + 2|a|\delta = \delta(1 + 2|a|)$. Hence we are led to choose

$$\delta(\epsilon) = \inf\left\{ 1, \frac{\epsilon}{1 + 2|a|} \right\}.$$

(e) Consider $\mathfrak{D} = \{x \in \mathbf{R} : x \ne 0\}$ and let f be defined by $f(x) = 1/x$, $x \in \mathfrak{D}$. If $a \in \mathfrak{D}$, then

$$|f(x) - f(a)| = |1/x - 1/a| = \frac{|x - a|}{|ax|}.$$

Again we wish to find a bound for the coefficient of $|x - a|$ which is valid in a neighborhood of $a \ne 0$. We note that if $|x - a| < \frac{1}{2}|a|$, then $\frac{1}{2}|a| < |x|$, and we have

$$|f(x) - f(a)| \le \frac{2}{|a|^2}|x - a|.$$

Thus we are led to take $\delta(\epsilon) = \inf\{\frac{1}{2}|a|, \frac{1}{2}\epsilon|a|^2\}$.

(f) Let f be defined for $\mathfrak{D} = \mathbf{R}$ by

$$f(x) = 0, \ x \le 0,$$
$$= 1, \ x > 0.$$

It may be seen that f is continuous at all points $a \ne 0$. We shall show that f is not continuous at 0 by using the Discontinuity Criterion 15.3. In fact, if $x_n = 1/n$, then the sequence $(f(1/n)) = (1)$ does not converge to $f(0)$. (See Figure 15.3 on the next page.)

(g) Let $\mathfrak{D} = \mathbf{R}$ and let f be Dirichlet's† discontinuous function defined by

$$f(x) = 1, \ \text{if} \ x \ \text{is rational},$$
$$= 0, \ \text{if} \ x \ \text{is irrational}.$$

---

† PETER GUSTAV LEJEUNE DIRICHLET (1805–1859) was born in the Rhineland and taught at Berlin for almost thirty years before going to Göttingen as Gauss' successor. He made fundamental contributions to number theory and analysis.

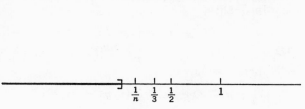

Figure 15.3

If a is a rational number, let $X = (x_n)$ be a sequence of irrational numbers converging to a. (Theorem 5.17 assures us of the existence of such a sequence.) Since $f(x_n) = 0$ for all $n \in \mathbf{N}$, the sequence $(f(x_n))$ does not converge to $f(a) = 1$ and f is not continuous at the rational number a. On the other hand, if b is an irrational number, then there exists a sequence $Y = (y_n)$ of rational numbers converging to b. The sequence $(f(y_n))$ does not converge to $f(b)$, so f is not continuous at b.Therefore, Dirichlet's function is *not continuous at any point*.

(h) Let $\mathfrak{D} = \{x \in \mathbf{R} : x > 0\}$. For any irrational number $x > 0$, we define $f(x) = 0$; for a rational number of the form m/n, with the natural numbers m, n having no common factor except 1, we define $f(m/n) = 1/n$. We shall show that f is continuous at every irrational number in $\mathfrak{D}$ and discontinuous at every rational number in $\mathfrak{D}$. The latter statement follows by taking a sequence of irrational numbers converging to the given rational number and using the Discontinuity Criterion. Let a be an irrational number and $\epsilon > 0$; then there is a natural number n such that $1/n < \epsilon$. If δ is chosen so small that the interval $(a - \delta, a + \delta)$ contains no rational number with denominator less than n, then it follows that for x in this interval we have $|f(x) - f(a)| = |f(x)| \leq 1/n < \epsilon$. Thus f is continuous at the irrational number a. Therefore, this function is *continuous precisely at the irrational points in its domain*.

(i) This time, let $\mathfrak{D} = \mathbf{R}^2$ and let f be the function on $\mathbf{R}^2$ with values in $\mathbf{R}^2$ defined by

$$f(x, y) = (2x + y, x - 3y).$$

Let (a, b) be a fixed point in $\mathbf{R}^2$; we shall show that f is continuous at this point. To do this, we need to show that we can make the expression

$$|f(x, y) - f(a, b)| = \{(2x + y - 2a - b)^2 + (x - 3y - a + 3b)^2\}^{1/2}$$

arbitrarily small by choosing (x, y) sufficiently close to (a, b). Since $\{p^2 + q^2\}^{1/2} \leq \sqrt{2}\sup\{|p|, |q|\}$, it is evidently enough to show that we can make the terms

$$|2x + y - 2a - b|, \qquad |x - 3y - a + 3b|,$$

arbitrarily small by choosing (x, y) sufficiently close to (a, b). In fact, by the Triangle Inequality,

$$|2x + y - 2a - b| = |2(x - a) + (y - b)| \leq 2|x - a| + |y - b|.$$

Now $|x - a| \leq \{(x - a)^2 + (y - b)^2\}^{1/2} = |(x, y) - (a, b)|$, and similarly for $|y - b|$; hence we have

$$|2x + y - 2a - b| \leq 3|(x, y) - (a, b)|.$$

Similarly,

$$|x - 3y - a + 3b| \leq |x - a| + 3|y - b| \leq 4|(x, y) - (a, b)|.$$

Therefore, if $\epsilon > 0$, we can take $\delta(\epsilon) = \epsilon/(4\sqrt{2})$ and be certain that if $|f(x, y) - f(a, b)| < \delta(\epsilon)$, then $|f(x, y) - f(a, b)| < \epsilon$, although a larger value of δ can be attained by a more refined analysis (for example, by using the C.-B.-S. Inequality 7.7).

(j) Again let $\mathfrak{D} = \mathbf{R}^2$ and let f be defined by

$$f(x, y) = (x^2 + y^2, \ 2xy).$$

If (a, b) is a fixed point in $\mathbf{R}^2$, then

$$|f(x, y) - f(a, b)| = \{(x^2 + y^2 - a^2 - b^2)^2 + (2xy - 2ab)^2\}^{1/2}.$$

As in (i), we examine the two terms on the right side separately. It will be seen that we need to obtain elementary estimates of magnitude. From the Triangle Inequality, we have

$$|x^2 + y^2 - a^2 - b^2| \leq |x^2 - a^2| + |y^2 - b^2|.$$

If the point (x, y) is within a distance of 1 of (a, b), then $|x| \leq |a| + 1$ whence $|x + a| \leq 2|a| + 1$ and $|y| \leq |b| + 1$ so that $|y + b| \leq 2|b|+1$. Thus we have

$$|x^2 + y^2 - a^2 - b^2| \leq |x - a|(2|a| + 1) + |y - b|(2|b| + 1)$$
$$\leq 2(|a| + |b| + 1)|(x, y) - (a, b)|.$$

In a similar fashion, we have

$$|2xy - 2ab| = 2|xy - xb + xb - ab| \leq 2|x|\,|y - b| + 2|b|\,|x - a|$$
$$\leq 2(|a| + |b| + 1)|(x, y) - (a, b)|.$$

Therefore, we set

$$\delta(\epsilon) = \inf\left\{1, \ \frac{\epsilon}{2\sqrt{2}(|a| + |b| + 1)}\right\};$$

if $|(x, y) - (a, b)| < \delta(\epsilon)$, then we have $|f(x, y) - f(a, b)| < \epsilon$, proving that f is continuous at the point (a, b).

Combinations of Functions

The next result is a direct consequence of Theorems 11.14 and 15.2(c), so we shall not write out the details. Alternatively, it could be proved directly by using arguments quite parallel to those employed in the proof of Theorem 11.14. We recall that if f and g are functions with domains $\mathfrak{D}(f)$ and $\mathfrak{D}(g)$ in $\mathbf{R}^p$ and ranges in $\mathbf{R}^q$, then we define their **sum** $f + g$, their **difference** $f - g$ and their **inner product** $f \cdot g$ for each x in $\mathfrak{D}(f) \cap \mathfrak{D}(g)$ by the formulas

$$f(x) + g(x), \quad f(x) - g(x), \quad f(x) \cdot g(x).$$

Similarly, if c is a real number and if φ is a function with domain $\mathfrak{D}(\varphi)$ in $\mathbf{R}^p$ and range in $\mathbf{R}$, we define the **products** cf for x in $\mathfrak{D}(f)$ and φf for x in $\mathfrak{D}(\varphi) \cap \mathfrak{D}(f)$ by the formulas

$$c f(x), \qquad \varphi(x) f(x).$$

In particular, if $\varphi(x) \neq 0$ for $x \in \mathfrak{D}_0$, then we can define the **quotient** f/φ for x in $\mathfrak{D}(f) \cap \mathfrak{D}_0$ by

$$\frac{f(x)}{\varphi(x)}.$$

With these definitions, we now state the result.

15.6   **Theorem.**   *If the functions f, g, φ are continuous at a point, then the algebraic combinations*

$$f + g, \ f - g, \ f \cdot g, \ cf, \ \varphi f \ \text{ and } \ f/\varphi$$

are also continuous at this point.

There is another algebraic combination that is often useful. If f is defined on $\mathfrak{D}(f)$ in $\mathbf{R}^p$ to $\mathbf{R}^q$, we define the *absolute value* $|f|$ of f to be the function with range in the real numbers $\mathbf{R}$ whose value at x in $\mathfrak{D}(f)$ is given by $|f(x)|$.

15.7   **Theorem.**   *If f is continuous at a point, then $|f|$ is also continuous there.*

proof.   From the Triangle Inequality 7.8, we have

$$\big|\, |f(x)| - |f(a)| \,\big| \leq |f(x) - f(a)|,$$

from which the result is immediate.

Q.E.D.

We recall the notion of the composition of two functions. Let f have domain $\mathfrak{D}(f)$ in $\mathbf{R}^p$ and range in $\mathbf{R}^q$ and let g have domain $\mathfrak{D}(g)$ in $\mathbf{R}^q$ and range in $\mathbf{R}^r$. In Definition 2.2, we defined the composition $h = g \circ f$ to have domain $\mathfrak{D}(h) = \{x \in \mathfrak{D}(f) : f(x) \in \mathfrak{D}(g)\}$ and for x in $\mathfrak{D}(h)$ we set $h(x) = g[f(x)]$. Thus $h = g \circ f$ is a function mapping $\mathfrak{D}(h)$, which is a subset of $\mathfrak{D}(f) \subseteq \mathbf{R}^p$, into $\mathbf{R}^r$. We now establish the continuity of this function.

15.8   THEOREM. *If f is continuous at a and g is continuous at* $b = f(a)$, *then the composition* $g \circ f$ *is continuous at a.*

PROOF.   Let W be a neighborhood of the point $c = g(b)$. Since g is continuous at b, there is a neighborhood V of b such that if y belongs to $V \cap \mathfrak{D}(g)$, then $g(y) \in W$. Since f is continuous at a, there exists a neighborhood U of a such that if x belongs to $U \cap \mathfrak{D}(f)$, then $f(x)$ is in V.

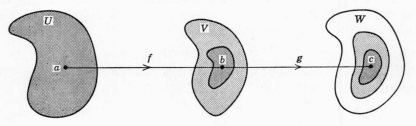

Figure 15.4

Therefore, if x belongs to $U \cap \mathfrak{D}(g \circ f)$, then $f(x)$ is in $V \cap \mathfrak{D}(g)$ and $g[f(x)]$ belongs to W. (See Figure 15.4.) This shows that $h = g \circ f$ is continuous at a.

Q.E.D.

Linear Functions

The preceding discussion pertained to general functions defined on a part of $\mathbf{R}^p$ into $\mathbf{R}^q$. We now mention a simple but extremely important special kind of function, namely the linear functions. In most applications, the domain of such functions is all of $\mathbf{R}^p$, and so we shall restrict our attention to this case.

15.9   DEFINITION. A function f with domain $\mathbf{R}^p$ and range in $\mathbf{R}^q$ is said to be **linear** if, for all vectors x, y in $\mathbf{R}^p$ and real numbers c,

(15.3) $f(x + y) = f(x) + f(y), \quad f(cx) = cf(x).$

Often linear functions are called **linear transformations**.

It is readily seen that the functions in Examples 15.6(b) and 15.6(i) are linear functions for the case $p = q = 1$ and $p = q = 2$, respectively. In fact, it is not difficult to characterize the most general linear function from $\mathbf{R}^p$ to $\mathbf{R}^q$.

15.10 THEOREM. *If f is a linear function with domain $\mathbf{R}^p$ and range in $\mathbf{R}^q$, then there are pq real numbers (c_{ij}), $1 \le i \le q$, $1 \le j \le p$, such that if $x = (\xi_1, \xi_2, \ldots, \xi_p)$ is any point in $\mathbf{R}^p$, and if $y = (\eta_1, \eta_2, \ldots, \eta_q) = f(x)$ is its image under f, then*

$$\eta_1 = c_{11}\xi_1 + c_{12}\xi_2 + \cdots + c_{1p}\xi_p,$$

$$\eta_2 = c_{21}\xi_1 + c_{22}\xi_2 + \cdots + c_{2p}\xi_p,$$

(15.4)
$$\cdots \cdots \cdots \cdots \cdots \cdots$$

$$\eta_q = c_{q1}\xi_1 + c_{q2}\xi_2 + \cdots + c_{qp}\xi_p.$$

Conversely, if (c_{ij}) is a collection of pq real numbers, then the function which assigns to x in $\mathbf{R}^p$ the element y in $\mathbf{R}^q$ according to the equations (15.4) is a linear function with domain $\mathbf{R}^p$ and range in $\mathbf{R}^q$.

PROOF.   Let $e_1, e_2, \ldots, e_p$ be the elements of $\mathbf{R}^p$ given by $e_1 = (1, 0, \ldots, 0)$, $e_2 = (0, 1, \ldots, 0)$, $\ldots$, $e_p = (0, 0, \ldots, 1)$. We examine the images of these vectors under the linear function f. Suppose that

$$f(e_1) = (c_{11}, c_{21}, \ldots, c_{q1}),$$

$$f(e_2) = (c_{12}, c_{22}, \ldots, c_{q2}),$$

(15.5)
$$\cdots \cdots \cdots \cdots \cdots$$

$$f(e_p) = (c_{1p}, c_{2p}, \ldots, c_{qp}).$$

Thus the real number c_{ij} is the ith coordinate of the point $f(e_j)$.

An arbitrary element $x = (\xi_1, \xi_2, \ldots, \xi_p)$ of $\mathbf{R}^p$ can be expressed simply in terms of the vectors $e_1, e_2, \ldots, e_p$; in fact,

$$x = \xi_1 e_1 + \xi_2 e_2 + \cdots + \xi_p e_p.$$

Since f is linear, it follows that

$$f(x) = \xi_1 f(e_1) + \xi_2 f(e_2) + \cdots + \xi_p f(e_p).$$

If we use the equations (15.5), we have

$$f(x) = \xi_1(c_{11}, c_{21}, \ldots, c_{q1}) + \xi_2(c_{12}, c_{22}, \ldots, c_{q2})$$

$$+ \cdots + \xi_p(c_{1p}, c_{2p}, \ldots, c_{qp})$$

$$= (c_{11}\xi_1, c_{21}\xi_1, \ldots, c_{q1}\xi_1) + (c_{12}\xi_2, c_{22}\xi_2, \ldots, c_{q2}\xi_2)$$

$$+ \cdots + (c_{1p}\xi_p, c_{2p}\xi_p, \ldots, c_{qp}\xi_p)$$

$$= (c_{11}\xi_1 + c_{12}\xi_2 + \cdots + c_{1p}\xi_p, c_{21}\xi_1 + c_{22}\xi_2 + \cdots + c_{2p}\xi_p,$$

$$\ldots, c_{q1}\xi_1 + c_{q2}\xi_2 + \cdots + c_{qp}\xi_p).$$

This shows that the coordinates of $f(x)$ are given by the relations (15.4), as asserted.

Conversely, it is easily verified by direct calculation that if the relations (15.4) are used to obtain the coordinates η_j of y from the coordinates ξ_i of x, then the resulting function satisfies the relations (15.3) and so is linear. We shall omit this calculation, since it is straight-forward.

Q.E.D.

It should be mentioned that the rectangular array of numbers

$$(15.6) \qquad \begin{bmatrix} c_{11} & c_{12} & \cdots & c_{1p} \\ c_{21} & c_{22} & \cdots & c_{2p} \\ \cdots\cdots\cdots\cdots \\ c_{q1} & c_{q2} & \cdots & c_{qp} \end{bmatrix},$$

consisting of q rows and p columns, is often called the **matrix** corresponding to the linear function f. There is a one-one correspondence between linear functions of R^p into R^q and $q \times p$ matrices of real numbers. As we have seen, the action of f is completely described in terms of its matrix. We shall not find it necessary to develop any of the extensive theory of matrices, however, but will regard the matrix (15.6) as being shorthand for a more elaborate description of the linear function f.

We shall now prove that a linear function from R^p to R^q is automatically continuous. To do this, we first observe that if $M = \sup \{|c_{ij}| : 1 \leq i \leq q, 1 \leq j \leq p\}$, then since $|\xi_j| \leq |x|$, it follows from equation (15.4) that if $1 \leq i \leq q$, then

$$|\eta_i| \leq |c_{i1}||\xi_1| + |c_{i2}||\xi_2| + \cdots + |c_{ip}||\xi_p| \leq pM\,|x|.$$

Since $|y|^2 = |\eta_1|^2 + \cdots + |\eta_q|^2$, we conclude that

$$|y|^2 \leq qp^2 M^2\,|x|^2,$$

so that we have

$$(15.7) \qquad |y| = |f(x)| \leq p\,\sqrt{q}M\,|x|.$$

Actually, the estimate $p\,\sqrt{q}M$ is not usually very sharp and can be improved with little effort. Instead of using the Triangle Inequality to estimate $|\eta_j|$, we restate the C.-B.-S. Inequality in the form

$$|a_1b_1 + a_2b_2 + \cdots + a_pb_p|^2 \leq \{a_1{}^2 + a_2{}^2 + \cdots + a_p{}^2\}$$
$$\times \{b_1{}^2 + b_2{}^2 + \cdots + b_p{}^2\}.$$

We apply this inequality to each expression in equation (15.4) to obtain, for $1 \leq i \leq q$, the estimate

$$|\eta_i|^2 \leq (|c_{i1}|^2 + |c_{i2}|^2 + \cdots + |c_{ip}|^2) \, |x|^2 = \sum_{j=1}^{p} |c_{ij}|^2 \, |x|^2.$$

Adding these inequalities, we have

$$|y|^2 \leq \left\{ \sum_{i=1}^{q} \sum_{j=1}^{p} |c_{ij}|^2 \right\} |x|^2,$$

from which we conclude that

(15.8) $$|y| = |f(x)| \leq \left\{ \sum_{i=1}^{q} \sum_{j=1}^{p} |c_{ij}|^2 \right\}^{1/2} |x|.$$

Although the coefficient of $|x|$ is more complicated than in (15.7), it is a more precise estimate since some of the (c_{ij}) may be small. Even in the most unfavorable case, where $|c_{ij}| = M$, for all i, j, the second estimate yields $\sqrt{pq} \, M$ instead of the larger term $p \, \sqrt{q} \, M$.

15.11 THEOREM. *If f is a linear function with domain $\mathbf{R}^p$ and range in $\mathbf{R}^q$, then there exists a positive constant A such that if u, v are any two vectors in $\mathbf{R}^p$,*

(15.9) $$|f(u) - f(v)| \leq A \, |u - v|.$$

Therefore, a linear function on $\mathbf{R}^p$ to $\mathbf{R}^q$ is continuous at every point.

PROOF. We have seen, in deriving equations (15.7) and (15.8), that there exists a constant A such that if x is any element of $\mathbf{R}^p$ then $|f(x)| \leq A \, |x|$. Now let $x = u - v$ and use the linearity of f to obtain $f(x) = f(u - v) = f(u) - f(v)$. Therefore, the equation (15.9) results. It is clear that this relation implies the continuity of f, for we can make $|f(u) - f(v)| < \epsilon$ by taking $|u - v| < \epsilon/A$.

Q.E.D.

Exercises

15.A. Prove that if f is defined for $x \geq 0$ by $f(x) = \sqrt{x}$, then f is continuous at every point of its domain.

15.B. Show that a polynomial function f, given by

$$f(x) = a_n x^n + a_{n-1} x^{n-1} + \ldots + a_1 x + a_0, \qquad x \in \mathbf{R},$$

is continuous at every point of $\mathbf{R}$.

15.C. Show that a rational function (that is, the quotient of two polynomials) is continuous at every point where it is defined.

15.D. Using the C.-B.-S. Inequality, show that one can take $\delta(\epsilon) = \epsilon/\sqrt{15}$ in Example 15.5(i).

15.E. Let f be the function on $\mathbf{R}$ to $\mathbf{R}$ defined by

$$f(x) = x, \qquad x \text{ irrational},$$
$$= 1 - x, \qquad x \text{ rational}.$$

Show that f is continuous at $x = \frac{1}{2}$ and discontinuous elsewhere.

15.F. Let f be continuous on $\mathbf{R}$ to $\mathbf{R}$. Show that if $f(x) = 0$ for rational x then $f(x) = 0$ for all x in $\mathbf{R}$.

15.G. Let f and g be continuous on $\mathbf{R}$ to $\mathbf{R}$. Is it true that $f(x) = g(x)$ for $x \in \mathbf{R}$ if and only if $f(y) = g(y)$ for all rational numbers y in $\mathbf{R}$?

15.H. Use the inequality

$$|\sin(x)| \leq |x|$$

to show that the sine function is continuous at $x = 0$. Use this fact, together with the identity

$$\sin(x) - \sin(u) = 2 \sin\left(\frac{x - u}{2}\right) \cos\left(\frac{x + u}{2}\right),$$

to prove that the sine function is continuous at any point of $\mathbf{R}$.

15.I. Using the results of the preceding exercise, show that the function g, defined on $\mathbf{R}$ to $\mathbf{R}$ by

$$g(x) = x \sin (1/x), \qquad x \neq 0,$$
$$= 0, \qquad x = 0,$$

is continuous at every point.

15.J. Let h be defined for $x \neq 0$, $x \in \mathbf{R}$, by

$$h(x) = \sin (1/x), \qquad x \neq 0.$$

Show that no matter how h is defined at $x = 0$, it will be discontinuous at $x = 0$.

15.K. Let f be monotone increasing on $J = [a, b]$ to $\mathbf{R}$. If $c \in (a, b)$, define

$$l(c) = \sup \{f(x) : x < c\},$$
$$r(c) = \inf \{f(x) : x > c\},$$
$$j(c) = r(c) - l(c).$$

Show that $l(c) \leq f(c) \leq r(c)$ and that f is continuous at c if and only if $j(c) = 0$. Prove that there are at most countably many points in (a, b) at which the monotone function is discontinuous.

15.L. We say that a function f on $\mathbf{R}$ to $\mathbf{R}$ is **additive** if it satisfies

$$f(x + y) = f(x) + f(y)$$

for all $x, y \in \mathbf{R}$. Show that an additive function which is continuous at $x = 0$ is continuous at any point of $\mathbf{R}$. Show that a monotone additive function is continuous at every point.

15.M. Suppose that f is a continuous additive function on $\mathbf{R}$. If $c = f(1)$, show that $f(x) = cx$ for all x in $\mathbf{R}$. (Hint: first show that if r is a rational number, then $f(r) = cr$.)

15.N. Let g be a function on R to R which satisfies the identity

$$g(x + y) = g(x) \, g(y), \qquad x, y \in R.$$

Show that, if g is continuous at $x = 0$, then g is continuous at every point of R. In addition, show that if g vanishes at a single point of R, then g vanishes at every point of R.

15.O. If $|f|$ is continuous at a point, then is it true that f is also continuous at this point?

15.P. Is it possible for f and g to be discontinuous and yet for $g \cdot f$ to be continuous? How about $g \circ f$?

15.Q. If f is a linear function of R^p into R^q, show that the columns of the matrix representation (15.6) of f indicate the elements in R^q into which the elements $e_1 = (1, 0, \ldots, 0)$, $e_2 = (0, 1, \ldots, 0)$, $\ldots$, $e_p = (0, 0, \ldots, 1)$ of R^p are mapped by f.

15.R. Let f be a linear function of R^2 into R^3 which sends the elements $e_1 = (1, 0)$, $e_2 = (0, 1)$ of R^2 into the vectors $f(e_1) = (2, 1, 0)$, $f(e_2) = (1, 0, -1)$ of R^3. Give the matrix representation of f. What vectors in R^3 are the images under f of the elements

$$(2, 0), \ (1, 1), \ (1, 3)?$$

15.S. If f denotes the linear function of Exercise 15.R, show that not every vector in R^3 is the image under f of a vector in R^2.

15.T. Let g be any linear function on R^2 to R^3. Show that not every element of R^3 is the image under g of a vector in R^2.

15.U. Let h be any linear function on R^3 to R^2. Show that there exist non-zero vectors in R^3 which are mapped into the zero vector of R^2 by h.

15.V. Let f be a linear function on R^2 to R^2 and let the matrix representation of f be given by

$$\begin{bmatrix} a & b \\ c & d \end{bmatrix}$$

Show that $f(x) \neq 0$ when $x \neq \theta$ if and only if $\Delta = ad - bc \neq 0$.

15.W. Let f be as in Exercise 15.V. Show that f maps R^2 onto R^2 if and only if $\Delta = ad - bc \neq 0$. Show that if $\Delta \neq 0$, then the inverse function f^{-1} is linear and has the matrix representation

$$\begin{bmatrix} d/\Delta & -b/\Delta \\ -c/\Delta & a/\Delta \end{bmatrix}$$

15.X. Let g be a linear function from R^p to R^q. Show that g is one-one if and only if $g(x) = \theta$ implies that $x = \theta$.

15.Y. If h is a one-one linear function from R^p onto R^p, show that the inverse h^{-1} is a linear function from R^p onto R^p.

15.Z. Show that the sum and the composition of two linear functions are linear functions. Calculate the corresponding matrices for $p = 2$, $q = 3$, $r = 2$.

Section 16   Global Properties of Continuous Functions

In the preceding section we considered "local" continuity; that is, we were concerned with continuity at a point. In this section we shall be concerned with establishing some deeper properties of continuous functions. Here we shall be concerned with "global" continuity in the sense that we will assume that the functions are continuous at every point of their domain.

Unless there is a special mention to the contrary, f will denote a function with domain $\mathfrak{D}$ contained in $\mathbf{R}^p$ and with range in $\mathbf{R}^q$. We recall that if B is a subset of the range space $\mathbf{R}^q$, the *inverse image* of B under f is the set

$$f^{-1}(B) = \{x \in \mathfrak{D} : f(x) \in B\}.$$

Observe that $f^{-1}(B)$ is automatically a subset of $\mathfrak{D}$ even though B is not necessarily a subset of the range of f.

In topology courses, where one is more concerned with global than local continuity, the next result is often taken as the definition of (global) continuity. Its importance will soon be evident.

16.1 GLOBAL CONTINUITY THEOREM.   *The following statements are equivalent:*

(a) *f is continuous on its domain $\mathfrak{D}$.*

(b) *If G is any open set in $\mathbf{R}^q$, then there exists an open set G_1 in $\mathbf{R}^p$ such that $G_1 \cap \mathfrak{D} = f^{-1}(G)$.*

(c) *If H is any closed set in $\mathbf{R}^q$, then there exists a closed set H_1 in $\mathbf{R}^p$ such that $H_1 \cap \mathfrak{D} = f^{-1}(H)$.*

PROOF.   First, we shall suppose that (a) holds and let G be an open subset of $\mathbf{R}^q$. If a belongs to $f^{-1}(G)$, then since G is a neighborhood of $f(a)$, it follows from the continuity of f at a that there is an open set $U(a)$ such that if $x \in \mathfrak{D} \cap U(a)$, then $f(x) \in G$. Select $U(a)$ for each a in $f^{-1}(G)$ and let G_1 be the union of the sets $U(a)$. By Theorem 8.3(c), the set G_1 is open and it is plain that $G_1 \cap \mathfrak{D} = f^{-1}(G)$. Hence (a) implies (b).

We shall now show that (b) implies (a). If a is an arbitrary point of $\mathfrak{D}$ and G is an open neighborhood of $f(a)$, then condition (b) implies that there exists an open set G_1 in $\mathbf{R}^p$ such that $G_1 \cap \mathfrak{D} = f^{-1}(G)$. Since $f(a) \in G$, it follows that $a \in G_1$, so G_1 is a neighborhood of a. If $x \in G_1 \cap \mathfrak{D}$, then $f(x) \in G$ whence f is continuous at a. This proves that condition (b) implies (a).

We now prove the equivalence of conditions (b) and (c). First we observe that if B is any subset of $\mathbf{R}^q$ and if $C = \mathbf{R}^q \backslash B$, then we have $f^{-1}(B) \cap f^{-1}(C) = \emptyset$ and

(16.1) $$\mathfrak{D} = f^{-1}(B) \cup f^{-1}(C).$$

If B_1 is a subset of $\mathbf{R}^p$ such that $B_1 \cap \mathfrak{D} = f^{-1}(B)$ and $C_1 = \mathbf{R}^p \backslash B_1$, then $C_1 \cap f^{-1}(B) = \emptyset$ and

$$(16.2) \qquad \mathfrak{D} = (B_1 \cap \mathfrak{D}) \cup (C_1 \cap \mathfrak{D}) = f^{-1}(B) \cup (C_1 \cap \mathfrak{D}).$$

The formulas (16.1) and (16.2) are two representations of $\mathfrak{D}$ as the union of $f^{-1}(B)$ with another set with which it has no common points. Therefore, we have

$$C_1 \cap \mathfrak{D} = f^{-1}(C).$$

Suppose that (b) holds and that H is closed in $\mathbf{R}^q$. Apply the argument just completed in the case where $B = \mathbf{R}^q \backslash H$ and $C = H$. Then B and B_1 are open sets in $\mathbf{R}^q$ and $\mathbf{R}^p$, respectively, so $C_1 = \mathbf{R}^q \backslash B_1$ is closed in $\mathbf{R}^p$. This shows that (b) implies (c).

To see that (c) implies (b), use the above argument with $B = \mathbf{R}^p \backslash G$, where G is an open set in $\mathbf{R}^q$.

Q.E.D.

In the case where $\mathfrak{D} = \mathbf{R}^p$, the preceding result simplifies to some extent.

16.2 COROLLARY. *Let f be defined on all of $\mathbf{R}^p$ and with range in $\mathbf{R}^q$. Then the following statements are equivalent:*
(a) *f is continuous on $\mathbf{R}^p$.*
(b) *If G is open in $\mathbf{R}^q$, then $f^{-1}(G)$ is open in $\mathbf{R}^p$.*
(c) *If H is closed in $\mathbf{R}^q$, then $f^{-1}(H)$ is closed in $\mathbf{R}^p$.*

It should be emphasized that the Global Continuity Theorem 16.1 does *not* say that if f is continuous and if G is an open set in $\mathbf{R}^p$, then the direct image $f(G) = \{f(x) : x \in G\}$ is open in $\mathbf{R}^q$. In general, a continuous function need not send open sets to open sets or closed sets to closed sets. For example, the function f on $\mathfrak{D} = \mathbf{R}$ to $\mathbf{R}$, defined by

$$f(x) = \frac{1}{1 + x^2}$$

is continuous on $\mathbf{R}$. [In fact, it was seen in Examples 15.5(a) and (c) that the functions

$$f_1(x) = 1, \qquad f_2(x) = x^2, \qquad x \in \mathbf{R},$$

are continuous at every point. From Theorem 15.6, it follows that

$$f_3(x) = 1 + x^2, \qquad x \in \mathbf{R},$$

is continuous at every point and, since f_3 never vanishes, this same theorem implies that the function f given above is continuous on $\mathbf{R}$.] If G is the open set $G = (-1, 1)$, then

$$f(G) = (\tfrac{1}{2}, 1],$$

which is not open in R. Similarly, if H is the closed set $H = \{x \in R : x \geq 1\}$, then

$$f(H) = (0, \tfrac{1}{2}],$$

which is not closed in R. Similarly, the function f maps the set R, which is both open and closed in R, into the set $f(R) = (0, 1]$, which is neither open nor closed in R.

The moral of the preceding remarks is that the property of a set being open or closed is not necessarily preserved under mapping by a continuous function. However, there are important properties of a set which are preserved under continuous mapping. For example, we shall now show that the properties of connectedness and compactness of sets have this character.

Preservation of Connectedness

We recall from Definition 8.14 that a set H in R^p is disconnected if there exist open sets A, B in R^p such that $A \cap H$ and $B \cap H$ are disjoint non-empty sets whose union is H. A set is connected if it is not disconnected.

16.3 PRESERVATION OF CONNECTEDNESS. *If H is connected and f is continuous on H, then $f(H)$ is connected.*

PROOF. Assume that $f(H)$ is disconnected in R^q, so that there exist open sets A, B in R^q such that $A \cap f(H)$ and $B \cap f(H)$ are disjoint non-empty sets whose union is $f(H)$. By the Global Continuity Theorem 16.1, there exist open sets A_1, B_1 in R^p such that

$$A_1 \cap H = f^{-1}(A), \quad B_1 \cap H = f^{-1}(B).$$

These intersections are non-empty and their disjointness follows from the disjointness of the sets $A \cap f(H)$ and $B \cap f(H)$. The assumption that the union of $A \cap f(H)$ and $B \cap f(H)$ is $f(H)$ implies that the union of $A_1 \cap H$ and $B_1 \cap H$ is H. Therefore, the disconnectedness of $f(H)$ implies the disconnectedness of H.

Q.E.D.

The very word "continuous" suggests that there are no sudden "breaks" in the graph of the function; hence the next result is by no means unexpected. However, the reader is invited to attempt to provide a different proof of this theorem and he will come to appreciate its depth.

16.4 BOLZANO'S INTERMEDIATE VALUE THEOREM. *Let H be a connected subset of R^p and let f be bounded and continuous on H and with values in R. If k is any real number satisfying*

$$\inf \{f(x) : x \in H\} < k < \sup \{f(x) : x \in H\},$$

then there is at least one point of H where f takes the value k.

PROOF. Let $A = \{t \in \mathbf{R} : t < k\}$ and let $B = \{t \in \mathbf{R} : t > k\}$ so that A and B are disjoint open sets in $\mathbf{R}$. By the Global Continuity Theorem 16.1 there exist open subsets A_1 and B_1 of $\mathbf{R}^p$ such that

$$A_1 \cap H = f^{-1}(A), \quad B_1 \cap H = f^{-1}(B).$$

If f never takes the value k, then the sets $A_1 \cap H$ and $B_1 \cap H$ are nonempty disjoint sets whose union is H. But this implies that H is disconnected, contrary to hypothesis.

Q.E.D.

Preservation of Compactness

We now demonstrate that the important property of compactness is preserved under continuous mapping. In the discussion to follow, we do not assume a close familiarity with Section 9, and we shall offer two proofs of the main results to be presented here. We recall that it is a consequence of the important Heine-Borel Theorem 9.3 that a subset K of $\mathbf{R}^p$ is compact if and only if it is both closed and bounded in $\mathbf{R}^p$. Thus the next result could be rephrased by saying that if K is closed and bounded in $\mathbf{R}^p$ and if f is continuous on K and with range in $\mathbf{R}^q$, then $f(K)$ is closed and bounded in $\mathbf{R}^q$.

16.5 PRESERVATION OF COMPACTNESS. *If K is compact and f is continuous on K, then $f(K)$ is compact.*

FIRST PROOF. We assume that K is closed and bounded in $\mathbf{R}^p$ and shall show that $f(K)$ is closed and bounded in $\mathbf{R}^q$. If $f(K)$ is not bounded, for each $n \in \mathbf{N}$ there exists a point x_n in K with $|f(x_n)| \geq n$. Since K is bounded, the sequence $X = (x_n)$ is bounded; hence it follows from the Bolzano-Weierstrass Theorem 12.4 that there is a subsequence of X which converges to an element x. Since $x_n \in K$ for $n \in \mathbf{N}$, the point x belongs to the closed set K. Hence f is continuous at x, so f is bounded by $|f(x)| + 1$ on a neighborhood of x. Since this contradicts the assumption that $|f(x_n)| \geq n$, the set $f(K)$ is bounded.

We shall prove that $f(K)$ is closed by showing that any cluster point y of $f(K)$ must be contained in this set. In fact, if n is a natural number, there is a point z_n in K such that

$$|f(z_n) - y| < 1/n.$$

By the Bolzano-Weierstrass Theorem 12.4, the sequence $Z = (z_n)$ has a subsequence $Z' = (z_{n(k)})$ which converges to an element z. Since K is closed, then $z \in K$ and f is continuous at z. Therefore,

$$f(z) = \lim_k \, (f(z_{n(k)})) = y,$$

which proves that y belongs to $f(K)$. Hence $f(K)$ is closed.

SECOND PROOF.   We shall base this proof on Definition 9.1 of compactness and the Global Continuity Theorem 16.1. Let $\mathcal{G} = \{G_\alpha\}$ be a family of open subsets of $\mathbf{R}^q$ whose union contains $f(K)$. By Theorem 16.1, for each set G_α in $\mathcal{G}$ there is an open subset C_α of $\mathbf{R}^p$ such that $C_\alpha \cap D = f^{-1}(G_\alpha)$. The family $\mathcal{C} = \{C_\alpha\}$ consists of open subsets of $\mathbf{R}^p$; we claim that the union of these sets contains K. For, if $x \in K$, then $f(x)$ is contained in $f(K)$; hence $f(x)$ belongs to some set G_α and by construction x belongs to the corresponding set C_α. Since K is compact, it is contained in the union of a finite number of sets in $\mathcal{C}$ and its image $f(K)$ is contained in the union of the corresponding finite number of sets in $\mathcal{G}$. Since this holds for an arbitrary family $\mathcal{G}$ of open sets covering $f(K)$, the set $f(K)$ is compact in $\mathbf{R}^q$.

Q.E.D.

When the range of the function is $\mathbf{R}$, the next theorem is sometimes reformulated by saying that *a continuous function on a compact set attains its maximum and minimum values.*

16.6   MAXIMUM AND MINIMUM VALUE THEOREM.   *Let f be continuous on a compact set K in $\mathbf{R}^p$ and with values in $\mathbf{R}^q$. Then there are points x^* and x_* in K such that*

$$|f(x^*)| = \sup \{|f(x)| : x \in K\}, \quad |f(x_*)| = \inf \{|f(x)| : x \in K\}.$$

FIRST PROOF.   Since f is continuous on K, its absolute value function $|f|$, which is defined for $x \in K$ to be $|f(x)|$, is also continuous on K. According to the preceding theorem, the set $\{|f(x)| : x \in K\}$ is a bounded set of real numbers. Let M be the supremum of this set and let $X = (x_n)$ be a sequence with

$$|f(x_n)| \geq M - 1/n, \quad n \in \mathbf{N}.$$

As before, some subsequence of X converges to a limit x^* which belongs to K. Since $|f|$ is continuous at x^* we must have $|f(x^*)| = M$. The assertion about x_* is proved in a similar way.

SECOND PROOF.   If there is no point x^* with $|f(x^*)| = M = \sup \{|f(x)| : x \in K\}$, then for each natural number n let $G_n = \{u \in \mathbf{R} : u < M - 1/n\}$. Since G_n is open and $|f|$ is continuous on K, it follows from Theorem 16.1 that there is an open set C_n in $\mathbf{R}^p$ such that $C_n \cap K = \{x \in K : |f(x)| < M - 1/n\}$. Now, if the value M is not attained, then it is plain that the union of the family $\mathcal{C} = \{C_n\}$ of open sets contains all of K. Since K is compact and the family $\{C_n \cap K\}$ is increasing, there is a natural number r such that $K \subseteq C_r$. But then we have

$$|f(x)| < M - 1/r, \quad \text{for all } x \in K,$$

whence $M = \sup \{|f(x)| : x \in K\} < M$, a contradiction.

Q.E.D.

16.7 COROLLARY. *If f is continuous on a compact subset K of $\mathbf{R}^p$ and has real values, then there exist points x^* , x_* in K such that*

$$f(x^*) = \sup \{f(x): x \in K\}, \quad f(x_*) = \inf \{f(x): x \in K\}.$$

As an application, we note that the set S in $\mathbf{R}^p$, defined by $S = \{x \in \mathbf{R}^p : |x| = 1\}$, is obviously bounded and is readily seen to be closed. Therefore, it follows that if f is continuous on S, then there are points x^*, x_* in S as described above. In the special case where f is linear, we have the relation

$$f\left(\frac{x}{|x|}\right) = \frac{1}{|x|} f(x) \quad \text{for} \quad x \neq \theta;$$

since the norm of the vector $x/|x|$ is 1, it follows that if M and m are the supremum and the infimum of $|f(u)|$ for u in S, then

$$m|x| \leq |f(x)| \leq M|x|,$$

for all x in $\mathbf{R}^p$. We have already seen in Theorem 15.11 that if f is linear on $\mathbf{R}^p$ to $\mathbf{R}^q$, then there exists a positive constant M such that

$$|f(x)| \leq M|x|, \quad x \in \mathbf{R}^p,$$

and this provides an alternative proof. However, it is not always true that there is a *positive* constant m such that

$$m|x| \leq |f(x)|, \quad x \in \mathbf{R}^p.$$

In fact, if m is positive, then $f(x) = \theta$ implies $x = \theta$. We now prove that this necessary condition is also sufficient when f is linear.

16.8 COROLLARY. *If f is a one-one linear function on $\mathbf{R}^p$ to $\mathbf{R}^q$, then there is a positive number m such that $|f(x)| \geq m|x|$ for all x in $\mathbf{R}^p$.*

PROOF. We suppose that the linear function f is one-one. It follows that if $x \neq \theta$, then $f(x) \neq \theta$; otherwise, f maps some $x \neq \theta$ and θ into the zero element of $\mathbf{R}^q$. We assert that $m = \inf \{|f(x)| : |x| = 1\} > 0$. For, if $m = 0$, then by the preceding results there exists an element x_* with $|x_*| = 1$ such that $0 = m = |f(x_*)|$, whence $f(x_*) = \theta$, contrary to hypothesis.

Q.E.D.

We recall that if a function f is one-one, then the inverse function f^{-1} exists and is the function whose domain is the range of f, and which is such that

$$f^{-1}(y) = x \quad \text{if and only if} \quad y = f(x).$$

It is easy to establish that the inverse of a one-one linear function from $\mathbf{R}^p$ into $\mathbf{R}^q$ is also linear (except that its domain may not coincide with

all of R^q). One could modify the argument in Theorem 15.11 to show
that this inverse function is continuous. Such modification is not necessary, however, as the continuity of f^{-1} follows from Corollary 16.8.
For, if y_1, y_2 belong to the domain of f^{-1} (= the range of f), then there
exist unique elements x_1, x_2 in R^p such that $f(x_1) = y_1$ and $f(x_2) = y_2$;
hence $f(x_1 - x_2) = f(x_1) - f(x_2) = y_1 - y_2$. From Corollary 16.8, we
infer that

$$m|x_1 - x_2| \leq |f(x_1 - x_2)| = |y_1 - y_2|.$$

Since $x_1 = f^{-1}(y_1)$ and $x_2 = f^{-1}(y_2)$, then

$$|f^{-1}(y_1) - f^{-1}(y_2)| \leq (1/m)|y_1 - y_2|,$$

from which the continuity of f^{-1} is evident.

We shall now show that the continuity of f^{-1} can also be established
for non-linear functions with a compact domain.

16.9   CONTINUITY OF THE INVERSE FUNCTION.   *Let K be a compact
subset of R^p and let f be a continuous one-one function with domain K and
range $f(K)$ in R^q. Then the inverse function is continuous with domain
$f(K)$ and range K.*

PROOF.   We observe that since K is compact, then Theorem 16.5 on
the preservation of compactness implies that $f(K)$ is compact and hence
closed. Since f is one-one by hypothesis, the inverse function $g = f^{-1}$ is
defined. Let H be any closed set in R^p and consider $H \cap K$; since this
set is bounded and closed [by Theorem 8.6(c)], the Heine-Borel Theorem
assures that $H \cap K$ is a compact subset of R^p. By Theorem 16.5, we
conclude that $H_1 = f(H \cap K)$ is compact and hence closed in R^q. Now
if $g = f^{-1}$, then

$$H_1 = f(H \cap K) = g^{-1}(H).$$

Since H_1 is a subset of $f(K) = \mathfrak{D}(g)$, we can write this last equation as

$$H_1 \cap \mathfrak{D}(g) = g^{-1}(H).$$

From the Global Continuity Theorem 16.1(c), we infer that $g = f^{-1}$
is continuous.

Q.E.D.

Uniform Continuity

If f is defined on a subset $\mathfrak{D}$ of R^p and with range in R^q, then it is
readily seen that the following statements are equivalent:
   (i) f is continuous on $\mathfrak{D}$.

(ii) Given $\epsilon > 0$ and $u \in \mathfrak{D}$, there is a $\delta(\epsilon, u) > 0$ such that if x belongs to $\mathfrak{D}$ and $|x - u| < \delta$, then $|f(x) - f(u)| < \epsilon$.

The thing that is to be noted here is that the δ depends, in general, on both ϵ and u. That δ depends on u is a reflection of the fact that the function f may change its values rapidly in the neighborhood of certain points.

Now it can happen that a function is such that the number δ can be chosen to be independent of the point u in $\mathfrak{D}$ and depending only on ϵ. For example, if $f(x) = 2x$, then

$$|f(x) - f(u)| = 2 |x - u|$$

and so we can choose $\delta(\epsilon, u) = \epsilon/2$ for all values of u.

On the other hand, if $g(x) = 1/x$ for $x > 0$, then

$$g(x) - g(u) = \frac{u - x}{ux}.$$

If $\delta < u$ and $|x - u| \le \delta$, then a little juggling with inequalities shows that

$$|g(x) - g(u)| \le \frac{\delta}{u(u - \delta)}$$

and this inequality cannot be improved, since equality actually holds for $x = u - \delta$. If we want to make $|g(x) - g(u)| \le \epsilon$, then the largest value of δ we can select is

$$\delta(\epsilon, u) = \frac{\epsilon u^2}{1 + \epsilon u}.$$

Thus if $u > 0$, then g is continuous at u because we can select $\delta(\epsilon, u) = \epsilon u^2/(1 + \epsilon u)$, and this is the largest value we can choose. Since

$$\inf \left\{ \frac{\epsilon u^2}{1 + \epsilon u} : u > 0 \right\} = 0,$$

we cannot obtain a positive $\delta(\epsilon, u)$ which is independent of the choice of u for all $u > 0$.

We shall now restrict g to a smaller domain. In fact, let $a > 0$ and define $h(x) = 1/x$ for $x \ge a$. Then the analysis just made shows that we can use the same value of $\delta(\epsilon, u)$. However, this time the domain is smaller and

$$\inf \left\{ \frac{\epsilon u^2}{1 + \epsilon u} : u \ge a \right\} = \frac{\epsilon a^2}{1 + \epsilon a} > 0.$$

Hence if we define $\delta(\epsilon) = \epsilon a^2/(1 + \epsilon a)$, then we can use this number for all points $u \ge a$.

In order to help fix these ideas, the reader should look over Examples 15.5 and determine in which examples the δ was chosen to depend on the point in question and in which ones it was chosen independently of the point.

With these preliminaries we now introduce the formal definition.

16.10 Definition. Let f have domain $\mathfrak{D}$ in $\mathbf{R}^p$ and range in $\mathbf{R}^q$. We say that f is **uniformly continuous** on $\mathfrak{D}$ if for each positive real number ϵ there is a positive number $\delta(\epsilon)$ such that if x and u belong to $\mathfrak{D}$ and $|x - u| < \delta(\epsilon)$, then $|f(x) - f(u)| < \epsilon$.

It is clear that if f is uniformly continuous on $\mathfrak{D}$, then it is continuous at every point of $\mathfrak{D}$. In general, however, the converse does not hold. It is useful to have in mind what is meant by saying that a function is **not** uniformly continuous, so we state such a criterion, leaving its proof to the reader.

16.11 Lemma. *A necessary and sufficient condition that the function f is not uniformly continuous on its domain is that there exist a positive number ϵ_0 and two sequences $X = (x_n)$, $Y = (y_n)$ in $\mathfrak{D}$ such that if $n \in \mathbf{N}$, then $|x_n - y_n| < 1/n$ and $|f(x_n) - f(y_n)| \geq \epsilon_0$.*

As an exercise the reader should apply this criterion to show that $g(x) = 1/x$ is not uniformly continuous on $\mathfrak{D} = \{x : x > 0\}$.

We now present a very useful result which assures that a continuous function with compact domain is automatically uniformly continuous on its domain.

16.12 Uniform Continuity Theorem. *Let f be a continuous function with domain K in $\mathbf{R}^p$ and range in $\mathbf{R}^q$. If K is compact then f is uniformly continuous on K.*

First proof. Suppose that f is not uniformly continuous on K. By Lemma 16.11 there exists $\epsilon_0 > 0$ and two sequences $X = (x_n)$ and $Y = (y_n)$ in K such that if $n \in \mathbf{N}$, then

$$(16.3) \qquad |x_n - y_n| < 1/n, \qquad |f(x_n) - f(y_n)| \geq \epsilon_0.$$

Since K is compact in $\mathbf{R}^p$, the sequence X is bounded; by the Bolzano-Weierstrass Theorem 12.4, there is a subsequence $X' = (x_{n(k)})$ of X which converges to an element z. Since K is closed, the limit z belongs to K and f is continuous at z. It is clear that the corresponding subsequence $Y' = (y_{n(k)})$ of Y also converges to z.

It follows from Theorem 15.2(c) that both sequences $(f(x_{n(k)}))$ and $(f(y_{n(k)}))$ converge to $f(z)$. Therefore, when k is sufficiently great, we have $|f(x_{n(k)}) - f(y_{n(k)})| < \epsilon_0$. But this contradicts the second relation in (16.3).

SECOND PROOF. (A short proof could be based on the Lebesgue Covering Theorem 9.5, but we prefer to use the definition of compactness.) Suppose that f is continuous at every point of the compact set K. According to Theorem 15.2(b), given $\epsilon > 0$ and u in K there is a positive number $\delta(\epsilon/2, u)$ such that if $x \in K$ and $|x - u| < \delta(\epsilon/2, u)$ then $|f(x) - f(u)| < \epsilon/2$. For each u in K, form the open set $G(u) = \{x \in \mathbf{R}^p : |x - u| < (\frac{1}{2}) \delta(\epsilon/2, u)\}$; then the set K is certainly contained in the union of the family $\mathcal{G} = \{G(u) : u \in K\}$ since to each point u in K there is an open set $G(u)$ which contains it. Since K is compact, it is contained in the union of a finite number of sets in the family $\mathcal{G}$, say $G(u_1), \ldots, G(u_N)$. We now define

$$\delta(\epsilon) = (\tfrac{1}{2}) \inf \{\delta(\epsilon/2, u_1), \ldots, \delta(\epsilon/2, u_N)\}$$

and we shall show that $\delta(\epsilon)$ has the desired property. For, suppose that x, u belong to K and that $|x - u| < \delta(\epsilon)$. Then there exists a natural number k with $1 \le k \le N$ such that x belongs to the set $G(u_k)$; that is, $|x - u_k| < (\frac{1}{2})\delta(\epsilon/2, u_k)$. Since $\delta(\epsilon) \le (\frac{1}{2})\delta(\epsilon/2, u_k)$, it follows that

$$|u - u_k| \le |u - x| + |x - u_k| < \delta(\epsilon/2, u_k).$$

Therefore, we have the relations

$$|f(x) - f(u_k)| < \epsilon/2, \qquad |f(u) - f(u_k)| < \epsilon/2,$$

whence it follows that $|f(x) - f(u)| < \epsilon$. We have shown that if x, u are any two points of K for which $|x - u| < \delta(\epsilon)$, then $|f(x) - f(u)| < \epsilon$.
Q.E.D.

In later sections we shall make use of the idea of uniform continuity on many occasions, so we shall not give any applications here. However, we shall introduce here another property which is often available and is sufficient to guarantee uniform continuity.

16.13 DEFINITION. If f has domain $\mathfrak{D}$ contained in $\mathbf{R}^p$ and range in $\mathbf{R}^q$, we say that f satisfies a Lipschitz† condition if there exists a positive constant A such that

(16.4) $$|f(x) - f(u)| \le A |x - u|$$

for all points x, u in $\mathfrak{D}$. In case the inequality (16.4) holds with a constant $A < 1$, the function is called a **contraction**.

It is clear that if relation (16.4) holds, then on setting $\delta(\epsilon) = \epsilon/A$ one can establish the uniform continuity of f on $\mathfrak{D}$. Therefore, if f

---

† RUDOLPH LIPSCHITZ (1832–1903) was a professor at Bonn. He made contributions to algebra, number theory, differential geometry, and analysis.

satisfies a Lipschitz condition, then f is uniformly continuous. The converse, however, is not true as may be seen by considering the function defined for $\mathfrak{D} = \{x \in \mathbf{R} : 0 \leq x \leq 1\}$ by $f(x) = \sqrt{x}$. If (16.4) holds, then setting $u = 0$ one must have $|f(x)| \leq A |x|$ for some constant A, but it is readily seen that the latter inequality cannot hold.

By recalling Theorem 15.11, we can see that a linear function with domain $\mathbf{R}^p$ and range in $\mathbf{R}^q$ satisfies a Lipschitz condition. Moreover, it will be seen in Section 19 that any real function with a bounded derivative also satisfies a Lipschitz condition.

Fixed Point Theorems

If f is a function with domain $\mathfrak{D}$ and range in the same space $\mathbf{R}^p$, then a point u in $\mathfrak{D}$ is said to be a **fixed point** of f in case $f(u) = u$. A number of important results can be proved on the basis of the existence of fixed points of functions so it is of importance to have some affirmative criteria in this direction. The first theorem we give is elementary in character, yet it is often useful and has the important advantage that it provides a construction of the fixed point. For simplicity, we shall first state the result when the domain of the function is the entire space.

16.14.   FIXED POINT THEOREM FOR CONTRACTIONS. *Let f be a contraction with domain $\mathbf{R}^p$ and range contained in $\mathbf{R}^p$. Then f has a unique fixed point.*

PROOF.   We are supposing that there exists a constant C with $0 < C < 1$ such that $|f(x) - f(y)| \leq C |x - y|$ for all x, y in $\mathbf{R}^p$. Let x_1 be an arbitrary point in $\mathbf{R}^p$ and set $x_2 = f(x_1)$; inductively, set

$$(16.5) \qquad x_{n+1} = f(x_n), \qquad n \in \mathbf{N}.$$

We shall show that the sequence (x_n) converges to a unique fixed point u of f and estimate the rapidity of the convergence.

To do this, we observe that

$$|x_3 - x_2| = |f(x_2) - f(x_1)| \leq C |x_2 - x_1|,$$

and, inductively, that

$$(16.6) \quad |x_{n+1} - x_n| = |f(x_n) - f(x_{n-1})| \leq C|x_n - x_{n-1}| \leq C^{n-1} |x_2 - x_1|.$$

If $m \geq n$, then repeated use of (16.6) yields

$$|x_m - x_n| \leq |x_m - x_{m-1}| + |x_{m-1} - x_{m-2}| + \cdots + |x_{n+1} - x_n|$$
$$\leq \{C^{m-2} + C^{m-3} + \cdots + C^{n-1}\} |x_2 - x_1|.$$

Hence it follows that, for $m \geq n$, then

(16.7)
$$|x_m - x_n| \leq \frac{C^{n-1}}{1 - C} |x_2 - x_1|.$$

Since $0 < C < 1$, the sequence (C^{n-1}) converges to zero. Therefore, (x_n) is a Cauchy sequence. If $u = \lim (x_n)$, then it is clear from (16.5) that u is a fixed point of f. From (16.7) and Lemma 11.16, we obtain the estimate

(16.8)
$$|u - x_n| \leq \frac{C^{n-1}}{1 - C} |x_2 - x_1|$$

for the rapidity of the convergence.

Finally, we show that there is only one fixed point for f. In fact, if u, v are two distinct fixed points of f, then

$$|u - v| = |f(u) - f(v)| \leq C |u - v|.$$

Since $u \neq v$, then $|u - v| \neq 0$, so this relation implies that $1 \leq C$, contrary to the hypothesis that $C < 1$.

Q.E.D.

It will be observed that we have actually established the following result.

16.15 COROLLARY. *If f is a contraction with constant $C < 1$, if x_1 is an arbitrary point in $\mathbf{R}^p$, and if the sequence $X = (x_n)$ is defined by equation (16.5), then X converges to the unique fixed point u of f with the rapidity estimated by (16.8).*

In case the function f is not defined on all of $\mathbf{R}^p$, then somewhat more care needs to be exercised to assure that the iterative definition (16.5) of the sequence can be carried out and that the points remain in the domain of f. Although some other formulations are possible, we shall content ourselves with the following one.

16.16 THEOREM. *Suppose that f is a contraction with constant C which is defined for $\mathfrak{D} = \{x \in \mathbf{R}^p : |x| \leq B\}$ and that $|f(\theta)| \leq B(1 - C)$. Then the sequence*

$$x_1 = \theta, x_2 = f(x), \ldots, x_{n+1} = f(x_n), \ldots$$

converges to the unique fixed point of f which lies in the set $\mathfrak{D}$.

PROOF. We shall check only that the sequence (x_n) remains in $\mathfrak{D}$. By hypothesis, $|x_2| = |f(\theta)| \leq B(1 - C) \leq B$ whence $x_2 \in \mathfrak{D}$. Thus $x_3 = f(x_2)$ can be defined and

$$|x_3 - x_2| = |f(x_2) - f(x_1)| \leq C |x_2 - \theta| = C |x_2|.$$

Therefore,

$$|x_3| \leq |x_2| + C\,|x_2| = (1 + C)|x_2| \leq B(1 - C^2).$$

This argument can be continued inductively to prove that $|x_{n+1}| \leq B(1 - C^n)$. Hence the sequence (x_n) lies in the set $\mathfrak{D}$ and the result follows as before.

Q.E.D.

The Contraction Theorem established above has certain advantages: it is constructive, the error of approximation can be estimated, and it guarantees a unique fixed point. However, it has the disadvantage that the requirement that f be a contraction is a very severe restriction. It is a deep and important fact, first proved in 1910 by L. E. J. Brouwer,† that *any* continuous function with domain $\mathfrak{D} = \{x \in \mathbf{R}^p : |x| \leq B\}$ and range contained in $\mathfrak{D}$ must have at least one fixed point.

16.17   BROUWER FIXED POINT THEOREM.   *Let $B > 0$ and let $\mathfrak{D} = \{x \in \mathbf{R}^p : |x| \leq B\}$. Then any continuous function with domain $\mathfrak{D}$ and range contained in $\mathfrak{D}$ has at least one fixed point.*

Since the proof of this result would take us too far afield, we shall not give it. For a proof based on elementary notions only, see the book of Dunford and Schwartz listed in the References. For a more systematic account of fixed point and related theorems, consult the book of Lefschetz.

Exercises

16.A. Interpret the Global Continuity Theorem 16.1 for the real functions $f(x) = x^2$ and $g(x) = 1/x$, $x \neq 0$. Take various open and closed sets and consider their inverse images under f and g.

16.B. Let h be defined on $\mathbf{R}$ by

$$h(x) = 1, \quad 0 \leq x \leq 1,$$
$$= 0, \quad \text{otherwise.}$$

Exhibit an open set G such that $h^{-1}(G)$ is not open, and a closed set F such that $h^{-1}(F)$ is not closed.

16.C. If f is defined and continuous on $\mathbf{R}^p$ to $\mathbf{R}$ and if $f(x_0) > 0$, then is f positive on some neighborhood of the point x_0? Does the same conclusion follow if f is merely continuous at the point x_0?

† L. E. J. BROUWER (1881–   ) is professor at Amsterdam and dean of the Dutch school of mathematics. In addition to his early contributions to topology, he is noted for his work on the foundations of mathematics and logic.

16.D. Let f and g be continuous functions on $\mathbf{R}^p$ to $\mathbf{R}$ and let h, k be defined for x in $\mathbf{R}^p$ by

$$h(x) = \sup \{f(x), g(x)\}, \qquad k(x) = \inf \{f(x), g(x)\}.$$

Show that h and k are continuous on $\mathbf{R}^p$. [Hint: use the relations $\sup \{a, b\} = \frac{1}{2} \{a + b + |a - b|\}$, $\inf \{a, b\} = \frac{1}{2} \{a + b - |a - b|\}$.]

16.E. Let f be continuous on $\mathbf{R}^2$ to $\mathbf{R}^q$. Define the functions g_1, g_2 on $\mathbf{R}$ to $\mathbf{R}^q$ by

$$g_1(t) = f(t, 0), \qquad g_2(t) = f(0, t).$$

Show that g_1 and g_2 are continuous.

16.F. Let f, g_1, g_2 be related by the formulas in the preceding exercise. Show that from the continuity of g_1 and g_2 at $t = 0$ one cannot prove the continuity of f at $(0, 0)$.

16.G. Give an example of a function on $\mathbf{I} = [0, 1]$ to $\mathbf{R}$ which is not bounded.

16.H. Give an example of a bounded function f on $\mathbf{I}$ to $\mathbf{R}$ which does not take on either of the numbers

$$\sup \{f(x) : x \in \mathbf{I}\}, \qquad \inf \{f(x) : x \in \mathbf{I}\}.$$

16.I. Give an example of a bounded and continuous function g on $\mathbf{R}$ to $\mathbf{R}$ which does not take on either of the numbers

$$\sup \{g(x) : x \in \mathbf{R}\}, \qquad \inf \{g(x) : x \in \mathbf{R}\}.$$

16.J. Show that every polynomial of odd degree and real coefficients has a real root. Show that the polynomial $p(x) = x^4 + 7x^3 - 9$ has at least two real roots.

16.K. If $c > 0$ and n is a natural number, there exists a unique positive number b such that $b^n = c$.

16.L. Let f be continuous on $\mathbf{I}$ to $\mathbf{R}$ with $f(0) < 0$ and $f(1) > 0$. If $N = \{x \in \mathbf{I} : f(x) < 0\}$, and if $c = \sup N$, show that $f(c) = 0$.

16.M. Let f be a continuous function on $\mathbf{R}$ to $\mathbf{R}$ which is strictly increasing in the sense that if $x' < x''$ then $f(x') < f(x'')$. Prove that f is one-one and that its inverse function f^{-1} is continuous and strictly increasing.

16.N. Let f be a continuous function on $\mathbf{R}$ to $\mathbf{R}$ which does not take on any of its values twice. Is it true that f must either be strictly increasing or strictly decreasing?

16.O. Let g be a function on $\mathbf{I}$ to $\mathbf{R}$. Prove that if g takes on each of its values exactly twice, then g cannot be continuous at every point of $\mathbf{I}$.

16.P. Let f be continuous on the interval $[0, 2\pi]$ to $\mathbf{R}$ and such that $f(0) = f(2\pi)$. Prove that there exists a point c in this interval such that $f(c) = f(c + \pi)$. (Hint: consider $g(x) = f(x) - f(x + \pi)$.) Conclude that there are, at any time, antipodal points on the equator of the earth which have the same temperature.

16.Q. Consider each of the functions given in Example 15.5 and either show that the function is uniformly continuous or that it is not.

16.R. Give a proof of the Uniform Continuity Theorem 16.12 by using the Lebesgue Covering Theorem 9.5.

16.S. If f is uniformly continuous on a bounded subset B of $\mathbf{R}^p$ and has values in $\mathbf{R}^q$, then must f be bounded on B?

16.T. A function g on $\mathbf{R}$ to $\mathbf{R}^q$ is periodic if there exists a positive number p such that $g(x + p) = g(x)$ for all x in $\mathbf{R}$. Show that a continuous periodic function is bounded and uniformly continuous on all of $\mathbf{R}$.

16.U. Suppose that f is uniformly continuous on $(0, 1)$ to $\mathbf{R}$. Can f be defined at $x = 0$ and $x = 1$ in such a way that it becomes continuous on $[0, 1]$?

16.V. Let $\mathfrak{D} = \{x \in \mathbf{R}^p : |x| < 1\}$. Is it true that a continuous function f on $\mathfrak{D}$ to $\mathbf{R}^q$ can be extended to a continuous function on $\mathfrak{D}_1 = \{x \in \mathbf{R}^p : |x| \leq 1\}$ if and only if f is uniformly continuous on $\mathfrak{D}$?

Projects

16.α. The purpose of this project is to show that many of the theorems of this section hold for continuous functions whose domains and ranges are contained in metric spaces. In establishing these results, we must either observe that earlier definitions apply to metric spaces or can be reformulated to do so.

(a) Show that Theorem 15.2 can be reformulated for a function from one metric space to another.

(b) Show that the Global Continuity Theorem 16.1 holds without change.

(c) Prove that the Preservation of Connectedness Theorem 16.3 holds.

(d) Show that the Preservation of Compactness Theorem 16.5 holds.

(e) Show that the Uniform Continuity Theorem 16.12 can be reformulated.

16.β. Let g be a function on $\mathbf{R}$ to $\mathbf{R}$ which is not identically zero and which satisfies the functional equation

$$g(x + y) = g(x)g(y) \quad \text{for} \quad x, y \in \mathbf{R}.$$

The purpose of this project is to show that g must be an exponential function.

(a) Show that g is continuous at every point of $\mathbf{R}$ if and only if it is continuous at one point of $\mathbf{R}$.

(b) Show that g does not vanish at any point.

(c) Prove that $g(0) = 1$. If $a = g(1)$, then $a > 0$ and $g(r) = a^r$ for $r \in \mathbf{Q}$.

(d) If $g(x) > 1$, $0 < x < \delta$, for some positive δ, then g is positive on all of $\mathbf{R}$. In this case, g is strictly increasing and continuous on $\mathbf{R}$.

(e) If g is continuous on $\mathbf{R}$, then g is positive on all of $\mathbf{R}$.

(f) Show that there exists at most one continuous function satisfying this functional equation and such that $g(1) = a$ for $a > 0$.

(g) Referring to Project 6.β, show that there exists a unique continuous function satisfying this functional equation and such that $g(1) = a$ for $a > 0$.

16.γ. Let h be a function on $P = \{x \in \mathbf{R} : x > 0\}$ to $\mathbf{R}$ which is not identically zero and which satisfies the functional equation

$$h(xy) = h(x) + h(y) \quad \text{for} \quad x, y \in P.$$

The purpose of this project is to show that h must be a logarithmic function.

(a) Show that h is continuous at every point of P if and only if it is continuous at one point of P.

(b) Show that h cannot be defined at $x = 0$ to satisfy this functional equation for $\{x \in \mathbf{R} : x \geq 0\}$.

(c) Prove that $h(1) = 0$. If $x > 0$ and $r \in \mathbf{Q}$, then $h(x^r) = r\, h(x)$.

(d) Show that, if h is positive on some interval in $\{x \in \mathbf{R} : x \geq 1\}$, then h is strictly increasing and continuous on P.

(e) If h is continuous on P, then h is positive for $x > 1$.

(f) Show that there exists at most one continuous function satisfying this functional equation and such that $h(b) = 1$ for $b > 1$.

(g) Referring to Project 6.γ, show that there exists a unique continuous function satisfying this functional equation and such that $h(b) = 1$ for $b > 1$.

Section 17   Sequences of Continuous Functions

There are many occasions when it is not enough to consider one or two continuous functions, but it is necessary to consider a *sequence* of continuous functions. In this section we shall present several interesting and important results along this line. The most important one is Theorem 17.1, which will be used often in the following and is a key result. The remaining theorems in this section will not be used in this text, but the reader should be familiar with the statement of these results, at least.

In this section the importance of uniform convergence should become clearer. We recall that a sequence (f_n) of functions on a subset $\mathfrak{D}$ of $\mathbf{R}^p$ to $\mathbf{R}^q$ is said to converge uniformly on $\mathfrak{D}$ to f if for every $\epsilon > 0$ there is an $N(\epsilon)$ such that if $n \geq N(\epsilon)$ and $x \in \mathfrak{D}$, then $|f_n(x) - f(x)| < \epsilon$.

Interchange of Limit and Continuity

We observe that the limit of a sequence of continuous functions may not be continuous. It is very easy to see this; in fact, for each natural number n, let f_n be defined on the unit interval $\mathbf{I} = [0, 1]$ to $\mathbf{R}$ by

$$f_n(x) = x^n, \quad x \in \mathbf{I}.$$

We have already seen, in Example 13.2(b), that the sequence (f_n) converges on $\mathbf{I}$ to the function f, defined by

$$f(x) = 0, \quad 0 \leq x < 1,$$
$$= 1, \quad x = 1.$$

Thus despite the simple character of the continuous functions f_n, the limit function f is not continuous at the point $x = 1$.

Although the extent of discontinuity of the limit function in the example just given is not very great, it should be evident that more complicated examples can be constructed which will produce more extensive discontinuity. It would be interesting to investigate exactly how discontinuous the limit of a sequence of continuous functions can be, but this investigation would take us too far afield. Furthermore, for most applications it is more important to find additional conditions which will guarantee that the limit function is continuous.

We shall now establish the important fact that uniform convergence of a sequence of continuous functions is sufficient to guarantee the continuity of the limit function.

17.1 THEOREM. *Let $F = (f_n)$ be a sequence of continuous functions with domain $\mathfrak{D}$ in $\mathbf{R}^p$ and range in $\mathbf{R}^q$ and let this sequence converge uniformly on $\mathfrak{D}$ to a function f. Then f is continuous on $\mathfrak{D}$.*

PROOF. Since (f_n) converges uniformly on $\mathfrak{D}$ to f, given $\epsilon > 0$ there is a natural number $N = N(\epsilon/3)$ such that $|f_N(x) - f(x)| < \epsilon/3$ for all x in $\mathfrak{D}$. To show that f is continuous at a point a in $\mathfrak{D}$, we note that

$$(17.1) \quad |f(x) - f(a)| \leq |f(x) - f_N(x)| + |f_N(x) - f_N(a)|$$
$$+ |f_N(a) - f(a)| \leq \epsilon/3 + |f_N(x) - f_N(a)| + \epsilon/3.$$

Since f_N is continuous, there exists a positive number, $\delta = \delta(\epsilon/3, a, f_N)$ such that if $|x - a| < \delta$ and $x \in \mathfrak{D}$, then $|f_N(x) - f_N(a)| < \epsilon/3$. (See Figure 17.1.) Therefore, for such x we have $|f(x) - f(a)| < \epsilon$. This establishes the continuity of the limit function f at the arbitrary point a in $\mathfrak{D}$.

Q.E.D.

We remark that, although the uniform convergence of the sequence of continuous functions is sufficient for the continuity of the limit function, it is *not* necessary. Thus if (f_n) is a sequence of continuous functions

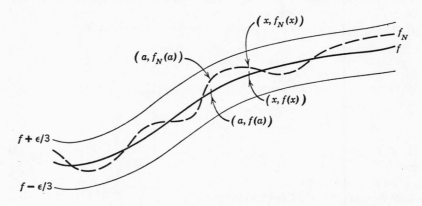

Figure 17.1

which converges to a continuous function f, then it does *not* follow that the convergence is uniform (see Exercise 17.A).

Approximation Theorems

For many applications it is convenient to "approximate" continuous functions by functions of an elementary nature. Although there are several reasonable definitions that one can use to make the word "approximate" more precise, one of the most natural as well as one of the most important is to require that at every point of the given domain the approximating function shall not differ from the given function by more than the preassigned error. This sense is sometimes referred to as "uniform approximation" and it is intimately connected with uniform convergence. We suppose that f is a given function with domain $\mathfrak{D}$ contained in $\mathbf{R}^p$ and range in $\mathbf{R}^q$. We say that a function g **approximates** f **uniformly** on $\mathfrak{D}$ to within $\epsilon > 0$, if

$$|g(x) - f(x)| \leq \epsilon \quad \text{for all} \quad x \in \mathfrak{D};$$

or, what amounts to the same thing, if

$$\|g - f\|_{\mathfrak{D}} = \sup \{|g(x) - f(x)| : x \in \mathfrak{D}\} \leq \epsilon.$$

Here we have used the $\mathfrak{D}$-norm which was introduced in Definition 13.7. We say that the function f can be **uniformly approximated** on $\mathfrak{D}$ by functions in a class $\mathcal{G}$ if, for each positive number ϵ there is a function g_ϵ in $\mathcal{G}$ such that $\|g_\epsilon - f\|_{\mathfrak{D}} < \epsilon$; or, equivalently, if there exists a sequence of functions in $\mathcal{G}$ which converges uniformly on $\mathfrak{D}$ to f.

17.2 DEFINITION. A function g with domain $\mathbf{R}^p$ and range in $\mathbf{R}^q$ is called a **step function** if it assumes only a finite number of distinct values in $\mathbf{R}^q$, each non-zero value being taken on an interval in $\mathbf{R}^p$.

For example, if $p = q = 1$, then the function g defined explicitly by

$$\begin{aligned}
g(x) &= 0, & x &\leq -2 \\
&= 1, & -2 &< x \leq 0, \\
&= 3, & 0 &< x < 1, \\
&= -5, & 1 &\leq x \leq 3, \\
&= 0, & x &> 3
\end{aligned}$$

is a step function. (See Figure 17.2 on the next page.)

We now show that a continuous function whose domain is a compact interval can be uniformly approximated by step functions.

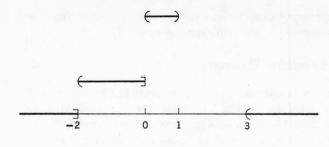

Figure 17.2.   A step function.

17.3 THEOREM. *Let f be a continuous function whose domain $\mathfrak{D}$ is a compact interval in $\mathbf{R}^p$ and whose values belong to $\mathbf{R}^q$. Then f can be uniformly approximated on $\mathfrak{D}$ by step functions.*

PROOF. Let $\epsilon > 0$ be given; since f is uniformly continuous (Theorem 16.12), there is a number $\delta(\epsilon) > 0$ such that if x, y belong to $\mathfrak{D}$ and $|x - y| < \delta(\epsilon)$, then $|f(x) - f(y)| < \epsilon$. Divide the domain $\mathfrak{D}$ of f into disjoint intervals $I_1, \ldots, I_n$ such that if x, y belong to I_k, then $|x - y| < \delta(\epsilon)$. Let x_k be any point belonging to the interval I_k, $k = 1, \ldots, n$ and define $g_\epsilon(x) = f(x_k)$ for $x \in I_k$ and $g_\epsilon(x) = 0$ for $x \notin \mathfrak{D}$. Then it is clear that $|g_\epsilon(x) - f(x)| < \epsilon$ for $x \in \mathfrak{D}$ so that g_ϵ approximates f uniformly on $\mathfrak{D}$ to within ϵ. (See Figure 17.3.)

Q.E.D.

It is natural to expect that a continuous function can be uniformly approximated by simple functions which are also continuous (as the step functions are not). For simplicity, we shall establish the next result only in the case where $p = q = 1$ although there evidently is a generalization for higher dimensions.

We say that a function g defined on a compact interval $J = [a, b]$ of $\mathbf{R}$ with values in $\mathbf{R}$ is **piecewise linear** if there are a finite number of points c_k with $a = c_0 < c_1 < c_2 < \cdots < c_n = b$ and corresponding real

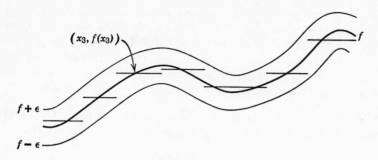

Figure 17.3.   Approximation by a step function.

numbers A_k, B_k, $k = 0, 1, \ldots, n$, such that when x satisfies the relation $c_k < x < c_{k+1}$, the function g has the form

$$g(x) = A_k x + B_k, \qquad k = 0, 1, \ldots, n.$$

If g is continuous on J, then the constants A_k, B_k must satisfy certain relations, of course.

17.4   THEOREM.   *Let f be a continuous function whose domain is a compact interval J in $\mathbf{R}$. Then f can be uniformly approximated on J by continuous piecewise linear functions.*

PROOF.   As before, f is uniformly continuous on the compact set J. Therefore, given $\epsilon > 0$, we divide $J = [a, b]$ into subintervals by adding intermediate points c_k, $k = 0, 1, \ldots, n$, with $a = c_0 < c_1 < c_2 < \cdots < c_n = b$ so that $c_k - c_{k-1} < \delta(\epsilon)$. Connect the points $(c_k, f(c_k))$ by line segments, and define the resulting continuous piecewise linear function g_ϵ. It is clear that g_ϵ approximates f uniformly on J within ϵ. (See Figure 17.4.)

Q.E.D.

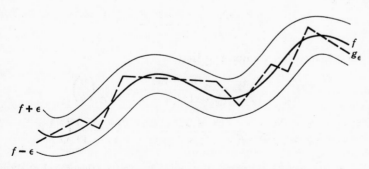

Figure 17.4.   Approximation by a piecewise linear function.

We shall now prove a deeper, more useful, and more interesting result concerning the approximation by polynomials. First, we prove the Weierstrass Approximation Theorem for $p = q = 1$, by using the polynomials of S. Bernstein.[†] Next, we shall establish the R^p case of M. H. Stone's generalization of the Weierstrass Theorem. We shall then be able to obtain easily the general case of polynomial approximation.

17.5 DEFINITION. Let f be a function with domain $I = [0, 1]$ and range in R. The nth Bernstein polynomial for f is defined to be

$$(17.2) \qquad B_n(x) = B_n(x; f) = \sum_{k=0}^{n} f\left(\frac{k}{n}\right)\binom{n}{k} x^k(1 - x)^{n-k}.$$

These Bernstein polynomials are not as terrifying as they look at first glance. A reader with some experience with probability should see the Binomial Distribution lurking in the background. Even without such experience, the reader should note that the value $B_n(x; f)$ of the polynomial at the point x is calculated from the values $f(0), f(1/n),$ $f(2/n), \ldots, f(1)$, with certain non-negative weight factors $\varphi_k(x) = \binom{n}{k} x^k(1 - x)^{n-k}$ which may be seen to be very small for those values of k for which k/n is far from x. In fact, the function φ_k is non-negative on I and takes its maximum value at the point k/n. Moreover, as we shall see below, the sum of all the $\varphi_k(x)$, $k = 0, 1, \ldots, n$, is 1 for each x in I.

We recall that the Binomial Theorem asserts that

$$(17.3) \qquad (s + t)^n = \sum_{k=0}^{n} \binom{n}{k} s^k t^{n-k},$$

where $\binom{n}{k}$ denotes the binomial coefficient

$$\binom{n}{k} = \frac{n!}{k!(n - k)!}.$$

By direct inspection we observe that

$$(17.4) \qquad \binom{n-1}{k-1} = \frac{(n-1)!}{(k-1)!(n-k)!} = \frac{k}{n}\binom{n}{k},$$

$$(17.5) \qquad \binom{n-2}{k-2} = \frac{(n-2)!}{(k-2)!(n-k)!} = \frac{k(k-1)}{n(n-1)}\binom{n}{k}.$$

---

† SERGE N. BERNSTEIN (1880–   ), dean of Russian mathematical analysis, has made profound contributions to analysis, approximation theory, and probability.

Now let $s = x$ and $t = 1 - x$ in (17.3), to obtain

(17.6) $$1 = \sum_{k=0}^{n} \binom{n}{k} x^k (1 - x)^{n-k}.$$

Writing (17.6) with n replaced by $n - 1$ and k by j, we have

$$1 = \sum_{j=0}^{n-1} \binom{n-1}{j} x^j (1 - x)^{n-1-j}.$$

Multiply this last relation by x and apply the identity (17.4) to obtain

$$x = \sum_{j=0}^{n-1} \frac{j+1}{n} \binom{n}{j+1} x^{j+1} (1 - x)^{n-(j+1)}.$$

Now let $k = j + 1$, whence

$$x = \sum_{k=1}^{n} \frac{k}{n} \binom{n}{k} x^k (1 - x)^{n-k}.$$

We also note that the term corresponding to $k = 0$ can be included, since it vanishes. Hence we have

(17.7) $$x = \sum_{k=0}^{n} \frac{k}{n} \binom{n}{k} x^k (1 - x)^{n-k}.$$

A similar calculation, based on (17.6) with n replaced by $n - 2$ and identity (17.5), shows that

$$(n^2 - n)x^2 = \sum_{k=0}^{n} (k^2 - k) \binom{n}{k} x^k (1 - x)^{n-k}.$$

Therefore we conclude that

(17.8) $$\left(1 - \frac{1}{n}\right) x^2 + \frac{1}{n} x = \sum_{k=0}^{n} \left(\frac{k}{n}\right)^2 \binom{n}{k} x^k (1 - x)^{n-k}.$$

Multiplying (17.6) by x^2, (17.7) by $-2x$, and adding them to (17.8), we obtain

(17.9) $$(1/n)x(1 - x) = \sum_{k=0}^{n} (x - k/n)^2 \binom{n}{k} x^k (1 - x)^{n-k},$$

which is an estimate that will be needed below.

Examining Definition 17.5, formula (17.6) says that the nth Bernstein polynomial for the constant function $f_0(x) = 1$ coincides with f_0. Formula (17.7) says the same thing for the function $f_1(x) = x$. Formula (17.8) asserts that the nth Bernstein polynomial for the function $f_2(x) = x^2$ is

$$B_n(x; f_2) = (1 - 1/n)x^2 + (1/n)x,$$

which converges uniformly on I to f_2. We shall now prove that if f is any continuous function on I to R, then the sequence of Bernstein polynomials has the property that it converges uniformly on I to f. This will give us a constructive proof of the Weierstrass Approximation Theorem. In the process of proving this theorem we shall need formula (17.9).

17.6 Bernstein Approximation Theorem. *Let f be continuous on I with values in R. Then the sequence of Bernstein polynomials for f, defined in equation (17.2), converges uniformly on I to f.*

PROOF.   On multiplying formula (17.6) by $f(x)$, we get

$$f(x) = \sum_{k=0}^{n} f(x) \binom{n}{k} x^k (1 - x)^{n-k}.$$

Therefore, we obtain the relation

$$f(x) - B_n(x) = \sum_{k=0}^{n} \{f(x) - f(k/n)\} \binom{n}{k} x^k (1 - x)^{n-k}$$

from which it follows that

$$(17.10) \quad |f(x) - B_n(x)| \leq \sum_{k=0}^{n} |f(x) - f(k/n)| \binom{n}{k} x^k (1 - x)^{n-k}.$$

Now f is bounded, say by M, and also uniformly continuous. Note that if k is such that k/n is near x, then the corresponding term in the sum (17.10) is small because of the continuity of f at x; on the other hand, if k/n is far from x, the factor involving f can only be said to be less than $2M$ and any smallness must arise from the other factors. We are led, therefore, to break (17.10) into two parts: those values of k where $x - k/n$ is small and those for which $x - k/n$ is large.

Let $\epsilon > 0$ and let $\delta(\epsilon)$ be as in the definition of uniform continuity for f. It turns out to be convenient to choose n so large that

$$(17.11) \quad\quad\quad n \geq \sup \{ (\delta(\epsilon))^{-4}, M^2/\epsilon^2 \},$$

and break (17.10) into two sums. The sum taken over those k for which $|x - k/n| < n^{-1/4} \leq \delta(\epsilon)$ yields the estimate

$$\sum_{k} \epsilon \binom{n}{k} x^k (1 - x)^{n-k} \leq \epsilon \sum_{k=1}^{n} \binom{n}{k} x^k (1 - x)^{n-k} = \epsilon.$$

The sum taken over those k for which $|x - k/n| \geq n^{-1/4}$, that is, $(x - k/m)^2 \geq n^{-1/2}$, can be estimated by using formula (17.9). For this part of the sum in (17.10) we obtain the upper bound

$$\sum_k 2M \binom{n}{k} x^k (1 - x)^{n-k}$$

$$= 2M \sum_k \frac{(x - k/n)^2}{(x - k/n)^2} \binom{n}{k} x^k (1 - x)^{n-k}$$

$$\leq 2M \sqrt{n} \sum_{k=1}^{n} (x - k/n)^2 \binom{n}{k} x^k (1 - x)^{n-k}$$

$$\leq 2M \sqrt{n} \left\{ \frac{1}{n} x(1 - x) \right\} \leq \frac{M}{2 \sqrt{n}},$$

since $x(1 - x) \leq \frac{1}{4}$ on the interval I. Recalling the determination (17.11) for n, we conclude that each of these two parts of (17.10) is bounded above by ϵ. Hence, for n chosen in (17.11) we have

$$|f(x) - B_n(x)| < 2\epsilon,$$

independently of the value of x. This shows that the sequence (B_n) converges uniformly on I to f.

Q.E.D.

As a direct corollary of the theorem of Bernstein, we have the following important result.

17.7 WEIERSTRASS APPROXIMATION THEOREM. *Let f be a continuous function on a compact interval of $\mathbf{R}$ and with values in $\mathbf{R}$. Then f can be uniformly approximated by polynomials.*

PROOF. If f is defined on $[a, b]$, then the function g defined on $\mathbf{I} = [0, 1]$ by

$$g(t) = f((b - a)t + a), \qquad t \in \mathbf{I},$$

is continuous. Hence g can be uniformly approximated by Bernstein polynomials and a simple change of variable yields a polynomial approximation to f.

Q.E.D.

We have chosen to go through the details of the Bernstein Theorem 17.6 because it gives a constructive method of finding a sequence of polynomials which converges uniformly on I to the given continuous function. Also, by using the relation (17.11), the rapidity of the convergence can be estimated. In addition, the method of proof of Theorem 17.6 is characteristic of many analytic arguments and it is important to develop an understanding of such arguments. Finally, although we shall establish more general approximation results, in order to do so we shall need to know that the absolute value function can be uniformly approximated on a compact interval by polynomials. Although it would be possible to establish this special case without the Bernstein polynomials, the required argument is not so simple as to overbalance the considerations just mentioned for including Theorem 17.6.

To facilitate the statement of the next theorem, we introduce the following terminology. If f and g are functions with domain $\mathfrak{D}$ in $\mathbf{R}^p$ and with values in $\mathbf{R}$, then the functions h and k defined for x in $\mathfrak{D}$ by

$$h(x) = \sup \{f(x), g(x)\}, \qquad k(x) = \inf \{f(x), g(x)\},$$

are called the **supremum** and **infimum**, respectively, of the functions f and g. If f and g are continuous on $\mathfrak{D}$, then both h and k are also continuous. This follows from Theorem 15.7 and the observation that if a, b are real numbers, then

$$\sup \{a, b\} = (\tfrac{1}{2})\{a + b + |a - b|\},$$
$$\inf \{a, b\} = (\tfrac{1}{2})\{a + b - |a - b|\}.$$

We now state one form of Stone's† generalization of the Weierstrass Approximation Theorem. This result is the most recent theorem that appears in this text, having been first proved in 1937 in somewhat different form and given in this form in 1948. Despite its recent discovery it has already become "classical" and should be a part of the background of every student of mathematics. The reader should refer to the article by Stone listed in the References for extensions, applications, and a much fuller discussion than is presented here.

17.8 STONE APPROXIMATION THEOREM. *Let K be a compact subset of $\mathbf{R}^p$ and let $\mathfrak{L}$ be a collection of continuous functions on K to $\mathbf{R}$ with the properties:*

(a) *If f, g belong to $\mathfrak{L}$, then $\sup \{f, g\}$ and $\inf \{f, g\}$ belong to $\mathfrak{L}$.*

(b) *If $a, b \in \mathbf{R}$ and $x \neq y \in K$, then there exists a function f in $\mathfrak{L}$ such that $f(x) = a, f(y) = b$.*

Then any continuous function on K to $\mathbf{R}$ can be uniformly approximated on K by functions in $\mathfrak{L}$.

PROOF. Let F be a continuous function on K to $\mathbf{R}$. If x, y belong to K, let $g_{xy} \in \mathfrak{L}$ be such that $g_{xy}(x) = F(x)$ and $g_{xy}(y) = F(y)$. Since the functions F, g_{xy} are continuous and have the same value at y; given $\epsilon > 0$, there is an open neighborhood $U(y)$ of y such that if z belongs to $K \cap U(y)$, then

$$(17.12) \qquad\qquad g_{xy}(z) > F(z) - \epsilon.$$

---

† MARSHALL H. STONE (1903–   ) studied at Harvard and is a professor at Chicago. The son of a chief justice, he has made basic contributions to modern analysis, especially to the theories of Hilbert space and Boolean algebras.

Hold x fixed and for each $y \in K$, select an open neighborhood $U(y)$ with this property. From the compactness of K, it follows that K is contained in a finite number of such neighborhoods: $U(y_1), \ldots, U(y_n)$. If $h_x = \sup\{g_{xy_1}, \ldots, g_{xy_n}\}$, then it follows from relation (17.12) that

(17.13) $h_x(z) > F(z) - \epsilon$ for $z \in K$.

Since $g_{xy_j}(x) = F(x)$, it is seen that $h_x(x) = F(x)$ and hence there is an open neighborhood $V(x)$ of x such that if z belongs to $K \cap V(x)$, then

(17.14) $h_x(z) < F(z) + \epsilon$.

Use the compactness of K once more to obtain a finite number of neighborhoods $V(x_1), \ldots, V(x_m)$ and set $h = \inf\{h_{x_1}, \ldots, h_{x_m}\}$. Then h belongs to $\mathcal{L}$ and it follows from (17.13) that

$$h(z) > F(z) - \epsilon \quad \text{for} \quad z \in K$$

and from (17.14) that

$$h(z) < F(z) + \epsilon \quad \text{for} \quad z \in K.$$

Combining these results, we have $|h(z) - F(z)| < \epsilon$, $z \in K$, which yields the desired approximation.

Q.E.D.

The reader will have observed that the preceding result made no use of the Weierstrass Approximation Theorem. In the next result, we replace condition (a) above by three algebraic conditions on the set of functions. Here we make use of the classical Weierstrass Theorem 17.7 for the special case of the absolute value function φ defined for t in R by $\varphi(t) = |t|$, to conclude that φ can be approximated by polynomials on every compact set of real numbers.

17.9 STONE-WEIERSTRASS THEOREM. *Let K be a compact subset of $\mathbf{R}^p$ and let $\mathcal{A}$ be a collection of continuous functions on K to R with the properties:*

(a) *The constant function $e(x) = 1$, $x \in K$, belongs to $\mathcal{A}$.*

(b) *If f, g belong to $\mathcal{A}$, then $\alpha f + \beta g$ belongs to $\mathcal{A}$.*

(c) *If f, g belong to $\mathcal{A}$, then fg belong to $\mathcal{A}$.*

(d) *If $x \neq y$ are two points of K, there exists a function f in $\mathcal{A}$ such that $f(x) \neq f(y)$.*

Then any continuous function on K to R can be uniformly approximated on K by functions in $\mathcal{A}$.

PROOF. Let $a, b \in \mathbf{R}$ and $x \neq y$ belong to K. According to (d), there is a function f in $\mathcal{A}$ such that $f(x) \neq f(y)$. Since $e(x) = 1 = e(y)$, it follows that there are real numbers α, β such that

$$\alpha f(x) + \beta e(x) = a, \qquad \alpha f(y) + \beta e(y) = b.$$

Therefore, by (b) there exists a function g in α such that $g(x) = a$ and $g(y) = b$.

Now let f be a continuous function on K to $\mathbf{R}$. It follows that f is bounded on K and we suppose that $|f(x)| \leq M$ for $x \in K$. By the Weierstrass Approximation Theorem 17.7 applied to the absolute value function $\varphi(t) = |t|$ on the interval $|t| \leq M$, we conclude that given $\epsilon > 0$ there is a polynomial p such that

$$||t| - p(t)| < \epsilon \quad \text{for} \quad |t| \leq M.$$

Therefore, we infer that

$$||f(x)| - p[f(x)]| < \epsilon \quad \text{for} \quad x \in K.$$

If f belongs to α, then by (b) and (c), the function $p \circ f$ also belongs to α and the remark just made shows that we can approximate the function $|f|$ by functions in α. Since

$$\sup \{f, g\} = \tfrac{1}{2}\{f + g + |f - g|\},$$
$$\inf \{f, g\} = \tfrac{1}{2}\{f + g - |f - g|\},$$

any function that can be uniformly approximated by linear combinations, suprema and infima of functions in α can also be uniformly approximated by polynomials of functions in α. Therefore, it follows from the preceding theorem that any continuous function on K can be uniformly approximated by functions in α.

Q.E.D.

We now obtain, as a special case of the Stone-Weierstrass Theorem, a strong form of Theorem 17.7. This result strengthens the latter result in two ways: (i) it permits the domain to be an arbitrary compact subset of $\mathbf{R}^p$ and not just a compact interval in $\mathbf{R}$, and (ii) it permits the range to lie in any space $\mathbf{R}^q$, and not just $\mathbf{R}$. To understand the statement, we recall that a function f with domain $\mathfrak{D}$ in $\mathbf{R}^p$ and range in $\mathbf{R}^q$ can be regarded as q functions on $\mathfrak{D}$ to $\mathbf{R}$ by the coordinate representation:

$$(17.15) \qquad f(x) = (f_1(x), \ldots, f_q(x)) \quad \text{for} \quad x \in \mathfrak{D}.$$

If each coordinate function f_j is a polynomial in the p coordinates $(\xi_1, \ldots, \xi_p)$, then we say that f is a *polynomial function*.

17.10   POLYNOMIAL APPROXIMATION THEOREM.   *Let f be a continuous function whose domain K is a compact subset of $\mathbf{R}^p$ and whose range belongs to $\mathbf{R}^q$ and let ϵ be a positive real number. Then there exists a polynomial function p on $\mathbf{R}^p$ to $\mathbf{R}^q$ such that*

$$|f(x) - p(x)| < \epsilon \quad \text{for} \quad x \in K.$$

PROOF.   Represent f by its q coordinate functions, as in (17.15). Since f is continuous on K, each of the coordinate functions f_j is continuous on K to R. The polynomial functions defined on $\mathbf{R}^p$ to R evidently satisfy the properties of the Stone-Weierstrass Theorem. Hence the coordinate function f_j can be uniformly approximated on K within $\epsilon/\sqrt{q}$ by a polynomial function p_j. Letting p be defined by

$$p(x) = (p_1(x), \ldots, p_q(x)),$$

we obtain a polynomial function from $\mathbf{R}^p$ to $\mathbf{R}^q$ which yields the desired approximation on K to the given function f.

Q.E.D.

Extension of Continuous Functions

Sometimes it is desirable to extend the domain of a continuous function to a larger set without changing the values on the original domain. This can always be done in a trivial way by defining the function to be 0 outside the original domain, but in general this method of extension does not yield a continuous function. After some reflection, the reader should see that it is not always possible to obtain a continuous extension. For example, if $\mathfrak{D} = \{x \in \mathbf{R} : x \neq 0\}$ and if f is defined for $x \in \mathfrak{D}$ to be $f(x) = 1/x$, then it is not possible to extend f in such a way as to obtain a continuous function on all of R. However, it is important to know that an extension is always possible when the domain is a closed set. Furthermore, it is not necessary to increase the bound of the function.

Before we prove this extension theorem, we observe that if A and B are two disjoint closed subsets of $\mathbf{R}^p$, then there exists a continuous function φ defined on $\mathbf{R}^p$ with values in R such that

$$\varphi(x) = 0, x \in A; \qquad \varphi(x) = 1, x \in B; \qquad 0 \leq \varphi(x) \leq 1, x \in \mathbf{R}^p.$$

In fact, if $d(x, A) = \inf \{|x - y| : y \in A\}$ and $d(x, B) = \inf \{|x - y| : y \in B\}$, then we can define φ for $x \in \mathbf{R}^p$ by the equation

$$\varphi(x) = \frac{d(x, A)}{d(x, A) + d(x, B)}.$$

17.11   TIETZE† EXTENSION THEOREM.   *Let f be a bounded continuous function defined on a closed subset $\mathfrak{D}$ of $\mathbf{R}^p$ and with values in R. Then there exists a continuous function g on $\mathbf{R}^p$ to R such that $g(x) = f(x)$ for x in $\mathfrak{D}$ and such that $\sup \{|g(x)| : x \in \mathbf{R}^p\} = \sup \{|f(x)| : x \in \mathfrak{D}\}$.*

---

† HEINRICH TIETZE (1880–1964), professor at Munich, has contributed to topology, geometry, and algebra. This extension theorem goes back to 1914.

PROOF. Let $M = \sup\{|f(x)|:x \in \mathfrak{D}\}$ and consider $A_1 = \{x \in \mathfrak{D}: f(x) \le M/3\}$ and $B_1 = \{x \in \mathfrak{D}:f(x) \ge M/3\}$. From the continuity of f and the fact that $\mathfrak{D}$ is closed, it follows from Theorem 16.1(c) that A_1 and B_1 are closed subsets of $\mathbf{R}^p$. According to the observation preceding the statement of the theorem, there is a continuous function φ_1 on $\mathbf{R}^p$ to R such that

$$\varphi_1(x) = -M/3, \, x \in A_1; \qquad \varphi_1(x) = M/3, \, x \in B_1;$$
$$-M/3 \le \varphi_1(x) \le M/3, \, x \in \mathbf{R}^p.$$

We now set $f_2 = f - \varphi_1$ and note that f_2 is continuous on $\mathfrak{D}$ and that $\sup\{|f_2(x)|:x \in \mathfrak{D}\} \le \frac{2}{3}M$.

Proceeding, we define $A_2 = \{x \in \mathfrak{D} : f_2(x) \le -(\frac{1}{3})(\frac{2}{3})M\}$ and $B_2 = \{x \in \mathfrak{D}:f_2(x) \ge (\frac{1}{3})(\frac{2}{3})M\}$ and obtain a continuous function φ_2 on $\mathbf{R}^p$ to R such that

$$\varphi_2(x) = -(\tfrac{1}{3})(\tfrac{2}{3})M, \, x \in A_2; \qquad \varphi_2(x) = (\tfrac{1}{3})(\tfrac{2}{3})M, \, x \in B_2;$$
$$-(\tfrac{1}{3})(\tfrac{2}{3})M \le \varphi_2(x) \le (\tfrac{1}{3})(\tfrac{2}{3})M, \, x \in \mathbf{R}^p.$$

Having done this, we set $f_3 = f_2 - \varphi_2$ and note that $f_3 = f - \varphi_1 - \varphi_2$ is continuous on $\mathfrak{D}$ and that $\sup\{|f_3(x)|:x \in \mathfrak{D}\} \le (\frac{2}{3})^2M$.

By proceeding in this manner, we obtain a sequence (φ_n) of functions defined on $\mathbf{R}^p$ to R such that, for each n,

(17.15) $$|f(x) - [\varphi_1(x) + \varphi_2(x) + \cdots + \varphi_n(x)]| \le (\tfrac{2}{3})^n M,$$

for all x in $\mathfrak{D}$ and such that

(17.16) $$|\varphi_n(x)| \le (\tfrac{1}{3})(\tfrac{2}{3})^{n-1}M \quad \text{for} \quad x \in \mathbf{R}^p.$$

Let g_n be defined on $\mathbf{R}^p$ to R by the equation

$$g_n = \varphi_1 + \varphi_2 + \cdots + \varphi_n,$$

whence it follows that g_n is continuous. From inequality (17.16) we infer that if $m \ge n$ and $x \in \mathbf{R}^p$, then

$$|g_m(x) - g_n(x)| = |\varphi_{n+1}(x) + \cdots + \varphi_m(x)|$$
$$\le (\tfrac{1}{3})(\tfrac{2}{3})^n M[1 + \tfrac{2}{3} + (\tfrac{2}{3})^2 + \cdots] \le (\tfrac{2}{3})^n M,$$

which proves that the sequence (g_n) converges uniformly on $\mathbf{R}^p$ to a function we shall denote by g. Since each g_n is continuous on $\mathbf{R}^p$, then Theorem 17.1 implies that g is continuous at every point of $\mathbf{R}^p$. Also, it is seen from the inequality (17.15) that

$$|f(x) - g_n(x)| \le (\tfrac{2}{3})^n M \quad \text{for} \quad x \in \mathfrak{D}.$$

We conclude, therefore, that $f(x) = g(x)$ for x in $\mathfrak{D}$. Finally, inequality (17.16) implies that for any x in $\mathbf{R}^p$ we have

$$|g_n(x)| \leq (\tfrac{1}{3})M[1 + \tfrac{2}{3} + \cdots + (\tfrac{2}{3})^{n-1}] \leq M,$$

which establishes the final statement of the theorem.

Q.E.D.

17.12   COROLLARY.   *Let f be a bounded continuous function defined on a closed subset $\mathfrak{D}$ of $\mathbf{R}^p$ and with values in $\mathbf{R}^q$. Then there exists a continuous function g on $\mathbf{R}^p$ to $\mathbf{R}^q$ with $g(x) = f(x)$ for x in $\mathfrak{D}$ and such that*

$$\sup \{|g(x)| : x \in \mathbf{R}^p\} = \sup \{|f(x)| : x \in \mathfrak{D}\}.$$

PROOF.   This result has just been proved for $q = 1$. In the general case, we note that f defines q continuous real-valued coordinate functions on $\mathfrak{D}$:

$$f(x) = (f_1(x), f_2(x), \ldots, f_q(x)).$$

Since each of the f_j, $1 \leq j \leq q$, has a continuous extension g_j on $\mathbf{R}^p$ to $\mathbf{R}$, we define g on $\mathbf{R}^p$ to $\mathbf{R}^q$ by

$$g(x) = (g_1(x), g_2(x), \ldots, g_q(x)).$$

The function g is seen to have the required properties.

Q.E.D.

Equicontinuity

We have made frequent use of the Bolzano-Weierstrass Theorem 8.13 for sets (which asserts that every bounded infinite subset of $\mathbf{R}^p$ has a cluster point) and the corresponding Theorem 12.4 for sequences (which asserts that every bounded sequence in $\mathbf{R}^p$ has a convergent subsequence). We now present a theorem which is entirely analogous to the Bolzano-Weierstrass Theorem except that it pertains to *sets of continuous functions* and not sets of points. For the sake of brevity and simplicity, we shall present here only the sequential form of this theorem, although it would be possible to define neighborhoods of a function, open and closed sets of functions, and cluster points of a set of functions.

In what follows we let K be a fixed compact subset of $\mathbf{R}^p$, and we shall be concerned with functions which are continuous on K and have their range in $\mathbf{R}^q$. In view of Theorem 16.5, each such function is bounded, and we write

$$||f|| = ||f||_K = \sup \{|f(x)| : x \in K\}.$$

We say that a set $\mathfrak{F}$ of continuous functions on K to $\mathbf{R}^q$ is bounded (or uniformly bounded) on K if there exists a constant M such that

$$\|f\| \leq M,$$

for all functions f in $\mathfrak{F}$. It is clear that any finite set $\mathfrak{F}$ of such functions is bounded; for if $\mathfrak{F} = \{f_1, f_2, \ldots, f_n\}$, then we can set

$$M = \sup \{\|f_1\|, \|f_2\|, \ldots, \|f_n\|\}.$$

In general, an infinite set of continuous functions on K to $\mathbf{R}^q$ will not be bounded. However, a uniformly convergent sequence of continuous functions is bounded, as we now show. (Compare this proof with Lemma 11.6.)

17.13 LEMMA. *If $\mathfrak{F} = (f_n)$ is a sequence of continuous functions on the compact set K to $\mathbf{R}^q$ which converges uniformly on K, then $\mathfrak{F}$ is bounded on K.*

PROOF. If f is the limit of the sequence $\mathfrak{F}$, there exists a natural number N such that if $n \geq N$, then $\|f_n - f\| < 1$. By using the Triangle Inequality 13.8(c) for the norm, we infer that

$$\|f_n\| \leq \|f\| + 1 \text{ for } n \geq N.$$

If we let $M = \sup \{\|f_1\|, \|f_2\| \ldots, \|f_{N-1}\|, \|f\| + 1\}$, we see that M is a bound for the set $\mathfrak{F}$.

Q.E.D.

If f is a continuous function on the compact set K of $\mathbf{R}^p$, then Theorem 16.12 implies that it is uniformly continuous. Hence, if $\epsilon > 0$ there exists a positive number $\delta(\epsilon)$, such that if x, y belong to K and $|x - y| < \delta(\epsilon)$, then $|f(x) - f(y)| < \epsilon$. Of course, the value of δ may depend on the function f as well as on ϵ and so we often write $\delta(\epsilon, f)$. (When we are dealing with more than one function it is well to indicate this dependence explicitly.) We notice that if $\mathfrak{F} = \{f_1, \ldots, f_n\}$ is a finite set of continuous functions on K, then, by setting

$$\delta(\epsilon, \mathfrak{F}) = \inf \{\delta(\epsilon, f_1), \ldots, \delta(\epsilon, f_n)\},$$

we obtain a δ which "works" for all the functions in this finite set.

17.14 DEFINITION. A set $\mathfrak{F}$ of functions on K to $\mathbf{R}^q$ is said to be equicontinuous on K if, for each positive real number ϵ there is a positive number $\delta(\epsilon)$ such that if x, y belong to K and $|x - y| < \delta(\epsilon)$ and f is a function in $\mathfrak{F}$, then $|f(x) - f(y)| < \epsilon$.

It has been seen that a finite set of continuous functions on K is equicontinuous. We shall now show that a sequence of continuous functions which converges uniformly on K is also equicontinuous.

17.15 LEMMA. If $\mathfrak{F} = (f_n)$ *is a sequence of continuous functions on a compact set K to $\mathbf{R}^q$ which converges uniformly on K, then the set $\mathfrak{F}$ is equicontinuous on K.*

PROOF. Let f be the uniform limit of the sequence $\mathfrak{F}$ and let $N(\epsilon/3)$ be such that if $n \geq N(\epsilon/3)$, then

$$|f_n(z) - f(z)| \leq \|f_n - f\| < \epsilon/3 \quad \text{for} \quad z \in K.$$

By Theorem 17.1, the function f is continuous and hence uniformly continuous on the compact set K. Therefore, there exists a number $\delta(\epsilon/3, f)$ such that if $x, y \in K$ and $|x - y| < \delta(\epsilon/3, f)$, then we have $|f(x) - f(y)| < \epsilon/3$. Thus if $n \geq N(\epsilon/3)$, then

$$|f_n(x) - f_n(y)| \leq |f_n(x) - f(x)| +$$
$$+ |f(x) - f(y)| + |f(y) - f_n(y)| < \epsilon.$$

As an abbreviation, let $N = N(\epsilon/3)$, and set

$$\delta(\epsilon) = \inf \{\delta(\epsilon, f_1), \ldots, \delta(\epsilon, f_{N-1}), \delta(\epsilon/3, f)\}.$$

Therefore, if $x, y \in K$ and $|x - y| < \delta(\epsilon)$, then $|f_n(x) - f_n(y)| < \epsilon$ for all $n \in \mathbf{N}$. This shows that the sequence is equicontinuous on K.

Q.E.D.

It follows that, in order for a sequence of functions on K to $\mathbf{R}^q$ to be uniformly convergent on K, it is necessary that the sequence be bounded and equicontinuous on K. We shall now show that these two properties are necessary and sufficient for a set $\mathfrak{F}$ of continuous functions on K to have the property that every sequence of functions from $\mathfrak{F}$ has a subsequence which converges uniformly on K. This may be regarded as a generalization of the Bolzano-Weierstrass Theorem to sets of continuous functions and plays an important role in the theory of differential and integral equations.

17.16 ARZELÀ-ASCOLI† THEOREM. *Let K be a compact subset of $\mathbf{R}^p$ and let $\mathfrak{F}$ be a collection of functions which are continuous on K and have values in $\mathbf{R}^q$. The following properties are equivalent:*

(a) *The family $\mathfrak{F}$ is bounded and equicontinuous on K.*

(b) *Every sequence from $\mathfrak{F}$ has a subsequence which is uniformly convergent on K.*

---

† CESARE ARZELÀ (1847–1912) was a professor at Bologna. He gave necessary and sufficient conditions for the limit of a sequence of continuous functions on a closed interval to be continuous, and he studied related topics.
GIULIO ASCOLI (1843–1896), a professor at Milan, formulated the definition of equicontinuity in a geometrical setting. He also made contributions to Fourier series.

PROOF. First, we shall show that if (a) fails, then so does (b). If the family $\mathfrak{F}$ is not bounded, there is a sequence (f_n) of functions in $\mathfrak{F}$ such that for each natural number n we have $||f_n|| \geq n$. In view of Lemma 17.13 no subsequence of (f_n) can converge uniformly on K. Also, if the set $\mathfrak{F}$ is not equicontinuous, then for some $\epsilon_0 > 0$ there is a sequence (f_n) from $\mathfrak{F}$ such that $\delta(\epsilon_0, f_n) \geq 1/n$. If this sequence (f_n) has a uniformly convergent subsequence, we obtain a contradiction to Lemma 17.15.

We now show that, if the set $\mathfrak{F}$ satisfies (a), then given any sequence (f_n) in $\mathfrak{F}$ there is a subsequence which converges uniformly on K. To do this we notice that it follows from Exercise 8.5 that there exists a countable set C in K such that if $y \in K$ and $\epsilon > 0$, then there exists an element x in C such that $|x - y| < \epsilon$. If $C = \{x_1, x_2, \ldots\}$, then the sequence $(f_n(x_1))$ is bounded in $\mathbf{R}^q$. It follows from the Bolzano-Weierstrass Theorem 12.4 that there is a subsequence

$$(f_{11}(x_1), f_{12}(x_1), \ldots, f_{1n}(x_1), \ldots)$$

of $(f_n(x_1))$ which is convergent. Next we note that the sequence $(f_{1k}(x_2): k \in \mathbf{N})$ is bounded in $\mathbf{R}^q$; hence it has a subsequence

$$(f_{21}(x_2), f_{22}(x_2), \ldots, f_{2n}(x_2), \ldots)$$

which is convergent. Again, the sequence $(f_{2n}(x_3): n \in \mathbf{N})$ is bounded in $\mathbf{R}^q$, so some subsequence

$$(f_{31}(x_3), f_{32}(x_3), \ldots, f_{3n}(x_3), \ldots)$$

is convergent. We proceed in this way and then set $g_n = f_{nn}$ so that g_n is the nth function in the nth subsequence. It is clear from the construction that the sequence (g_n) converges at each point of C.

We shall now prove that the sequence (g_n) converges at each point of K and that the convergence is uniform. To do this, let $\epsilon > 0$ and let $\delta(\epsilon)$ be as in the definition of equicontinuity. Let $C_1 = \{y_1, \ldots, y_k\}$ be a finite subset of C such that every point in K is within $\delta(\epsilon)$ of some point in C_1. Since the sequences

$$(g_n(y_1)), (g_n(y_2)), \ldots, (g_n(y_k))$$

converge, there exists a natural number M such that if $m, n \geq M$, then

$$|g_m(y_i) - g_n(y_i)| < \epsilon \quad \text{for} \quad i = 1, 2, \ldots, k.$$

Given $x \in K$, there exists a $y_i \in C_1$ such that $|x - y_i| < \delta(\epsilon)$. Hence, by the equicontinuity, we have

$$|g_n(x) - g_n(y_i)| < \epsilon$$

for all $n \in \mathbf{N}$; in particular, this inequality holds for $n \geq M$. Therefore, we have

$$|g_n(x) - g_m(x)| \leq |g_n(x) - g_n(y_j)| + |g_n(y_j) - g_m(y_j)|$$
$$+ |g_m(y_j) - g_m(x)| < \epsilon + \epsilon + \epsilon = 3\epsilon,$$

provided $m, n > M$. This shows that

$$\|g_n - g_m\|_K \leq 3\epsilon \quad \text{for} \quad m, n \geq M,$$

so the uniform convergence of the sequence (g_n) on K follows from the Cauchy Criterion for uniform convergence, given in 13.11.

Q.E.D.

In the proof of this result, we constructed a sequence of subsequences of functions and then selected the "diagonal" sequence (g_n), where $g_n = f_{nn}$. Such a construction is often called a "diagonal process" or "Cantor's diagonal method" and is frequently useful. The reader should recall that a similar type of argument was used in Section 3 to prove that the real numbers do not form a countable set.

Exercises

17.A. Give an example of a sequence of continuous functions which converges to a continuous function, but where the convergence is not uniform.

17.B. Can a sequence of discontinuous functions converge uniformly to a continuous function?

17.C. Give an example of a sequence of continuous functions which converges on a compact set to a function that has an infinite number of discontinuities.

17.D. Suppose that f_n is continuous on $\mathfrak{D} \subseteq \mathbf{R}^p$ to $\mathbf{R}^q$, that (f_n) converges uniformly on $\mathfrak{D}$ to f, and that a sequence (x_n) of elements in $\mathfrak{D}$ converges to x in $\mathfrak{D}$. Does it follow that $(f_n(x))$ converges to $f(x)$?

17.E. Consider the sequences (f_n) defined on $\{x \in \mathbf{R} : x \geq 0\}$ to $\mathbf{R}$ by the formulas

(a) $\dfrac{x^n}{n}$,

(c) $\dfrac{x^n}{n + x^n}$,

(e) $\dfrac{x^n}{1 + x^{2n}}$,

(b) $\dfrac{x^n}{1 + x^n}$,

(d) $\dfrac{x^{2n}}{1 + x^n}$,

(f) $\dfrac{x}{n} e^{-(x/n)}$.

Discuss the convergence and the uniform convergence of these sequences (f_n) and the continuity of the limit functions. Consider both the entire half-line and appropriately chosen intervals as the domains.

17.F. Let (f_n) be a sequence of functions on $\mathfrak{D} \subseteq \mathbf{R}^p$ to $\mathbf{R}^q$ which converges on $\mathfrak{D}$ to f. Suppose that each f_n is continuous at a point c in $\mathfrak{D}$ and that the sequence converges uniformly on a neighborhood of c. Prove that f is continuous at c.

17.G. Let (f_n) be a sequence of continuous functions on $\mathfrak{D} \subseteq \mathbf{R}^p$ to $\mathbf{R}$ which is monotone decreasing in the sense that if $x \in \mathfrak{D}$, then

$$f_1(x) \geq f_2(x) \geq \ldots \geq f_n(x) \geq f_{n+1}(x) \geq \ldots$$

If $(f_n(c))$ converges to 0 and $\epsilon > 0$, then there exists a natural number M and a neighborhood U of c such that if $n \geq M$ and $x \in U \cap \mathfrak{D}$ then $f_n(x) < \epsilon$.

17.H. Using the preceding exercise, establish the following result of U. Dini.†
If (f_n) is a monotone sequence of real-valued continuous functions which converges at each point of a compact subset K of $\mathbf{R}^p$ to a continuous function f, then the convergence is uniform on K.

17.I. Can Dini's Theorem fail if the hypothesis that K is compact is dropped? Can it fail if the hypothesis that f is continuous is dropped? Can it fail if the hypothesis that the sequence is monotone is dropped?

17.J. Prove the following result of G. Pólya.‡ If for each $n \in \mathbf{N}$, f_n is a monotone increasing function on $\mathbf{I}$ to $\mathbf{R}$, if f is continuous on $\mathbf{I}$ to $\mathbf{R}$, and if $f(x) = \lim (f_n(x))$ for all $x \in \mathbf{I}$, then the convergence is uniform on $\mathbf{I}$. Observe that it need not be assumed that the f_n are continuous.

17.K. Let (f_n) be a sequence of continuous functions on $\mathfrak{D} \subseteq \mathbf{R}^p$ to $\mathbf{R}^q$ and let $f(x) = \lim (f_n(x))$ for $x \in \mathfrak{D}$. Show that f is continuous at a point c in $\mathfrak{D}$ if and only if for each $\epsilon > 0$ there exists a natural number $m = m(\epsilon)$ and a neighborhood $U = U(\epsilon)$ of c such that if $x \in \mathfrak{D} \cap U$, then

$$|f_m(x) - f(x)| < \epsilon.$$

17.L. Consider the weight factors φ_k that appear in the nth Bernstein polynomials. By using elementary calculus or other means, show that φ_k takes its supremum on $\mathbf{I}$ at the point k/n. Write out explicitly the functions φ_k, $k = 0, 1, 2$, when $n = 2$ and the functions corresponding to $n = 3$, and note that $\sum \varphi_n(x) = 1$, for $x \in \mathbf{I}$. Draw graphs of some of these functions.

17.M. Carry out the details in the derivation of equation (17.8) and the equation immediately preceding this equation.

17.N. Differentiate equation (17.3) twice with respect to s and then substitute $s = x$, $t = 1 - x$. From what is obtained, give another derivation of equations (17.7) and (17.8).

17.O. Let K be the circumference of the unit circle in $\mathbf{R}^2$; hence K is the set $\{(x, y) : x^2 + y^2 = 1\}$. Note that K can be parametrized by the angle θ, where $\tan \theta = y/x$. A **trigonometric polynomial** is a function p on K to $\mathbf{R}$ of the form

$$p(\theta) = A_0 + (A_1 \cos \theta + B_1 \sin \theta) + \ldots +$$
$$+ (A_n \cos n\theta + B_n \sin n\theta),$$

---

† ULISSE DINI (1845–1918) studied and taught at Pisa. He worked on geometry and analysis, particularly Fourier series.

‡ GEORGE PÓLYA (1887–   ) was born in Budapest and taught at Zürich and Stanford. He is widely known for his work in complex analysis, probability, number theory, and the theory of inference.

where the A_i, B_j are real numbers. Use the Stone-Weierstrass Theorem and show that any continuous function on K to $\mathbf{R}$ can be uniformly approximated by trigonometric polynomials.

17.P. Let D be the unit circle in $\mathbf{R}^2$; in polar coordinates, D is the set $\{(r \cos \theta, r \sin \theta) : 0 \leq \theta \leq 2\pi, \, 0 \leq r \leq 1\}$. Show that any continuous function on D to $\mathbf{R}$ can be uniformly approximated by functions of the form

$$A_0 + r(A_1 \cos \theta + B_1 \sin \theta) + \ldots + r^n(A_n \cos n\theta + B_n \sin n\theta).$$

17.Q. Let I_2 denote the square $I \times I$ in $\mathbf{R}^2$. Show that any continuous function on I_2 to $\mathbf{R}$ can be uniformly approximated by functions having the form

$$f_1(x)g_1(y) + \ldots + f_n(x)g_n(y),$$

where f_i, g_j are continuous functions on I to $\mathbf{R}$.

17.R. Show that the Tietze Theorem 17.11 may fail if the domain $\mathfrak{D}$ is not closed.

17.S. Use the Tietze Theorem to show that if $\mathfrak{D}$ is a closed subset of $\mathbf{R}^p$ and f is a (possibly unbounded) continuous function on $\mathfrak{D}$ to $\mathbf{R}$, then there exists a continuous extension of f which is defined on all of $\mathbf{R}^p$. (Hint: consider the composition of $\varphi \circ f$, where $\varphi(x) = \text{Arc tan } x$ or $\varphi(x) = x/(1 + |x|)$.)

17.T. Let $\mathfrak{F}$ be a family of functions with compact domain K in $\mathbf{R}^p$ and with range in $\mathbf{R}^q$. Suppose that for each $c \in K$ and $\epsilon > 0$ there is a $\delta(c, \epsilon) > 0$ such that if $x \in K$ and $|x - c| < \delta(c, \epsilon)$, then $|f(x) - f(c)| < \epsilon$ for all $f \in \mathfrak{F}$. Prove that the family $\mathfrak{F}$ is equicontinuous in the sense of Definition 17.14.

17.U. Show that the family $\mathfrak{F}$ has the property stated in the preceding exercise at the point c if and only if for each sequence (x_n) in K with $c = \lim (x_n)$, then $f(c) = \lim (f(x_n))$ uniformly for f in $\mathfrak{F}$.

17.V. Let $\mathfrak{F}$ be a bounded and equicontinuous set of functions with domain $\mathfrak{D}$ contained in $\mathbf{R}^p$ and with range in $\mathbf{R}$. Let f^* be defined on $\mathfrak{D}$ to $\mathbf{R}$ by

$$f^*(x) = \sup \{f(x) : f \in \mathfrak{F}\}.$$

Show that f^* is continuous on $\mathfrak{D}$ to $\mathbf{R}$.

17.W. Show that the conclusion of the preceding exercise may fail if it is not assumed that $\mathfrak{F}$ is an equicontinuous set.

17.X. Let (f_n) be a sequence of continuous functions on $\mathbf{R}$ to $\mathbf{R}^q$ which converges at each point of the set Q of rationals. If the set $\mathfrak{F} = \{f_n\}$ is equicontinuous on $\mathbf{R}$, show that the sequence is actually convergent at every point of $\mathbf{R}$ and that this convergence is uniform on $\mathbf{R}$.

17.Y. Show that the Arzelà-Ascoli Theorem 17.16 may fail if the hypothesis that the domain is compact is dropped.

Section 18 Limits of Functions

Although it is not easy to draw a definite borderline, it is fair to characterize analysis as that part of mathematics where systematic use is made of various limiting concepts. If this is a reasonably accurate statement, it may seem odd to the reader that we have waited this long before inserting a section dealing with limits. There are several reasons for this delay, the main one being that elementary analysis deals with several different types of limit operations. We have already discussed the convergence of sequences and the limiting implicit in the study of continuity. In the next chapters, we shall bring in the limiting operations connected with the derivative and the integral. Although all of these limit notions are special cases of a more general one, the general notion is of a rather abstract character. For that reason, we prefer to introduce and discuss the notions separately, rather than to develop the general limiting idea first and then specialize. Once the special cases are well understood it is not difficult to comprehend the abstract notion. For an excellent exposition of this abstract limit, see the expository article of E. J. McShane cited in the References.

In this section we shall be concerned with the limit of a function at a point and some slight extensions of this idea. Often this idea is studied *before* continuity; in fact, the very definition of a continuous function is sometimes expressed in terms of this limit instead of using the definition we have given in Section 15. One of the reasons why we have chosen to study continuity separately from the limit is that we shall introduce two slightly different definitions of the limit of a function at a point. Since both definitions are widely used, we shall present them both and attempt to relate them to each other.

Unless there is specific mention to the contrary, we shall let f be a function with domain $\mathfrak{D}$ contained in $\mathbf{R}^p$ and values in $\mathbf{R}^q$ and we shall consider the limiting character of f at a cluster point c of $\mathfrak{D}$. Therefore, every neighborhood of c contains infinitely many points of $\mathfrak{D}$.

18.1 DEFINITION.   (i) An element b of $\mathbf{R}^q$ is said to be the **deleted limit of** f **at** c if for every neighborhood V of b there is a neighborhood U of c such that if x belongs to $U \cap \mathfrak{D}$ and $x \neq c$, then $f(x)$ belongs to V. In this case we write

$$(18.1) \qquad b = \lim_c f \quad \text{or} \quad b = \lim_{x \to c} f(x).$$

(ii) An element b of $\mathbf{R}^q$ is said to be the **non-deleted limit of** f **at** c if for every neighborhood V of b there is a neighborhood U of c such that if x belongs to $U \cap \mathfrak{D}$, then $f(x)$ belongs to V. In this case we write

$$(18.2) \qquad b = \operatorname{Lim}_c f \quad \text{or} \quad b = \operatorname{Lim}_{x \to c} f(x).$$

It is important to observe that the difference between these two notions centers on whether the value $f(c)$, when it exists, is considered or not. Note also the rather subtle notational distinction we have introduced in equations (18.1) and (18.2). It should be realized that most authors introduce only one of these notions, in which case they refer to it merely as "the limit" and generally employ the notation in (18.1). Since the deleted limit is the most popular, we have chosen to preserve the conventional symbolism in referring to it.

The uniqueness of either limit, when it exists, is readily established. We content ourself with the following statement.

18.2 LEMMA.   (a) *If either of the limits*

$$\lim_{c} f, \qquad \operatorname{Lim}_{c} f,$$

exist, then it is uniquely determined.

(b) *If the non-deleted limit exists, then the deleted limit exists and*

$$\lim_{c} f = \operatorname{Lim}_{c} f.$$

(c) *If c does not belong to the domain $\mathfrak{D}$ of f, then the deleted limit exists if and only if the non-deleted limit exists.*

Part (b) of the lemma just stated shows that the notion of the non-deleted limit is somewhat more restrictive than that of the deleted limit. Part (c) shows that they can be different only in the case where c belongs to $\mathfrak{D}$. To give an example where these notions differ, consider the function f on $\mathbf{R}$ to $\mathbf{R}$ defined by

$$(18.3) \qquad\qquad f(x) = 0, \qquad x \neq 0,$$
$$= 1, \qquad x = 0.$$

If $c = 0$, then the deleted limit of f at $c = 0$ exists and equals 0, while the non-deleted limit does not exist.

We now state some necessary and sufficient conditions for the existence of the limits, leaving their proof to the reader. It should be realized that in part (c) of both results the limit refers to the limit of a *sequence*, which was discussed in Section 11.

18.3 THEOREM.   *The following statements, pertaining to the deleted limit, are equivalent.*

(a) *The deleted limit $b = \lim_{c} f$ exists.*

(b) *If $\epsilon > 0$, there is a $\delta > 0$ such that if $x \in \mathfrak{D}$ and $0 < |x - c| < \delta$, then $|f(x) - b| < \epsilon$.*

(c) *If (x_n) is any sequence in $\mathfrak{D}$ such that $x_n \neq c$ and $c = \lim (x_n)$, then $b = \lim (f(x_n))$.*

18.4   THEOREM.   *The following statements, pertaining to the non-deleted limit, are equivalent.*

(a) *The non-deleted limit* $b = \underset{c}{\text{Lim}} f$ *exists.*

(b) *If* $\epsilon > 0$, *there is a* $\delta > 0$ *such that if* $x \in \mathfrak{D}$ *and* $|x - c| < \delta$, *then* $|f(x) - b| < \epsilon$.

(c) *If* (x_n) *is any sequence in* $\mathfrak{D}$ *such that* $c = \lim (x_n)$, *then we have* $b = \lim (f(x_n))$.

The next result yields an instructive connection between these two limits and continuity of f at c.

18.5   THEOREM.   *If c is a cluster point belonging to the domain $\mathfrak{D}$ of f, then the following statements are equivalent.*

(a) *The function f is continuous at c.*

(b) *The deleted limit $\underset{c}{\lim} f$ exists and equals $f(c)$.*

(c) *The non-deleted limit $\underset{c}{\text{Lim}} f$ exists.*

PROOF.   If (a) holds, and V is a neighborhood of $f(c)$, then there exists a neighborhood U of c such that if x belongs to $U \cap \mathfrak{D}$, then $f(x)$ belongs to V. Clearly, this implies that $\text{Lim} f$ exists at c and equals $f(c)$. Similarly, $f(x)$ belongs to V for all $x \neq c$ for which $x \in U \cap \mathfrak{D}$, in which case $\lim f$ exists and equals $f(c)$. Conversely, statements (b) and (c) are readily seen to imply (a).

Q.E.D.

If f and g are two functions which have deleted (respectively, non-deleted) limits at a cluster point c of $\mathfrak{D}(f + g) = \mathfrak{D}(f) \cap \mathfrak{D}(g)$, then their sum $f + g$ has a deleted (respectively, non-deleted) limit at c and

$$\underset{c}{\lim} (f + g) = \underset{c}{\lim} f + \underset{c}{\lim} g,$$

$$(\text{respectively, } \underset{c}{\text{Lim}} (f + g) = \underset{c}{\text{Lim}} f + \underset{c}{\text{Lim}} g).$$

Similar results hold for other algebraic combinations of functions, as is easily seen. The following result, concerning the composition of two functions, is deeper and is a place where the non-deleted limit is simpler than the deleted limit.

18.6   THEOREM.   *Suppose that f has domain $\mathfrak{D}(f)$ in $\mathbf{R}^p$ and range in $\mathbf{R}^q$ and that g has domain $\mathfrak{D}(g)$ in $\mathbf{R}^q$ and range in $\mathbf{R}^r$. Let $g \circ f$ be the composition of g and f and let c be a cluster point of $\mathfrak{D}(g \circ f)$.*

(a) *If the deleted limits*

$$b = \underset{c}{\lim} f, \qquad a = \underset{b}{\lim} g$$

both exist and if either g is continuous at b or f(x) ≠ b for x in a neighbor-
hood of c, then the deleted limit of g ∘ f exists at c and

$$a = \lim_c g \circ f.$$

(b) *If the non-deleted limits*

$$b = \operatorname{Lim}_c f, \qquad a = \operatorname{Lim}_b g$$

both exist, then the non-deleted limit of g ∘ f exists at c and

$$a = \operatorname{Lim}_c g \circ f.$$

PROOF.   (a) Let W be a neighborhood of a in $\mathbf{R}^r$; since $a = \lim g$ at b, there is a neighborhood V of b such that if y belongs to $V \cap \mathfrak{D}(g)$ and $y \neq b$, then $g(y) \in W$. Since $b = \lim f$ at c, there is a neighborhood U of c such that if x belongs to $U \cap \mathfrak{D}(f)$ and $x \neq c$, then $f(x) \in V$. Hence, if x belongs to the possibly smaller set $U \cap \mathfrak{D}(g \circ f)$, and $x \neq c$, then $f(x) \in V \cap \mathfrak{D}(g)$. If $f(x) \neq b$ on some neighborhood U_1 of c, it follows that for $x \neq c$ in $(U_1 \cap U) \cap \mathfrak{D}(g \circ f)$, then $(g \circ f)(x) \in W$, so that a is the deleted limit of $g \circ f$ at c. If g is continuous at b, then $(g \circ f)(x) \in W$ for x in $U \cap \mathfrak{D}(g \circ f)$ and $x \neq c$.

To prove part (b), we note that the exceptions made in the proof of (a) are no longer necessary. Hence if x belongs to $U \cap \mathfrak{D}(g \circ f)$, then $f(x) \in V \cap \mathfrak{D}(g)$ and, therefore, $(g \circ f)(x) \in W$.

Q.E.D.

The conclusion in part (a) of the preceding theorem may fail if we drop the condition that g is continuous at b or that $f(x) \neq b$ on a neighborhood of c. To substantiate this remark, let f be the function on $\mathbf{R}$ to $\mathbf{R}$ defined in formula (18.3) and let $g = f$ and $c = 0$. Then $g \circ f$ is given by

$$(g \circ f)(x) = 1, \qquad x \neq 0,$$
$$= 0, \qquad x = 0.$$

Furthermore, we have

$$\lim_{x \to 0} f(x) = 0, \qquad \lim_{y \to 0} g(y) = 0,$$

whereas it is clear that

$$\lim_{x \to 0} (g \circ f)(x) = 1.$$

Note that the non-deleted limits do not exist for these functions.

Upper Limits at a Point

For the remainder of the present section, we shall consider the case where $q = 1$. Thus f is a function with domain $\mathfrak{D}$ in $\mathbf{R}^p$ and values in $\mathbf{R}$ and the point c in $\mathbf{R}^p$ is a cluster point of $\mathfrak{D}$. We shall define the limit superior or the upper limit of f at c. Again there are two possibilities depending on whether deleted or non-deleted neighborhoods are considered, and we shall discuss both possibilities. It is clear that we can define the limit inferior in a similar fashion. One thing to be noted here is that, although the existence of the limit (deleted or not) is a relatively delicate matter, the limits superior to be defined have the virtue that (at least if f is bounded) their existence is guaranteed.

The ideas in this part are parallel to the notion of the limit superior of a sequence in $\mathbf{R}^p$ which was introduced in Section 14. However, we shall not assume familiarity with what was done there, except in some of the exercises.

18.7 DEFINITION. Suppose that f is bounded on a neighborhood of the point c. If $r > 0$, define $\varphi(r)$ and $\varphi(r)$ by

(18.4a) $\varphi(r) = \sup \{f(x) : 0 < |x - c| < r, x \in \mathfrak{D}\}$,

(18.4b) $\Phi(r) = \sup \{f(x) : |x - c| < r, x \in \mathfrak{D}\}$.

and set

(18.5a) $\displaystyle \limsup_{x \to c} f = \inf \{\varphi(r) : r > 0\}$,

(18.5b) $\displaystyle \operatorname{Lim\,sup}_{x \to c} f = \inf \{\Phi(r) : r > 0\}$.

These quantities are called the **deleted limit superior** and the **non-deleted limit superior** of f at c, respectively.

Since these quantities are defined as the infima of the image under f of ever-decreasing neighborhoods of c, it is probably not clear that they deserve the terms "limit superior." The next lemma indicates a justification for the terminology.

18.8 LEMMA. *If φ, Φ are as defined in equations (18.4), then*

(18.6a) $\displaystyle \limsup_{x \to c} f = \lim_{r \to 0} \varphi(r)$,

(18.6b) $\displaystyle \operatorname{Lim\,sup}_{x \to c} f = \lim_{r \to 0} \Phi(r)$.

PROOF. We observe that if $0 < r < s$, then

$$\limsup_{x \to c} f \le \varphi(r) \le \varphi(s).$$

Furthermore, by (18.5a), if $\epsilon > 0$ there exists an $r_\epsilon > 0$ such that

$$\varphi(r_\epsilon) < \limsup_{x \to c} f + \epsilon.$$

Therefore, if r satisfies $0 < r < r_\epsilon$, we have

$$\left| \varphi(r) - \limsup_{x \to c} f \right| < \epsilon,$$

which proves (18.6a). The proof of (18.6b) is similar and will be omitted.

Q.E.D.

18.9   Lemma.   (a) *If $M > \limsup\limits_{x \to c} f$, then there exists a neighborhood U of c such that*

$$f(x) < M \quad for \quad c \neq x \in \mathfrak{D} \cap U.$$

(b) *If $M > \operatorname{Lim\,sup}\limits_{x \to c} f$, then there exists a neighborhood U of c such that*

$$f(x) < M \quad for \quad x \in \mathfrak{D} \cap U.$$

PROOF.   (a) By (18.5a), we have

$$\inf \{\varphi(r) : r > 0\} < M.$$

Hence there exists a real number $r_1 > 0$ such that $\varphi(r_1) < M$ and we can take $U = \{x \in \mathbb{R}^p : |x - c| < r_1\}$. The proof of (b) is similar.

Q.E.D.

18.10   Lemma.   *Let f and g be bounded on a neighborhood of c and suppose that c is a cluster point of $\mathfrak{D}(f + g)$. Then*

(18.7a) $\quad \limsup\limits_{x \to c} (f + g) \leq \limsup\limits_{x \to c} f + \limsup\limits_{x \to c} g,$

(18.7b) $\quad \operatorname{Lim\,sup}\limits_{x \to c} (f + g) \leq \operatorname{Lim\,sup}\limits_{x \to c} f + \operatorname{Lim\,sup}\limits_{x \to c} g.$

PROOF.   In view of the relation
$$\sup \{f(x) + g(x) : x \in A\} \leq \sup \{f(x) : x \in A\} + \sup \{g(x) : x \in A\},$$
it is clear that, using notation as in Definition 18.7, we have

$$\varphi_{f+g}(r) \leq \varphi_f(r) + \varphi_g(r).$$

Now use Lemma 18.8 and let $r \to 0$ to obtain (18.7a).

Q.E.D.

Results concerning other algebraic combinations will be found in Exercise 18.F.

Although we shall have no occasion to pursue these matters, in some areas of analysis it is useful to have the following generalization of the notion of continuity.

18.11   DEFINITION.   A function f on $\mathfrak{D}$ to R is said to be **upper semi-continuous** at a point c in $\mathfrak{D}$ in case

$$(18.8) \qquad\qquad f(c) = \operatorname*{Lim\,sup}_{x \to c} f.$$

It is said to be **upper semi-continuous** on $\mathfrak{D}$ if it is upper semi-continuous at every point of $\mathfrak{D}$.

Instead of defining upper semi-continuity by means of equation (18.8) we could require the equivalent, but less elegant, condition

$$(18.9) \qquad\qquad f(c) \geq \operatorname*{lim\,sup}_{x \to c} f.$$

One of the keys to the importance and the utility of upper semi-continuous functions is suggested by the following lemma, which may be compared with the Global Continuity Theorem 16.1.

18.12   LEMMA.   *Let f be an upper semi-continuous function with domain $\mathfrak{D}$ in $\mathbf{R}^p$ and let k be an arbitrary real number. Then there exists an open set G and a closed set F such that*

$$(18.10) \qquad\qquad G \cap \mathfrak{D} = \{x \in \mathfrak{D} : f(x) < k\},$$

$$F \cap \mathfrak{D} = \{x \in \mathfrak{D} : f(x) \geq k\}.$$

PROOF.   Suppose that c is a point in $\mathfrak{D}$ such that $f(c) < k$. According to Definition 18.11 and Lemma 18.9(b), there is a neighborhood $U(c)$ of c such that $f(x) < k$ for all x in $\mathfrak{D} \cap U(c)$. Without loss of generality we can select $U(c)$ to be an open neighborhood; setting

$$G = \mathsf{U}\, \{U(c) : c \in \mathfrak{D}\},$$

we have an open set with the property stated in (18.10). If F is the complement of G, then F is closed in $\mathbf{R}^p$ and satisfies the stated condition.
                                                                Q.E.D.

It is possible to show, using the lemma just proved, (cf. Exercise 18.M) that if K is a compact subset of $\mathbf{R}^p$ and f is upper semi-continuous on K, then f is bounded above on K and *there exists a point in K where f attains its supremum.* Thus upper semi-continuous functions on compact sets possess some of the properties we have established for continuous functions, even though an upper semi-continuous function can have many points of discontinuity.

Exercises

18.A. Discuss the existence of both the deleted and the non-deleted limits of the following functions at the point $x = 0$.

(a) $f(x) = |x|$,

(b) $f(x) = 1/x, \qquad x \neq 0$,

(c) $f(x) = x \sin (1/x), \qquad x \neq 0$,

(d) $f(x) = \begin{cases} x \sin (1/x), & x \neq 0, \\ 1, & x = 0, \end{cases}$

(e) $f(x) = \sin (1/x), \qquad x \neq 0$,

(f) $f(x) = \begin{cases} 0, & x \leq 0, \\ 1, & x > 0. \end{cases}$

18.B. Prove Lemma 18.2.

18.C. If f denotes the function defined in equation (18.3), show that the deleted limit at $x = 0$ equals 0 and that the non-deleted limit at $x = 0$ does not exist. Discuss the existence of these two limits for the composition $f \circ f$.

18.D. Prove Lemma 18.4.

18.E. Show that statements 18.5(b) and 18.5(c) imply statement 18.5(a).

18.F. Show that if f and g have deleted limits at a cluster point c of the set $\mathfrak{D}(f) \cap \mathfrak{D}(g)$, then the sum $f + g$ has a deleted limit at c and

$$\lim_{c} (f + g) = \lim_{c} f + \lim_{c} g.$$

Under the same hypotheses, the inner product $f \cdot g$ has a deleted limit at c and

$$\lim_{c} (f \cdot g) = (\lim_{c} f) \cdot (\lim_{c} g).$$

18.G. Let f be defined on a subset $\mathfrak{D}(f)$ of $\mathbf{R}$ into $\mathbf{R}^q$. If c is a cluster point of the set

$$V = \{x \in \mathbf{R} : x \in \mathfrak{D}(f), x > c\},$$

and if f_1 is the restriction of f to V [that is, if f_1 is defined for $x \in V$ by $f_1(x) = f(x)$], then we define the **right-hand (deleted) limit** of f at c to be $\lim_{c} f_1$, whenever this limit exists. Sometimes this limit is denoted by $\lim_{c+} f$ or by $f(c + 0)$. Formulate and establish a result analogous to Lemma 18.3 for the right-hand deleted limit. (A similar definition can be given for the **right-hand non-deleted limit** and both left-hand limits at c.)

18.H. Let f be defined on $\mathfrak{D} = \{x \in \mathbf{R} : x \geq 0\}$ to $\mathbf{R}$. We say that a number L is the **limit of f at $+\infty$** if for each $\epsilon > 0$ there exists a real number $m(\epsilon)$ such that if $x \geq m(\epsilon)$, then $|f(x) - L| < \epsilon$. In this case we write $L = \lim_{x \to +\infty} f$. Formulate and prove a result analogous to Lemma 18.3 for this limit.

18.I. If f is defined on a set $\mathfrak{D}(f)$ in $\mathbf{R}$ to $\mathbf{R}$ and if c is a cluster point of $\mathfrak{D}(f)$, then we say that $f(x) \to +\infty$ as $x \to c$, or that

$$\lim_{x \to c} f = +\infty$$

in case for each positive number M there exists a neighborhood U of c such that if $x \in U \cap \mathfrak{D}(f)$, $x \neq c$, then $f(x) > M$. Formulate and establish a result analogous to Lemma 18.3 for this limit.

18.J. In view of Exercises 18.H and 18.I, give a definition of what is meant by the expressions

$$\lim_{x \to +\infty} f = +\infty, \qquad \lim_{x \to c} f = -\infty.$$

18.K. Establish Lemma 18.8 for the non-deleted limit superior. Give the proof of Lemma 18.9(b).

18.L. Define what is meant by

$$\limsup_{x \to +\infty} f = L, \qquad \liminf_{x \to +\infty} f = -\infty.$$

18.M. Show that if f is an upper semi-continuous function on a compact subset K of $\mathbf{R}^p$ with values in $\mathbf{R}$, then f is bounded above and attains its supremum on K.

18.N. Show that an upper semi-continuous function on a compact set may not be bounded below and may not attain its infimum.

18.O. Show that if A is an open subset of $\mathbf{R}^p$ and if f is defined on $\mathbf{R}^p$ to $\mathbf{R}$ by

$$f(x) = 1, \qquad x \in A,$$
$$0, \qquad x \notin A,$$

then f is a lower semi-continuous function. If A is a closed subset of $\mathbf{R}^p$, show that f is upper semi-continuous.

18.P. Give an example of an upper semi-continuous function which has an infinite number of points of discontinuity.

18.Q. Is it true that function on $\mathbf{R}^p$ to $\mathbf{R}$ is continuous at a point if and only if it is both upper and lower semi-continuous at this point?

18.R. If (f_n) is a bounded sequence of continuous functions on $\mathbf{R}^p$ to $\mathbf{R}$ and if f^* is defined on $\mathbf{R}^p$ by

$$f^*(x) = \sup \{f_n(x) : n \in \mathbf{N}\}, \, x \in \mathbf{R}^p,$$

then is it true that f^* is upper semi-continuous on $\mathbf{R}^p$?

18.S. If (f_n) is a bounded sequence of continuous functions on $\mathbf{R}^p$ to $\mathbf{R}$ and if f_* is defined on $\mathbf{R}^p$ by

$$f_*(x) = \inf \{f_n(x) : n \in \mathbf{N}\}, x \in \mathbf{R}^p,$$

then is it true that f_* is upper semi-continuous on $\mathbf{R}^p$?

18.T. Let f be defined on a subset $\mathfrak{D}$ of $\mathbf{R}^p \times \mathbf{R}^q$ and with values in $\mathbf{R}^r$. Let (a, b) be a cluster point of $\mathfrak{D}$. By analogy with Definition 14.9, define the double and the two iterated limits of f at (a, b). Show that the existence of the double and the iterated limits implies their equality. Show that the double limit can exist without either iterated limit existing and that both iterated limits can exist and be equal without the double limit existing.

18.U. Let f be as in the preceding exercise. By analogy with Definitions 13.4 and 14.13, define what it means to say that

$$g(y) = \lim_{x \to a} f(x, y)$$

uniformly for y in a set $\mathfrak{D}_2$. Formulate and prove a result analogous to Theorem 14.15.

18.V. Let f be as in Definition 18.1 and suppose that the deleted limit at c exists and that for some element A in $\mathbf{R}^q$ and $r > 0$ the inequality $|f(x) - A| < r$ holds on some neighborhood of c. Prove that

$$\left| \lim_{x \to c} f - A \right| \leq r.$$

Does the same conclusion hold for the non-deleted limit?

V

Differentiation

We shall now consider the important operation of differentiation and shall establish the basic theorems concerning this operation. Although we expect that the reader has had experience with differential calculus and that the ideas are somewhat familiar, we shall not require any explicit results to be known and shall establish the entire theory on a rigorous basis.

For pedagogical reasons we shall first treat the main outlines of the theory of differentiation for functions with domain and range in R— our objective being to obtain the fundamental Mean Value Theorem and a few of its consequences. After this has been done, we turn to the theory for functions with domain and range in Cartesian spaces. In Section 20, we introduce the derivative of a function f on $\mathbf{R}^p$ to $\mathbf{R}^q$ as a linear function approximating f at the given point. In Section 21, it is seen that the local character of the function is faithfully reflected by its derivative. Finally, the derivative is used to locate extreme points of a real valued function on $\mathbf{R}^p$.

Section 19   The Derivative in **R**

Since the reader is assumed to be already familiar with the connection between the derivative of a function and the slope of a curve and rate of change, we shall focus our attention entirely on the mathematical aspects of the derivative and not go into its many applications. In this section we shall consider a function f which has its domain $\mathfrak{D}$ and range contained in R. Although we are primarily interested with the derivative at a point which is interior to $\mathfrak{D}$, we shall define the derivative more generally. We shall require that the point at which the derivative is being defined belongs to $\mathfrak{D}$ and that every neighborhood of the points contains other points of $\mathfrak{D}$.

19.1   DEFINITION.   If c is a cluster point of $\mathfrak{D}$ and belongs to $\mathfrak{D}$, we say that a real number L is the **derivative** of f at c if for every positive number ϵ there is a positive number $\delta(\epsilon)$ such that if x belongs to $\mathfrak{D}$ and if $0 < |x - c| < \delta(\epsilon)$, then

$$(19.1) \qquad\qquad \left| \frac{f(x) - f(c)}{x - c} - L \right| < \epsilon.$$

In this case we write $f'(c)$ for L.

Alternatively, we could define $f'(c)$ as the limit

$$(19.2) \qquad\qquad \lim_{x \to c} \frac{f(x) - f(c)}{x - c} \quad (x \in \mathfrak{D}).$$

It is to be noted that if c is an interior point of $\mathfrak{D}$, then in (19.1) we consider the points x both to the left and the right of the point c. On the other hand, if $\mathfrak{D}$ is an interval and c is the left end point of $\mathfrak{D}$, then in relation (19.1) we can only take x to the right of c. In this case we sometimes say that "L is the right-hand derivative of f at $x = c$." However, for our purposes it is not necessary to introduce such terminology.

Whenever the derivative of f at c exists, we denote its value by $f'(c)$. In this way we obtain a function f' whose domain is a subset of the domain of f. We now show that continuity of f at c is a necessary condition for the existence of the derivative at c.

19.2   LEMMA.   *If f has a derivative at c, then f is continuous there.*

PROOF.   Let $\epsilon = 1$ and take $\delta = \delta(1)$ such that

$$\left| \frac{f(x) - f(c)}{x - c} - f'(c) \right| < 1,$$

for all $x \in \mathfrak{D}$ satisfying $0 < |x - c| < \delta$. From the Triangle Inequality, we infer that for these values of x we have

$$|f(x) - f(c)| \leq |x - c|\{|f'(c)| + 1\}.$$

The left side of this expression can be made less than ϵ if we take x in $\mathfrak{D}$ with

$$|x - c| < \inf \left\{ \delta, \frac{\epsilon}{|f'(c)| + 1} \right\}.$$

Q.E.D.

It is easily seen that continuity at c is not a sufficient condition for the derivative to exist at c. For example, if $\mathfrak{D} = \mathbf{R}$ and $f(x) = |x|$, then f is continuous at every point of $\mathbf{R}$ but has a derivative at a point c if and only if $c \neq 0$. By taking simple algebraic combinations, it is easy to construct continuous functions which do not have a derivative at a finite or even a countable number of points. In 1872, Weierstrass shocked the mathematical world by giving an example of a *function which is continuous at every point but whose derivative does not exist anywhere*. (In fact, the function defined by the series

$$f(x) = \sum_{n=0}^{\infty} \frac{1}{2^n} \cos(3^n x),$$

can be proved to have this property. We shall not go through the details, but refer the reader to the books of Titchmarsh and Boas for further details and references.)

19.3 LEMMA. (a) *If f has a derivative at c and $f'(c) > 0$, there exists a positive number δ such that if $x \in \mathfrak{D}$ and $c < x < c + \delta$, then $f(c) < f(x)$.*

(b) *If $f'(c) < 0$, there exists a positive number δ such that if $x \in \mathfrak{D}$ and $c - \delta < x < c$, then $f(c) < f(x)$.*

PROOF. (a) Let ϵ_0 be such that $0 < \epsilon_0 < f'(c)$ and let $\delta = \delta(\epsilon_0)$ correspond to ϵ_0 as in Definition 19.1. If $x \in \mathfrak{D}$ and $c < x < c + \delta$, then we have

$$-\epsilon_0 < \frac{f(x) - f(c)}{x - c} - f'(c).$$

Since $x - c > 0$, this relation implies that

$$0 < [f'(c) - \epsilon_0](x - c) < f(x) - f(c),$$

which proves the assertion in (a). The proof of (b) is similar.

Q.E.D.

We recall that the function f is said to have a **relative maximum** at a point c in $\mathfrak{D}$ if there exists a $\delta > 0$ such that $f(x) \leq f(c)$ when $x \in \mathfrak{D}$ satisfies $|x - c| < \delta$. A similar definition applies to the term **relative minimum**. The next result provides the theoretical justification for the familiar process of finding points at which f has relative maxima and minima by examining the zeros of the derivative. It is to be noted that this procedure applies only to interior points of the interval. In fact, if $f(x) = x$ on $\mathfrak{D} = [0, 1]$, then the end point $x = 0$ yields the unique relative minimum and the end point $x = 1$ yields the unique relative maximum of f, but neither is a root of the derivative. For simplicity, we shall state this result only for relative maxima, leaving the formulation of the corresponding result for relative minima to the reader.

19.4 INTERIOR MAXIMUM THEOREM. *Let c be an interior point of $\mathfrak{D}$ at which f has a relative maximum. If the derivative of f at c exists, then it must be equal to zero.*

PROOF. If $f'(c) > 0$, then from Lemma 19.3(a) there is a $\delta > 0$ such that if $c < x < c + \delta$ and $x \in \mathfrak{D}$, then $f(c) < f(x)$. This contradicts the assumption that f has a relative maximum at c. If $f'(c) < 0$, we use Lemma 19.3(b).

Q.E.D.

19.5 ROLLE'S THEOREM.† *Suppose that f is continuous on a closed interval $J = [a, b]$, that the derivative f' exists in the open interval (a, b), and that $f(a) = f(b) = 0$. Then there exists a point c in (a, b) such that $f'(c) = 0$.*

PROOF. If f vanishes identically on J, we can take $c = (a + b)/2$. Hence we suppose that f does not vanish identically; replacing f by $-f$, if necessary, we may suppose that f assumes some positive values. By Corollary 16.7, the function f attains the value sup $\{f(x):x \in J\}$ at some point c of J. Since $f(a) = f(b) = 0$, the point c satisfies $a < c < b$.

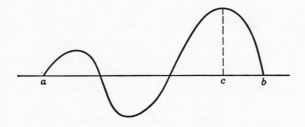

Figure 19.1

(See Figure 19.1.) By hypothesis $f'(c)$ exists and, since f has a relative maximum point at c, the Interior Maximum Theorem implies that $f'(c) = 0$.

Q.E.D.

As a consequence of Rolle's Theorem, we obtain the very important Mean Value Theorem.

† This theorem is generally attributed to MICHEL ROLLE (1652–1719), a member of the French Academy, who made contributions to analytic geometry and the early work leading to calculus.

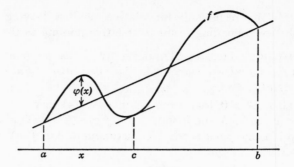

Figure 19.2.   The mean value theorem.

19.6   MEAN VALUE THEOREM. *Suppose that f is continuous on a closed interval $J = [a, b]$ and has a derivative in the open interval (a, b). Then there exists a point c in (a, b) such that*

$$f(b) - f(a) = f'(c)(b - a).$$

PROOF.   Consider the function φ defined on J by

$$\varphi(x) = f(x) - f(a) - \frac{f(b) - f(a)}{b - a}(x - a).$$

[It is easily seen that φ is the difference of f and the function whose graph consist of the line segment passing through the points $(a, f(a))$ and $(b, f(b))$; see Figure 19.2.] It follows from the hypotheses that φ is continuous on $J = [a, b]$ and it is easily checked that φ has a derivative in (a, b). Furthermore, we have $\varphi(a) = \varphi(b) = 0$. Applying Rolle's Theorem, there exists a point c inside J such that

$$0 = \varphi'(c) = f'(c) - \frac{f(b) - f(a)}{b - a}$$

from which the result follows.

Q.E.D.

19.7   COROLLARY. *If f has a derivative on $J = [a, b]$, then there exists a point c in (a, b) such that*

$$f(b) - f(a) = f'(c)(b - a).$$

Sometimes it is convenient to have a more general version of the Mean Value Theorem involving two functions.

19.8   CAUCHY MEAN VALUE THEOREM. *Let f, g be continuous on $J = [a, b]$ and have derivatives inside (a, b). Then there exists a point c in (a, b) such that*

$$f'(c)[g(b) - g(a)] = g'(c)[f(b) - f(a)].$$

PROOF.   When $g(b) = g(a)$ the result is immediate if we take c so that $g'(c) = 0$. If $g(b) \neq g(a)$, consider the function φ defined on J by

$$\varphi(x) = f(x) - f(a) - \frac{f(b) - f(a)}{g(b) - g(a)} [g(x) - g(a)].$$

Applying Rolle's Theorem to φ, we obtain the desired result.

Q.E.D.

Although the derivative of a function need not be continuous, there is an elementary but striking theorem due to Darboux† asserting that the derivative f' attains every value between $f'(a)$ and $f'(b)$ on the interval $[a, b]$. (See Exercise 19.N.)

Suppose that the derivative f' exists at every point of a set $\mathfrak{D}$. We can consider the existence of the derivative of f' at a point c in $\mathfrak{D}$. In case the function f' has a derivative at c, we refer to the resulting number as the **second derivative** of f at c and ordinarily denote this number by $f''(c)$. In a similar fashion we define the **third derivative** $f'''(c), \ldots$ and the nth derivative $f^{(n)}(c), \ldots$, whenever these derivatives exist.

Before we turn to some applications, we obtain the celebrated theorem of Brook Taylor‡, which plays an important role in many investigations and is an extension of the Mean Value Theorem.

19.9   TAYLOR'S THEOREM.   *Suppose that n is a natural number, that f and its derivatives $f', f'', \ldots, f^{(n-1)}$ are defined and continuous on $J = [a, b]$, and that $f^{(n)}$ exists in (a, b). If α, β belong to J, then there exists a number γ between α and β such that*

$$f(\beta) = f(\alpha) + \frac{f'(\alpha)}{1!} (\beta - \alpha) + \frac{f''(\alpha)}{2!} (\beta - \alpha)^2$$
$$+ \cdots + \frac{f^{(n-1)}(\alpha)}{(n-1)!} (\beta - \alpha)^{n-1} + \frac{f^{(n)}(\gamma)}{n!} (\beta - \alpha)^n.$$

PROOF.   Let P be the real number defined by the relation

$$(19.3) \quad \frac{(\beta - \alpha)^n}{n!} P = f(\beta) - \left\{ f(\alpha) + \frac{f'(\alpha)}{1!} (\beta - \alpha) \right.$$
$$\left. + \cdots + \frac{f^{(n-1)}(\alpha)}{(n-1)!} (\beta - \alpha)^{n-1} \right\}.$$

---

† GASTON DARBOUX (1842–1917) was a student of Hermite and a professor at the Collège de France. Although he is known primarily as a geometer, he made important contributions to analysis as well.

‡ BROOK TAYLOR (1685–1731) was an early English mathematician. In 1715 he gave the infinite series expansion, but — true to the spirit of the time — did not discuss questions of convergence. The remainder was supplied by Lagrange.

and consider the function φ defined on J by

$$\varphi(x) = f(\beta) - \left\{ f(x) + \frac{f'(x)}{1!} (\beta - x) \right.$$
$$\left. + \cdots + \frac{f^{(n-1)}(x)}{(n-1)!} (\beta - x)^{n-1} + \frac{P}{n!} (\beta - x)^n \right\}.$$

Clearly, φ is continuous on J and has a derivative on (a, b). It is evident that $\varphi(\beta) = 0$ and it follows from the definition of P that $\varphi(\alpha) = 0$. By Rolle's Theorem, there exists a point γ between α and β such that $\varphi'(\gamma) = 0$. On calculating the derivative φ' (using the usual formula for the derivative of a sum and product of two functions), we obtain the telescoping sum

$$\varphi'(x) = - \left\{ f'(x) - f'(x) + \frac{f''(x)}{1!} (\beta - x) + \cdots \right.$$
$$+ (-1) \frac{f^{(n-1)}(x)}{(n-2)!} (\beta - x)^{n-2} + \frac{f^{(n)}(x)}{(n-1)!} (\beta - x)^{n-1}$$
$$\left. - \frac{P}{(n-1)!} (\beta - x)^{n-1} \right\} = \frac{P - f^{(n)}(x)}{(n-1)!} (\beta - x)^{n-1}.$$

Since $\varphi'(\gamma) = 0$, then $P = f^{(n)}(\gamma)$, proving the assertion.

Q.E.D.

REMARK.   The remainder term

(19.4) $$R_n = \frac{f^{(n)}(\gamma)}{n!} (\beta - \alpha)^n$$

given above is often called the **Lagrange form** of the remainder. There are many other expressions for the remainder, but for the present, we mention only the **Cauchy form** which asserts that for some number θ with $0 < \theta < 1$, then

(19.5) $$R_n = (1 - \theta)^{n-1} \cdot \frac{f^{(n)}((1 - \theta)\alpha + \theta\beta)}{(n-1)!} (\beta - \alpha)^n.$$

This form can be established as above, except that on the left side of equation (19.3) we put $(\beta - \alpha)Q/(n-1)!$ and we define φ as above except its last term is $(\beta - x)Q/(n-1)!$ We leave the details as an exercise. (In Section 23 we shall obtain another form involving use of the integral to evaluate the remainder term.)

19.10   CONSEQUENCES.   We now mention some elementary consequences of the Mean Value Theorem which are frequently of use. As before, we assume that f is continuous on $J = [a, b]$ and its derivative exists in (a, b).

(i) If $f'(x) = 0$ for $a < x < b$, then f is constant on J.

(ii) If $f'(x) = g'(x)$ for $a < x < b$, then f and g differ on J by a constant.

(iii) If $f'(x) \geq 0$ for $a < x < b$ and if $x_1 \leq x_2$ belong to J, then $f(x_1) \leq f(x_2)$.

(iv) If $f'(x) > 0$ for $a < x < b$ and if $x_1 < x_2$ belong to J, then $f(x_1) < f(x_2)$.

(v) If $f'(x) \geq 0$ for $a < x < a + \delta$, then a is a relative minimum point of f.

(vi) If $f'(x) \geq 0$ for $b - \delta < x < b$, then b is a relative maximum point of f.

(vii) If $|f'(x)| \leq M$ for $a < x < b$, then f satisfies the Lipschitz condition:

$$|f(x_1) - f(x_2)| \leq M |x_1 - x_2| \quad \text{for} \quad x_1, x_2 \text{ in } J.$$

Applications of the Mean Value Theorem

It is hardly possible to overemphasize the importance of the Mean Value Theorem, for it plays a crucial role in many theoretical considerations. At the same time it is very useful in many practical matters. In 19.10 we indicated some immediate consequences of the Mean Value Theorem which are often useful. We shall now suggest some other areas in which it can be applied; in doing so we shall draw more freely than before on the past experience of the reader and his knowledge concerning the derivatives of certain well-known functions.

19.11 APPLICATIONS. (a) Rolle's Theorem can be used for the location of roots of a function. For, if a function g can be identified as the derivative of a function f, then between any two roots of f there is at least one root of g. For example, let $g(x) = \cos x$; then g is known to be the derivative of $f(x) = \sin x$. Hence, between any two roots of $\sin x$ there is at least one root of $\cos x$. On the other hand, $g'(x) = -\sin x = -f(x)$, so another application of Rolle's Theorem tells us that between any two roots of $\cos x$ there is at least one root of $\sin x$. Therefore, we conclude that *the roots of* $\sin x$ *and* $\cos x$ *interlace each other*. This conclusion is probably not news to the reader; however, the same type of argument can be applied to *Bessel*† *functions* J_n of integral order by using the relations

$$[x^n J_n(x)]' = x^n J_{n-1}(x), \qquad [x^{-n} J_n(x)]' = -x^{-n} J_{n+1}(x).$$

† FRIEDRICH WILHELM BESSEL (1784–1846) was an astronomer and mathematician. A close friend of Gauss, he is best known for the differential equation which bears his name.

The details of this argument should be supplied by the reader.

(b) We can apply the Mean Value Theorem for approximate calculations and to obtain error estimates. For example, suppose it is desired to evaluate $\sqrt{105}$. We employ the Mean Value Theorem with $f(x) = \sqrt{x}$, $a = 100$, $b = 105$ to obtain

$$\sqrt{105} - \sqrt{100} = \frac{5}{2\sqrt{c}},$$

for some number c with $100 < c < 105$. Since $10 < \sqrt{c} < \sqrt{105} < \sqrt{121} = 11$, we can assert that

$$\frac{5}{2(11)} < \sqrt{105} - 10 < \frac{5}{2(10)},$$

whence it follows that $10.22 < \sqrt{105} < 10.25$. This estimate may not be as sharp as desired. It is clear that the estimate $\sqrt{c} < \sqrt{105} < \sqrt{121}$ was wasteful and can be improved by making use of our conclusion that $\sqrt{105} < 10.25$. Thus, $\sqrt{c} < 10.25$ and we easily determine that

$$0.243 < \frac{5}{2(10.25)} < \sqrt{105} - 10.$$

Our improved estimate is $10.243 < \sqrt{105} < 10.250$ and more accurate estimates can be obtained in this way.

(c) The Mean Value Theorem and its corollaries can be used to establish inequalities and to extend inequalities that are known for integral or rational values to real values.

For example, we recall that Bernoulli's Inequality 5.E asserts that if $1 + x > 0$ and $n \in \mathbf{N}$, then $(1 + x)^n \geq 1 + nx$. We shall show that this inequality holds for any real exponent $r \geq 1$. To do so, let

$$f(x) = (1 + x)^r,$$

so that

$$f'(x) = r(1 + x)^{r-1}.$$

If $-1 < x < 0$, then $f'(x) < r$, while if $x > 0$, then $f'(x) > r$. If we apply the Mean Value Theorem to both of these cases, we obtain the result

$$(1 + x)^r \geq 1 + rx,$$

when $1 + x > 0$ and $r \geq 1$. Moreover, if $r > 1$, then the equality occurs if and only if $x = 0$.

As a similar result, let α be a real number satisfying $0 < \alpha < 1$ and let

$$g(x) = \alpha x - x^\alpha \qquad \text{for} \qquad x \geq 0.$$

Then

$$g'(x) = \alpha(1 - x^{\alpha-1}),$$

so that $g'(x) < 0$ for $0 < x < 1$ and $g'(x) > 0$ for $x > 1$. Consequently, if $x \geq 0$, then $g(x) \geq g(1)$ and $g(x) = g(1)$ if and only if $x = 1$. Therefore, if $x \geq 0$ and $0 < \alpha < 1$, then we have

$$x^\alpha \leq \alpha x + (1 - \alpha).$$

If a, b are non-negative real numbers and if we let $x = a/b$ and multiply by b, we obtain the inequality

$$a^\alpha b^{1-\alpha} \leq \alpha a + (1 - \alpha)b.$$

where equality holds if and only if $a = b$. This inequality is often the starting point in establishing the important Hölder Inequality (cf. Project 7.β).

(d) Some of the familiar rules of L'Hospital† on the evaluation of "indeterminant forms" can be established by means of the Cauchy Mean Value Theorem. For example, suppose that f, g are continuous on $[a, b]$ and have derivatives in (a, b), that $f(a) = g(a) = 0$, but that g, g' do not vanish for $x \neq a$. Then there exists a point c with $a < c < b$ such that

$$\frac{f(b)}{g(b)} = \frac{f'(c)}{g'(c)}.$$

It follows that if the limit

$$\lim_{x \to a} \frac{f'(x)}{g'(x)}$$

exists, then

$$\lim_{x \to a} \frac{f(x)}{g(x)} = \lim_{x \to a} \frac{f'(x)}{g'(x)}.$$

The case where the functions become infinite at $x = a$, or where the point at which the limit is taken is infinite, or where we have an "indeterminant" of some other form, can often be treated by taking logarithms, exponentials or some similar manipulation.

For example, if $a = 0$ and we wish to evaluate the limit of $h(x) = x \log x$ as $x \to 0$, we cannot apply the above argument. We write $h(x)$

† GUILLAUME FRANÇOIS L'HOSPITAL (1661–1704) was a student of Johann Bernoulli (1667–1748). The Marquis de L'Hospital published his teacher's lectures on differential calculus in 1696, thereby presenting the first textbook on calculus to the world.

in the form $f(x)/g(x)$ where $f(x) = \log x$ and $g(x) = 1/x, x > 0$. It is seen that

$$\frac{f'(x)}{g'(x)} = \frac{\dfrac{1}{x}}{\dfrac{-1}{x^2}} = -x \to 0, \quad \text{as} \quad x \to 0.$$

Let $\epsilon > 0$ and choose a fixed positive number $x_1 < 1$ such that if $0 < x < x_1$, then

$$\left| \frac{f'(x)}{g'(x)} \right| < \epsilon.$$

Applying the Cauchy Mean Value Theorem, we have

$$\left| \frac{f(x) - f(x_1)}{g(x) - g(x_1)} \right| = \left| \frac{f'(x_2)}{g'(x_2)} \right| < \epsilon,$$

with x_2 satisfying $0 < x < x_2 < x_1$. Since $f(x) \neq 0$ and $g(x) \neq 0$ for $0 < x < x_1$, we can write the quantity appearing on the left side in the more convenient form

$$\frac{f(x)}{g(x)} \left[\frac{1 - \dfrac{f(x_1)}{f(x)}}{1 - \dfrac{g(x_1)}{g(x)}} \right].$$

Holding x_1 fixed, we let $x \to 0$. Since the quantity in braces converges to 1, it exceeds $\frac{1}{2}$ for x sufficiently small. We infer from the above that

$$|h(x)| = \left| \frac{f(x)}{g(x)} \right| < 2\epsilon,$$

for x sufficiently near 0. Thus the limit of h at $x = 0$ is 0.

Interchange of Limit and Derivative

Let (f_n) be a sequence of functions defined on an interval J of R and with values in R. It is easy to give an example of a sequence of functions which have derivatives at every point of J and which converges on J to a function f which does not have a derivative at some points of J. (Do so!) Moreover, the example of Weierstrass mentioned before can be used to give an example of a sequence of functions possessing derivatives at every point of R and converging uniformly on R to a continuous function which has a derivative at no point. Thus it is not permissible, in general, to differentiate the limit of a convergent sequence of functions possessing derivatives even when the convergence is uniform.

We shall now show that if the sequence of *derivatives* is uniformly convergent, then all is well. If one adds the hypothesis that the derivatives are continuous, then it is possible to give a short proof based on the Riemann integral. However, if the derivatives are not assumed to be continuous, a somewhat more delicate argument is required.

19.12   THEOREM.   *Let (f_n) be a sequence of functions defined on an interval J of* **R** *and with values on* **R**. *Suppose that there is a point x_0 in J at which the sequence $(f_n(x_0))$ converges, that the derivatives $f_n{}'$ exist on J, and that the sequence $(f_n{}')$ converges uniformly on J to a function g. Then the sequence (f_n) converges uniformly on J to a function f which has a derivative at every point of J and $f' = g$.*

PROOF.   Suppose the end points of J are $a < b$ and let x be any point of J. If m, n are natural numbers, we apply the Mean Value Theorem to the difference $f_m - f_n$ on the interval with end points x_0, x to conclude that there exists a point y (depending on m, n) such that

$$f_m(x) - f_n(x) = f_m(x_0) - f_n(x_0) + (x - x_0)\{f_m{}'(y) - f_n{}'(y)\}.$$

Hence we infer that

$$\|f_m - f_n\| \le |f_m(x_0) - f_n(x_0)| + (b - a)\|f_m{}' - f_n{}'\|,$$

so the sequence (f_n) converges uniformly on J to a function we shall denote by f. Since the f_n are continuous and the convergence of (f_n) to f is uniform, then f is continuous on J.

To establish the existence of the derivative of f at a point c in J, we apply the Mean Value Theorem to the difference $f_m - f_n$ on an interval with end points c, x to infer that there exists a point z (depending on m, n) such that

$$\{f_m(x) - f_n(x)\} - \{f_m(c) - f_n(c)\} = (x - c)\{f_m{}'(z) - f_n{}'(z)\}.$$

We infer that, when $c \ne x$, then

$$\left| \frac{f_m(x) - f_m(c)}{x - c} - \frac{f_n(x) - f_n(c)}{x - c} \right| \le \|f_m{}' - f_n{}'\|.$$

In virtue of the uniform convergence of the sequence $(f_n{}')$, the right hand side is dominated by ϵ when $m, n \ge M(\epsilon)$. Taking the limit with respect to m, we infer from Lemma 11.16 that

$$\left| \frac{f(x) - f(c)}{x - c} - \frac{f_n(x) - f_n(c)}{x - c} \right| \le \epsilon,$$

when $n \geq M(\epsilon)$. Since $g(c) = \lim (f_n'(c))$, there exists an $N(\epsilon)$ such that if $n \geq N(\epsilon)$, then

$$|f_n'(c) - g(c)| < \epsilon.$$

Now let $K = \sup \{M(\epsilon), N(\epsilon)\}$. In view of the existence of $f_K'(c)$, if $0 < |x - c| < \delta_K(\epsilon)$, then

$$\left| \frac{f_K(x) - f_K(c)}{x - c} - f_K'(c) \right| < \epsilon.$$

Therefore, it follows that if $0 < |x - c| < \delta_K(\epsilon)$, then

$$\left| \frac{f(x) - f(c)}{x - c} - g(c) \right| < 3\epsilon.$$

This shows that $f'(c)$ exists and equals $g(c)$.

Q.E.D.

Exercises

19.A. Using the definition, calculate the derivative (when it exists) of the functions given by the expressions:

(a) $f(x) = x^2$,

(b) $g(x) = x^n$,

(c) $h(x) = \sqrt{x}$, $x \geq 0$

(d) $F(x) = 1/x$, $x \neq 0$,

(e) $G(x) = |x|$,

(f) $H(x) = 1/x^2$, $x \neq 0$.

19.B. If f and g are real-valued functions defined on an interval J, and if they are differentiable at a point c, show that their product h, defined by $h(x) = f(x)g(x)$, $x \in J$, is differentiable at c and

$$h'(c) = f'(c)g(c) + f(c)g'(c).$$

19.C. Show that the function defined for $x \neq 0$ by

$$f(x) = \sin (1/x)$$

is differentiable at each non-zero real number. Show that its derivative is not bounded on a neighborhood of $x = 0$. (You may make use of trigonometric identities, the continuity of the sine and cosine functions, and the elementary limiting relation

$$\frac{\sin u}{u} \to 1 \quad \text{as} \quad u \to 0.)$$

19.D. Show that the function defined by

$$g(x) = x^2 \sin (1/x), \qquad x \neq 0,$$
$$= 0, \qquad\qquad\quad x = 0,$$

is differentiable for all real numbers, but that g' is not continuous at $x = 0$.

19.E. The function defined on R by

$$h(x) = x^2, \qquad x \text{ rational},$$
$$= 0, \qquad x \text{ irrational},$$

is continuous at exactly one point. Is it differentiable there?

19.F. Construct a continuous function which does not have a derivative at any rational number.

19.G. If f' exists on a neighborhood of $x = 0$ and if $f'(x) \to a$ as $x \to 0$, then $a = f'(0)$.

19.H. Does there exist a continuous function with a unique relative maximum point but such that the derivative does not exist at this point?

19.I. Justify the expression for φ' that is stated in the proof of the Mean Value Theorem 19.6.

19.J. Verify Rolle's Theorem for the polynomial $f(x) = x^m(1 - x)^n$ on the interval $I = [0, 1]$.

19.K. If $a < b$ are consecutive roots of a polynomial, there are an odd number (counting multiplicities) of roots of its derivative in (a, b).

19.L. If p is a polynomial whose roots are real, then the roots of p' are real. If, in addition, the roots of p are simple, then the roots of p' are simple.

19.M. If $f(x) = (x^2 - 1)^n$ and if g is the nth derivative of f, then g is a polynomial of degree n whose roots are simple and lie in the open interval $(-1, 1)$.

19.N. (Darboux) If f is differentiable on $[a, b]$, if $f'(a) = A$, $f'(b) = B$, and if C lies between A and B, then there exists a point c in (a, b) for which $f'(c) = C$. (Hint: consider the lower bound of the function $g(x) = f(x) - C(x - a)$.)

19.O. Establish the Cauchy form of the remainder given in formula (19.5).

19.P. Establish the statements listed in 19.10 (i–vii).

19.Q. Show that the roots of the Bessel functions J_0 and J_1 interlace each other. (Hint: refer to 19.11(a).)

19.R. If $f(x) = \sin x$, show that the remainder term R_n in Taylor's Theorem approaches zero as n increases.

19.S. If $f(x) = (1 + x)^m$, where m is a rational number, the usual differentiation formulas from calculus and Taylor's Theorem lead to the expansion

$$(1 + x)^m = 1 + \binom{m}{1} x + \binom{m}{2} x^2 + \cdots + \binom{m}{n-1} x^{n-1} + R_n,$$

where the remainder R_n can be given (in Lagrange's form) by

$$R_n = \frac{x^n}{n!} f^{(n)}(\theta_n x), \qquad 0 < \theta_n < 1.$$

Show that if $0 \le x < 1$, then $\lim(R_n) = 0$.

19.T. In the preceding exercise, use Cauchy's form of the remainder to obtain

$$R_n = \frac{m(m - 1) \cdots (m - n + 1)}{1 \cdot 2 \cdots (n - 1)} \frac{(1 - \theta_n)^{n-1} x^n}{(1 + \theta_n x)^{n-m}},$$

where $0 < \theta_n < 1$. When $-1 < x < +1$,

$$\left| \frac{1 - \theta_n}{1 + \theta_n x} \right| < 1.$$

Show that if $|x| < 1$, then $\lim(R_n) = 0$.

19.U. (a) If $f'(a)$ exists, then

$$f'(a) = \lim_{h \to 0} \frac{f(a + h) - f(a - h)}{2h}.$$

(b) If $f''(a)$ exists, then

$$f''(a) = \lim_{h \to 0} \frac{f(a + h) - 2f(a) + f(a - h)}{h^2}.$$

19.V. (a) If $f(x) \to a$ and $f'(x) \to b$ as $x \to +\infty$, then $b = 0$.

(b) If $f'(x) \to a \neq 0$ as $x \to +\infty$, then $\dfrac{f(x)}{ax} \to 1$ as $x \to +\infty$.

(c) If $f'(x) \to 0$ as $x \to +\infty$, then $\dfrac{f(x)}{x} \to 0$ as $x \to +\infty$.

19.W. Give an example of a sequence of functions which are differentiable at each point and which converge to a function which fails to have a derivative at some points.

19.X. Give an example of the situation described in the preceding exercise where the convergence is uniform.

Projects

19.α. In this project we consider the exponential function from the point of view of differential calculus.

(a) Suppose that a function E on $J = (a, b)$ to $\mathbf{R}$ has a derivative at every point of J and that $E'(x) = E(x)$ for all $x \in J$. Observe that E has derivatives of all orders on J and they all equal E.

(b) If $E(\alpha) = 0$ for some $\alpha \in J$, apply Taylor's Theorem 19.9 and Exercise 11.N to show that $E(x) = 0$ for all $x \in J$.

(c) Show that there exists at most one function E on $\mathbf{R}$ to $\mathbf{R}$ which satisfies

$$E'(x) = E(x) \quad \text{for } x \in \mathbf{R}, \qquad E(0) = 1.$$

(d) Prove that if E satisfies the conditions in part (c), then it also satisfies the functional equation

$$E(x + y) = E(x)E(y) \quad \text{for} \quad x, y \in \mathbf{R}.$$

(Hint: if $f(x) = E(x + y)/E(y)$, then $f'(x) = f(x)$ and $f(0) = 1$.)

(e) Let (E_n) be the sequence of functions defined on $\mathbf{R}$ by

$$E_1(x) = 1 + x, \qquad E_n(x) = E_{n-1}(x) + x^n/n!.$$

Let A be any positive number; if $|x| \leq A$ and if $m \geq n > 2A$, then

$$|E_m(x) - E_n(x)| \leq \frac{A^{n+1}}{(n+1)!}\left[1 + \frac{A}{n} + \cdots + \left(\frac{A}{n}\right)^{m-n}\right]$$

$$< \frac{2A^{n+1}}{(n+1)!}.$$

Hence the sequence (E_n) converges uniformly for $|x| \leq A$.

(f) If (E_n) is the sequence of functions defined in part (e), then

$$E_n'(x) = E_{n-1}(x), \qquad x \in \mathbf{R}.$$

Show that the sequence (E_n) converges on **R** to a function E with the properties displayed in part (c). Therefore, E is the unique function with these properties.

(g) Let E be the function with $E' = E$ and $E(0) = 1$. If we define e to be the number

$$e = E(1),$$

then e lies between $2\frac{2}{3}$ and $2\frac{3}{4}$. (Hint: $1 + 1 + \frac{1}{2} + \frac{1}{6} < e < 1 + 1 + \frac{1}{2} + \frac{1}{6} + \frac{1}{12}$. More precisely, we can show that

$$2.708 < 2 + \tfrac{17}{24} < e < 2 + \tfrac{13}{18} < 2.723.)$$

19.β. In this project, you may use the results of the preceding one. Let E denote the unique function on **R** such that

$$E' = E \qquad \text{and} \qquad E(0) = 1$$

and let $e = E(1)$.

(a) Show that E is strictly increasing and has range $P = \{x \in \mathbf{R} : x > 0\}$.

(b) Let L be the inverse function of E, so that the domain of L is P and its range is all of **R**. Prove that L is strictly increasing on P, that $L(1) = 0$, and that $L(e) = 1$.

(c) Show that $L(xy) = L(x) + L(y)$ for all x, y in P.

(d) If $0 < x < y$, then

$$\frac{1}{y}(y - x) < L(y) - L(x) < \frac{1}{x}(y - x).$$

(Hint: apply the Mean Value Theorem to E.)

(e) The function L has a derivative for $x > 0$ and $L'(x) = 1/x$.

(f) The number e satisfies

$$e = \lim\left(\left(1 + \frac{1}{n}\right)^n\right).$$

(Hint: evaluate $L'(1)$ by using the sequence $((1 + 1/n))$ and the continuity of E.)

19.γ. In this project we shall introduce the sine and cosine.

(a) Let h be defined on an interval $J = (a, b)$ to R and satisfy

$$h''(x) + h(x) = 0$$

for all x in J. Show that h has derivatives of all orders and that if there is a point α in J such that $h(\alpha) = 0$, $h'(\alpha) = 0$, then $h(x) = 0$ for all $x \in J$. (Hint: use Taylor's Theorem 19.9.)

(b) Show that there exists at most one function C on R satisfying the conditions

$$C'' + C = 0, \qquad C(0) = 1, \qquad C'(0) = 0,$$

and at most one function S on R satisfying

$$S'' + S = 0, \qquad S(0) = 0, \qquad S'(0) = 1.$$

(c) We define a sequence (C_n) by

$$C_1(x) = 1 - x^2/2, \qquad C_n(x) = C_{n-1}(x) + (-1)^n \frac{x^{2n}}{(2n)!}.$$

Let A be any positive number; if $|x| \leq A$ and if $m \geq n > A$, then

$$|C_m(x) - C_n(x)| \leq \frac{A^{2n+2}}{(2n + 2)!} \left[1 + \left(\frac{A}{2n}\right)^2 + \cdots + \left(\frac{A}{2n}\right)^{2m-2n} \right]$$

$$< \left(\frac{4}{3}\right) \frac{A^{2n+2}}{(2n + 2)!}.$$

Hence the sequence (C_n) converges uniformly for $|x| \leq A$. Show also that $C_n'' = -C_{n-1}$, and $C_n(0) = 1$ and $C_n'(0) = 0$. Prove that the limit C of the sequence (C_n) is the unique function with the properties in part (b).

(d) Let (S_n) be defined by

$$S_1(x) = x, \qquad S_n(x) = S_{n-1}(x) + (-1)^{n-1} \frac{x^{2n-1}}{(2n - 1)!}.$$

Show that (S_n) converges uniformly for $|x| \leq A$ to the unique function S with the properties in part (b).

(e) Prove that $S' = C$ and $C' = -S$.

(f) Establish the Pythagorean Identity $S^2 + C^2 = 1$. (Hint: calculate the derivative of $S^2 + C^2$.)

19.δ. This project continues the discussion of the sine and cosine functions. Free use may be made of the properties established in the preceding project.

(a) Suppose that h is a function on R which satisfies the equation

$$h'' + h = 0.$$

Show that there exist constants α, β such that $h = \alpha C + \beta S$. (Hint: $\alpha = h(0)$, $\beta = h'(0)$.)

(b) The function C is even and S is odd in the sense that

$$C(-x) = C(x), \qquad S(-x) = -S(x), \qquad \text{for all } x \text{ in } R.$$

(c) Show that the "addition formulas"

$$C(x + y) = C(x)C(y) - S(x)S(y),$$
$$S(x + y) = S(x)C(y) + C(x)S(y),$$

hold for all x, y in $\mathbf{R}$. (Hint: let y be fixed, define $h(x) = C(x + y)$, and show that $h'' + h = 0$.)

(d) Show that the "duplication formulas"

$$C(2x) = 2[C(x)]^2 - 1 = 2[S(x)]^2 + 1,$$
$$S(2x) = 2S(x)C(x),$$

hold for all x in $\mathbf{R}$.

(e) Prove that C satisfies the inequality

$$C_1(x) = 1 - \frac{x^2}{2} \leq C(x) \leq 1 - \frac{x^2}{2} + \frac{x^4}{24} = C_2(x).$$

Therefore, the smallest positive root γ of C lies between the positive root of $x^2 - 2 = 0$ and the smallest positive root of $x^4 - 12x^2 + 24 = 0$. Using this, prove that $\sqrt{2} < \gamma < \sqrt{3}$.

(f) We define π to be the smallest positive root of S. Prove that $\pi = 2\gamma$ and hence that $2\sqrt{2} < \pi < 2\sqrt{3}$.

(g) Prove that both C and S are periodic functions with period 2π in the sense that $C(x + 2\pi) = C(x)$ and $S(x + 2\pi) = S(x)$ for all x in $\mathbf{R}$. Also show that

$$S(x) = C\left(\frac{\pi}{2} - x\right) = -C\left(x + \frac{\pi}{2}\right),$$
$$C(x) = S\left(\frac{\pi}{2} - x\right) = S\left(x + \frac{\pi}{2}\right),$$

for all x in $\mathbf{R}$.

19.ε. Following the model of the preceding two exercises, introduce the hyperbolic cosine and sine as functions satisfying

$$c'' = c, \quad c(0) = 1, \quad c'(0) = 0,$$
$$s'' = s, \quad s(0) = 0, \quad s'(0) = 1,$$

respectively. Establish the existence and the uniqueness of these functions and show that

$$c^2 - s^2 = 1.$$

Prove results similar to (a)–(d) of Project 19.δ and show that, if the exponential function is denoted by E, then

$$c(x) = \tfrac{1}{2}(E(x) + E(-x)),$$
$$s(x) = \tfrac{1}{2}(E(x) - E(-x)).$$

19.ϛ. A function φ on an interval J of R to R is said to be **convex** in case

$$\varphi\left(\frac{x+y}{2}\right) \leq \frac{1}{2}\left(\varphi(x) + \varphi(y)\right)$$

for each x, y in J. (In geometrical terms: the midpoint of any chord of the curve $y = \varphi(x)$, lies above or on the curve.) In this project we shall always suppose that φ is a continuous convex function.

(a) If $n = 2^m$ and if $x_1, \ldots, x_n$ belong to J, then

$$\varphi\left(\frac{x_1 + x_2 + \cdots + x_n}{n}\right) \leq \frac{1}{n}\left(\varphi(x_1) + \cdots + \varphi(x_n)\right).$$

(b) If $n < 2^m$ and if $x_1, \ldots, x_n$ belong to J, let x_j for $j = n+1, \ldots, 2^m$ be equal to

$$\bar{x} = \left(\frac{x_1 + x_2 + \cdots + x_n}{n}\right).$$

Show that the same inequality holds as in part (a).

(c) Since φ is continuous, show that if x, y belong to J and $t \in I$, then

$$\varphi((1-t)x + ty) \leq (1-t)\varphi(x) + t\varphi(y).$$

(In geometrical terms: the entire chord lies above or on the curve.)

(d) Suppose that φ has a second derivative on J. Then a necessary and sufficient condition that φ be convex on J is that $\varphi''(x) \geq 0$ for $x \in J$. (Hint: to prove the necessity, use Exercise 19.U. To prove the sufficiency, use Taylor's Theorem and expand about $\bar{x} = (x+y)/2$.)

(e) If φ is a continuous convex function on J and if $x \leq y \leq z$ belong to J, show that

$$\frac{\varphi(y) - \varphi(x)}{y - x} \leq \frac{\varphi(z) - \varphi(x)}{z - x}.$$

Therefore, if $w \leq x \leq y \leq z$ belong to J, then

$$\frac{\varphi(x) - \varphi(w)}{x - w} \leq \frac{\varphi(z) - \varphi(y)}{z - y}.$$

(f) Prove that a continuous convex function φ on J has a left-hand derivative and a right-hand derivative at every point. Furthermore, the subset where φ' does not exist is countable.

Section 20   The Derivative in $\mathbf{R}^p$

In the preceding section we considered the derivative of a function with domain and range in R. In the present section we shall consider a function defined on a subset of $\mathbf{R}^p$ and with values in $\mathbf{R}^q$.

If the reader will review Definition 19.1, he will note that it applies equally well to a function defined on an interval J in R and with values in the Cartesian space $\mathbf{R}^q$. Of course, in this case L is a vector in $\mathbf{R}^q$. The only change required for this extension is to replace the absolute value in equation (19.1) by the norm in the space $\mathbf{R}^q$. Except for this, Definition 19.1 applies *verbatim* to this more general situation. That this situation is worthy of study should be clear when it is realized that a function f on J to $\mathbf{R}^q$ can be regarded as being a *curve* in the space $\mathbf{R}^q$ and that the derivative (when it exists) of this function at the point $x = c$ yields a *tangent vector* to the curve at the point $f(c)$. Alternatively, if we think of x as denoting time, then the function f is the trajectory of a point in $\mathbf{R}^q$ and the derivative $f'(c)$ denotes the *velocity vector* of the point at time $x = c$.

A fuller investigation of these lines of thought would take us farther into differential geometry and dynamics than is desirable at present. Our aims are more modest: we wish to organize the analytical machinery that would make a satisfactory investigation possible and to remove the restriction that the domain is in a one-dimensional space and allow the domain to belong to the Cartesian space $\mathbf{R}^p$. We shall now proceed to do this.

An analysis of Definition 19.1 shows that the only place where it is necessary for the domain to consist of a subset of $\mathbf{R}$ is in equation (19.1), where a quotient appears. Since we have no meaning for the quotient of a vector in $\mathbf{R}^q$ by a vector in $\mathbf{R}^p$, we cannot interpret equation (19.1) as it stands. We are led, therefore, to find reformulations of this equation. One possibility which is of considerable interest is to take one-dimensional "slices" passing through the point c in the domain. For simplicity it will be supposed that c is an interior point of the domain $\mathfrak{D}$ of the function; then for any u in $\mathbf{R}^p$, the point $c + tu$ belongs to $\mathfrak{D}$ for sufficiently small real numbers t.

20.1 DEFINITION. Let f be defined on a subset $\mathfrak{D}$ of $\mathbf{R}^p$ and have values in $\mathbf{R}^q$, let c be an interior point of $\mathfrak{D}$, and let u be any point in $\mathbf{R}^p$. A vector L_u in $\mathbf{R}^q$ is said to be the **directional derivative of f at c in the direction of u** if for each positive real number ϵ there is a positive number $\delta(\epsilon)$ such that if $0 < |t| < \delta(\epsilon)$, then

$$(20.1) \qquad \left| \frac{1}{t} \{f(c + tu) - f(c)\} - L_u \right| < \epsilon.$$

It is readily seen that the directional derivative L_u defined in (20.1) is uniquely determined when it exists. Alternatively, we can define L_u as the limit

$$\lim_{t \to 0} \frac{1}{t} \{f(c + tu) - f(c)\}.$$

We shall write $f_u(c)$ for the directional derivative of f at c in the direction u and use f_u for the resulting function with values in $\mathbf{R}^q$, which is defined for those interior points c in $\mathfrak{D}$ for which the required limit exists.

It is clear that if f is real-valued (so that $q = 1$) and if u is the vector $e_1 = (1, 0, \ldots, 0)$ in $\mathbf{R}^p$, then the directional derivative of f in the direction e_1 coincides with the **partial derivative of f with respect to ξ_1**, which is often denoted by

$$f_{\xi_1} \quad \text{or} \quad \frac{\partial f}{\partial \xi_1}.$$

In the same way, taking $e_2 = (0, 1, \ldots, 0), \ldots, e_p = (0, 0, \ldots, 1)$, we obtain the **partial derivatives with respect to** $\xi_2, \ldots, \xi_p$, denoted by

$$f_{\xi_2} = \frac{\partial f}{\partial \xi_2}, \ldots, f_{\xi_p} = \frac{\partial f}{\partial \xi_p}.$$

Thus the notion of partial derivative is a special case of Definition 20.1.

Observe that the directional derivative of a function at a point in one direction may exist, yet the derivative in another direction need not exist. It is also plain that, under appropriate hypotheses, there are algebraic relations between the directional derivatives of sums and products of functions, and so forth. We shall not bother to obtain these relations, since they are either special cases of what we shall do below or can be proved in a similar fashion.

A word about terminology is in order. Some authors refer to $f_u(c)$ as "the derivative of f at c with respect to the vector u" and use the term "directional derivative" only in the case where u is a unit vector.

The Derivative

In order to motivate the notion of the derivative, we shall consider a special example. Let f be the function defined for $x = (\xi_1, \xi_2)$ in $\mathbf{R}^2$ to $\mathbf{R}^3$ given by

$$f(x) = f(\xi_1, \xi_2) = (\xi_1, \xi_2, \xi_1{}^2 + \xi_2{}^2).$$

Geometrically, the graph of f can be represented by the surface of the paraboloid in $\mathbf{R}^3$ given by the equation

$$\xi_3 = \xi_1{}^2 + \xi_2{}^2.$$

Let $c = (\gamma_1, \gamma_2)$ be a point in $\mathbf{R}^2$; we shall calculate the directional derivative of f at c in the direction of an element $w = (\omega_1, \omega_2)$ of $\mathbf{R}^2$. Since

$$f(c + tw) = (\gamma_1 + t\omega_1, \gamma_2 + t\omega_2, (\gamma_1 + t\omega_1)^2 + (\gamma_2 + t\omega_2)^2),$$
$$f(c) = (\gamma_1, \gamma_2, \gamma_1{}^2 + \gamma_2{}^2),$$

it follows that the directional derivative is given by

$$f_w(c) = (\omega_1, \omega_2, 2\gamma_1\omega_1 + 2\gamma_2\omega_2)$$

from which it is seen that

$$f_w(c) = \omega_1(1, 0, 2\gamma_1) + \omega_2(0, 1, 2\gamma_2).$$

From the formula just given it follows that the directional derivative of f exists in any direction and that it depends linearly on w in the sense that

$$f_{\alpha w}(c) = \alpha f_w(c) \quad \text{for} \quad \alpha \in \mathbf{R},$$

$$f_{w+z}(c) = f_w(c) + f_z(c) \quad \text{for} \quad w, z \in \mathbf{R}^2.$$

Thus the function which sends the element w of $\mathbf{R}^2$ into the element $f_w(c)$ of $\mathbf{R}^3$ is a linear function. Moreover, it is readily seen that

$$f(c + w) - f(c) - f_w(c) = (0, 0, \omega_1{}^2 + \omega_2{}^2),$$

from which it follows that

$$|f(c + w) - f(c) - f_w(c)| = |\omega_1{}^2 + \omega_2{}^2| = |w|^2.$$

If we think of the directional derivatives $f_w(c)$ as elements of $\mathbf{R}^3$ depending on $w \in \mathbf{R}^2$, then the fact that $f_w(c)$ depends linearly on w can be interpreted geometrically as meaning that the vectors $\{f_w(c) : w \in \mathbf{R}^2\}$ belong to a plane in $\mathbf{R}^3$ which passes through the origin. Adding the point $f(c)$ of $\mathbf{R}^3$, we obtain the set

$$P = \{f(c) + f_w(c) : w \in \mathbf{R}^2\},$$

which is a plane in $\mathbf{R}^3$ which passes through $f(c)$. In geometrical terms this latter plane is precisely the *plane tangent to the surface at the point* $f(c)$. (See Figure 20.1 on the next page.)

Therefore, we are led to inquire if, given $\epsilon > 0$ and a general function f on $\mathbf{R}^p$ to $\mathbf{R}^q$, does there exist a linear function L on $\mathbf{R}^p$ to $\mathbf{R}^q$ such that

$$|f(c + w) - f(c) - L(w)| \leq \epsilon |w|$$

for w in $\mathbf{R}^p$ which are such that $|w|$ is sufficiently small.

20.2 DEFINITION.   Let f have domain $\mathfrak{D}$ in $\mathbf{R}^p$ and range in $\mathbf{R}^q$ and let c be an interior point of $\mathfrak{D}$. We say that f is **differentiable at** c if there exists a linear function L on $\mathbf{R}^p$ to $\mathbf{R}^q$ such that for every positive number ϵ there exists a positive number $\delta(\epsilon)$ such that if $|x - c| < \delta(\epsilon)$, then $x \in \mathfrak{D}$ and

(20.2) $$|f(x) - f(c) - L(x - c)| \leq \epsilon |x - c|.$$

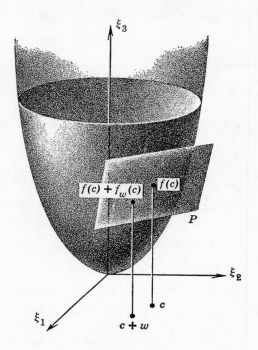

Figure 20.1

We shall see below that the linear function L is uniquely determined when it exists and that it enables us to calculate the directional derivative very easily. This linear function is called the **derivative** of f at c.

Usually we shall denote the derivative of f at c by

$$Df(c) \quad \text{or} \quad f'(c),$$

instead of L. When we write $Df(c)$ for L, we shall denote $L(x - c)$ by $Df(c)(x - c)$.

Some authors refer to $Df(c)$ as the *differential* of f at c. However, the most conventional use of the term "differential" is for the function which takes the point (c, u) of $R^p \times R^p$ into the point $Df(c)(u)$ of R^q.

20.3 LEMMA. *A function has at most one derivative at a point.*

PROOF. Suppose that L_1 and L_2 are linear functions on R^p to R^q which satisfy the inequality (20.2) when $|x - c| < \delta(\epsilon)$. If L_1 and L_2 are different, then there exists an element $z \in R^p$ with $|z| = 1$ such that

$$0 < |L_1(z) - L_2(z)|.$$

Let α be a non-zero real number with $|\alpha| < \delta(\epsilon)$ and set $x = c + \alpha z$. It follows that

$$0 < |\alpha|\,|L_1(z) - L_2(z)| = |L_1(\alpha z) - L_2(\alpha z)|$$
$$\leq |f(x) - f(c) - L_1(x - c)| + |f(x) - f(c) - L_2(x - c)|$$
$$\leq 2\epsilon\,|x - c| = 2\epsilon\,|\alpha z| = 2\epsilon\,|\alpha|.$$

Therefore, for any $\epsilon > 0$, then

$$0 < |L_1(z) - L_2(z)| \leq 2\epsilon,$$

which is a contradiction.

Q.E.D.

20.4 LEMMA. *If f is differentiable at a point c, then there exist positive real numbers δ, K such that if $|x - c| < \delta$, then*

(20.3) $$|f(x) - f(c)| \leq K\,|x - c|.$$

In particular, f is continuous at $x = c$.

PROOF.   According to Definition 20.2, there exists a positive real number δ_1 such that if $|x - c| < \delta_1$, then $x \in \mathfrak{D}$ and relation (20.2) holds with $\epsilon = 1$. Using the Triangle Inequality, we have

$$|f(x) - f(c)| \leq |L(x - c)| + |x - c|.$$

According to Theorem 15.11, there is a positive constant M such

$$|L(x - c)| \leq M\,|x - c|,$$

from which it follows that

$$|f(x) - f(c)| \leq (M + 1)\,|x - c|$$

provided that $|x - c| < \delta_1$.

Q.E.D.

20.5 EXAMPLES.   (a) Let $p = q = 1$ and let the domain $\mathfrak{D}$ of f be a subset of R. Then f is differentiable at an interior point c of $\mathfrak{D}$ if and only if the derivative $f'(c)$ of f exists at c. In this case the derivative $Df(c)$ of f at c is the linear function on R to R which sends the real number u into the real number

(20.4) $$f'(c)u$$

obtained by multiplying by $f'(c)$. Traditionally, instead of writing u for the real number on which this linear function operates, we write the somewhat peculiar symbol dx; here the "d" plays the role of a prefix and has no other significance. When this is done and the Leibniz† notation for the derivative is used, the formula (20.4) becomes

$$Df(c)(dx) = \frac{df}{dx}(c)\,dx.$$

(b) Let $p = 1$, $q > 1$, and let $\mathfrak{D}$ be a subset of $\mathbf{R}$. A function f, defined on $\mathfrak{D}$ to $\mathbf{R}^q$, can be represented by the "coordinate functions":

$$(20.5) \qquad f(x) = \big(f_1(x), f_2(x), \ldots, f_q(x)\big),\ x \in \mathfrak{D}.$$

It can be verified that the function f is differentiable at an interior point c in $\mathfrak{D}$ if and only if each of the real-valued coordinate functions f_1, $f_2, \ldots, f_q$ has a derivative at c. In this case, the derivative $Df(c)$ is the linear function of $\mathbf{R}$ into $\mathbf{R}^q$ which sends the real number u into the vector

$$(20.6) \qquad \big(f_1{}'(c)u, f_2{}'(c)u, \ldots, f_q{}'(c)u\big)$$

of $\mathbf{R}^q$. It may be noted that $Df(c)$ sends a real number u into the product of u and a fixed vector in $\mathbf{R}^q$.

(c) Let $p > 1$, $q = 1$, and let $\mathfrak{D}$ be a subset of $\mathbf{R}^p$. Then for $x = (\xi_1, \ldots, \xi_p)$ in $\mathfrak{D}$, we often write

$$f(x) = f(\xi_1, \ldots, \xi_p).$$

It can be verified that if f is differentiable at a point $c = (\gamma_1, \ldots, \gamma_p)$ of $\mathfrak{D}$, then each of the partial derivatives

$$f_{\xi_1}(c), \ldots, f_{\xi_p}(c).$$

must exist at c. However, the existence of these partial derivatives is not sufficient, in general, for the differentiability of f at c, as we shall show in the exercises. If f is differentiable at c, then the derivative Df is the linear function of $\mathbf{R}^p$ into $\mathbf{R}$ which sends the point $w = (\omega_1, \ldots, \omega_p)$ into the real number given by the sum

$$(20.7) \qquad f_{\xi_1}(c)\omega_1 + \cdots + f_{\xi_p}(c)\omega_p.$$

Sometimes, instead of w we write $dx = (d\xi_1, d\xi_2, \ldots, d\xi_p)$ for the point in $\mathbf{R}^p$ on which the derivative is to act. When this notation is used and when Leibniz's notation is employed for the partial derivatives of f, then formula (20.7) becomes

$$Df(c)(dx) = \frac{\partial f}{\partial \xi_1}(c)d\xi_1 + \cdots + \frac{\partial f}{\partial \xi_p}(c)d\xi_p.$$

† GOTTFRIED WILHELM LEIBNIZ (1646–1716) is, with ISAAC NEWTON (1642–1727), one of the coinventors of calculus. Leibniz spent most of his life serving the dukes of Hanover and was a universal genius. He contributed greatly to mathematics, law, philosophy, theology, linguistics, and history.

(d) Let us consider the case $p > 1$, $q > 1$, but restrict our attention first to a *linear* function f on $\mathbf{R}^p$ to $\mathbf{R}^q$. Then $f(x) - f(c) = f(x - c)$, and hence

$$|f(x) - f(c) - f(x - c)| = 0.$$

This shows that when f is linear, then f is differentiable at every point and $Df(c) = f$ for any point c in $\mathbf{R}^p$.

(e) We now consider the case $p > 1$, $q > 1$, and do not restrict the function f, defined on $\mathfrak{D}$ in $\mathbf{R}^p$ to $\mathbf{R}^q$ to be linear. In this case we can represent $y = f(x)$ by system

$$\eta_1 = f_1(\xi_1, \ldots, \xi_p),$$

(20.8) $\qquad \cdot \quad \cdot \quad \cdot \quad \cdot \quad \cdot \quad \cdot \quad \cdot$

$$\eta_q = f_q(\xi_1, \ldots, \xi_p),$$

of q functions of p arguments. If f is differentiable at a point $c = (\gamma_1, \ldots, \gamma_p)$ in $\mathfrak{D}$, then it follows that the partial derivatives of each of the f_j with respect to the ξ_k must exist at c. (Again this latter condition is not sufficient, in general, for the differentiability of f at c.) When $Df(c)$ exists, it is the linear function which sends the point $u = (v_1, \ldots, v_p)$ of $\mathbf{R}^p$ into the point w of $\mathbf{R}^q$ whose coordinates $(\omega_1, \ldots, \omega_q)$ are given by

$$\omega_1 = \frac{\partial f_1}{\partial \xi_1}(c)v_1 + \frac{\partial f_1}{\partial \xi_2}(c)v_2 + \cdots + \frac{\partial f_1}{\partial \xi_p}(c)v_p,$$

(20.9) $\qquad \cdot \quad \cdot \quad \cdot \quad \cdot \quad \cdot \quad \cdot \quad \cdot \quad \cdot \quad \cdot \quad \cdot \quad \cdot$

$$\omega_q = \frac{\partial f_q}{\partial \xi_1}(c)v_1 + \frac{\partial f_q}{\partial \xi_2}(c)v_2 + \cdots + \frac{\partial f_q}{\partial \xi_p}(c)v_p.$$

The derivative $Df(c)$ is the linear function of $\mathbf{R}^p$ into $\mathbf{R}^q$ determined by the $q \times p$ matrix whose elements are

(20.10)
$$\begin{bmatrix} \dfrac{\partial f_1}{\partial \xi_1}(c) & \dfrac{\partial f_1}{\partial \xi_2}(c) & \cdots & \dfrac{\partial f_1}{\partial \xi_p}(c) \\[2ex] \dfrac{\partial f_2}{\partial \xi_1}(c) & \dfrac{\partial f_2}{\partial \xi_2}(c) & \cdots & \dfrac{\partial f_2}{\partial \xi_p}(c) \\[2ex] \cdot & \cdot & \cdots & \cdot \\[2ex] \dfrac{\partial f_q}{\partial \xi_1}(c) & \dfrac{\partial f_q}{\partial \xi_2}(c) & \cdots & \dfrac{\partial f_q}{\partial \xi_p}(c) \end{bmatrix}$$

We have already remarked in Theorem 15.10 that such an array of real numbers determines a linear function on R^p to R^q. The matrix (20.10) is called the Jacobian† matrix of the system (20.8) at the point c. When $p = q$, the determinant of the matrix (20.10) is called the Jacobian determinant (or simply, the Jacobian) of the system (20.8) at the point c. Frequently, this Jacobian determinant is denoted by

$$\frac{\partial f}{\partial x}(c), \qquad \left.\frac{\partial(f_1, f_2, \ldots, f_p)}{\partial(\xi_1, \xi_2, \ldots, \xi_p)}\right|_{x=c}, \qquad \text{or } J_f(c).$$

The next result shows that if f is differentiable at c, then all the directional derivatives of f at c exist and can be calculated by a very simple method.

20.6 THEOREM. *Let f be defined on $\mathfrak{D}$ in R^p and have range in R^q. If f is differentiable at the point c in $\mathfrak{D}$ and u is any point in R^p, then the directional derivative of f at c in the direction u exists and equals $Df(c)(u)$.*

PROOF.   Applying Definition 20.2 with $x = c + tu$, we have

$$|f(c + tu) - f(c) - Df(c)(tu)| \le \epsilon |tu|,$$

when $|tu| < \delta(\epsilon)$. If $u = \theta$, the directional derivative is clearly θ; hence we suppose that $u \neq \theta$. If $0 < |t| < \delta(\epsilon)/|u|$, then

$$\left|\frac{1}{t}\{f(c + tu) - f(c)\} - Df(c)(u)\right| \le \epsilon |u|.$$

This shows that $Df(c)(u)$ is the directional derivative of f at c in the direction u.

Q.E.D.

Existence of the Derivative

It follows from Theorem 20.6 that the existence of the derivative at a point implies the existence of any directional derivative (and hence any partial derivative) at the point. Therefore, the existence of the partial derivatives is a necessary condition for the existence of the derivative. It is not a sufficient condition, however. In fact, if f is defined on R^2 to R by

$$f(\xi, \eta) = 0, \qquad (\xi, \eta) = (0, 0),$$

$$= \frac{\xi\eta}{\xi^2 + \eta^2}, \qquad (\xi, \eta) \neq (0, 0),$$

† CARL (G. J.) JACOBI (1804–1851) was professor at Königsberg and Berlin. His main work was concerned with elliptic functions, but he is also known for his work in determinants.

then the partial derivatives

$$\frac{\partial f}{\partial \xi}(0, 0), \qquad \frac{\partial f}{\partial \eta}(0, 0)$$

both exist and equal zero and every directional derivative exists. However, the function f is not even continuous at $\theta = (0, 0)$, so that f does not have a derivative at θ.

Although the existence of the partial derivatives is not a sufficient condition for the existence of the derivative, the *continuity* of these partial derivatives is a sufficient condition.

20.7 Theorem. *If the partial derivatives of f exist in a neighborhood of c and are continuous at c, then f is differentiable at c.*

proof. We shall treat the case $q = 1$ in detail. If $\epsilon > 0$, let $\delta(\epsilon) > 0$ be such that if $|y - c| < \delta(\epsilon)$ and $j = 1, 2, \ldots, p$, then

$$(20.11) \qquad \left| \frac{\partial f}{\partial \xi_j}(y) - \frac{\partial f}{\partial \xi_j}(c) \right| < \epsilon.$$

If $x = (\xi_1, \xi_2, \ldots, \xi_p)$ and $c = (\gamma_1, \gamma_2, \ldots, \gamma_p)$, let $x_1, x_2, \ldots, x_{p-1}$ denote the points

$$x_1 = (\gamma_1, \xi_2, \ldots, \xi_p), \quad x_2 = (\gamma_1, \gamma_2, \xi_3, \ldots, \xi_p),$$

$$\ldots, x_{p-1} = (\gamma_1, \gamma_2, \ldots, \gamma_{p-1}, \xi_p)$$

and let $x_0 = x$ and $x_p = c$. If $|x - c| < \delta(\epsilon)$, then it is easily seen that $|x_j - c| < \delta(\epsilon)$ for $j = 0, 1, \ldots, p$. We write the difference $f(x) - f(c)$ in the telescoping sum

$$f(x) - f(c) = \sum_{j=1}^{p} \{f(x_{j-1}) - f(x_j)\}.$$

Applying the Mean Value Theorem 19.6 to the jth term of this sum, we obtain a point $\bar{x}_j$, lying on the line segment joining x_{j-1} and x_j, such that

$$f(x_{j-1}) - f(x_j) = (\xi_j - \gamma_j) \frac{\partial f}{\partial \xi_j}(\bar{x}_j).$$

Therefore, we obtain the expression

$$f(x) - f(c) - \sum_{j=1}^{p} (\xi_j - \gamma_j) \frac{\partial f}{\partial \xi_j}(c) = \sum_{j=1}^{p} (\xi_j - \gamma_j) \left\{ \frac{\partial f}{\partial \xi_j}(\bar{x}_j) - \frac{\partial f}{\partial \xi_j}(c) \right\}.$$

Employing the inequality (20.11), each quantity appearing in braces in the last formula is dominated by ϵ. Applying the C.-B.-S. Inequality to this last sum, we obtain the estimate

$$\left| f(x) - f(c) - \sum_{j=1}^{p} (\xi_j - \gamma_j) \frac{\partial f}{\partial \xi_j}(c) \right| \leq |x - c|(\epsilon \sqrt{p}),$$

whenever $|x - c| < \delta(\epsilon)$.

We have proved that f is differentiable at c and that its derivative $Df(c)$ is the linear function from $\mathbf{R}^p$ to $\mathbf{R}$ which takes the value

$$Df(c)(z) = \sum_{j=1}^{p} \zeta_j \frac{\partial f}{\partial \xi_j} (c)$$

at the point $z = (\zeta_1, \zeta_2, \ldots, \zeta_p)$ in $\mathbf{R}^p$.

In the case where f takes values in $\mathbf{R}^q$ with $q > 1$, we apply the same argument to the real-valued functions f_i, $i = 1, 2, \ldots, q$, which occur in the coordinate representation (20.8) of the mapping f. We shall omit the details of this argument.

Q.E.D.

Properties of the Derivative

We now establish the basic algebraic relations concerning the derivative.

20.8 THEOREM. (a) *If f, g are differentiable at a point c in $\mathbf{R}^p$ and have values in $\mathbf{R}^q$ and if α, β are real numbers, then the function $h = \alpha f + \beta g$ is differentiable at c and $Dh(c) = \alpha\, Df(c) + \beta\, Dg(c)$.*

(b) *If f, g are as in (a), then the inner product $k = f \cdot g$ is differentiable at c and*

$$Dk(c)(u) = Df(c)(u) \cdot g(c) + f(c) \cdot Dg(c)(u).$$

(c) *If φ is differentiable at c in $\mathbf{R}^p$ and has values in $\mathbf{R}$, then the product φf is differentiable at c and*

$$D(\varphi f)(c)(u) = D\varphi(c)(u)f(c) + \varphi(c)Df(c)(u).$$

PROOF. (a) If $\epsilon > 0$, then there exist $\delta_1(\epsilon) > 0$ and $\delta_2(\epsilon) > 0$ such that if $|x - c| < \inf\{\delta_1(\epsilon), \delta_2(\epsilon)\}$, then

$$|f(x) - f(c) - Df(c)(x - c)| \leq \epsilon\, |x - c|,$$

$$|g(x) - g(c) - Dg(c)(x - c)| \leq \epsilon\, |x - c|.$$

Thus if $|x - c| < \inf\{\delta_1(\epsilon), \delta_2(\epsilon)\}$, then

$$|h(x) - h(c) - \{\alpha\, Df(c)(x - c) + \beta\, Dg(c)(x - c)\}|$$
$$\leq (|\alpha| + |\beta|)\, \epsilon\, |x - c|.$$

Since $\alpha\, Df(c) + \beta\, Dg(c)$ is a linear function of $\mathbf{R}^p$ into $\mathbf{R}^q$, it follows that h is differentiable at c and that $Dh(c) = \alpha\, Df(c) + \beta\, Dg(c)$.

(b) From an inspection of both sides, we obtain the relation

$$k(x) - k(c) - \{Df(c)(x - c) \cdot g(c) + f(c) \cdot Dg(c)(x - c)\}$$
$$= \{f(x) - f(c) - Df(c)(x - c)\} \cdot g(x)$$
$$+ Df(c)(x - c) \cdot \{g(x) - g(c)\}$$
$$+ f(c) \cdot \{g(x) - g(c) - Dg(c)(x - c)\}.$$

Since $Dg(c)$ exists, we infer from Lemma 20.4 that g is continuous at c; hence there exists a constant M such that $|g(x)| < M$ for $|x - c| < \delta$. From this it is seen that all the terms on the right side of the last equation can be made arbitrarily small by choosing $|x - c|$ small enough. This establishes part (b).

Statement (c) follows in exactly the same way as (b), so its proof will be omitted.

Q.E.D.

The next result asserts that the derivative of the composition of two functions is the composition of their derivatives.

20.9   CHAIN RULE.   *Let f be a function with domain $\mathfrak{D}(f)$ in R^p and range in R^q and let g have domain $\mathfrak{D}(g)$ in R^q and range in R^r. Suppose that f is differentiable at c and that g is differentiable at $b = f(c)$. Then the composition $h = g \circ f$ is differentiable at c and*

$$(20.13) \qquad\qquad Dh(c) = Dg(b) \circ Df(c).$$

PROOF.   The hypotheses imply that c is an interior point of $\mathfrak{D}(f)$ and that $b = f(c)$ is an interior point of $\mathfrak{D}(g)$ whence it follows that c is an interior point of $\mathfrak{D}(h)$. (Why?) Let $\epsilon > 0$ and let $\delta(\epsilon, f)$ and $\delta(\epsilon, g)$ be as in Definition 20.2. It follows from Lemma 20.4 there exist positive numbers γ, K such that if $|x - c| < \gamma$, then $f(x) \in \mathfrak{D}(g)$ and

$$(20.14) \qquad\qquad |f(x) - f(c)| \le K |x - c|.$$

For simplicity, we let $L_f = Df(c)$ and $L_g = Dg(b)$. By Theorem 15.11 there is a constant M such that

$$(20.15) \qquad\qquad |L_g(u)| \le M |u|, \quad \text{for} \quad u \in R^q.$$

If $|x - c| < \inf \{\gamma, (1/K)\delta(\epsilon, g)\}$, then (20.14) implies that $|f(x) - f(c)| \le \delta(\epsilon, g)$, which means that

$$(20.16) \quad |g[f(x)] - g[f(c)] - L_g[f(x) - f(c)]|$$
$$\le \epsilon |f(x) - f(c)| \le K \epsilon |x - c|.$$

If we also require that $|x - c| < \delta(\epsilon, f)$, then we infer from (20.15) that

$$|L_g[f(x) - f(c) - L_f(x - c)]| \le M \epsilon |x - c|.$$

If we combine this last relation with (20.16), we infer that if $\delta_1 = \inf \{\gamma, (1/K)\delta(\epsilon, g), \delta(\epsilon, f)\}$ and if $|x - c| < \delta_1$, then $x \in \mathfrak{D}(h)$ and

$$|g[f(x)] - g[f(c)] - L_g[L_f(x - c)]| \le (K + M) \epsilon |x - c|.$$

Q.E.D.

Maintaining the notation of the proof of the theorem, $L_f = Df(c)$ is a linear function of $\mathbf{R}^p$ into $\mathbf{R}^q$ and $L_g = Dg(b)$ is a linear function of $\mathbf{R}^q$ into $\mathbf{R}^r$. The composition $L_g \circ L_f$ is a linear function of $\mathbf{R}^p$ into $\mathbf{R}^r$, as is required, since $h = g \circ f$ is a function defined on part of $\mathbf{R}^p$ with values in $\mathbf{R}^r$. We now consider some examples of this result.

20.10 EXAMPLES. (a) Let $p = q = r = 1$; then the derivative $Df(c)$ is the linear function which takes the real number u into $f'(c)u$, and similarly for $Dg(b)$. It follows that the derivative of $g \circ f$ sends the real number u into $g'(b)f'(c)u$.

(b) Let $p > 1, q = r = 1$. According to Example 20.5(c), the derivative of f at c takes the point $w = (\omega_1, \ldots, \omega_p)$ of $\mathbf{R}^p$ into the real number

$$f_{\xi_1}(c)\omega_1 + \cdots + f_{\xi_p}(c)\omega_p$$

and so the derivative of $g \circ f$ at c takes this point of $\mathbf{R}^p$ into the real number

$$(20.17) \qquad g'(b)[f_{\xi_1}(c)\omega_1 + \cdots + f_{\xi_p}(c)\omega_p].$$

(c) Let $q > 1, p = r = 1$. According to Examples 20.5(b), (c) the derivative $Df(c)$ takes the real number u into the point

$$Df(c)(u) = (f_1'(c)u, \ldots, f_q'(c)u) \quad \text{in} \quad \mathbf{R}^q,$$

and the derivative $Dg(b)$ takes the point $w = (\omega_1, \ldots, \omega_q)$ in $\mathbf{R}^q$ into the real number

$$g_{\eta_1}(b)\omega_1 + \cdots + g_{\eta_q}(b)\omega_q.$$

It follows that the derivative of $h = g \circ f$ takes the real number u into the real number

$$(20.18) \qquad Dh(c)u = \{g_{\eta_1}(b)f_1'(c) + \cdots + g_{\eta_q}(b)f_q'(c)\}u.$$

The quantity in the braces is sometimes denoted by the less precise symbolism

$$(20.19) \qquad \frac{\partial g}{\partial \eta_1}\frac{df_1}{dx} + \cdots + \frac{\partial g}{\partial \eta_q}\frac{df_q}{dx}.$$

In this connection, it must be understood that the derivatives are to be evaluated at appropriate points.

(d) We consider the case where $p = q = 2$ and $r = 3$. For simplicity in notation, we denote the coordinate variables in $\mathbf{R}^p$ by (x, y), in $\mathbf{R}^q$ by (w, z), and in $\mathbf{R}^r$ by (r, s, t). Then a function f on $\mathbf{R}^p$ to $\mathbf{R}^q$ can be expressed in the form

$$w = W(x, y), \qquad z = Z(x, y)$$

and a function g on $\mathbf{R}^q$ to $\mathbf{R}^r$ can be expressed in the form

$$r = R(w, z), \qquad s = S(w, z), \qquad t = T(w, z).$$

The derivative $Df(c)$ sends (ξ, η) into (ω, ζ) according to the formulas

(20.20)
$$\omega = W_x(c)\xi + W_y(c)\eta,$$
$$\zeta = Z_x(c)\xi + Z_y(c)\eta.$$

Also the derivative $Dg(b)$ sends (ω, ζ) into (ρ, σ, τ) according to the relations

(20.21)
$$\rho = R_w(b)\omega + R_z(b)\zeta,$$
$$\sigma = S_w(b)\omega + S_z(b)\zeta,$$
$$\tau = T_w(b)\omega + T_z(b)\zeta.$$

A routine calculation shows that the derivative of $g \circ f$ sends (ξ, η) into (ρ, σ, τ) by

(20.22)

$$\rho = \{R_w(b)W_x(c) + R_z(b)Z_x(c)\}\xi + \{R_w(b)W_y(c) + R_z(b)Z_y(c)\}\eta,$$
$$\sigma = \{S_w(b)W_x(c) + S_z(b)Z_x(c)\}\xi + \{S_w(b)W_y(c) + S_z(b)Z_y(c)\}\eta,$$
$$\tau = \{T_w(b)W_x(c) + T_z(b)Z_x(c)\}\xi + \{T_w(b)W_y(c) + T_z(b)Z_y(c)\}\eta.$$

A more classical notation would be to write dx, dy instead of ξ, η; dw, dz instead of ω, ζ; and dr, ds, dt instead of ρ, σ, τ. If we denote the values of the partial derivative W_x at the point c by $\dfrac{\partial w}{\partial x}$, etc., then (20.20) becomes

$$dw = \frac{\partial w}{\partial x}\, dx + \frac{\partial w}{\partial y}\, dy,$$

$$dz = \frac{\partial z}{\partial x}\, dx + \frac{\partial z}{\partial y}\, dy;$$

similarly, (20.21) becomes

$$dr = \frac{\partial r}{\partial w}\, dw + \frac{\partial r}{\partial z}\, dz,$$

$$ds = \frac{\partial s}{\partial w}\, dw + \frac{\partial s}{\partial z}\, dz,$$

$$dt = \frac{\partial t}{\partial w}\, dw + \frac{\partial t}{\partial z}\, dz;$$

and (20.22) is written in the form

$$dr = \left(\frac{\partial r}{\partial w}\frac{\partial w}{\partial x} + \frac{\partial r}{\partial z}\frac{\partial z}{\partial x}\right) dx + \left(\frac{\partial r}{\partial w}\frac{\partial w}{\partial y} + \frac{\partial r}{\partial z}\frac{\partial z}{\partial y}\right) dy,$$

$$ds = \left(\frac{\partial s}{\partial w}\frac{\partial w}{\partial x} + \frac{\partial s}{\partial z}\frac{\partial z}{\partial x}\right) dx + \left(\frac{\partial s}{\partial w}\frac{\partial w}{\partial y} + \frac{\partial s}{\partial z}\frac{\partial z}{\partial y}\right) dy,$$

$$dt = \left(\frac{\partial t}{\partial w}\frac{\partial w}{\partial x} + \frac{\partial t}{\partial z}\frac{\partial z}{\partial x}\right) dx + \left(\frac{\partial t}{\partial w}\frac{\partial w}{\partial y} + \frac{\partial t}{\partial z}\frac{\partial z}{\partial y}\right) dy.$$

In these last three sets of formulas it is important to realize that all of the indicated partial derivatives are to be evaluated at appropriate points. Hence the coefficients of dx, dy, and so forth turn out to be real numbers.

We can express equation (20.20) in matrix terminology by saying that the mapping $Df(c)$ of (ξ, η) into (ω, ζ) is given by the 2×2 matrix

(20.23)
$$\begin{bmatrix} W_x(c) & W_y(c) \\ Z_x(c) & Z_y(c) \end{bmatrix} = \begin{bmatrix} \dfrac{\partial w}{\partial x}(c) & \dfrac{\partial w}{\partial y}(c) \\ \dfrac{\partial z}{\partial x}(c) & \dfrac{\partial z}{\partial y}(c) \end{bmatrix}.$$

Similarly, (20.21) asserts that the mapping $Dg(b)$ of (ω, ζ) into (ρ, σ, τ) is given by the 3×2 matrix

(20.24)
$$\begin{bmatrix} R_w(b) & R_z(b) \\ S_w(b) & S_z(b) \\ T_w(b) & T_z(b) \end{bmatrix} = \begin{bmatrix} \dfrac{\partial r}{\partial w}(b) & \dfrac{\partial r}{\partial z}(b) \\ \dfrac{\partial s}{\partial w}(b) & \dfrac{\partial s}{\partial z}(b) \\ \dfrac{\partial t}{\partial w}(b) & \dfrac{\partial t}{\partial z}(b) \end{bmatrix}.$$

Finally, relation (20.22) asserts that the mapping $D(g \circ f)(c)$ of (ξ, η) into (ρ, σ, τ) is given by the 3×2 matrix

$$\begin{bmatrix} R_w(b)W_x(c) + R_z(b)Z_x(c) & R_w(b)W_y(c) + R_z(b)Z_y(c) \\ S_w(b)W_x(c) + S_z(b)Z_x(c) & S_w(b)W_y(c) + S_z(b)Z_y(c) \\ T_w(b)W_x(c) + T_z(b)Z_x(c) & T_w(t)W_y(c) + T_z(b)Z_y(c) \end{bmatrix}$$

which is the product of the matrix in (20.24) with the matrix in (20.23) in that order.

Mean Value Theorem

We now turn to the problem of obtaining a generalization of the Mean Value Theorem 19.6 for differentiable functions on $\mathbf{R}^p$ to $\mathbf{R}^q$. It will be seen that the direct analog of Theorem 19.6 does not hold when $q > 1$. It might be expected that if f is differentiable at every point of $\mathbf{R}^p$ with values in $\mathbf{R}^q$, and if a, b belong to $\mathbf{R}^p$, then there exists a point c (lying between a, b) such that

(20.25) $$f(b) - f(a) = Df(c)(b - a).$$

This conclusion fails even when $p = 1$ and $q = 2$ as is seen by the function f defined on $\mathbf{R}$ to $\mathbf{R}^2$ by the formula

$$f(x) = (x - x^2, x - x^3).$$

Then $Df(c)$ is the linear function on $\mathbf{R}$ to $\mathbf{R}^2$ which sends the real number u into the element

$$Df(c)(u) = ((1 - 2c)u, (1 - 3c^2)u).$$

Now $f(0) = (0, 0)$ and $f(1) = (0, 0)$, but there is no point c such that $Df(c)(u) = (0, 0)$ for any non-zero u in $\mathbf{R}$. Hence the formula (20.25) cannot hold in general when $q > 1$, even when $p = 1$. However, for many applications it is sufficient to consider the case where $q = 1$ and here it is easy to extend the Mean Value Theorem.

20.11 MEAN VALUE THEOREM. *Let f be defined on a subset $\mathfrak{D}$ of $\mathbf{R}^p$ and have values in $\mathbf{R}$. Suppose that the set $\mathfrak{D}$ contains the points a, b and the line segment joining them and that f is differentiable at every point of this segment. Then there exists a point c on this line segment such that*

(20.25) $$f(b) - f(a) = Df(c)(b - a).$$

PROOF. Consider the function φ defined on $\mathbf{I} = [0, 1]$ to $\mathbf{R}$ by

$$\varphi(t) = f((1 - t)a + tb), t \in \mathbf{I}.$$

Observe that $\varphi(0) = f(a), \varphi(1) = f(b)$ and that it follows from the Chain Rule that

$$\varphi'(t) = Df((1 - t)a + tb)(b - a).$$

From the Mean Value Theorem 19.6, we conclude that there exists a point t_0 with $0 < t_0 < 1$ such that

$$\varphi(1) - \varphi(0) = \varphi'(t_0).$$

Letting $c = (1 - t_0)a + t_0 b$, we obtain (20.25).

Q.E.D.

Sometimes one of the following results can be used in place of the Mean Value Theorem when $q > 1$.

20.12 COROLLARY. *Let f be defined on a subset $\mathfrak{D}$ of $\mathbf{R}^p$ and with values in $\mathbf{R}^q$. Suppose that the set $\mathfrak{D}$ contains the points a, b and the line segment joining them and that f is differentiable at every point of this segment. If y belongs to $\mathbf{R}^q$, then there exists a point c on this line segment such that*

$$\{f(b) - f(a)\}\cdot y = \{Df(c)(b - a)\}\cdot y.$$

PROOF. Let F be defined on $\mathfrak{D}$ to $\mathbf{R}$ by $F(x) = f(x)\cdot y$. Applying the Mean Value Theorem 20.11, there exists a point c on this line segment such that $F(b) - F(a) = DF(c)(b - a)$, from which the assertion of this corollary is immediate.

Q.E.D.

20.13 COROLLARY. *Let f be defined on a subset $\mathfrak{D}$ of $\mathbf{R}^p$ and with values in $\mathbf{R}^q$. Suppose that the set $\mathfrak{D}$ contains the points a, b and the line segment joining them and that f is differentiable at every point of this segment. Then there exists a linear function L of $\mathbf{R}^p$ into $\mathbf{R}^q$ such that*

$$f(b) - f(a) = L(b - a).$$

PROOF. Let $y_1, y_2, \ldots, y_q$ be the points $y_1 = (1, 0, \ldots, 0)$, $y_2 = (0, 1, \ldots, 0), \ldots, y_q = (0, 0, \ldots, 1)$, lying in $\mathbf{R}^q$. We observe that the q functions $f_1, f_2, \ldots, f_q$ on $\mathfrak{D}$ to $\mathbf{R}$ which give the coordinate representation of the mapping f are obtained by

$$f_i(x) = f(x)\cdot y_i \quad \text{for} \quad i = 1, 2, \ldots, q.$$

Applying the preceding corollary to each of these functions, we obtain q points c_i on the line segment joining a and b such that

$$f_i(b) - f_i(a) = Df(c_i)(b - a)\cdot y_i.$$

Since the matrix representation of $Df(c)$ is given by the $q \times p$ matrix with entries

$$\frac{\partial f_i}{\partial \xi_j}(c), \quad i = 1, 2, \ldots, q, \quad j = 1, 2, \ldots, p;$$

it is easily seen that the desired linear function L has the matrix representation

$$\frac{\partial f_i}{\partial \xi_j}(c_i), \quad i = 1, 2, \ldots, q, \quad j = 1, 2, \ldots, p.$$

Q.E.D.

We remark that the proof yields more information about L than was announced in the statement. Each of the q rows of the matrix for L is obtained by evaluating the partial derivatives of $f_i = f \cdot y_i, i = 1, 2, \ldots, q$, at some point c_i lying on the line segment joining a and b. However, as we have already seen, it is not always possible to use the same point c for different rows in this matrix.

Interchange of the Order of Differentiation

If f is a function with domain in $\mathbf{R}^p$ and range in $\mathbf{R}$, then f may have p (first) partial derivatives, which we denote by

$$f_{\xi_i} \quad \text{or} \quad \frac{\partial f}{\partial \xi_i}, \quad i = 1, 2, \ldots, p.$$

Each of the partial derivatives is a function with domain in $\mathbf{R}^p$ and range in $\mathbf{R}$ and so each of these p functions may have p partial derivatives. Following the accepted American notation, we shall refer to the resulting p^2 functions (or to such ones that exist) as the second partial derivatives of f and we shall denote them by

$$f_{\xi_i \xi_j} \quad \text{or} \quad \frac{\partial^2 f}{\partial \xi_j \partial \xi_i}, \quad i, j = 1, 2, \ldots, p.$$

It should be observed that the partial derivative intended by either of the latter symbols is the partial derivative with respect to ξ_j of the partial derivative of f with respect to ξ_i. (In other words: first ξ_i, then ξ_j; however, note the difference in the order in the two symbols!)

In like manner, we can inquire into the existence of the third partial derivatives and those of still higher order. In principle, a function on $\mathbf{R}^p$ to $\mathbf{R}$ can have as many as p^n nth partial derivatives. However, it is a considerable convenience that if the resulting derivatives are continuous, then the order of differentiation is not significant. In addition to decreasing the number of (potentially distinct) higher partial derivatives, this result largely removes the danger from the rather subtle notational distinction employed for different orders of differentiation.

It is enough to consider the interchange of order for second derivatives. By holding all the other coordinates constant, we see that it is no loss of generality to consider a function on $\mathbf{R}^2$ to $\mathbf{R}$. In order to simplify our notation we let (x, y) denote a point in $\mathbf{R}^2$ and we shall show that if f_x, f_y, and f_{xy} exist and if f_{xy} is continuous at a point, then the partial derivative f_{yx} exists at this point and equals f_{xy}. It will be seen in Exercise 20.U that it is possible that both f_{xy} and f_{yx} exists at a point and yet are not equal.

The device that will be used in this proof is to show that both of these mixed partial derivatives at the point $(0, 0)$ are the limit of the quotient

$$\frac{f(h, k) - f(h, 0) - f(0, k) + f(0, 0)}{hk},$$

as (h, k) approaches $(0, 0)$.

20.14 LEMMA. *Suppose that f is defined on a neighborhood U of the origin in R^2 with values in R, that the partial derivatives f_x and f_{xy} exist in U, and that f_{xy} is continuous at $(0, 0)$. If A is the mixed difference*

(20.26) $A(h, k) = f(h, k) - f(h, 0) - f(0, k) + f(0, 0),$

then we have

$$f_{xy}(0, 0) = \lim_{(h,k)\to(0,0)} \frac{A(h, k)}{hk}.$$

PROOF.   Let $\epsilon > 0$ and let $\delta > 0$ be so small that if $|h| < \delta$ and $|k| < \delta$, then the point (h, k) belongs to U and

(20.27) $|f_{xy}(h, k) - f_{xy}(0, 0)| < \epsilon.$

If $|k| < \delta$, we define B for $|h| < \delta$ by

$$B(h) = f(h, k) - f(h, 0),$$

from which it follows that $A(h, k) = B(h) - B(0)$. By hypothesis, the partial derivative f_x exists in U and hence B has a derivative. Applying the Mean Value Theorem 19.6 to B, there exists a number h_0 with $0 < |h_0| < |h|$ such that

(20.28) $A(h, k) = B(h) - B(0) = hB'(h_0).$

(It is noted that the value of h_0 depends on the value of k, but this will not cause any difficulty.) Referring to the definition of B, we have

$$B'(h_0) = f_x(h_0, k) - f_x(h_0, 0).$$

Applying the Mean Value Theorem to the right-hand side of the last equation, there exists a number k_0 with $0 < |k_0| < |k|$ such that

(20.29) $B'(h_0) = k\{f_{xy}(h_0, k_0)\}.$

Combining equations (20.28) and (20.29), we conclude that if $0 < |h| < \delta$ and $0 < |k| < \delta$, then

$$\frac{A(h, k)}{hk} = f_{xy}(h_0, k_0),$$

where $0 < |h_0| < |h|$, $0 < |k_0| < |k|$. It follows from inequality (20.27) and the preceding expression

$$\left| \frac{A(h, k)}{hk} - f_{xy}(0, 0) \right| < \epsilon$$

whenever $0 < |h| < \delta$ and $0 < |k| < \delta$.

Q.E.D.

We can now obtain a useful sufficient condition (due to H. A. Schwarz) for the equality of the two mixed partial derivatives.

20.15   THEOREM. *Suppose that f is defined on a neighborhood U of a point (x, y) in $\mathbf{R^2}$ with values in $\mathbf{R}$. Suppose that the partial derivatives f_x, f_y, and f_{xy} exist in U and that f_{xy} is continuous at (x, y). Then the partial derivative f_{yx} exists at (x, y) and $f_{yx}(x, y) = f_{xy}(x, y)$.*

PROOF.   It is no loss of generality to suppose that $(x, y) = (0, 0)$ and we shall do so. If A is the function defined in the preceding lemma, then it was seen that

$$(20.30) \qquad\qquad f_{xy}(0, 0) = \lim_{(h,k)\to(0,0)} \frac{A(h, k)}{hk} ,$$

the existence of this double limit being part of the conclusion. By hypothesis f_y exists in U, so that

$$(20.31) \qquad\qquad \lim_{k\to 0} \frac{A(h, k)}{hk} = \frac{1}{h} \{ f_y(h, 0) - f_y(0, 0) \}, \qquad h \neq 0.$$

If $\epsilon > 0$, there exists a number $\delta(\epsilon) > 0$ such that if $0 < |h| < \delta(\epsilon)$ and $0 < |k| < \delta(\epsilon)$, then

$$\left| \frac{A(h, k)}{hk} - f_{xy}(0, 0) \right| < \epsilon.$$

By taking the limit in this inequality with respect to k and using (20.31), we obtain

$$\left| \frac{1}{h} \{ f_y(h, 0) - f_y(0, 0) \} - f_{xy}(0, 0) \right| \leq \epsilon,$$

for all h satisfying $0 < |h| < \delta(\epsilon)$. Therefore, $f_{yx}(0, 0)$ exists and equals $f_{xy}(0, 0)$.

Q.E.D.

Higher Derivatives

If f is a function with domain in $\mathbf{R}^p$ and range in $\mathbf{R}$, then the derivative $Df(c)$ of f at c is the linear function on $\mathbf{R}^p$ to $\mathbf{R}$ such that

$$|f(c + z) - f(c) - Df(c)(z)| \leq \epsilon |z|,$$

for sufficiently small z. This means that $Df(c)$ is the linear function which most closely approximates the difference $f(c + z) - f(c)$ when z is small. Any other linear function would lead to a less exact approximation for small z. From this defining property, it is seen that if $Df(c)$ exists, then it is necessarily given by the formula

$$Df(c)(z) = f_{\xi_1}(c)\zeta_1 + \cdots + f_{\xi_p}(c)\zeta_p,$$

where $z = (\zeta_1, \ldots, \zeta_p)$ in $\mathbf{R}^p$.

Although linear approximations are particularly simple and are sufficiently exact for many purposes, it is sometimes desirable to obtain a finer degree of approximation than is possible by using linear functions. In such cases it is natural to turn to quadratic functions, cubic functions, etc., to effect closer approximations. Since our functions are to have their domains in $\mathbf{R}^p$, we would be led into the study of multilinear functions on $\mathbf{R}^p$ to $\mathbf{R}$ for a thorough discussion of such functions. Although such a study is not particularly difficult, it would take us rather far afield in view of the limited applications we have in mind.

For this reason we shall define the second derivative $D^2f(c)$ of f at c to be the function on $\mathbf{R}^p \times \mathbf{R}^p$ to $\mathbf{R}$ such that if (y, z) belongs to this product and $y = (\eta_1, \ldots, \eta_p)$ and $z = (\zeta_1, \ldots, \zeta_p)$, then

$$D^2f(c)(y, z) = \sum_{i,j=1}^{p} f_{\xi_i \xi_j}(c)\eta_i \zeta_j.$$

In discussing the second derivative, we shall assume in the following that the second partial derivatives of f exist and are continuous on a neighborhood of c. Similarly, we define the third derivative $D^3f(c)$ of f at c to be the function of (y, z, w) in $\mathbf{R}^p \times \mathbf{R}^p \times \mathbf{R}^p$ given by

$$D^3f(c)(y, z, w) = \sum_{i,j,k=1}^{p} f_{\xi_i \xi_j \xi_k}(c)\eta_i \zeta_j \omega_k.$$

In discussing the third derivative, we shall assume that all of the third partial derivatives of f exist and are continuous in a neighborhood of c.

By now the method of formation of the higher differentials should be clear. (In view of our preceding remarks concerning the interchange of order in differentiation, if the resulting mixed partial derivatives are

continuous, then they are independent of the order of differentiation.)
One further notational device: we write

$$D^2f(c)(w)^2 \quad \text{for} \quad D^2f(c)(w, w),$$
$$D^3f(c)(w)^3 \quad \text{for} \quad D^3f(c)(w, w, w),$$

$$\cdot\ \cdot\ \cdot\ \cdot\ \cdot\ \cdot\ \cdot\ \cdot\ \cdot\ \cdot\ \cdot\ \cdot\ \cdot\ \cdot$$

$$D^nf(c)(w)^n \quad \text{for} \quad D^nf(c)(w, w, \ldots, w).$$

If $p = 2$ and if we denote an element of $\mathbb{R}^2$ by (ξ, η) and $w = (h, k)$,
then $D^2f(c)(w)^2$ equals the expression

$$f_{\xi\xi}(c)h^2 + 2f_{\xi\eta}(c)hk + f_{\eta\eta}(c)k^2;$$

similarly, $D^3f(c)(w)^3$ equals

$$f_{\xi\xi\xi}(c)h^3 + 3f_{\xi\xi\eta}(c)h^2k + 3f_{\xi\eta\eta}(c)hk^2 + f_{\eta\eta\eta}(c)k^3,$$

and $D^nf(c)(w)^n$ equals the expression

$$f_{\xi\ldots\xi}(c)h^n + \binom{n}{1} f_{\xi\ldots\xi\eta}(c)h^{n-1}k + \binom{n}{2} f_{\xi\ldots\xi\eta\eta}(c)h^{n-2}k^2$$
$$+ \cdots + f_{\eta\ldots\eta}(c)k^n.$$

Now that we have introduced this notation we shall establish an
important generalization of Taylor's Theorem for functions on $\mathbb{R}^p$ to $\mathbb{R}$.

20.16 TAYLOR'S THEOREM. *Suppose that f is a function with domain*
$\mathfrak{D}$ *in* $\mathbb{R}^p$ *and range in* $\mathbb{R}$, *and suppose that f has continuous partial deriva-*
tives of order n in a neighborhood of every point on a line segment joining
two points u, v in $\mathfrak{D}$. *Then there exists a point* $\bar{u}$ *on this line segment*
such that

$$f(v) = f(u) + \frac{1}{1!} Df(u)(v - u) + \frac{1}{2!} D^2f(u)(v - u)^2$$
$$+ \cdots + \frac{1}{(n-1)!} D^{n-1}f(u)(v - u)^{n-1} + \frac{1}{n!} D^nf(\bar{u})(v - u)^n.$$

PROOF. Let F be defined for t in $\mathbf{I}$ to $\mathbb{R}$ by

$$F(t) = f(u + t(v - u)).$$

In view of the assumed existence of the partial derivatives of f, it
follows that

$$F'(t) = Df(u + t(v - u))(v - u),$$
$$F''(t) = D^2f(u + t(v - u))(v - u)^2,$$

$$\cdot\ \cdot\ \cdot\ \cdot\ \cdot\ \cdot\ \cdot\ \cdot\ \cdot\ \cdot\ \cdot\ \cdot\ \cdot\ \cdot$$

$$F^{(n)}(t) = D^nf(u + t(v - u))(v - u)^n.$$

If we apply the one-dimensional version of Taylor's Theorem 19.9 to the function F on I, we infer that there exists a real number ψ in I such that

$$F(1) = F(0) + \frac{1}{1!} F'(0) + \cdots + \frac{1}{(n-1)!} F^{(n-1)}(0) + \frac{1}{n!} F^{(n)}(\psi).$$

If we set $\bar{u} = u + \psi(v - u)$, then the result follows.

Q.E.D.

Exercises

20.A. If f is defined for (ξ, η, ζ) in $\mathbf{R}^3$ to $\mathbf{R}$ by the formula

$$f(\xi, \eta, \zeta) = 2\xi^2 - \eta + 6\xi\eta - \zeta^3 + 3\zeta,$$

calculate the directional derivative of f at the origin $\theta = (0, 0, 0)$ in the direction of the points

$$x = (1, 2, 0), \qquad y = (2, 1, -3).$$

20.B. Let f be defined for (ξ, η) in $\mathbf{R}^2$ to $\mathbf{R}$ by

$$f(\xi, \eta) = \xi/\eta, \qquad \eta \neq 0,$$
$$= 0, \qquad \eta = 0,$$

Show that the partial derivatives f_ξ, f_η exist for $\theta = (0, 0)$ but that if $u = (\alpha, \beta)$ with $\alpha\beta \neq 0$, then the directional derivative of f at θ in the direction of u does not exist. Show also that f is not continuous at θ; in fact, f is not even bounded at θ.

20.C. If f is defined on $\mathbf{R}^2$ to $\mathbf{R}$ by

$$f(\xi, \eta) = 0, \qquad \text{if } \xi\eta = 0,$$
$$= 1, \qquad \text{otherwise,}$$

then f has partial derivatives f_ξ, f_η at $\theta = (0, 0)$, but f does not have directional derivatives in the direction $u = (\alpha, \beta)$ if $\alpha\beta \neq 0$. The function f is not continuous at θ, but it is bounded.

20.D. Let f be defined on $\mathbf{R}^2$ to $\mathbf{R}$ by

$$f(\xi^3 \eta) = \frac{\xi^2 \eta}{\xi^3 - \eta^2}, \qquad \xi^3 \neq \eta^2,$$
$$= 0, \qquad \xi^3 = \eta^2.$$

Then f has a directional derivative at $\theta = (0, 0)$ in every direction, but f is not continuous at θ. However, f is bounded on a neighborhood of θ.

20.F. Let f be defined on $\mathbf{R}^2$ to $\mathbf{R}$ by

$$f(\xi, \eta) = \frac{\xi\eta}{\sqrt{\xi^2 + \eta^2}}, \qquad (\xi, \eta) \neq (0, 0),$$
$$= 0, \qquad (\xi, \eta) = (0, 0).$$

Then f is continuous and has partial derivatives at $\theta = (0, 0)$, but f is not differentiable at θ.

20.G. Let f be defined on $\mathbf{R}^2$ to $\mathbf{R}$ by

$$f(\xi, \eta) = \xi^2 + \eta^2, \qquad \text{both } \xi, \eta \text{ rational,}$$
$$= 0, \qquad\qquad \text{otherwise.}$$

Then f is continuous only at the point $\theta = (0, 0)$, but it is differentiable there.

20.H. Let f be defined on $\mathbf{R}^2$ to $\mathbf{R}$ by

$$f(\xi, \eta) = (\xi^2 + \eta^2) \sin 1/(\xi^2 + \eta^2), \qquad (\xi, \eta) \neq (0, 0),$$
$$= 0, \qquad\qquad\qquad\qquad\quad (\xi, \eta) = (0, 0).$$

Then f is differentiable at θ, but its partial derivatives are not continuous (or even bounded) on a neighborhood of θ.

20.I. Suppose the real-valued function f has a derivative at a point c in $\mathbf{R}^p$. Express the directional derivative of f at c in the direction of a unit vector $w = (\omega_1, \ldots, \omega_p)$. Using the C.-B.-S. Inequality, show that there is a direction in which the derivative is maximum and this direction is uniquely determined if at least one of the partial derivatives is not zero. This direction is called the **gradient direction** of f at c. Show that there exists a unique vector v_c such that $Df(c)(w) = v_c \cdot w$ for all unit vectors w. This vector v_c is called the **gradient** of f at c and is often denoted by $\nabla_c f$ or grad $f(c)$.

20.J. Suppose that f and g are real-valued functions which are differentiable at a point c in $\mathbf{R}^p$ and that α is a real number. Show that the gradient of f at c is given by

$$\nabla_c f = \big(f_{\xi_1}(c), \ldots, f_{\xi_p}(c)\big),$$

and that

$$\nabla_c(\alpha f) = \alpha \, \nabla_c f,$$
$$\nabla_c(f + g) = \nabla_c f + \nabla_c g,$$
$$\nabla_c(fg) = (\nabla_c f)g(c) + f(c)(\nabla_c g).$$

20.K. If f is differentiable on an open subset $\mathfrak{D}$ of $\mathbf{R}^p$ and has values in $\mathbf{R}^q$ such that $|f(x)| = 1$ for $x \in \mathfrak{D}$, then

$$f(x) \cdot Df(x)(u) = 0 \qquad \text{for } x \in \mathfrak{D}, \ u \in \mathbf{R}^p.$$

If $p = 1$, give a physical interpretation of this equation.

20.L. Suppose that f is defined for $x = (\xi_1, \xi_2)$ in $\mathbf{R}^2$ to $\mathbf{R}$ by the formula

$$f(x) = f(\xi_1, \xi_2) = A\xi_1{}^2 + B\xi_1\xi_2 + C\xi_2{}^2.$$

Calculate Df at the point $y = (\eta_1, \eta_2)$. Show that

(i) $\qquad f(tx) = t^2 f(x) \qquad \text{for } t \in \mathbf{R}, \ x \in \mathbf{R}^2;$

(ii) $Df(x)(y) = Df(y)(x);$

(iii) $Df(x)(x) = 2f(x);$

(iv) $f(x + y) = f(x) + Df(x)(y) + f(y).$

20.M. Let f be defined on an open set $\mathfrak{D}$ of $\mathbf{R}^p$ into $\mathbf{R}^q$ and satisfy the relation

(20.33) $f(tx) = t^k f(x)$ for $t \in \mathbf{R}$, $x \in \mathfrak{D}$.

In this case we say that f is **homogeneous** of degree k. If this function f is differentiable at x, show that

(20.34) $Df(x)(x) = kf(x)$.

(Hint: differentiate equation (20.33) with respect to t and set $t = 1$.) Conclude that Euler's† Relation (20.34) holds even when f is **positively homogeneous** in the sense that (20.33) holds only for $t \geq 0$. If $q = 1$ and $x = (\xi_1, \ldots, \xi_p)$, then Euler's Relation becomes

$$kf(x) = \xi_1 \frac{\partial f}{\partial \xi_1}(x) + \cdots + \xi_p \frac{\partial f}{\partial \xi_p}(x).$$

20.N. Let f be a twice differentiable function on $\mathbf{R}$ to $\mathbf{R}$. If we define F on $\mathbf{R}^2$ to $\mathbf{R}$ by

(a) $F(\xi, \eta) = f(\xi\eta)$,   then $\xi\dfrac{\partial F}{\partial \xi} = \eta\dfrac{\partial F}{\partial \eta}$;

(b) $F(\xi, \eta) = f(a\xi + b\eta)$,   then $b\dfrac{\partial F}{\partial \xi} = a\dfrac{\partial F}{\partial \eta}$;

(c) $F(\xi, \eta) = f(\xi^2 + \eta^2)$,   then $\eta\dfrac{\partial F}{\partial \xi} = \xi\dfrac{\partial F}{\partial \eta}$;

(d) $F(\xi, \eta) = f(\xi + c\eta) + f(\xi - c\eta)$,   then $c^2\dfrac{\partial^2 F}{\partial \xi^2} = \dfrac{\partial^2 F}{\partial \eta^2}$.

20.O. If f is defined on an open subset $\mathfrak{D}$ of $\mathbf{R}^2$ to $\mathbf{R}$ and if the partial derivatives f_ξ, f_η exist on $\mathfrak{D}$, then is it true that f is continuous on $\mathfrak{D}$?

20.P. Let f be defined on a neighborhood of a point c in $\mathbf{R}^2$ to $\mathbf{R}$. Suppose that f_ξ exists and is continuous on a neighborhood of c and that f_η exists at c. Then is f differentiable at c?

20.Q. Let f be defined on a subset $\mathfrak{D}$ of $\mathbf{R}^p$ with values in $\mathbf{R}^q$ and suppose that f is differentiable at every point of a line segment L joining two points a, b in $\mathfrak{D}$. If $|Df(c)(u)| \leq M|u|$ for all u in $\mathbf{R}^p$ and for all points c on this line segment L, then

$$|f(b) - f(a)| \leq M\,|b - a|.$$

(This result can often be used as a replacement for the Mean Value Theorem when $q > 1$.)

---

† Leonard Euler (1707–1783), a native of Basle, studied with Johann Bernoulli. He resided many years at the court in St. Petersburg, but this stay was interrupted by twenty-five years in Berlin. Despite the fact that he was the father of thirteen children and became totally blind, he was still able to write over eight hundred papers and books and make fundamental contributions to all branches of mathematics.

20.R. Suppose that $\mathfrak{D}$ is a connected open subset of $\mathbf{R}^p$, that f is differentiable on $\mathfrak{D}$ to $\mathbf{R}^q$, and that $Df(x) = 0$ for all x in $\mathfrak{D}$. Show that $f(x) = f(y)$ for all x, y in $\mathfrak{D}$.

20.S. The conclusion in the preceding exercise may fail if $\mathfrak{D}$ is not connected.

20.T. Suppose that f is differentiable on an interval J in $\mathbf{R}^p$ and has values in $\mathbf{R}$. If the partial derivatives f_{ξ_1} vanishes on J, then f does not depend on ξ_1.

20.U. Let f be defined on $\mathbf{R}^2$ to $\mathbf{R}$ by

$$f(\xi, \eta) = \frac{\xi\eta(\xi^2 - \eta^2)}{\xi^2 + \eta^2}, \qquad (\xi, \eta) \neq (0, 0),$$

$$= 0, \qquad (\xi, \eta) = (0, 0).$$

Show that the second partial derivatives $f_{\xi\eta}, f_{\eta\xi}$ exist at $\theta = (0, 0)$ but that they are not equal.

Section 21 Mapping Theorems and Extremum Problems

Throughout the first part of this section we shall suppose that f is a function with domain $\mathfrak{D}$ in $\mathbf{R}^p$ and with range in $\mathbf{R}^q$. Unless there is special mention, it is not assumed that $p = q$.

It will be shown that if f is differentiable at a point c, then the local character of the mapping of f is indicated by the linear function $Df(c)$. More precisely, if $Df(c)$ is one-one, then f is locally one-one; if $Df(c)$ maps onto $\mathbf{R}^q$, then f maps a neighborhood of c onto a neighborhood of $f(c)$. As a by-product of these mapping theorems, we obtain some inversion theorems and the important Implicit Function Theorem. It is possible to give a slightly shorter proof of this theorem than is presented here (see Project 21.α), but it is felt that the mapping theorems that are presented add sufficient insight to be worth the detour needed to establish them.

In the second part of this section we shall discuss extrema of a real-valued function on $\mathbf{R}^p$ and present the most frequently used results in this direction, including Lagrange's Method of finding extreme points when constraints are imposed.

We recall that a function f on a subset $\mathfrak{D}$ of $\mathbf{R}^p$ into $\mathbf{R}^q$ can be expressed in the form of a system

$$\begin{aligned}\eta_1 &= f_1(\xi_1, \xi_2, \ldots, \xi_p), \\ \eta_2 &= f_2(\xi_1, \xi_2, \ldots, \xi_p), \\ &\quad\cdots\cdots\cdots\cdots \\ \eta_q &= f_q(\xi_1, \xi_2, \ldots, \xi_p),\end{aligned}$$

(21.1)

of q real-valued functions f_i defined on $\mathfrak{D} \subseteq \mathbf{R}^p$. Each of the functions $f_i, i = 1, 2, \ldots, q$, can be examined as to whether it has partial derivatives with respect to each of the p coordinates in $\mathbf{R}^p$. We are interested in the case where each of the qp partial derivatives

$$\frac{\partial f_i}{\partial \xi_j} \qquad (i = 1, 2, \ldots, q : j = 1, 2, \ldots, p)$$

exists in a neighborhood of c and is continuous at c. It is convenient to have an abbreviation for this and closely related concepts and so we shall introduce some terminology.

21.1 DEFINITION. If the partial derivatives of f exist and are continuous at a point c interior to $\mathfrak{D}$, then we say that f belongs to Class C' at c. If $\mathfrak{D}_0 \subseteq \mathfrak{D}$ and if f belongs to Class C' at every point of $\mathfrak{D}_0$, we say that f belongs to Class C' on $\mathfrak{D}_0$.

It follows from Theorem 20.7 that if f belongs to Class C' on an open set $\mathfrak{D}$, then f is differentiable at every point of $\mathfrak{D}$. We shall now show that under this hypothesis, the derivative varies continuously, in a sense to be made precise.

21.2 LEMMA. *If f is in Class C' on a neighborhood of a point c and if $\epsilon > 0$, then there exists a $\delta(\epsilon) > 0$ such that if $|x - c| < \delta(\epsilon)$, then*

$$(21.2) \qquad |Df(x)(z) - Df(c)(z)| \leq \epsilon |z|,$$

for all z in $\mathbf{R}^p$.

PROOF. It follows from the continuity of the partial derivatives $\partial f_i / \partial \xi_j$ on a neighborhood of c that if $\epsilon > 0$, there exists $\delta(\epsilon) > 0$ such that if $|x - c| < \delta(\epsilon)$, then

$$\left| \frac{\partial f_i}{\partial \xi_j}(x) - \frac{\partial f_i}{\partial \xi_j}(c) \right| < \frac{\epsilon}{\sqrt{pq}} \cdot$$

Applying the estimate (15.8), we infer that (21.2) holds for all z in $\mathbf{R}^p$.
Q.E.D.

It will be seen in Exercise 21.I that the conclusion of this lemma implies that the partial derivatives are continuous at c.

The next result is a partial replacement for the Mean Value Theorem which (as we have seen) may fail when $q > 1$. This lemma provides the key for the mapping theorems to follow.

21.3 APPROXIMATION LEMMA. *If f is in Class C' on a neighborhood of a point c and if $\epsilon > 0$, then there exists a number $\delta(\epsilon) > 0$ such that if $|x_i - c| < \delta(\epsilon), i = 1, 2$, then*

$$(21.3) \qquad |f(x_1) - f(x_2) - Df(c)(x_1 - x_2)| \leq \epsilon |x_1 - x_2|.$$

PROOF. If $\epsilon > 0$, choose $\delta(\epsilon) > 0$ according to Lemma 21.2 so that if $|x - c| < \delta(\epsilon)$, then

$$|Df(x)(z) - Df(c)(z)| \leq \epsilon |z|$$

for all z in $\mathbf{R}^p$. If x_1, x_2 satisfy $|x_i - c| < \delta(\epsilon)$, we select $w \in \mathbf{R}^q$ such that $|w| = 1$ and

$$|f(x_1) - f(x_2) - Df(c)(x_1 - x_2)|$$
$$= \{f(x_1) - f(x_2) - Df(c)(x_1 - x_2)\} \cdot w.$$

If F is defined on $\mathbf{I}$ to $\mathbf{R}$ by

$$F(t) = \{f[t(x_1 - x_2) + x_2] - Df(c)(x_1 - x_2)\} \cdot w,$$

then F is differentiable on $0 < t < 1$ to $\mathbf{R}$ and

$$F'(t) = \{Df(t(x_1 - x_2) + x_2)(x_1 - x_2)\} \cdot w,$$
$$F(0) = \{f(x_2) - Df(c)(x_1 - x_2)\} \cdot w,$$
$$F(1) = \{f(x_1) - Df(c)(x_1 - x_2)\} \cdot w.$$

According to the Mean Value Theorem 19.6, there is a real number ψ with $0 < \psi < 1$ such that

$$F(1) - F(0) = F'(\psi).$$

Therefore, if $\bar{x} = \psi(x_1 - x_2) + x_2$, then

$$\{f(x_1) - f(x_2) - Df(c)(x_1 - x_2)\} \cdot w$$
$$= \{Df(\bar{x})(x_1 - x_2) - Df(c)(x_1 - x_2)\} \cdot w.$$

Since $|\bar{x} - c| < \delta(\epsilon)$ and $|w| = 1$, we employ the C.-B.-S. Inequality to infer that

$$|f(x_1) - f(x_2) - Df(c)(x_1 - x_2)|$$
$$\leq |Df(\bar{x})(x_1 - x_2) - Df(c)(x_1 - x_2)| \leq \epsilon |x_1 - x_2|.$$

Q.E.D.

Local One-One Mapping

It will now be seen that if f is in Class C' on a neighborhood of c and if the derivative $Df(c)$ is one-one, then f is one-one on a suitably small neighborhood of c. We sometimes describe this by saying that f is locally one-one at c.

21.4 LOCALLY ONE-ONE MAPPING. *If f is in Class C' on a neighborhood of c and the derivative $Df(c)$ is one-one, then there exists a positive* *constant δ such that the restriction of f to $U = \{x \in \mathbf{R}^p : |x - c| \leq \delta\}$ is one-one.*

PROOF. Since $Df(c)$ is a one-one linear function, it follows from Corollary 16.8 that there exists a constant $r > 0$ such that if $z \in \mathbf{R}^p$, then

$$(21.4) \qquad\qquad r\,|z| \leq |Df(c)(z)|.$$

Applying the Approximation Lemma 21.3 to $\epsilon = r/2$, we infer that there exists a constant $\delta > 0$ such that if $|x_i - c| \leq \delta$, $i = 1, 2$, then

$$|f(x_1) - f(x_2) - Df(c)(x_1 - x_2)| \leq \frac{r}{2}\,|x_1 - x_2|.$$

If we apply the Triangle Inequality to the left side of this inequality, we obtain

$$|Df(c)(x_1 - x_2)| - |f(x_1) - f(x_2)| \leq \frac{r}{2}\,|x_1 - x_2|.$$

Combining this with inequality (21.4), we conclude that

$$\frac{r}{2}\,|x_1 - x_2| \leq |f(x_1) - f(x_2)|.$$

Since this inequality holds for any two points in U, the function f cannot take the same value at two different points in U.

Q.E.D.

It follows from the theorem that the restriction of f to U has an inverse function. We now see that this inverse function is automatically continuous.

21.5 WEAK INVERSION THEOREM. *If f is in Class C' on a neighborhood of c and if $Df(c)$ is one-one, then there exists a positive real number δ such that the restriction of f to the compact neighborhood $U = \{x \in \mathbf{R}^p : |x - c| \leq \delta\}$ of c has a continuous inverse function with domain $f(U)$.*

PROOF. If $\delta > 0$ is as in the preceding theorem, then the restriction of f to U is a one-one function with compact domain. The conclusion then follows from Theorem 16.9.

Q.E.D.

We refer to this last result as the "Weak" Inversion Theorem, because it has the drawback that the local inverse function g need not be defined on a neighborhood of $f(c)$. Moreover, although we have assumed differentiability for f, we make no assertion concerning the differentiability of the inverse function. A stronger inversion theorem will be proved later under additional hypotheses.

Local Solvability

The next main result, the Local Solvability Theorem, is a companion to the Local One-One Mapping Theorem. It says that if f is in Class C' on a neighborhood of c and if $Df(c)$ maps $\mathbf{R}^p$ *onto* all of $\mathbf{R}^q$, then f maps a neighborhood of c onto a neighborhood of $f(c)$. Expressed differently, every point of $\mathbf{R}^q$ which is sufficiently close to $f(c)$ is the image under f of a point close to c. In order to establish this result for the general case we first establish it for linear functions and then prove that it holds for functions that can be approximated closely enough by linear functions.

21.6 Lemma. *If L is a linear function of $\mathbf{R}^p$ onto all of $\mathbf{R}^q$, then there exists a positive constant m such that every element y in $\mathbf{R}^q$ is the image under L of an element x in $\mathbf{R}^p$ such that $|x| \leq m\,|y|$.*

PROOF. Consider the following vectors in $\mathbf{R}^q$:

$$e_1 = (1, 0, \ldots, 0), \qquad e_2 = (0, 1, \ldots, 0), \ldots, \qquad e_q = (0, 0, \ldots, 1).$$

By hypothesis, there exist vectors u_j in $\mathbf{R}^p$ such that $L(u_j) = e_j$, $j = 1, 2, \ldots, q$. Let m be given by

$$(21.5) \qquad m = \left\{ \sum_{j=1}^{q} |u_j|^2 \right\}^{1/2}.$$

In view of the linearity of L, the vector $x = \sum_{j=1}^{q} \eta_j u_j$ is mapped into the vector

$$y = \sum_{j=1}^{q} \eta_j e_j = (\eta_1, \eta_2, \ldots, \eta_q).$$

By using the Triangle and the C.-B.-S. Inequalities, we obtain the estimate

$$|x| = \left| \sum_{j=1}^{q} \eta_j u_j \right| \leq \sum_{j=1}^{q} |\eta_j|\,|u_j| \leq m\,|y|.$$

Q.E.D.

21.7 Lemma. *Let g be continuous on $\mathfrak{D}(g) = \{x \in \mathbf{R}^p : |x| < \alpha\}$ with values in $\mathbf{R}^q$ and such that $g(\theta) = \theta$. Let L be linear and map $\mathbf{R}^p$ onto all of $\mathbf{R}^q$ and let $m > 0$ be as in the preceding lemma. Suppose that*

$$(21.6) \qquad |g(x_1) - g(x_2) - L(x_1 - x_2)| \leq \frac{1}{2m}\,|x_1 - x_2|$$

for $|x_i| < \alpha$. Then any vector y in $\mathbf{R}^q$ satisfying $|y| < \beta = \alpha/2m$ is the image under g of an element in $\mathfrak{D}(g)$.

PROOF.   To simplify later notation, let $x_0 = \theta$ and $y_0 = y$ and choose x_1 in $\mathbf{R}^p$ such that $y_0 = L(x_1 - x_0)$ and $|x_1 - x_0| \leq m\,|y|$. According to the preceding lemma, this is possible. Since

$$|x_1 - x_0| \leq m\,|y| < \alpha/2,$$

it follows that $x_1 \in \mathfrak{D}(g)$. We define y_1 by

$$y_1 = y_0 + g(x_0) - g(x_1) = -\{g(x_1) - g(x_0) - L(x_1 - x_0)\};$$

using the relation (21.6), we have

$$|y_1| \leq \frac{1}{2m}\,|x_1 - x_0| \leq \frac{1}{2}\,|y|.$$

Apply Lemma 21.6 again to obtain an element x_2 in $\mathbf{R}^p$ such that

$$y_1 = L(x_2 - x_1), \qquad |x_2 - x_1| \leq m\,|y_1|.$$

It follows that $|x_2 - x_1| \leq (\tfrac{1}{2})|x_1|$ and from the Triangle Inequality that $|x_2| \leq \tfrac{3}{2}|x_1| < \tfrac{3}{4}\alpha$, so that $x_2 \in \mathfrak{D}(g)$.

Proceeding inductively, suppose that $\theta = x_0, x_1, \ldots, x_n$ in $\mathfrak{D}(g)$ and $y = y_0, y_1, \ldots, y_n$ in $\mathbf{R}^q$ have been chosen to satisfy, for $1 \leq k \leq n$, the inequality

$$(21.7) \qquad\qquad |x_k - x_{k-1}| \leq m\,|y_{k-1}| \leq \frac{m}{2^{k-1}}\,|y|,$$

and to satisfy the relations

$$(21.8) \qquad\qquad y_{k-1} = L(x_k - x_{k-1}),$$

and

$$(21.9) \qquad\qquad y_k = y_{k-1} + g(x_{k-1}) - g(x_k).$$

Then it is seen from (21.7) and the Triangle Inequality that $|x_k| \leq 2m\,|y| < \alpha$.

We now carry the induction one step farther by choosing x_{n+1} so that

$$y_n = L(x_{n+1} - x_n), \qquad |x_{n+1} - x_n| \leq m\,|y_n|.$$

As before, it is easily seen that $|x_{n+1}| < \alpha$ so that $x_{n+1} \in \mathfrak{D}(g)$. We define y_{n+1} to be

$$y_{n+1} = y_n + g(x_n) - g(x_{n+1});$$

by (21.6), we conclude that

$$|y_{n+1}| \leq \frac{1}{2m}\,|x_{n+1} - x_n| \leq \frac{1}{2^{n+1}}\,|y|.$$

Another application of the Triangle Inequality shows that (x_n) is a Cauchy sequence and hence converges to an element x in $\mathbf{R}^p$ satisfying $|x| \leq 2m\,|y| < \alpha$. Since $|y_n| \leq (1/2^n)|y|$, the sequence (y_n) converges to the zero element θ of $\mathbf{R}^q$. Adding the relations (21.9) for $k = 1, 2, \ldots, n$, and recalling that $x_0 = \theta$ and $y_0 = y$, we obtain

$$y_n = y - g(x_n), \qquad n \in \mathbf{N}.$$

Since g is continuous and $x = \lim (x_n)$, we infer that $g(x) = y$. This proves that every element y with $|y| < \beta = \alpha/2m$ is the image under g of some element x in $\mathfrak{D}(g)$.

Q.E.D.

Since all the hard work has been done, we can derive the next result by a translation.

21.8 LOCAL SOLVABILITY THEOREM. *Suppose that f is in Class C' on a neighborhood of c and that the derivative $Df(c)$ maps $\mathbf{R}^p$ onto all of $\mathbf{R}^q$. There are positive numbers α, β such that if $y \in \mathbf{R}^q$ and $|y - f(c)| < \beta$, then there is an element x in $\mathbf{R}^p$ with $|x - c| < \alpha$ such that $f(x) = y$.*

PROOF. By hypothesis, the linear function $L = Df(c)$ maps onto $\mathbf{R}^q$ and we let m be as in Lemma 21.6. By the Approximation Lemma 21.3 there exists a number $\alpha > 0$ such that if $|x_i - c| < \alpha, i = 1, 2$, then

$$(21.10) \qquad |f(x_1) - f(x_2) - L(x_1 - x_2)| \leq \frac{1}{2m}|x_1 - x_2|.$$

Let g be defined on $\mathfrak{D}(g) = \{z \in \mathbf{R}^p : |z| < \alpha\}$ to $\mathbf{R}^q$ by the formula

$$g(z) = f(z + c) - f(c);$$

then g is continuous and $g(\theta) = f(c) - f(c) = \theta$. Moreover, if $|z_i| < \alpha$, $i = 1, 2$, and if $x_i = z_i + c$, then $x_1 - x_2 = z_1 - z_2$ and

$$g(z_1) - g(z_2) = f(x_1) - f(x_2),$$

whence it follows from inequality (21.10) that inequality (21.6) holds for g.

If $y \in \mathbf{R}^q$ satisfies $|y - f(c)| < \beta = \alpha/2m$ and if $w = y - f(c)$, then $|w| < \beta$. According to Lemma 21.7, there exists an element $z \in \mathbf{R}^p$ with $|z| < \alpha$ such that $g(z) = w$. If $x = c + z$, we have

$$w = g(z) = f(z + c) - f(c) = f(x) - f(c),$$

whence it follows that $f(x) = w + f(c) = y$.

Q.E.D.

21.9   OPEN MAPPING THEOREM.   *Let $\mathfrak{D}$ be an open subset of $\mathbf{R}^p$ and let f be in Class $C'(\mathfrak{D})$. If, for each x in $\mathfrak{D}$, the derivative $Df(x)$ maps $\mathbf{R}^p$ onto $\mathbf{R}^q$, then $f(\mathfrak{D})$ is open in $\mathbf{R}^q$. Moreover, if G is any open subset of $\mathfrak{D}$, then $f(G)$ is open in $\mathbf{R}^q$.*

PROOF.   If G is open and $c \in G$, then the Local Solvability Theorem implies that some open neighborhood of c maps onto an open neighborhood of $f(c)$, whence $f(G)$ is open.

Q.E.D.

The Inversion Theorem

We now combine our two mapping theorems in the case that $p = q$ and the derivative $Df(c)$ is both one-one and maps $\mathbf{R}^p$ onto $\mathbf{R}^p$. To be more explicit, if L is a linear function with domain $\mathbf{R}^p$ and range in $\mathbf{R}^p$, then L is one-one if and only if the range of L is all of $\mathbf{R}^p$. Furthermore, the linear function L has these properties if and only if its matrix representation has a non-vanishing determinant.

When applied to the derivative of a function f mapping part of $\mathbf{R}^p$ into $\mathbf{R}^p$, these latter remarks assert that $Df(c)$ is one-one if and only if it maps $\mathbf{R}^p$ onto all of $\mathbf{R}^p$ and that this is the case if and only if the Jacobian determinant

$$
J_f(c) = \det \begin{vmatrix}
\dfrac{\partial f_1}{\partial \xi_1}(c) & \dfrac{\partial f_1}{\partial \xi_2}(c) & \cdots & \dfrac{\partial f_1}{\partial \xi_p}(c) \\
\dfrac{\partial f_2}{\partial \xi_1}(c) & \dfrac{\partial f_2}{\partial \xi_2}(c) & \cdots & \dfrac{\partial f_2}{\partial \xi_p}(c) \\
\cdot & \cdot \cdot \cdot \cdot \cdot \cdot \cdot & \cdot & \cdot \\
\dfrac{\partial f_p}{\partial \xi_1}(c) & \dfrac{\partial f_p}{\partial \xi_2}(c) & \cdots & \dfrac{\partial f_p}{\partial \xi_p}(c)
\end{vmatrix}
$$

is not zero.

21.10   INVERSION THEOREM.   *Suppose that f is in Class C' on a neighborhood of c in $\mathbf{R}^p$ with values in $\mathbf{R}^p$ and that the derivative $Df(c)$ is a one-one map of $\mathbf{R}^p$ onto $\mathbf{R}^p$. Then there exists a neighborhood U of c such that $V = f(U)$ is a neighborhood of $f(c)$, f is a one-one mapping of U onto V, and f has a continuous inverse function g defined on V to U. Moreover, g is in Class C' on V and if $y \in V$ and $x = g(y) \in U$, then the linear function $Dg(y)$ is the inverse of the linear function $Df(x)$.*

PROOF. By hypothesis $Df(c)$ is one-one, so Corollary 16.8 implies that there exists a positive number r such that

$$2r\,|z| \leq |Df(c)(z)| \quad \text{for} \quad z \in \mathbf{R}^p.$$

By Lemma 21.2 there is a sufficiently small neighborhood of c on which f is in Class C' and Df satisfies

(21.11) $$r\,|z| \leq |Df(x)(z)| \quad \text{for} \quad z \in \mathbf{R}^p.$$

We further restrict our attention to a neighborhood U of c on which f is one-one and which is contained in the ball with center c and radius α (as in Theorem 21.8). Then $V = f(U)$ is a neighborhood of $f(c)$ and we infer from Theorems 21.5 and 21.8 that the restriction of f to U has a continuous inverse function g, defined on V.

In order to prove that g is differentiable at $y = f(x) \in V$, let $y_1 \in V$ be near y and let x_1 be the unique element of U with $f(x_1) = y_1$. Since f is differentiable at x, then

$$f(x_1) - f(x) - Df(x)(x_1 - x) = u(x_1)|x_1 - x|,$$

where $|u(x_1)| \to 0$ as $x_1 \to x$. If M_x is the inverse of the linear function $Df(x)$, then

$$x_1 - x = M_x \circ Df(x)(x_1 - x) = M_x[f(x_1) - f(x) - u(x_1)|x_1 - x|].$$

In view of the relations between x, y and x_1, y_1, this equation can be written in the form

$$g(y_1) - g(y) - M_x(y_1 - y) = -|x_1 - x|M_x[u(x_1)].$$

Since $Df(x)$ is one-one, it follows as in the proof of Theorem 21.4 that

$$|y_1 - y| = |f(x_1) - f(x)| \geq \frac{r}{2}\,|x_1 - x|,$$

provided that y_1 is chosen close enough to y. Moreover, it follows from (21.11) that $|M_x(u)| \leq (1/r)|u|$ for all $u \in \mathbf{R}^q$. Therefore, we have

$$|g(y_1) - g(y) - M_x(y_1 - y)| \leq \frac{1}{r}\,|x_1 - x|\,|u(x_1)| \leq \left\{\frac{2}{r^2}\,|u(x_1)|\right\}|y_1 - y|.$$

Therefore, g is differentiable at $y = f(x)$ and its derivative $Dg(y)$ is the linear function M_x, which is the inverse of $Df(x)$.

It remains to show that g is in Class C' on V. Let z be any element of $\mathbf{R}^p$ and let x, x_1, y, y_1 be as before; then it is seen directly from the fact that the linear function Dg is the inverse of the linear function Df that

$$Dg(y)(z) - Dg(y_1)(z) = Dg(y) \circ [Df(x_1) - Df(x)] \circ Dg(y_1)(z).$$

Since f is in Class C' at x, then

$$|Df(x_1)(w) - Df(x)(w)| \le \epsilon |w| \quad \text{for} \quad w \in \mathbf{R}^p,$$

when x_1 is sufficiently close to x. Moreover, it follows from (21.11) that if $u \in \mathbf{R}^p$, then both $|Dg(y_1)(u)|$ and $|Dg(y)(u)|$ are dominated by $(1/r)|u|$. Employing these estimates in the above expression, we infer that

$$|Dg(y)(z) - Dg(y_1)(z)| \le \frac{\epsilon}{r^2} |z| \quad \text{for} \quad z \in \mathbf{R}^p,$$

when y_1 is sufficiently close to y. If we take z to be the unit vector e_j (displayed in the proof of Lemma 21.6) and take the inner product with the vector e_i, we conclude that the partial derivative $\partial g_i/\partial \xi_j$ is continuous at y.

Q.E.D.

Implicit Functions

Suppose that F is a function which is defined on a subset of $\mathbf{R}^p \times \mathbf{R}^q$ into $\mathbf{R}^p$. If we make the obvious identification of $\mathbf{R}^p \times \mathbf{R}^q$ with $\mathbf{R}^{p+q}$, then we do not need to redefine what it means to say that F is continuous, or is differentiable, or is in Class C' at a point. Suppose that F takes the point (x_0, y_0) into the zero vector of $\mathbf{R}^p$. The problem of implicit functions is to solve the equation $F(x, y) = \theta$ for one argument (say x) in terms of the other in the sense that we find a function φ defined on a subset of $\mathbf{R}^q$ with values in $\mathbf{R}^p$ such that $\varphi(y_0) = x_0$ and

$$F[\varphi(y), y] = \theta,$$

for all y in the domain of φ. Naturally, we expect to assume that F is continuous on a neighborhood of (x_0, y_0) and we hope to conclude that the solution function φ is continuous on a neighborhood of y_0. It will probably be no surprise to the reader that we shall assume that F is in Class C' on a neighborhood of (x_0, y_0), but even this hypothesis is not enough to guarantee the existence and uniqueness of a continuous solution function defined on a neighborhood of y_0. In the case $p = q = 1$, the function $F(x, y) = x^2 - y^2$ has two continuous solution functions $\varphi_1(y) = y$ and $\varphi_2(y) = -y$ corresponding to the point $(0, 0)$. It also has discontinuous solutions, such as

$$\begin{aligned} \varphi_3(y) &= y, \quad y \text{ rational}, \\ &= -y, \quad y \text{ irrational}. \end{aligned}$$

The function $G(x, y) = y - x^2$ has two continuous solution functions corresponding to $(0, 0)$, but neither of them is defined on a neighborhood of the point $y = 0$. To give a more exotic example, the function

$$H(x, y) = 0, \qquad\qquad x = 0,$$
$$= y - x^3 \sin (1/x), \qquad x \neq 0,$$

is in Class C' on a neighborhood of $(0, 0)$ but there is no continuous solution functions defined on a neighborhood of $y = 0$.

In all three of these examples, the partial derivative with respect to x vanishes at the point under consideration. In the case $p = q = 1$, the additional assumption needed to guarantee the existence and uniqueness of the solution functions is that this partial derivative be non-zero. In the general case, we observe that the derivative $DF(x_0, y_0)$ is a linear function on $\mathbf{R}^p \times \mathbf{R}^q$ into $\mathbf{R}^p$ and induces a linear function L of $\mathbf{R}^p$ into $\mathbf{R}^p$, defined by

$$L(u) = DF(x_0, y_0)(u, \theta)$$

for all u in $\mathbf{R}^p$. In a very reasonable sense, L is the partial derivative of F with respect to x at the point (x_0, y_0). The additional hypothesis we shall impose is that L is a one-one linear function of $\mathbf{R}^p$ onto all of $\mathbf{R}^p$.

Before we proceed any further, we observe that it is no loss of generality to assume that the points x_0 and y_0 are the zero vectors in the spaces $\mathbf{R}^p$ and $\mathbf{R}^q$, respectively, Indeed, this can always be attained by a translation. Since it simplifies our notation somewhat, we shall make this assumption.

We also wish to interpret this problem in terms of the coordinates. If $x = (\xi_1, \xi_2, \ldots, \xi_p)$ and $y = (\eta_1, \eta_2, \ldots, \eta_q)$, the equation

$$F(x, y) = \theta$$

takes the form of p equations in the $p + q$ arguments $\xi_1, \ldots, \xi_p,$ $\eta_1, \ldots, \eta_q$:

$$f_1(\xi_1, \ldots, \xi_p, \eta_1, \ldots, \eta_q) = 0,$$

(21.12) $\qquad\qquad$ . . . .

$$f_p(\xi_1, \ldots, \xi_p, \eta_1, \ldots, \eta_q) = 0.$$

Here it is understood that the system of equations is satisfied for $\xi_1 = 0, \ldots, \eta_q = 0$, and it is desired to solve for the ξ_i in terms of the η_j, at least when the latter are sufficiently small. The hypotheses to be made amount to assuming that the partial derivatives of the functions f_i, with respect to the $p + q$ arguments, are continuuos near zero, and that the Jacobian of the f_i with respect to the ξ_i is not zero when $\xi_i = 0$,

$i = 1, \ldots, p$. Under these hypotheses, we shall show that there are functions φ_i, $i = 1, \ldots, p$, which are continuous near $\eta_1 = 0, \ldots, \eta_q = 0$, and such that if we substitute

$$\xi_1 = \varphi_1(\eta_1, \ldots, \eta_q),$$

(21.13) $\cdot \quad \cdot \quad \cdot \quad \cdot \quad \cdot \quad \cdot \quad \cdot \quad \cdot$

$$\xi_p = \varphi_p(\eta_1, \ldots, \eta_q),$$

into the system of equations (21.12), then we obtain an identity in the η_j.

21.11 IMPLICIT FUNCTION THEOREM. *Suppose that F is in Class C' on a neighborhood of (θ, θ) in $\mathbf{R}^p \times \mathbf{R}^q$ and has values in $\mathbf{R}^p$. Suppose that $F(\theta, \theta) = \theta$ and that the linear function L, defined by*

$$L(u) = DF(\theta, \theta)(u, \theta), \qquad u \in \mathbf{R}^p,$$

is a one-one function of $\mathbf{R}^p$ onto $\mathbf{R}^p$. Then there exists a function φ which is in Class C' on a neighborhood W of θ in $\mathbf{R}^q$ to $\mathbf{R}^p$ such that $\varphi(\theta) = \theta$ and

$$F[\varphi(y), y] = \theta \quad for \quad y \in W.$$

PROOF. Let H be the function defined on a neighborhood of (θ, θ) in $\mathbf{R}^p \times \mathbf{R}^q$ to $\mathbf{R}^p \times \mathbf{R}^q$ by

(21.14) $H(x, y) = (F(x, y), y).$

Then H is in Class C' on a neighborhood of (θ, θ) and

$$DH(\theta, \theta)(u, v) = (DF(\theta, \theta)(u, v), v).$$

In view of the hypothesis that L is a one-one function of $\mathbf{R}^p$ onto $\mathbf{R}^p$, then $DH(\theta, \theta)$ is a one-one function of $\mathbf{R}^p \times \mathbf{R}^q$ onto $\mathbf{R}^p \times \mathbf{R}^q$. It follows from the Inversion Theorem 21.10 that there is a neighborhood U of (θ, θ) such that $V = H(U)$ is a neighborhood of (θ, θ) and H is a one-one mapping of U onto V and has a continuous inverse function G. In addition, the function G is in Class C' on V and its derivative DG at a point in V is the inverse of the linear function DH at the corresponding point in U. In view of the formula (21.14) defining H, its inverse function G has the form

$$G(x, y) = (G_1(x, y), y),$$

where G_1 is in Class C' on V to $\mathbf{R}^p$.

Let W be a neighborhood of θ in $\mathbf{R}^q$ such that if $y \in W$ then $(\theta, y) \in V$, and let φ be defined on W to $\mathbf{R}^p$ by the formula

$$\varphi(y) = G_1(\theta, y) \quad \text{for} \quad y \in W.$$

If (x, y) is in V, then we have

$$(x, y) = H \circ G(x, y) = H(G_1(x, y), y)$$
$$= (F[G_1(x, y), y], y).$$

If we take $x = \theta$ in this relation, we obtain

$$(\theta, y) = (F[\varphi(y), y], y) \quad \text{for} \quad y \in W.$$

Therefore, we infer that

$$F[\varphi(y), y] = \theta \quad \text{for} \quad y \in W.$$

Since G_1 is in Class C' on V to $\mathbf{R}^p$, it follows that φ is in Class C' on W to $\mathbf{R}^p$.

Q.E.D.

It is sometimes useful to have an explicit formula for the derivative of φ. In order to give this, it is convenient to introduce the **partial derivatives** of F. Indeed, if (a, b) is a point near (θ, θ) in $\mathbf{R}^p \times \mathbf{R}^q$, then the partial derivative $D_x F$ of F at (a, b) is the linear function on $\mathbf{R}^p$ to $\mathbf{R}^p$ defined by

$$D_x F(a, b)(u) = DF(a, b)(u, \theta) \quad \text{for} \quad u \in \mathbf{R}^p.$$

Similarly, the partial derivative $D_y F$ is the linear function on $\mathbf{R}^q$ to $\mathbf{R}^p$ defined by

$$D_y F(a, b)(v) = DF(a, b)(\theta, v) \quad \text{for} \quad v \in \mathbf{R}^q.$$

It may be noted that

$$(21.15) \qquad DF(a, b)(u, v) = D_x F(a, b)(u) + D_y F(a, b)(v).$$

21.12   COROLLARY.   *With the hypotheses of the theorem and the notation just introduced, the derivative of φ at a point y in W is the linear function on $\mathbf{R}^q$ to $\mathbf{R}^p$ given by*

$$(21.16) \qquad D\varphi(y) = - (D_x F)^{-1} \circ (D_y F).$$

Here it is understood that the partial derivatives of F are evaluated at the point $(\varphi(y), y)$.

PROOF.   We shall apply the Chain Rule 20.9 to the composite function which sends y in W into

$$F[\varphi(y), y] = \theta.$$

For the sake of clarity, let K be defined for $y \in \mathbf{R}^q$ to $\mathbf{R}^p \times \mathbf{R}^q$ by

$$K(y) = (\varphi(y), y);$$

then $F \circ K$ is identically equal to θ. Moreover,

$$DK(y)(v) = (D\varphi(y)(v), v) \quad \text{for} \quad v \in \mathbf{R}^q.$$

Calculating $DF \circ DK$, and using (21.15), we obtain

$$\theta = D_x F \circ D\varphi + D_y F,$$

where the partial derivatives of F are evaluated at the point $(\varphi(y), y)$. Since $D_x F$ is invertible, the formula (21.16) results.

Q.E.D.

Extremum Problems

The use of the derivative to determine the relative maximum and relative minimum points of a function on **R** to **R** is well-known to students of calculus. In the Interior Maximum Theorem 19.4, we have presented the main tool in the case where the relative extreme is taken at an interior point. The question as to whether a *critical point* (that is, a point at which the derivative vanishes) is actually an extreme point is not always easily settled, but can often be handled by use of Taylor's Theorem 19.9. The discussion of extreme points which belong to the boundary, often yields to application of the Mean Value Theorem 19.6.

In the case of a function with domain in $\mathbf{R}^p$, $p > 1$, and range in **R**, the situation is more complicated and each function needs to be examined in its own right since there are few general statements that can be made. However, the next result is a familiar and very useful necessary condition.

21.13   THEOREM.   *Let f be a function with domain $\mathfrak{D}$ in $\mathbf{R}^p$ and with range in* **R**. *If c is an interior point of $\mathfrak{D}$ at which f is differentiable and has a relative extremum, then $Df(c) = 0$.*

PROOF.   By hypothesis, the restriction of f to any line passing through c will have an extremum at c. Therefore, by the Interior Maximum Theorem 19.4, any directional derivative of f must vanish at c. In particular,

$$(21.17) \qquad \frac{\partial f}{\partial \xi_1}(c) = 0, \ldots, \frac{\partial f}{\partial \xi_p}(c) = 0,$$

whence it follows that $Df(c) = 0$.

Q.E.D.

A more elegant proof of the preceding result, under the hypothesis that f is in Class C' on a neighborhood of c, can be obtained from the Local Solvability Theorem 21.8. For, we notice that if $w = (\omega_1, \ldots, \omega_p)$, then

$$Df(c)(w) = \frac{\partial f}{\partial \xi_1}(c)\,\omega_1 + \cdots + \frac{\partial f}{\partial \xi_p}(c)\,\omega_p.$$

It is clear that if one of these partial derivatives of f at c is not zero, then $Df(c)$ maps $\mathbf{R}^p$ onto all of **R**. According to the Local Solvability Theorem

21.8, f maps a neighborhood of c onto a neighborhood of $f(c)$; therefore the function f cannot have an extremum at c. Consequently, if f has an extremum at an interior point c of the domain of f, then $Df(c) = 0$.

If c is a point at which $Df(c) = 0$, we say that c is a **critical point** of the function f on $\mathfrak{D} \subseteq \mathbf{R}^p$ into R. It is well-known that not every critical point of f is a relative extremum of f. For example, if f is defined on $\mathbf{R}^2$ to R by $f(\xi, \eta) = \xi\eta$, then the origin $(0, 0)$ is a critical point of f, but f takes on values larger than $f(0, 0)$ in the first and third quadrants, while it takes on values less than $f(0, 0)$ in the second and fourth quadrants. Hence the origin is neither a relative maximum nor a relative minimum of f; it is an example of a **saddle point** (i.e., a critical point which is not an extremum). In the example just cited, the function has a relative minimum at the origin along some lines $\xi = \alpha t$, $\eta = \beta t$, and a relative maximim at the origin along other lines. This is not always the case for, as will be seen in Exercise 21.W, it is possible that a function may have a relative minimum along every line passing through a saddle point. The adjoining figure provides a representation of such a function. (See Figure 21.1.)

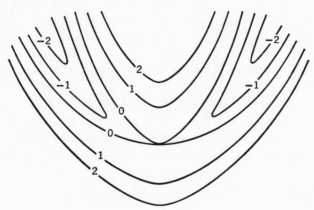

Figure 21.1

In view of these remarks, it is convenient to have a condition which is sufficient to guarantee that a critical point is an extremum or that it is a saddle point. The next result, which is a direct analog of the "second derivative test," gives such a sufficient condition.

21.14   THEOREM.   *Let the real-valued function f have continuous second partial derivatives on a neighborhood of a critical point c in $\mathbf{R}^p$, and consider the second derivative*

$$(21.18) \qquad D^2f(c)(w)^2 = \sum_{i,j=1}^{p} \frac{\partial^2 f}{\partial \xi_i \partial \xi_j} (c)\, \omega_i \omega_j,$$

evaluated at $w = (\omega_1, \ldots, \omega_p)$.

(a) *If* $D^2f(c)(w)^2 > 0$ *for all* $w \neq \theta$ *in* $\mathbf{R}^p$, *then* f *has a relative minimum at* c.

(b) *If* $D^2f(c)(w)^2 < 0$ *for all* $w \neq \theta$ *in* $\mathbf{R}^p$, *then* f *has a relative maximum at* c.

(c) *If* $D^2f(c)(w)^2$ *takes on both positive and negative values for* w *in* $\mathbf{R}^p$, *then* c *is a saddle point of* f.

PROOF.   (a) If $D^2f(c)(w)^2 > 0$ for points in the compact set $\{w \in \mathbf{R}^p : |w| = 1\}$, then there exists a constant $m > 0$ such that

$$D^2f(c)(w)^2 \geq m \quad \text{for} \quad |w| = 1.$$

Since the second partial derivatives of f are continuous at c, there exists a $\delta > 0$ such that if $|u - c| < \delta$, then

$$D^2f(u)(w)^2 \geq m/2 \quad \text{for} \quad |w| = 1.$$

According to Taylor's Theorem 20.16, if $0 \leq t \leq 1$, there exists a point $\bar{c}$ on the line segment joining c and $c + tw$ such that

$$f(c + tw) = f(c) + Df(c)(tw) + \tfrac{1}{2}D^2f(\bar{c})(tw)^2.$$

Since c is a critical point, it follows that if $|w| = 1$, and if $0 \leq t < \delta$, then

$$f(c + tw) - f(c) = \frac{t^2}{2} D^2f(\bar{c})(w)^2 \geq \frac{m}{4} t^2 \geq 0.$$

Hence f has a relative minimum at c. The proof of (b) is similar.

To prove part (c), let w_1 and w_2 be elements of unit length and such that

$$D^2f(c)(w_1)^2 > 0, \qquad D^2f(c)(w_2)^2 < 0.$$

It is easily seen that if t is a sufficiently small positive number, then

$$f(c + tw_1) > f(c), \qquad f(c + tw_2) < f(c).$$

In this case the point c is a saddle point for f.

Q.E.D.

The preceding result indicates that the nature of the critical point c is determined by the quadratic function given in (21.18). In particular, it is of importance to know whether this function can take on both positive and negative values or whether it is always of one sign. An important and well-known result of algebra can be used to determine this. For each $j = 1, 2, \ldots, p$, let Δ_j be the determinant of the matrix

$$\begin{bmatrix} f_{\xi_1\xi_1}(c) & \cdots & f_{\xi_1\xi_j}(c) \\ \cdot & \cdot \cdot \cdot \cdot \cdot & \cdot \\ f_{\xi_j\xi_1}(c) & \cdots & f_{\xi_j\xi_j}(c) \end{bmatrix}$$

If the numbers $\Delta_1, \Delta_2, \ldots, \Delta_p$ are all positive, the second derivative (21.18) takes only positive values and hence f has a relative minimum at c. If the numbers $\Delta_1, \Delta_2, \ldots, \Delta_p$ are alternately negative and positive, this derivative takes only negative values and hence f has a relative maximum at c. In other cases the point c is a saddle point.

We shall establish this remark only for $p = 2$, where a less elaborate formulation is more convenient. Here we need to examine a quadratic function

$$Q = A\xi^2 + 2B\xi\eta + C\eta^2.$$

If $\Delta = AC - B^2 > 0$, then $A \neq 0$ and we can complete the square and write

$$Q = \frac{1}{A}[(A\xi + B\eta)^2 + (AC - B^2)\eta^2].$$

Hence the sign of Q is the same as the sign of A. On the other hand, if $\Delta = AC - B^2 < 0$, then we shall see that Q has both positive and negative values. This is obvious if $A = C = 0$. If $A \neq 0$, we can complete the square in Q as above and observe that the quadratic function Q has opposite signs at the two points $(\xi, \eta) = (1, 0)$ and $(B, -A)$. If $A = 0$ but $C \neq 0$, a similar argument can be given.

We collect these remarks pertaining to a function on $\mathbf{R}^2$ in a formal statement.

21.15 COROLLARY. *Let the real-valued function f have continuous second partial derivatives in a neighborhood of a critical point c in $\mathbf{R}^2$, and let*

$$\Delta = f_{\xi\xi}(c)f_{\eta\eta}(c) - [f_{\xi\eta}(c)]^2.$$

(a) *If $\Delta > 0$ and if $f_{\xi\xi}(c) > 0$, then f has a relative minimum at c.*

(b) *If $\Delta > 0$ and if $f_{\xi\xi}(c) < 0$, then f has a relative maximum at c.*

(c) *If $\Delta < 0$, then the point c is a saddle point of f.*

Extremum Problems with Constraints

Until now we have been discussing the case where the extrema of the real-valued function f belong to the interior of its domain $\mathfrak{D}$ in $\mathbb{R}^p$. None of our remarks apply to the location of the extrema on the boundary. However, if the function is defined on the boundary of $\mathfrak{D}$ and if this boundary of $\mathfrak{D}$ can be parametrized by a function φ, then the extremum problem is reduced to an examination of the extrema of the composition $f \circ \varphi$.

There is a related problem which leads to an interesting and elegant procedure. Suppose that S is a surface contained in the domain $\mathfrak{D}$ of the real-valued function f. It is often desired to find the values of f that are maximum or minimum among all those attained on S. For example, if $\mathfrak{D} = \mathbb{R}^p$ and $f(x) = |x|$, then the problem we have posed is concerned with finding the points on the surface S which are closest to (or farthest from) the origin. If the surface S is given parametrically, then we can treat this problem by considering the composition of f with the parametric representation of S. However, it frequently is not convenient to express S in this fashion and another procedure is often more desirable.

Suppose S can be given as the points x in $\mathfrak{D}$ satisfying a relation of the form

$$g(x) = 0,$$

for a function g defined on $\mathfrak{D}$ to $\mathbb{R}$. We are attempting to find the relative extreme values of f for those points x in $\mathfrak{D}$ satisfying the *constraint* (or *side condition*) $g(x) = 0$. If we assume that f and g are in Class C' in a neighborhood of a point c in $\mathfrak{D}$ and that $Dg(c) \neq 0$, then a necessary condition that c be an extreme point of f relative to points x satisfying $g(x) = 0$, is that the derivative $Dg(c)$ is a multiple of $Df(c)$. In terms of partial derivatives, this condition is that there exists a real number λ such that

$$\frac{\partial f}{\partial \xi_1}(c) = \lambda \frac{\partial g}{\partial \xi_1}(c),$$

$$\cdot \;\; \cdot \;\; \cdot \;\; \cdot \;\; \cdot \;\; \cdot \;\; \cdot$$

$$\frac{\partial f}{\partial \xi_p}(c) = \lambda \frac{\partial g}{\partial \xi_p}(c).$$

In practice we wish to determine the p coordinates of the point c satisfying this necessary condition. However the real number λ, which is called the Lagrange multiplier, is not known either. The p equations given above, together with the equation

$$g(c) = 0,$$

are then solved for the $p + 1$ unknown quantities, of which the co-ordinates of c are of primary interest.

We shall now establish this result.

21.16   LAGRANGE'S METHOD. *Let f and g be in Class C' on a neighborhood of a point c in $\mathbf{R}^p$ and with values in $\mathbf{R}$. Suppose that there exists a neighborhood of c such that $f(x) \geq f(c)$ or $f(x) \leq f(c)$ for all points x in this neighborhood which also satisfy the constraint $g(x) = 0$. If $Dg(c) \neq 0$, then there exists a real number λ such that*

$$Df(c) = \lambda \, Dg(c).$$

PROOF.   Let F be defined on $\mathfrak{D}$ to $\mathbf{R}^2$ by

$$F(x) = \big(f(x), g(x)\big).$$

It is readily seen that F is in Class C' on a neighborhood of c and that

$$DF(x)(w) = \big(Df(x)(w), Dg(x)(w)\big)$$

for each x in this neighborhood and for w in $\mathbf{R}^p$. Moreover, an element x satisfies the constraint $g(x) = 0$ if and only if $F(x) = \big(f(x), 0\big)$.

Now suppose that c satisfies the constraint and is a relative extremum among such points. To be explicit, assume that $f(x) \leq f(c)$ for all points x in a neighborhood of c which also satisfy $g(x) = 0$. Then the derivative $Df(c)$ does not map $\mathbf{R}^p$ onto all of $\mathbf{R}^2$. For, if so, then the Local Solvability Theorem 21.8 implies that for some $\epsilon > 0$ the points $(\xi, 0)$ with $f(c) < \xi < f(c) + \epsilon$ are images of points in a neighborhood of c, contrary to hypothesis. Therefore, $DF(c)$ maps $\mathbf{R}^p$ into a line in $\mathbf{R}^2$. By hypothesis $Dg(c) \neq 0$, so that $DF(c)$ maps $\mathbf{R}^p$ into a line $\mathbf{R}^2$ which passes through a point $(\lambda, 1)$. Therefore, we have $Df(c) = \lambda \, Dg(c)$.

Q.E.D.

The condition $Df(c) = \lambda \, Dg(c)$ can be written in the form

$$\frac{\partial f}{\partial \xi_1}(c)\, \omega_1 + \cdots + \frac{\partial f}{\partial \xi_p}(c)\, \omega_p = \lambda \left[\frac{\partial g}{\partial \xi_1}(c)\, \omega_1 + \cdots + \frac{\partial g}{\partial \xi_p}(c)\, \omega_p \right]$$

for each element $w = (\omega_1, \ldots, \omega_p)$ in $\mathbf{R}^p$. By taking the elements

$$(1, 0, \ldots, 0), \ldots, (0, \ldots, 0, 1),$$

for w, we write this as a system

$$\frac{\partial f}{\partial \xi_1}(c) = \lambda \frac{\partial g}{\partial \xi_1}(c),$$

$$\cdots \cdots \cdots$$

$$\frac{\partial f}{\partial \xi_p}(c) = \lambda \frac{\partial g}{\partial \xi_p}(c),$$

which is to be solved together with the equation

$$g(c) = 0.$$

To give an elementary application of Lagrange's Method, let us find the point on the plane with the equation

$$2\xi + 3\eta - \zeta = 5,$$

which is nearest the origin in $\mathbf{R}^3$. We shall minimize the function which gives the square of the distance of the point (ξ, η, ζ) to the origin, namely

$$f(\xi, \eta, \zeta) = \xi^2 + \eta^2 + \zeta^2,$$

under the constraint

$$g(\xi, \eta, \zeta) = 2\xi + 3\eta - \zeta - 5 = 0.$$

Thus we have the system

$$2\xi = 2\lambda,$$
$$2\eta = 3\lambda,$$
$$2\zeta = -\lambda,$$
$$2\xi + 3\eta - \zeta - 5 = 0,$$

which is to be solved for the unknowns $\xi, \eta, \zeta, \lambda$. In this case the solution is simple and yields $(5/7, 15/14, -5/14)$ as the point on the plane nearest the origin.

Lagrange's Method is a necessary condition only, and the points obtained by solving the equations may yield relative maxima, relative minima, or neither. In many applications, the determination of whether the points are actually extrema can be based on geometrical or physical considerations; in other cases, it can lead to considerable analytic difficulties.

In conclusion, we observe that Lagrange's Method can readily be extended to handle the case where there is more than one constraint. In this case we must introduce one Lagrange multiplier for each constraint.

Exercises

21.A. Let f be the mapping of $\mathbf{R}^2$ into $\mathbf{R}^2$ which sends the point (x, y) into the point (u, v) given by

$$u = x + y, \quad v = 2x + ay.$$

Calculate the derivative Df. Show that Df is one-one if and only if it maps $\mathbf{R}^2$ onto $\mathbf{R}^2$, and that this is the case if and only if $a \neq 2$. Examine the image of the unit square $\{(x, y) : 0 \leq x \leq 1, 0 \leq y \leq 1\}$ in the three cases $a = 1$, $a = 2$, $a = 3$.

21.B. Let f be the mapping of $\mathbf{R}^2$ into $\mathbf{R}^2$ which sends the point (x, y) into the point (u, v) given by

$$u = x, \qquad v = xy.$$

Draw some curves $u = $ constant, $v = $ constant in the (x, y)-plane and some curves $x = $ constant, $y = $ constant in the (u, v)-plane. Is this mapping one-one? Does f map onto all of $\mathbf{R}^2$? Show that if $x \neq 0$, then f maps some neighborhood of (x, y) in a one-one fashion onto a neighborhood of (x, xy). Into what region in the (u, v)-plane does f map the rectangle $\{(x, y):1 \leq x \leq 2,\ 0 \leq y \leq 2\}$? What points in the (x, y)-plane map under f into the rectangle $\{(u, v):1 \leq u \leq 2,\ 0 \leq v \leq 2\}$?

21.C. Let f be the mapping of $\mathbf{R}^2$ into $\mathbf{R}^2$ which sends the point (x, y) into the point (u, v) given by

$$u = x^2 - y^2, \qquad v = 2xy.$$

What curves in the (x, y)-plane map under f into the lines $u = $ constant, $v = $ constant? Into what curves in the (u, v)-plane do the lines $x = $ constant, $y = $ constant map? Show that each non-zero point (u, v) is the image under f of two points. Into what region does f map the square $\{(x, y):0 \leq x \leq 1,\ 0 \leq y \leq 1\}$? What region is mapped by f into the square $\{(u, v):0 \leq u \leq 1,\ 0 \leq v \leq 1\}$?

21.D. Let f be the mapping in the preceding exercise. Show that f is locally one-one at every point except $\theta = (0, 0)$, but f is not one-one on $\mathbf{R}^2$.

21.E. Let f be in Class C' on $\mathbf{R}^p$ onto $\mathbf{R}^q$ and suppose that f has an inverse. Is it true that for each x in $\mathbf{R}^p$, then $Df(x)$ is a one-one linear function which maps $\mathbf{R}^p$ onto $\mathbf{R}^q$?

21.F. Let f be defined on $\mathbf{R}$ to $\mathbf{R}$ by

$$\begin{aligned} f(x) &= x + 2x^2 \sin (1/x), \qquad & x \neq 0, \\ &= 0, & x = 0. \end{aligned}$$

Then $Df(0)$ is one-one but f has no inverse near $x = 0$.

21.G. Let f be a function on $\mathbf{R}^p$ to $\mathbf{R}^p$ which is differentiable on a neighborhood of a point c and such that $Df(c)$ has an inverse. Then is it true that f has an inverse on a neighborhood of c?

21.H. Let f be a function on $\mathbf{R}^p$ to $\mathbf{R}^p$. If f is differentiable at c and has a differentiable inverse, then is it true that $Df(c)$ is one-one?

21.I. Suppose that f is differentiable on a neighborhood of a point c and that if $\epsilon > 0$ then there exists $\delta(\epsilon) > 0$ such that if $|x - c| < \delta(\epsilon)$, then $|Df(x)(z) - Df(c)(z)| \leq \epsilon|z|$ for all z in $\mathbf{R}^p$. Prove that the partial derivatives of f exist and are continuous at c.

21.J. Suppose that L_0 is a one-one linear function on $\mathbf{R}^p$ to $\mathbf{R}^q$. Show that there exists a positive number α such that if L is a linear function on $\mathbf{R}^p$ to $\mathbf{R}^p$ satisfying

$$|L(z) - L_0(z)| \leq \alpha|z| \qquad \text{for} \qquad z \in \mathbf{R}^p,$$

then L is one-one.

21.K. Suppose that L_0 is a linear function on $\mathbf{R}^p$ with range all of $\mathbf{R}^q$. Show that there exists a positive number β such that if L is a linear function on $\mathbf{R}^p$ into $\mathbf{R}^q$ satisfying

$$|L(z) - L_0(z)| \leq \beta|z| \qquad \text{for} \qquad z \in \mathbf{R}^p,$$

then the range of L is $\mathbf{R}^q$.

21.L. Let f be in Class C' on a neighborhood of a point c in $\mathbf{R}^p$ and with values in $\mathbf{R}^p$. If $Df(c)$ is one-one and has range equal to $\mathbf{R}^p$, then there exists a positive number δ such that if $|x - c| < \delta$, then $Df(x)$ is one-one and has range equal to $\mathbf{R}^p$.

21.M. Let f be defined on $\mathbf{R}^2$ to $\mathbf{R}^2$ by $f(x, y) = (x \cos y, x \sin y)$. Show that if $x_0 > 0$, then there exists a neighborhood of (x_0, y_0) on which f is one-one, but that there are infinitely many points which are mapped into $f(x_0, y_0)$.

21.N. Let F be defined on $\mathbf{R} \times \mathbf{R}$ to $\mathbf{R}$ by $F(x, y) = x^2 - y$. Show that F is in Class C' on a neighborhood of $(0, 0)$ but there does not exist a continuous function φ defined on a neighborhood of 0 such that $F[\varphi(y), y] = 0$.

21.O. Suppose that, in addition to the hypotheses of the Implicit Function Theorem 21.11, the function F has continuous partial derivatives of order n. Show that the solution function φ has continuous partial derivatives of order n.

21.P. Let F be the function on $\mathbf{R}^2 \times \mathbf{R}^2$ to $\mathbf{R}^2$ defined for $x = (\xi_1, \xi_2)$ and $y = (\eta_1, \eta_2)$ by the formula

$$F(x, y) = (\xi_1{}^3 + \xi_2\eta_1 + \eta_2, \xi_1\eta_2 + \xi_2{}^3 - \eta_1).$$

At what points (x, y) can one solve the equation $F(x, y) = \theta$ for x in terms of y. Calculate the derivative of this solution function, when it exists. In particular, calculate the partial derivatives of the coordinate functions of φ with respect to η_1, η_2.

21.Q. Let f be defined and continuous on the set $\mathfrak{D} = \{x \in \mathbf{R}^p : |x| \leq 1\}$ with values in $\mathbf{R}$. Suppose that f is differentiable at every interior point of $\mathfrak{D}$ and that $f(x) = 0$ for all $|x| = 1$. Prove that there exists an interior point c of $\mathfrak{D}$ and that $Df(c) = 0$ (This result may be regarded as a generalization of Rolle's Theorem.)

21.R. If we define f on $\mathbf{R}^2$ to $\mathbf{R}$ by

$$f(\xi, \eta) = \xi^2 + 4\xi\eta + \eta^2,$$

then the origin is not a relative extreme point but a saddle point of f.

21.S. (a) Let f_1 be defined on $\mathbf{R}^2$ to $\mathbf{R}$ by

$$f_1(\xi, \eta) = \xi^4 + \eta^4,$$

then the origin $\theta = (0, 0)$ is a relative minimum of f_1 and $\Delta = 0$ at θ. (Here $\Delta = f_{\xi\xi}f_{\eta\eta} - f_{\xi\eta}{}^2$.)

(b) If $f_2 = -f_1$, then the origin is a relative maximum of f_2 and $\Delta = 0$ at θ.

(c) If f_3 is defined on $\mathbf{R}^2$ to $\mathbf{R}$ by

$$f_3(\xi, \eta) = \xi^4 - \eta^4,$$

then the origin $\theta = (0, 0)$ is a saddle point of f_3 and $\Delta = 0$ at θ. (The moral of this exercise is that if $\Delta = 0$, then anything can happen.)

21.T. Let f be defined on $\mathfrak{D} = \{(\xi, \eta) \in \mathbf{R}^2 : \xi > 0, \eta > 0\}$ to $\mathbf{R}$ by the formula

$$f(\xi, \eta) = \frac{1}{\xi} + \frac{1}{\eta} + c\xi\eta.$$

Locate the critical points of f and determine whether they yield relative maxima, relative minima, or saddle points. If $c > 0$ and we set

$$\mathfrak{D}_1 = \{(\xi, \eta) : \xi > 0, \eta > 0, \xi + \eta \leq c\},$$

then locate the relative extrema of f on $\mathfrak{D}_1$.

21.U. Suppose we are given n points (ξ_j, η_j) in $\mathbf{R}^2$ and desire to find the linear function $F(x) = Ax + B$ for which the quantity

$$\sum_{j=1}^{n} [F(\xi_j) - \eta_j]^2$$

is minimized. Show that this leads to the equations

$$A \sum_{j=1}^{n} \xi_j^2 + B \sum_{j=1}^{n} \xi_j = \sum_{j=1}^{n} \xi_j\eta_j,$$

$$A \sum_{j=1}^{n} \xi_j + nB \qquad = \sum_{j=1}^{n} \eta_j,$$

for the numbers A, B. This linear function is referred to as the linear function which best fits the given n points in the sense of **least squares**.

21.V. Let f be defined and continuous on the set $\mathfrak{D} = \{x \in \mathbf{R}^p : |x| \leq 1\}$ with values in $\mathbf{R}$. If f is differentiable at every interior point of $\mathfrak{D}$ and if

$$\sum_{j=1}^{p} f_{\xi_j\xi_j}(x) = 0$$

for all $|x| < 1$, then f is said to be *harmonic* in $\mathfrak{D}$. Suppose that f is not constant and that f does not attain its supremum on $C = \{x : |x| = 1\}$ but at a point c interior to $\mathfrak{D}$. Then, if $\epsilon > 0$ is sufficiently small, the function g defined by

$$g(x) = f(x) + \epsilon|x - c|^2$$

does not attain its supremum on C but at some interior point c'. Since

$$g_{\xi_j\xi_j}(c') = f_{\xi_j\xi_j}(c') + 2\epsilon, \quad j = 1, \ldots, p,$$

it follows that

$$\sum_{j=1}^{p} g_{\xi_j\xi_j}(c') = 2\epsilon p > 0,$$

so that some $g_{\xi_j\xi_j}(c') > 0$, a contradiction. (Why?) Therefore, if f is harmonic in $\mathfrak{D}$ it attains its supremum (and also its infimum) on C. Show also that if f and h are harmonic in $\mathfrak{D}$ and $f(x) = h(x)$ for $x \in C$, then $f(x) = h(x)$ for $x \in \mathfrak{D}$.

21.W. Show that the function

$$f(\xi, \eta) = (\eta - \xi^2)(\eta - 2\xi^2)$$

does not have a relative extremum at $\theta = (0, 0)$ although it has a relative minimum along every line $\xi = \alpha t, \eta = \beta t$.

21.X. Find the dimensions of the box of maximum volume which can be fitted into the ellipsoid

$$\frac{\xi^2}{a^2} + \frac{\eta^2}{b^2} + \frac{\zeta^2}{c^2} = 1,$$

assuming that each edge of the box is parallel to a coordinate axis.

21.Y. (a) Find the maximum of

$$f(x_1, x_2, \ldots, x_n) = (x_1 x_2 \cdots x_n)^2,$$

subject to the constraint

$$x_1^2 + x_2^2 + \cdots + x_n^2 = 1.$$

(b) Show that the geometric mean of a collection of non-negative real numbers $\{a_1, a_2, \ldots, a_n\}$ does not exceed their arithmetic mean; that is,

$$(a_1 a_2 \cdots a_n)^{1/n} \le \frac{1}{n}(a_1 + a_2 + \cdots + a_n).$$

21.Z. (a) Let $p > 1, q > 1$, and $\dfrac{1}{p} + \dfrac{1}{q} = 1$. Show that the minimum of

$$f(\xi, \eta) = \frac{\xi^p}{p} + \frac{\eta^p}{q},$$

subject to the constraint $\xi \eta = 1$, is 1.

(b) From (a), show that if a, b are non-negative real numbers, then

$$ab \le \frac{a^p}{p} + \frac{b^q}{q}.$$

(c) Let $\{a_j\}, \{b_j\}, j = 1, \ldots, n$, be non-negative real numbers, and obtain Hölder's Inequality:

$$\sum_{j=1}^{n} a_j b_j \le \left(\sum_{j=1}^{n} a_j{}^p\right)^{1/p} \left(\sum_{j=1}^{n} b_j{}^q\right)^{1/q}.$$

[Hint: let $A = \left(\sum a_j{}^p\right)^{1/p}, B = \left(\sum b_j{}^q\right)^{1/q}$ and apply the inequality in (b) to $a = a_j/A, b = b_j/B$.]

(d) Note that

$$|a + b|^p = |a + b|\,|a + b|^{p/q} \le |a|\,|a + b|^{p/q} + |b|\,|a + b|^{p/q}.$$

Use Hölder's Inequality in (c) and derive the Minkowski Inequality

$$\left(\sum_{j=1}^{n} |a_j + b_j|^p\right)^{1/p} \le \left(\sum_{j=1}^{n} |a_j|^p\right)^{1/p} + \left(\sum_{j=1}^{n} |b_j|^p\right)^{1/p}.$$

Project

21.α. This project yields a more direct proof of the Inversion Theorem 21.10 (and hence of the Implicit Function Theorem) than given in the text. It uses ideas related to the Fixed Point Theorem for contractions given in 16.14.

(a) If F is a contraction in $\mathbf{R}^p$ with constant C and if $F(\theta) = \theta$, then for each element y in $\mathbf{R}^p$ there exists a unique element x in $\mathbf{R}^p$ such that $x + F(x) = y$. Moreover, x can be obtained as the limit of the sequence (x_n) defined by

$$x_1 = y, \quad x_{n+1} = y - F(x_n), \quad n \in \mathbf{N}.$$

(b) Let F be a contraction on $\{x \in \mathbf{R}^p : |x| \le B\}$ with constant C and let $F(\theta) = \theta$. If $|y| \le B(1 - C)$, then there exists a unique solution of the equation $x + F(x) = y$ with $|x| \le B$.

(c) If f is in Class C' on a neighborhood of θ and if $L = Df(\theta)$, use the Approximation Lemma 21.3 to prove that the function H defined by $H(x) = f(x) - L(x)$ is a contraction on a neighborhood of θ.

(d) Suppose that f is in Class C' on a neighborhood of θ, that $f(\theta) = \theta$, and that $L = Df(\theta)$ is a one-one map of $\mathbf{R}^p$ onto all of $\mathbf{R}^p$. If $M = L^{-1}$, show that the function F defined by $F(x) = M[f(x) - L(x)]$ is a contraction on a neighborhood of θ. Show also that the equation $f(x) = y$ is equivalent to the equation $x + F(x) = M(y)$.

(e) Show that, under the hypotheses in (d), there is a neighborhood U of θ such that $V = f(U)$ is a neighborhood of $\theta = f(\theta)$, f is a one-one mapping of U onto V, and f has a continuous inverse function g defined on V to U. (This is the first assertion of Theorem 21.10.)

VI

Integration

In this chapter, we shall develop a theory of integration. We assume that the reader is acquainted (informally at least) with the integral from a calculus course and shall not provide an extensive motivation for it. However, we shall not assume that the reader has seen a rigorous derivation of the properties of the integral. Instead, we shall define the integral and establish its most important properties without making appeal to geometrical or physical intuition.

In Section 22, we shall consider bounded real-valued functions defined on closed intervals of R and define the Riemann-Stieltjes† integral of one such function with respect to another. In the next section the connection between differentiation and integration is made and some other useful results are proved. In Section 24 we define a Riemann integral for functions with domain in R^p and range in R^q. Finally, we shall treat improper and infinite integrals and derive some important results pertaining to them.

The reader who continues his study of mathematical analysis will want to become familiar with the more general Lebesgue integral at an early date. However, since the Riemann and the Riemann-Stieltjes integrals are adequate for many purposes and are more familiar to the reader, we prefer to treat them here and leave the more advanced Lebesgue theory for a later course.

† (GEORG FRIEDRICH) BERNHARD RIEMANN (1826–1866) was the son of a poor country minister and was born near Hanover. He studied at Göttingen and Berlin and taught at Göttingen. He was one of the founders of the theory of analytic functions, but also made fundamental contributions to geometry, number theory, and mathematical physics.

THOMAS JOANNES STIELTJES (1856–1894) was a Dutch astronomer and mathematician. He studied in Paris with Hermite and obtained a professorship at Toulouse. His most famous work was a memoir on continued fractions, the moment problem, and the Stieltjes integral, which was published in the last year of his short life.

Section 22   Riemann-Stieltjes Integral

We shall consider bounded real-valued functions on closed intervals of the real number system, define the integral of one such function with respect to another, and derive the main properties of this integral. The type of integration considered here is somewhat more general than that considered in earlier courses and the added generality makes it very useful in certain applications, especially in statistics. At the same time, there is little additional complication to the theoretical machinery that a rigorous discussion of the ordinary Riemann integral requires. Therefore, it is worthwhile to develop this type of integration theory as far as its most frequent applications require.

Let f and g denote real-valued functions defined on a closed interval $J = [a, b]$ of the real line. *We shall suppose that both f and g are bounded on J;* this standing hypothesis will not be repeated. A **partition** of J is a finite collection of non-overlapping intervals whose union is J. Usually, we describe a partition P by specifying a finite set of real numbers $(x_0, x_1, \ldots, x_n)$ such that

$$a = x_0 \leq x_1 \leq \cdots \leq x_n = b$$

and such that the subintervals occurring in the partition P are the intervals $[x_{k-1}, x_k]$, $k = 1, 2, \ldots, n$. More properly, we refer to the end points x_k, $k = 0, 1, \ldots, n$ as the **partition points** corresponding to P. However, in practice it is often convenient and can cause no confusion to use the word "partition" to denote either the collection of subintervals or the collection of end points of these subintervals. Hence we write $P = (x_0, x_1, \ldots, x_n)$.

If P and Q are partitions of J, we say that Q is a **refinement** of P or that Q is **finer** than P in case every subinterval in Q is contained in some subinterval in P. This is equivalent to the requirement that every partition point in P is also a partition point in Q. For this reason, we write $P \subseteq Q$ when Q is a refinement of P.

22.1   **Definition.**   If P is a partition of J, then a **Riemann-Stieltjes sum** of f with respect to g and corresponding to $P = (x_0, x_1, \ldots, x_n)$ is a real number $S(P; f, g)$ of the form

$$(22.1) \qquad S(P; f, g) = \sum_{k=1}^{n} f(\xi_k) \{ g(x_k) - g(x_{k-1}) \}.$$

Here we have selected numbers ξ_k satisfying

$$x_{k-1} \leq \xi_k \leq x_k \quad \text{for} \quad k = 1, 2, \ldots, n.$$

Note that if the function g is given by $g(x) = x$, then the expression in equation (22.1) reduces to

$$(22.2) \qquad\qquad \sum_{k=1}^{n} f(\xi_k)(x_k - x_{k-1}).$$

The sum (22.2) is usually called a **Riemann sum** of f corresponding to the partition P and can be interpreted as the area of the union of rectangles with sides $[x_{k-1}, x_k]$ and heights $f(\xi_k)$. (See Figure 22.1.) Thus if the partition P is very fine, it is expected that the Riemann sum (22.2) yields an approximation to the "area under the graph of f." For a general function g, the reader should interpret the Riemann-Stieltjes sum (22.1) as being similar to the Riemann sum (22.2)—except that, instead of considering the *length* $x_k - x_{k-1}$ of the subinterval $[x_{k-1}, x_k]$, we are considering some other measure of magnitude of this subinterval; namely, the difference $g(x_k) - g(x_{k-1})$. Thus if $g(x)$ is the total "mass" or "charge" on the interval $[a, x]$, then $g(x_k) - g(x_{k-1})$ denotes the "mass" or "charge" on the subinterval $[x_{k-1}, x_k]$. The idea is that we want to be able to consider measures of magnitude of an interval other than length, so we allow for the slightly more general sums (22.1).

It will be noted that both of the sums (22.1) and (22.2) depend upon the choice of the "intermediate points"; that is, upon the numbers ξ_k, $1 \leq k \leq n$. Thus it might be thought advisable to introduce a notation displaying the choice of these numbers. However, by introducing a finer partition, it can always be assumed that the intermediate points ξ_k are partition points. In fact, if we introduce the partition $Q = (x_0, \xi_1, x_1, \xi_2, \ldots, \xi_n, x_n)$ and the sum $S(Q; f, g)$ where we take the intermediate points to be alternately the right and the left end points of the subinter-

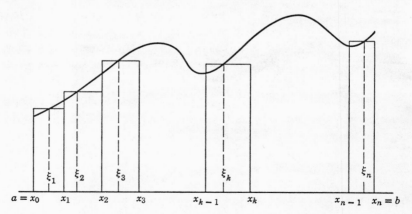

Figure 22.1. The Riemann sum as an area.

val, then the sum $S(Q; f, g)$ yields the same value as the sum in (22.1). We could always assume that the partition divides the interval into an even number of subintervals and the intermediate points are alternately the right and left end points of these subintervals. However, we shall not find it necessary to require this "standard" partitioning process, nor shall we find it necessary to display these intermediate points.

22.2 DEFINITION. We say that f is integrable with respect to g on J if there exists a real number I such that for every positive number ϵ there is a partition P_ϵ of J such that if P is any refinement of P_ϵ and $S(P; f,g)$ is any Riemann-Stieltjes sum corresponding to P, then

$$(22.3) \qquad\qquad |S(P; f, g) - I| < \epsilon.$$

In this case the number I is uniquely determined and is denoted by

$$I = \int_a^b f \, dg = \int_a^b f(t) \, dg(t);$$

it is called the **Riemann-Stieltjes integral** of f with respect to g over $J = [a, b]$. We call the function f the **integrand**, and g the **integrator**. In the special case $g(x) = x$, if f is integrable with respect to g, we usually say that f is **Riemann integrable**.

Before we develop any of the properties of the Riemann-Stieltjes integral, we shall consider some examples. In order to keep the calculations simple, some of these examples are chosen to be extreme cases; more typical examples are found by combining the ones given below.

22.3 EXAMPLES. (a) We have already noted that if $g(x) = x$, then the integral reduces to the ordinary Riemann integral of elementary calculus.

(b) If g is constant on the interval $[a, b]$, then any function f is integrable with respect to g and the value of the integral is 0. More generally, if g is constant on a subinterval J_1 of J, then any function f which vanishes on $J \backslash J_1$ is integrable with respect to g and the value of the integral is 0.

(c) Let g be defined on $J = [a, b]$ by

$$g(x) = 0, \qquad x = a,$$
$$= 1, \qquad a < x \le b.$$

We leave it as an exercise to show that a function f is integrable with respect to g if and only if f is continuous at a and that in this case the value of the integral is $f(a)$.

(d) Let c be an interior point of the interval $J = [a, b]$ and let g be defined by

$$g(x) = 0, \qquad a \leq x \leq c,$$
$$= 1, \qquad c < x \leq b.$$

It is an exercise to show that a function f is integrable with respect to g if and only if it is continuous at c from the right (in the sense that for every $\epsilon > 0$ there exists $\delta(\epsilon) > 0$ such that if $c \leq x < c + \delta(\epsilon)$ and $x \in J$, then $|f(x) - f(c)| < \epsilon$). If f satisfies this condition, then the value of the integral is $f(c)$. (Observe that the integrator function g is continuous at c from the left.)

(e) Modifying the preceding example, let h be defined by

$$h(x) = 0, \qquad a \leq x < c,$$
$$= 1, \qquad c \leq x \leq b.$$

Then h is continuous at c from the right and a function f is integrable with respect to h if and only if f is continuous at c from the left. In this case the value of the integral is $f(c)$.

(f) Let $c_1 < c_2$ be interior points of $J = [a, b]$ and let g be defined by

$$g(x) = \alpha_1, \qquad a \leq x \leq c_1,$$
$$= \alpha_2, \qquad c_1 < x \leq c_2,$$
$$= \alpha_3, \qquad c_2 < x \leq b.$$

If f is continuous at the points c_1, c_2, then f is integrable with respect to g and

$$\int_a^b f \, dg = (\alpha_2 - \alpha_1)f(c_1) + (\alpha_3 - \alpha_2)f(c_2).$$

By taking more points we can obtain a sum involving the values of f at points in J, weighted by the values of the jumps of g at these points.

(g) Let the function f be Dirichlet's discontinuous function [cf. Example 15.5(g)] defined by

$$f(x) = 1, \qquad \text{if } x \text{ is rational,}$$
$$= 0, \qquad \text{if } x \text{ is irrational,}$$

and let $g(x) = x$. Consider these functions on $I = [0, 1]$. If a partition P consists of n equal subintervals, then by selecting k of the intermediate points in the sum $S(P; f, g)$ to be rational and the remaining to be irrational, $S(P; f, g) = k/n$. It follows that f is *not* Riemann integrable.

(h) Let f be the function defined on I by $f(0) = 1$, $f(x) = 0$ for x irrational, and $f(m/n) = 1/n$ when m and n are natural numbers with no common factors except 1. It was seen in Example 15.5(h) that f is continuous at every irrational number and discontinuous at every rational number. If $g(x) = x$, then it is an exercise to show that f is integrable with respect to g and that the value of the integral is 0.

22.4 CAUCHY CRITERION FOR INTEGRABILITY. *The function f is integrable with respect to g over $J = [a, b]$ if and only if for each positive real number ϵ there is a partition Q_ϵ of J such that if P and Q are refinements of Q_ϵ and if $S(P; f, g)$ and $S(Q; f, g)$ are any corresponding Riemann-Stieltjes sums, then*

$$(22.4) \qquad |S(P; f, g) - S(Q; f, g)| < \epsilon.$$

PROOF. If f is integrable, there is a partition P_ϵ such that if P, Q are refinements of P_ϵ, then any corresponding Riemann-Stieltjes sums satisfy $|S(P; f, g) - I| < \epsilon/2$ and $|S(Q; f, g) - I| < \epsilon/2$. By using the Triangle Inequality, we obtain (22.4).

Conversely, suppose the criterion is satisfied. To show that f is integrable with respect to g, we need to produce the value of its integral and use Definition 22.2. Let Q_1 be a partition of J such that if P and Q are refinements of Q_1, then $|S(P; f, g) - S(Q; f, g)| < 1$. Inductively, we choose Q_n to be a refinement of Q_{n-1} such that if P and Q are refinements of Q_n, then

$$(22.5) \qquad |S(P; f, g) - S(Q; f, g)| < 1/n.$$

Consider a sequence $(S(Q_n; f, g))$ of real numbers obtained in this way. Since Q_n is a refinement of Q_m when $n \geq m$, this sequence of sums is a Cauchy sequence of real numbers, regardless of how the intermediate points are chosen. By Theorem 12.10, the sequence converges to some real number L. Hence, if $\epsilon > 0$, there is an integer N such that $2/N < \epsilon$ and

$$|S(Q_N; f, g) - L| < \epsilon/2.$$

If P is a refinement of Q_N, then it follows from the construction of Q_N that

$$|S(P; f, g) - S(Q_N; f, g)| < 1/N < \epsilon/2.$$

Hence, for any refinement P of Q_N and any corresponding Riemann-Stieltjes sum, we have

$$(22.6) \qquad |S(P; f, g) - L| < \epsilon,$$

This shows that f is integrable with respect to g over J and that the value of this integral is L.

Q.E.D.

The next property is sometimes referred to as the **bilinearity** of the Riemann-Stieltjes integral.

22.5 THEOREM. (a) *If f_1, f_2 are integrable with respect to g on J and α, β are real numbers, then $\alpha f_1 + \beta f_2$ is integrable with respect to g on J and*

$$(22.7) \qquad \int_a^b (\alpha f_1 + \beta f_2)\, dg = \alpha \int_a^b f_1\, dg + \beta \int_a^b f_2\, dg.$$

(b) *If f is integrable with respect to g_1 and g_2 on J and α, β are real numbers, then f is integrable with respect to $g = \alpha g_1 + \beta g_2$ on J and*

$$(22.8) \qquad \int_a^b f\, dg = \alpha \int_a^b f\, dg_1 + \beta \int_a^b f\, dg_2.$$

PROOF. (a) Let $\epsilon > 0$ and let $P_1 = (x_0, x_1, \ldots, x_n)$ and $P_2 = (y_0, y_1, \ldots, y_m)$ be partitions of $J = [a, b]$ such that if Q is a refinement of both P_1 and P_2, then for any corresponding Riemann-Stieltjes sums, we have

$$|I_1 - S(Q; f_1, g)| < \epsilon, \qquad |I_2 - S(Q; f_2, g)| < \epsilon.$$

Let P_ϵ be a partition of J which is a refinement of both P_1 and P_2 (for example, all the partition points in P_1 and P_2 are combined to form P_ϵ). If Q is a partition of J such that $P_\epsilon \subseteq Q$, then both of the relations above still hold. When the same intermediate points are used, we evidently have

$$S(Q; \alpha f_1 + \beta f_2, g) = \alpha S(Q; f_1, g) + \beta S(Q; f_2, g).$$

It follows from this and the preceding inequalities that

$$|\alpha I_1 + \beta I_2 - S(Q; \alpha f_1 + \beta f_2, g)| =$$
$$|\alpha \{ I_1 - S(Q; f_1, g)\} + \beta \{ I_2 - S(Q; f_2, g)\}| \leq (|\alpha| + |\beta|)\epsilon.$$

This proves that $\alpha I_1 + \beta I_2$ is the integral of $\alpha f_1 + \beta f_2$ with respect to g. This establishes part (a); the proof of part (b) is similar and will be left to the reader.

Q.E.D.

There is another useful additivity property possessed by the Riemann-Stieltjes integral; namely, with respect to the interval over which the integral is extended. (It is in order to obtain the next result that we employed the type of limiting introduced in Definition 22.2. A more restrictive type of limiting would be to require inequality (22.3) for any Riemann-Stieltjes sum corresponding to a partition $P = (x_0, x_1, \ldots, x_n)$ which is such that

$$\|P\| = \sup \{x_1 - x_0, x_2 - x_1, \ldots, x_n - x_{n-1}\} < \delta(\epsilon).$$

This type of limiting is generally used in defining the Riemann integral and sometimes used in defining the Riemann-Stieltjes integral. However, many authors employ the definition we introduced, which is due to S. Pollard, for it enlarges slightly the class of integrable functions. As a result of this enlargement, the next result is valid without any additional restriction. See Exercises 22.D–F.)

22.6   THEOREM.   (a)   *Suppose that $a < c < b$ and that f is integrable with respect to g over both of the subintervals $[a, c]$ and $[c, b]$. Then f is integrable with respect to g on the interval $[a, b]$ and*

$$(22.9) \qquad \int_a^b f \, dg = \int_a^c f \, dg + \int_c^b f \, dg.$$

(b)   *Let f be integrable with respect to g on the interval $[a, b]$ and let c satisfy $a < c < b$. Then f is integrable with respect to g on the subintervals $[a, c]$ and $[c, b]$ and formula (22.9) holds.*

PROOF.   (a)   If $\epsilon > 0$, let P_ϵ' be a partition of $[a, c]$ such that if P' is a refinement of P_ϵ', then inequality (22.3) holds for any Riemann-Stieltjes sum. Let P_ϵ'' be a corresponding partition of $[c, b]$. If P_ϵ is the partition of $[a, b]$ formed by using the partition points in both P_ϵ' and P_ϵ'', and if P is a refinement of P_ϵ, then

$$S(P; f, g) = S(P'; f, g) + S(P''; f, g),$$

where P', P'' denote the partitions of $[a, c]$, $[c, b]$ induced by P and where the corresponding intermediate points are used. Therefore, we have

$$\left| \int_a^c f \, dg + \int_c^b f \, dg - S(P; f, g) \right|$$

$$\leq \left| \int_a^c f \, dg - S(P'; f, g) \right| + \left| \int_c^b f \, dg - S(P''; f, g) \right| < 2\epsilon.$$

It follows that f is integrable with respect to g over $[a, b]$ and that the value of its integral is

$$\int_a^c f \, dg + \int_c^b f \, dg.$$

(b)   We shall use the Cauchy Criterion 22.4 to prove that f is integrable over $[a, c]$. Since f is integrable over $[a, b]$, given $\epsilon > 0$ there is a partition Q_ϵ of $[a, b]$ such that if P, Q are refinements of Q_ϵ, then relation (22.4) holds for any corresponding Riemann-Stieltjes sums. It is clear that we may suppose that the point c belongs to Q_ϵ, and we let Q_ϵ' be the partition of $[a, c]$ consisting of those points of Q_ϵ which belong to $[a, c]$. Suppose that P' and Q' are partitions of $[a, c]$ which are refinements of Q_ϵ' and extend them to partitions P and Q of $[a, b]$ by using the points in Q_ϵ which belong to $[c, b]$. Since P, Q are refinements of Q_ϵ, then relation (22.4) holds. However, it is clear from the fact that P, Q are identical on $[c, b]$ that, if we use the same intermediate points, then

$$|S(P'; f, g) - S(Q'; f, g)| = |S(P; f, g) - S(Q; f, g)| < \epsilon.$$

Therefore, the Cauchy Criterion establishes the integrability of f with respect to g over the subinterval $[a, c]$ and a similar argument also applies to the interval $[c, b]$. Once this integrability is known, part (a) yields the validity of formula (22.9).

Q.E.D.

Thus far we have not interchanged the roles of the integrand f and the integrator g, and it may not have occurred to the reader that it might be possible to do so. Although the next result is not exactly the same as the "integration by parts formula" of calculus, the relation is close and this result is usually referred to by that name.

22.7 INTEGRATION BY PARTS. *A function f is integrable with respect to g over $[a, b]$ if and only if g is integrable with respect to f over $[a, b]$. In this case,*

$$(22.10) \qquad \int_a^b f \, dg + \int_a^b g \, df = f(b)g(b) - f(a)g(a).$$

PROOF. We shall suppose that f is integrable with respect to g. Let $\epsilon > 0$ and let P_ϵ be a partition of $[a, b]$ such that if Q is a refinement of P_ϵ and $S(Q; f, g)$ is any corresponding Riemann-Stieltjes sum, then

$$(22.11) \qquad \left| S(Q; f, g) - \int_a^b f \, dg \right| < \epsilon.$$

Now let P be a refinement of P_ϵ and consider a Riemann-Stieltjes sum $S(P; g, f)$ given by

$$S(P; g, f) = \sum_{k=1}^n g(\xi_k)\{f(x_k) - f(x_{k-1})\},$$

where $x_{k-1} \le \xi_k \le x_k$. Let $Q = (y_0, y_1, \ldots, y_{2n})$ be the partition of $[a, b]$ obtained by using both the ξ_k and x_k as partition points; hence $y_{2k} = x_k$ and $y_{2k-1} = \xi_k$. Add and subtract the terms $f(y_{2k})g(y_{2k})$, $k = 0$, $1, \ldots, n$, to $S(P; g, f)$ and rearrange to obtain

$$S(P; g, f) = f(b)g(b) - f(a)g(a) - \sum_{k=1}^{2n} f(\eta_k)\{g(y_k) - g(y_{k-1})\},$$

where the intermediate points η_k are selected to be the points x_j. Thus we have

$$S(P; g, f) = f(b)g(b) - f(a)g(a) - S(Q; f, g),$$

where the partition $Q = (y_0, y_1, \ldots, y_{2n})$ is a refinement of P_ϵ. In view of formula (22.11),

$$|S(P; g, f) - \{f(b)g(b) - f(a)g(a) - \int_a^b f \, dg\}| < \epsilon$$

provided P is a refinement of P_ϵ. This proves that g is integrable with respect to f over $[a, b]$ and establishes formula (22.10).

Q.E.D

Integrability of Continuous Functions

We now establish a theorem which guarantees that every continuous function f on a closed bounded interval $J = [a, b]$ is integrable with respect to any monotone function g. This result is an existence theorem in that it asserts that the integral exists, but it does not yield information concerning the value of the integral or how to calculate this value.

To be explicit, we assume that g is monotone increasing on J; that is, we suppose that if x_1, x_2 are points in J and if $x_1 \leq x_2$, then $g(x_1) \leq g(x_2)$. The case of a monotone decreasing function can be handled similarly or reduced to a monotone increasing function by multiplying by -1. Actually, the proof we give below yields the existence of the integral of a continuous function f with respect to a function g which has bounded variation on J in the sense that there exists a constant M such that, for any partition $P = (x_0, x_1, \ldots, x_n)$ of $J = [a, b]$ the inequality

$$(22.12) \qquad \sum_{k=1}^{n} |g(x_k) - g(x_{k-1})| \leq M$$

holds. It is clear that, if g is monotone increasing, the sum in (22.12) telescopes and one can take $M = g(b) - g(a)$ so that a monotone function has bounded variation. Conversely, it can be shown that a real-valued function has bounded variation if and only if it can be expressed as the difference of two monotone increasing functions.

22.8 INTEGRABILITY THEOREM. *If f is continuous on J and g is monotone increasing, then f is integrable with respect to g over J.*

PROOF. Since f is uniformly continuous, given $\epsilon > 0$ there is a real number $\delta(\epsilon) > 0$ such that if x, y belong to J and $|x - y| < \delta(\epsilon)$, then $|f(x) - f(y)| < \epsilon$. Let $P_\epsilon = (x_0, x_1, \ldots, x_n)$ be a partition such that sup $\{x_k - x_{k-1}\} < \delta(\epsilon)$ and let $Q = (y_0, y_1, \ldots, y_m)$ be a refinement of P_ϵ; we shall estimate the difference $S(P_\epsilon; f, g) - S(Q; f, g)$. Since every point in P_ϵ appears in Q, we can express these Riemann-Stieltjes sums in the form

$$S(P_\epsilon; f, g) = \sum_{k=1}^{m} f(\xi_k)\{g(y_k) - g(y_{k-1})\},$$

$$S(Q; f, g) = \sum_{k=1}^{m} f(\eta_k)\{g(y_k) - g(y_{k-1})\}.$$

In order to write $S(P_\epsilon; f, g)$ in terms of the partition points in Q, we must permit repetitions for the intermediate points ξ_k and we do not require ξ_k to be contained in $[y_{k-1}, y_k]$. However, both ξ_k and η_k belong to some interval $[x_{h-1}, x_h]$ and, according to the choice of P_ϵ, we therefore have

$$|f(\xi_k) - f(\eta_k)| < \epsilon.$$

If we write the difference of the two Riemann-Stieltjes sums and employing the preceding estimate, we have

$$|S(P_\epsilon; f, g) - S(Q; f, g)| = \left| \sum_{k=1}^{m} \{f(\xi_k) - f(\eta_k)\}\{g(y_k) - g(y_{k-1})\} \right|$$

$$\leq \sum_{k=1}^{m} |f(\xi_k) - f(\eta_k)||g(y_k) - g(y_{k-1})| \leq \epsilon \sum_{k=1}^{m} |g(y_k) - g(y_{k-1})|$$

$$= \epsilon\{g(b) - g(a)\}.$$

Therefore, if P and Q are partitions of J which are refinements of P_ϵ and if $S(P; f, g)$ and $S(Q; f, g)$ are any corresponding Riemann-Stieltjes sums, then

$$|S(P; f, g) - S(Q; f, g)| \leq |S(P; f, g) - S(P_\epsilon; f, g)|$$

$$+ |S(P_\epsilon; f, g) - S(Q; f, g)| \leq 2\epsilon\{g(b) - g(a)\}.$$

From the Cauchy Criterion 22.4, we conclude that f is integrable with respect to g.

Q.E.D.

The next result is an immediate result of the theorem just proved and Theorem 22.7. It implies that any monotone function is Riemann integrable.

22.9   COROLLARY.   *If f is monotone and g is continuous on J, then f is integrable with respect to g over J.*

It is also convenient to have an estimate of the magnitude of the integral. For convenience, we use the notation $||f|| = \sup\{|f(x)| : x \in J\}$ and $|f|$ for the function whose value at x is $|f(x)|$.

22.10   LEMMA.   *Let f be continuous and let g be monotone increasing on J. Then we have the estimate*

$$(22.13) \qquad \left| \int_a^b f \, dg \right| \leq \int_a^b |f| \, dg \leq \|f\|\{g(b) - g(a)\}.$$

If $m \leq f(x) \leq M$ for all x in J, then

$$(22.14) \qquad m\{g(b) - g(a)\} \leq \int_a^b f \, dg \leq M\{g(b) - g(a)\}.$$

PROOF.   It follows from Theorems 15.7 and 22.8 that $|f|$ is integrable with respect to g. If $P = (x_0, x_1, \ldots, x_n)$ is a partition of J and (ξ_k) is a set of intermediate points, then for $k = 1, 2, \ldots, n$,

$$- \|f\| \leq - |f(\xi_k)| \leq f(\xi_k) \leq |f(\xi_k)| \leq \|f\|.$$

Multiply by $\{g(x_k) - g(x_{k-1})\} \geq 0$ and sum to obtain the estimate

$$- \|f\|\{g(b) - g(a)\} \leq -S(P; |f|, g)$$
$$\leq S(P; f, g) \leq S(P; |f|, g) \leq \|f\|\{g(b) - g(a)\},$$

whence it follows that

$$|S(P; f, g)| \leq S(P; |f|, g) \leq \|f\|\{g(b) - g(a)\}.$$

From this inequality we obtain inequality (22.13). The formula (22.14) is obtained by a similar argument which will be omitted.

Q.E.D.

NOTE.   It will be seen in Exercise 22.H that, if f is integrable with respect to a monotone function g, then $|f|$ is integrable with respect to g and (22.13) holds. Thus the continuity of f is sufficient, but not necessary, for the result. Similarly, inequality (22.14) holds when f is integrable. Both of these results will be used in the following.

Sequences of Integrable Functions

Suppose that g is a monotone increasing function on J and that (f_n) is a sequence of functions which are integrable with respect to g and which converge at every point of J to a function f. It is quite natural to expect that the limit function f is integrable and that

$$(22.15) \qquad \int_a^b f \, dg = \lim \int_a^b f_n \, dg.$$

However, this need not be the case even for very nice functions.

22.11   EXAMPLE.   Let $J = [0, 1]$, let $g(x) = x$, and let f_n be defined for $n \geq 2$ by

$$f_n(x) = n^2x, \quad 0 \leq x \leq 1/n,$$
$$= -n^2(x - 2/n), \quad 1/n \leq x \leq 2/n,$$
$$= 0, \quad 2/n \leq x \leq 1.$$

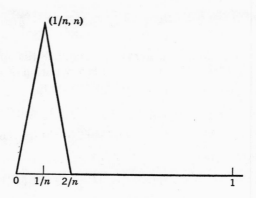

Figure 22.2.   Graph of f_n.

It is clear that for each n the function f_n is continuous on J, and hence it is integrable with respect to g. (See Figure 22.2.) Either by means of a direct calculation or referring to the significance of the integral as an area, we obtain

$$\int_0^1 f_n(x) \, dx = 1, \qquad n \geq 2.$$

In addition, the sequence (f_n) converges at every point of J to 0; hence the limit function f vanishes identically, is integrable, and

$$\int_0^1 f(x) \, dx = 0.$$

Therefore, equation (22.15) does not hold in this case even though both sides have a meaning.

Since equation (22.15) is very convenient, we inquire if there are any simple additional conditions that will imply it. We now show that, if the convergence is uniform, then this relation holds.

22.12   THEOREM.   *Let g be a monotone increasing function on J and let (f_n) be a sequence of functions which are integrable with respect to g over*

J. Suppose that the sequence (f_n) converges uniformly on J to a limit function f. Then f is integrable with respect to g and

$$(22.15) \qquad \int_a^b f \, dg = \lim \int_a^b f_n \, dg.$$

PROOF. Let $\epsilon > 0$ and let N be such that $||f_N - f|| < \epsilon$. Now let P_N be a partition of J such that if P, Q are refinements of P_N, then $|S(P;f_N, g) - S(Q;f_N, g)| < \epsilon$, for any choice of the intermediate points. If we use the same intermediate points for f and f_N, then

$$|S(P;f_N, g) - S(P;f, g)| \le \sum_{k=1}^{n} ||f_N - f|| \{g(x_k) - g(x_{k-1})\}$$
$$= ||f_N - f|| \{g(b) - g(a)\} < \epsilon \{g(b) - g(a)\}.$$

Since a similar estimate holds for the partition Q, then for refinements P, Q of P_N and corresponding Riemann-Stieltjes sums, we have

$$|S(P;f, g) - S(Q;f, g)| \le |S(P;f, g) - S(P;f_N, g)|$$
$$+ |S(P;f_N, g) - S(Q;f_N, g)| + |S(Q;f_N, g) - S(Q;f, g)|$$
$$\le \epsilon(1 + 2\{g(b) - g(a)\}).$$

According to the Cauchy Criterion 22.4, the limit function f is integrable with respect to g.

To establish (22.15), we employ Lemma 22.10:

$$\left| \int_a^b f \, dg - \int_a^b f_n \, dg \right| = \left| \int_a^b (f - f_n) \, dg \right| \le ||f - f_n|| \{g(b) - g(a)\}.$$

Since $\lim ||f - f_n|| = 0$, the desired conclusion follows.

Q.E.D.

The hypothesis made in Theorem 22.12, that the convergence of (f_n) is uniform, is rather severe and restricts the utility of this result. There is another theorem which does not restrict the convergence so heavily, but requires the integrability of the limit function. Although it can be established for a monotone integrator, for the sake of simplicity in notation, we shall limit our attention to the Riemann integral. In order to prove this convergence theorem, the following lemma will be used. This lemma says that if the integral is positive, then the function must be bounded away from zero on a reasonably large set.

22.13 LEMMA. *Let f be a non-negative Riemann integrable function on $J = [0, 1]$ and suppose that*

$$\alpha = \int_0^1 f > 0.$$

Then the set $E = \{x \in J : f(x) \geq \alpha/3\}$ contains a finite number of intervals of total length exceeding $\alpha/(3\|f\|)$.

PROOF.   Let P be a partition of $J = [0, 1]$ such that if $S(P; f)$ is any Riemann sum corresponding to P, then $|S(P; f) - \alpha| < \alpha/3$. Hence $2\alpha/3 < S(P; f)$. Now select the intermediate points to make $f(\xi_j) < \alpha/3$ whenever possible and break $S(P; f)$ into a sum over (i) subintervals contained in E, and (ii) subintervals which are not contained in E. Let L denote the sum of the lengths of the subintervals (i) contained in E. Since the contribution to the Riemann sum made by subintervals (ii) is less than $\alpha/3$, it follows that the contribution to the Riemann sum made by subintervals (i) is bounded below by $\alpha/3$ and above by $\|f\|\, L$. Therefore, $L > \alpha/(3\|f\|)$, as asserted.

Q.E.D.

22.14   BOUNDED CONVERGENCE THEOREM.   *Let (f_n) be a sequence of functions which are Riemann integrable on $J = [a, b]$ and such that*

(22.16) $$\|f_n\| < B \quad for \quad n \in \mathbf{N}.$$

If the sequence converges at each point of J to a Riemann integrable function f, then

$$\int_a^b f = \lim \int_a^b f_n.$$

PROOF.   It is no loss of generality to suppose that $J = [0, 1]$. Moreover, by introducing $g_n = |f_n - f|$, we may and shall assume that the f_n are non-negative and the limit function f vanishes identically. It is desired to show that $\lim \left(\int_0^1 f_n \right) = 0$. If this is not the case, there exists $\alpha > 0$ and a subsequence such that

$$\alpha < \int_a^b f_{n_k}.$$

By applying the lemma and the hypothesis (22.16), we infer that for each $k \in \mathbf{N}$, the set $E_k = \{x \in J : f_{n_k}(x) \geq \alpha/3\}$ contains a finite number of intervals of total length exceeding $\alpha/3B$. But this implies, although we omit the proof, that there exist points belonging to infinitely many of the sets E_k, which contradicts the supposition that the sequence (f_n) converges to f at every point of J.

Q.E.D.

We have used the fact that $|f_n - f|$ is Riemann integrable if f_n and f are. This statement has been established if $f_n - f$ is continuous; for the general case, we employ Exercise 22.H. Because of its importance, we shall state explicitly the following special case of the Bounded Convergence Theorem 22.14. This result can be proved by using the same argument as in the proof of 22.14, only here it is not necessary to appeal to Exercise 22.H.

22.15 MONOTONE CONVERGENCE THEOREM. *Let (f_n) be a monotone sequence of Riemann integrable functions which converges at each point of $J = [a, b]$ to a Riemann integrable function f. Then*

$$\int_a^b f = \lim \int_a^b f_n.$$

PROOF. Suppose that $f_1(x) \leq f_2(x) \leq \cdots \leq f(x)$ for $x \in J$. Letting $g_n = f - f_n$, we infer that g_n is non-negative and integrable. Moreover, $\|g_n\| \leq \|f\| + \|f_1\|$ for all $n \in N$. The remainder of the proof is as in Theorem 22.14.

Q.E.D.

The Riesz Representation Theorem

We shall conclude this section with a very important theorem, but it is convenient first to collect some results which we have already demonstrated or which are direct consequences of what we have done.

We denote the collection of all real-valued continuous functions defined on J by $C_R(J)$ and write

$$\|f\| = \sup \{|f(x)| : x \in J\}.$$

A linear functional on $C_R(J)$ is a real-valued function G defined for each function in $C_R(J)$ such that if f_1, f_2 belong to $C_R(J)$ and α, β are real numbers, then

$$G(\alpha f_1 + \beta f_2) = \alpha G(f_1) + \beta G(f_2).$$

The linear functional G on $C_R(J)$ is positive if, for each f in $C_R(J)$ such that $f(x) \geq 0$ for $x \in J$, then

$$G(f) \geq 0.$$

The linear functional G on $C_R(J)$ is bounded if there exists a constant M such that

$$|G(f)| \leq M \|f\|$$

for all f in $C_R(J)$.

22.16 LEMMA. *If g is a monotone increasing function and G is defined for f in $C_R(J)$ by*

$$G(f) = \int_a^b f \, dg,$$

then G is bounded positive linear functional on $C_R(J)$.

PROOF.   It follows from Theorem 22.5 (a) and Theorem 22.8 that G is a linear function on $C_R(J)$ and from Lemma 22.10 that G is bounded by $M = g(b) - g(a)$. If f belongs to $C_R(J)$ and $f(x) \geq 0$ for $x \in J$, then taking $m = 0$ in formula (22.14) we conclude that $G(f) \geq 0$.

Q.E.D.

We shall now show that, conversely, every bounded positive linear functional on $C_R(J)$ is generated by the Riemann-Stieltjes integral with respect to some monotone increasing function g. This is a form of the celebrated "Riesz Representation Theorem," which is one of the keystones for the subject of "functional analysis" and has many far-reaching generalizations and applications. The theorem was proved by the great Hungarian mathematician Frederic Riesz.†

22.17 RIESZ REPRESENTATION THEOREM.   *If G is a bounded positive linear functional on $C_R(J)$, then there exists a monotone increasing function g on J such that*

$$(22.17) \qquad\qquad G(f) = \int_a^b f \, dg,$$

for every f in $C_R(J)$.

PROOF.   We shall first define a monotone increasing function g and then show that (22.17) holds.

There exists a constant M such that if $0 \leq f_1(x) \leq f_2(x)$ for all x in J, then $0 \leq G(f_1) \leq G(f_2) \leq M \, \|f_2\|$. If t is any real number such that $a < t < b$, and if n is a sufficiently large natural number, we let $\varphi_{t,n}$ be the function (see Figure 22.3), on $C_R(J)$ defined by

$$(22.18) \qquad
\begin{aligned}
\varphi_{t,n}(x) &= 1, & a &\leq x \leq t, \\
&= 1 - n(x - t), & t &< x \leq t + 1/n, \\
&= 0, & t + 1/n &< x \leq b.
\end{aligned}$$

It is readily seen that if $n \leq m$, then for each t with $a < t < b$,

$$0 \leq \varphi_{t,m}(x) \leq \varphi_{t,n}(x) \leq 1,$$

so that the sequence $(G(\varphi_{t,n}) : n \in \mathbf{N})$ is a bounded decreasing sequence of real numbers which converges to a real number. We define $g(t)$ to be equal to this limit. If $a < t \leq s < b$ and $n \in \mathbf{N}$, then

$$0 \leq \varphi_{t,n}(x) \leq \varphi_{s,n}(x) \leq 1,$$

† FREDERIC RIESZ (1880–1955), a brilliant Hungarian mathematician, was one of the founders of topology and functional analysis. He also made beautiful contributions to potential, ergodic, and integration theory.

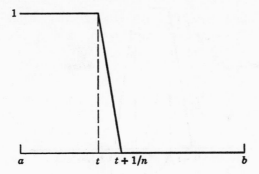

Figure 22.3.   Graph of $\varphi_{t,n}$.

whence it follows that $g(t) \leq g(s)$. We define $g(a) = 0$ and if $\varphi_{b,n}$ denotes the function $\varphi_{b,n}(x) = 1$, $x \in J$, then we set $g(b) = G(\varphi_{b,n})$. If $a < t < b$ and n is sufficiently large, then for all x in J we have

$$0 \leq \varphi_{t,n}(x) \leq \varphi_{b,n}(x) = 1,$$

so that $g(a) = 0 \leq G(\varphi_{t,n}) \leq G(\varphi_{b,n}) = g(b)$. This shows that $g(a) \leq g(t) \leq g(b)$ and completes the construction of the monotone increasing function g.

If f is continuous on J and $\epsilon > 0$, there is a $\delta(\epsilon) > 0$ such that if $|x - y| < \delta(\epsilon)$ and $x, y \in J$, then $|f(x) - f(y)| < \epsilon$. Since f is integrable with respect to g, there exists a partition P_ϵ of J such that if Q is a refinement of P_ϵ, then for any Riemann-Stieltjes sum, we have

$$\left| \int_a^b f \, dg - S(Q; f, g) \right| < \epsilon.$$

Now let $P = (t_0, t_1, \ldots, t_m)$ be a partition of J into distinct points which is a refinement of P_ϵ such that $\sup \{t_k - t_{k-1}\} < (\tfrac{1}{2})\delta(\epsilon)$ and let n be a natural number so large that

$$2/n < \inf \{t_k - t_{k-1}\}.$$

Then only consecutive intervals

(22.19) $[t_0, t_1 + 1/n], \ldots, [t_{k-1}, t_k + 1/n], \ldots, [t_{m-1}, t_m]$

have any points in common. (See Figure 22.4.) For each $k = 1, \ldots, m$, the decreasing sequence $(G(\varphi_{t_k, n}))$ converges to $g(t_k)$ and hence we may suppose that n is so large that

(22.20) $g(t_k) \leq G(\varphi_{t_k, n}) \leq g(t_k) + (\epsilon/m \, \|f\|).$

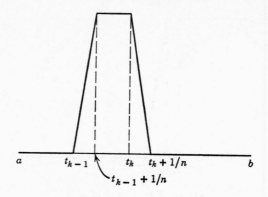

Figure 22.4.   Graph of $\varphi_{t_k, n} - \varphi_{t_{k-1}, n}$.

We now consider the function f^* defined on J by

$$(22.21) \qquad f^*(x) = f(t_1)\varphi_{t_1, n}(x) + \sum_{k=2}^{m} f(t_k)\{\varphi_{t_k, n}(x) - \varphi_{t_{k-1}, n}(x)\}.$$

An element x in J either belongs to one or two intervals in (22.19). If it belongs to one interval, then we must have $t_0 \leq x < t_1$ and $f^*(x) = f(t_1)$ or we have $t_{k-1} + (1/n) < x \leq t_k$ for some $k = 1, 2, \ldots, m$ in which case $f^*(x) = f(t_k)$. (See Figure 22.5.) Hence

$$|f(x) - f^*(x)| < \epsilon.$$

If the x belongs to two intervals in (22.19), then $t_k \leq x \leq t_k + 1/n$ for some $k = 1, \ldots, m - 1$ and we infer that

$$f^*(x) = f(t_k)\varphi_{t_k, n}(x) + f(t_{k+1})\{1 - \varphi_{t_k, n}(x)\}.$$

If we refer to the definition of the φ's in (22.18), we have

$$f^*(x) = f(t_k)(1 - n(x - t_k)) + f(t_{k+1})n(x - t_k).$$

Since $|x - t_k| < \delta(\epsilon)$ and $|x - t_{k+1}| < \delta(\epsilon)$, we conclude that

$$\begin{aligned} |f(x) - f^*(x)| &\leq |f(x) - f(t_k)|(1 - n(x - t_k)) \\ &\quad + |f(x) - f(t_{k+1})|n(x - t_k) \\ &< \epsilon\{1 - n(x - t_k) + n(x - t_k)\} = \epsilon. \end{aligned}$$

Consequently, we have the estimate

$$\|f - f^*\| = \sup \{|f(x) - f^*(x)| : x \in J\} \leq \epsilon.$$

Since G is a bounded linear functional on $C_{\mathbf{R}}(J)$, it follows that

$$(22.22) \qquad |G(f) - G(f^*)| \leq M\epsilon.$$

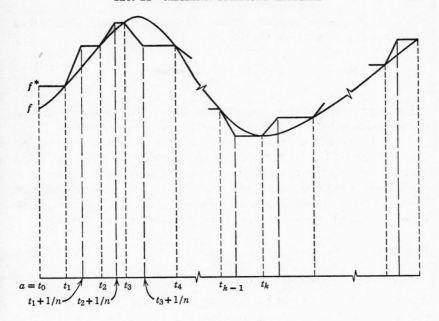

Figure 22.5.   Graphs of f and f^*.

In view of relation (22.20) we see that

$$|\{G(\varphi_{t_k,\,n}) - G(\varphi_{t_{k-1},\,n})\} - \{g(t_k) - g(t_{k-1})\}| < \epsilon/\,(m\,\|f\|)$$

for $k = 2, 3, \ldots, m$. Applying G to the function f^* defined by equation (22.21) and recalling that $g(t_0) = 0$, we obtain

$$\left| G(f^*) - \sum_{k=1}^{m} f(t_k)\{g(t_k) - g(t_{k-1})\} \right| < \epsilon.$$

But the second term on the left side is a Riemann-Stieltjes sum $S(P;f,g)$ for f with respect to g corresponding to the partition P which is a refinement of P_ϵ. Hence we have

$$\left| \int_a^b f\,dg - G(f^*) \right| \leq \left| \int_a^b f\,dg - S(P;f,g) \right| + |S(P;f,g) - G(f^*)| < 2\epsilon.$$

Finally, using relation (22.22), we find that

(22.23) $$\left| \int_a^b f\,dg - G(f) \right| < (M + 2)\epsilon.$$

Since ϵ is an arbitrary positive number and the left side of (22.23) does not depend on it, we conclude that

$$G(f) = \int_a^b f \, dg.$$

Q.E.D.

For some purposes it is important to know that there is a one-one correspondence between bounded positive linear functionals on $C_{\mathbf{R}}(J)$ and certain normalized monotone increasing functions. Our construction can be checked to show that it yields an increasing function g such that $g(a) = 0$ and g is continuous from the right at every interior point of J. With these additional conditions, there is a one-one correspondence between positive functionals and increasing functions. (In some applications it is useful to employ other normalizations, however.)

Exercises

22.A. Let g be defined on $\mathbf{I} = [0, 1]$ by

$$\begin{aligned} g(x) &= 0, \qquad 0 \le x \le \tfrac{1}{2}, \\ &= 1, \qquad \tfrac{1}{2} < x \le 1. \end{aligned}$$

Show that a bounded function f is integrable with respect to g on $\mathbf{I}$ if and only if f is continuous at $\tfrac{1}{2}$ from the right and in this case, then

$$\int_0^1 f \, dg = f(\tfrac{1}{2}).$$

22.B Show that the function f, given in Example 22.3(h) is Riemann integrable on $\mathbf{I}$ and that the value of its integral is 0.

22.C. Show that the function f, defined on $\mathbf{I}$ by

$$\begin{aligned} f(x) &= x, \qquad x \text{ rational}, \\ &= 0, \qquad x \text{ irrational}, \end{aligned}$$

is not Riemann integrable on $\mathbf{I}$.

22.D. If $P = (x_0, x_1, \ldots, x_n)$ is a partition of $J = [a, b]$, let $\|P\|$ be defined to be

$$\|P\| = \sup \{x_j - x_{j-1} : j = 1, 2, \ldots, n\};$$

we call $\|P\|$ the **norm** of the partition P. Define f to be (*)-**integrable** with respect to g on J in case there exists a number A with the property: if $\epsilon > 0$ then there is a $\delta(\epsilon) > 0$ such that if $\|P\| < \delta(\epsilon)$ and if $S(P; f, g)$ is any corresponding Riemann-Stieltjes sum, then $|S(P; f, g) - A| < \epsilon$. If this is satisfied the number A is called the (*)-**integral** of f with respect to g on J. Show that if f is (*)-integrable with respect to g on J, then f is integrable with respect to g (in the sense of Definition 22.2) and that the values of these integrals are equal.

22.E. Let g be defined on I as in Exercise 22.A. Show that a bounded function f is (*)-integrable with respect to g in the sense of the preceding exercise if and only if f is continuous at $\frac{1}{2}$ when the value of the (*)-integral is $f(\frac{1}{2})$. If h is defined by

$$h(x) = 0, \quad 0 \leq x < \frac{1}{2},$$
$$= 1, \quad \frac{1}{2} \leq x \leq 1,$$

then h is (*)-integrable with respect to g on $[0, \frac{1}{2}]$ and on $[\frac{1}{2}, 1]$ but it is not (*)-integrable with respect to g on $[0, 1]$. Hence Theorem 22.6(a) may fail for the (*)-integral.

22.F. Let $g(x) = x$ for $x \in J$. Show that for this integrator, a function f is integrable in the sense of Definition 22.2 if and only if it is (*)-integrable in the sense of Exercise 22.D.

22.G. Let g be monotone increasing on J (that is, if $x \leq x'$, then $g(x) \leq g(x')$). Show that f is integrable with respect to g if and only if for each $\epsilon > 0$ there is a partition P_ϵ of J and that if $P = (x_0, x_1, \ldots, x_n)$ is a refinement of P_ϵ and if ξ_j and η_j belong to $[x_{j-1}, x_j]$, then

$$\sum_{j=1}^{n} |f(\xi_j) - f(\eta_j)| \{g(x_j) - g(x_{j-1})\} < \epsilon.$$

22.H. Let g be montone increasing on J and suppose that f is integrable with respect to g. Prove that the function $|f|$ is integrable with respect to g. (Hint: $||f(\xi)| - |f(\eta)|| \leq |f(\xi) - f(\eta)|$.)

22.I. Give an example of a function f which is not Riemann integrable, but is such that $|f|$ is Riemann integrable.

22.J. Let g be monotone increasing on J and suppose that f is integrable with respect to g. Prove that the function f^2, defined by $f^2(x) = [f(x)]^2$ for $x \in J$, is also integrable with respect to g. (Hint: if M is an upper bound for $|f|$ on J, then

$$|f^2(\xi) - f^2(\eta)| \leq 2M|f(\xi) - f(\eta)|.)$$

22.K. Give an example of a function f which is not Riemann integrable, but which is such that f^2 is Riemann integrable.

22.L. Let g be monotone increasing on J. If f and h are integrable with respect to g on J, then their product fh is also integrable. (Hint: $2fh = (f + h)^2 - f^2 - h^2$.) If f and fh are known to be integrable, does it follow that h is integrable?

22.M. Let f be Riemann integrable on J and let $f(x) \geq 0$ for $x \in J$. If f is continuous at a point $c \in J$ and if $f(c) > 0$, then

$$\int_a^b f > 0.$$

22.N. Let f be Riemann integrable on J and let $f(x) > 0$ for $x \in J$. Show that

$$\int_a^b f > 0.$$

(Hint: for each $n \in N$, let H_n be the closure of the set of points x in J such that $f(x) > 1/n$ and apply Baire's Theorem 9.8.)

22.O. If f is Riemann integrable on I and if

$$a_n = \frac{1}{n} \sum_{k=1}^{n} f(k/n) \quad \text{for } n \in N,$$

then the sequence (a_n) converges and

$$\lim (a_n) = \int_0^1 f.$$

Show that if f is not Riemann integrable, then the sequence (a_n) may not converge.

22.P. (a) Show that a bounded function which has at most a finite number of discontinuities is Riemann integrable.

(b) Show that if f_1 and f_2 are Riemann integrable on J and if $f_1(x) = f_2(x)$ except for x in a finite subset of J, then their integrals over J are equal.

22.Q. Show that the Integrability Theorem 22.8 holds for an integrator function g which has bounded variation.

22.R. Let g be a fixed monotone increasing function on $J = [a, b]$. If f is any function which is integrable with respect to g on J, then we define $||f||_1$ by

$$||f||_1 = \int_a^b |f| \, dg.$$

Show that the following "norm properties" are satisfied:

(a) $||f||_1 \geq 0$;

(b) If $f(x) = 0$ for all $x \in J$, then $||f||_1 = 0$;

(c) If $c \in R$, then $||cf||_1 = |c| \, ||f||_1$;

(d) $| \, ||f||_1 - ||h||_1 \, | \leq ||f \pm h||_1 \leq ||f||_1 + ||h||_1$.

However, it is possible to have $||f||_1 = 0$ without having $f(x) = 0$ for all $x \in J$. (Can this occur when $g(x) = x$?)

22.S. If g is monotone increasing on J, and if f and f_n, $n \in N$, are functions which are integrable with respect to g, then we say that the sequence (f_n) **converges in mean** (with respect to g) in case

$$||f_n - f||_1 \to 0.$$

(The notation here is the same as in the preceding exercise.) Show that if (f_n) converges in mean to f, then

$$\int_a^b f_n \, dg \to \int_a^b f \, dg.$$

Prove that if a sequence (f_n) of integrable functions converges uniformly on J to f, then it also converges in mean to f. In fact,

$$||f_n - f||_1 \leq \{g(b) - g(a)\} \, ||f_n - f||_J.$$

However, if f_n denotes the function in Example 22.11, and if $g_n = (1/n)f_n$, then the sequence (g_n) converges in mean [with respect to $g(x) = x$] to the zero function, but the convergence is not uniform on I.

22.T. Let $g(x) = x$ on $J = [0, 2]$ and let (I_n) be a sequence of closed intervals in J such that (i) the length of I_n is $1/n$, (ii) $I_n \cap I_{n+1} = \emptyset$, and (iii) every point x in J belongs to infinitely many of the I_n. Let f_n be defined by

$$f_n(x) = 1, \quad x \in I_n,$$
$$= 0, \quad x \notin I_n.$$

Prove that the sequence (f_n) converges in mean [with respect to $g(x) = x$] to the zero function on J, but that the sequence (f_n) does not converge uniformly. Indeed, the sequence (f_n) does not converge at *any* point!

22.U. Let g be monotone increasing on $J = [a, b]$. If f and h are integrable with respect to g on J to $\mathbf{R}$, we define the **inner product** (f, h) of f and h by the formula

$$(f, h) = \int_a^b f(x)h(x) \, dg(x).$$

Verify that all of the properties of Theorem 7.5 are satisfied except (ii). If $f = h$ is the zero function on J, then $(f, f) = 0$; however, it may happen that $(f, f) = 0$ for a function f which does not vanish everywhere on J.

22.V. Define $||f||_2$ to be

$$||f||_2 = \left\{ \int_a^b |f(x)|^2 \, dg(x) \right\}^{1/2},$$

so that $||f||_2 = (f, f)^{1/2}$. Establish the C.-B.-S. Inequality

$$|(f, h)| \le ||f||_2 \, ||h||_2$$

(**see** Theorems 7.6 and 7.7). Show that the Norm Properties 7.8 hold, except that $||f||_2 = 0$ does not imply that $f(x) = 0$ for all x in J. Show that $||f||_1 \le \{g(b) - g(a)\}^{1/2}||f||_2$.

22.W. Let f and f_n, $n \in \mathbf{N}$, be integrable on J with respect to an increasing function g. We say that the sequence (f_n) **converges in mean square** (with respect to g on J) to f if $||f_n - f||_2 \to 0$.

(a) Show that if the sequence is uniformly convergent on J, then it also converges in mean square to the same function.

(b) Show that if the sequence converges in mean square, then it converges in mean to the same function.

(c) Show that Exercise 22.T proves that convergence in mean square does not imply convergence at *any* point of J.

(d) If, in Exercise 22.T, we take I_n to have length $1/n^2$ and if we set $h_n = nf_n$, then the sequence (h_n) converges in mean, but does not converge in mean square, to the zero function.

22.X. Show that if we define G_0, G_1, G_2 for f in $C_R(\mathbf{I})$ by

$$G_0(f) = f(0), \qquad G_2(f) = 2 \int_0^{\frac{1}{2}} f(x)\, dx,$$

$$G_1(f) = \tfrac{1}{2}\{f(0) + f(1)\};$$

then G_0, G_1, and G_2 are bounded positive linear functionals on $C_R(\mathbf{I})$. Give monotone increasing functions g_0, g_1, g_2 which represent these linear functionals as Riemann-Stieltjes integrals. Show that the choice of these g_j is not uniquely determined unless one requires that $g_j(0) = 0$ and that g_j is continuous from the right at each interior point of $\mathbf{I}$.

Projects

22.α. The following outline is sometimes used as an approach to the Riemann-Stieltjes integral when the integrator function g is monotone increasing on the interval J. [This development has the advantage that it permits the definition of upper and lower integrals which always exists for a bounded function f. However, it has the disadvantage that it puts an additional restriction on g and tends to blemish somewhat the symmetry of the Riemann-Stieltjes integral given by the Integration of Parts Theorem 22.7.] If $P = (x_0, x_1, \ldots, x_n)$ is a partition of $J = [a, b]$ and f is a bounded function on J, let m_j, M_j be defined to be the infimum and the supremum of $\{f(x) : x_{j-1} \le x \le x_j\}$, respectively. Corresponding to the partition P, define the **lower** and the **upper sums** of f with respect to g to be

$$L(P;f,g) = \sum_{j=1}^n m_j\{g(x_j) - g(x_{j-1})\},$$

$$U(P;f,g) = \sum_{j=1}^n M_j\{g(x_j) - g(x_{j-1})\}.$$

(a) If $S(P;f,g)$ is any Riemann-Stieltjes sum corresponding to P, then

$$L(P;f,g) \le S(P;f,g) \le U(P;f,g).$$

(b) If $\epsilon > 0$ then there exists a Riemann-Stieltjes sum $S_1(P;f,g)$ corresponding to P such that

$$S_1(P;f,g) \le L(P;f,g) + \epsilon,$$

and there exists a Riemann-Stieltjes sum $S_2(P;f,g)$ corresponding to P such that

$$U(P;f,g) - \epsilon \le S_2(P;f,g).$$

(c) If P and Q are partitions of J and if Q is a refinement of P (that is, $P \subseteq Q$), then

$$L(P;f,g) \le L(Q;f,g) \le U(Q;f,g) \le U(P;f,g).$$

(d) If P_1 and P_2 are any partitions of J, then $L(P_1;f,g) \le U(P_2;f,g)$. [Hint: let Q be a partition which is a refinement of both P_1 and P_2 and apply (c).]

(e) Define the **lower** and the **upper integral** of f with respect to g to be, respectively

$$L(f, g) = \sup \{L(P; f, g)\},$$

$$U(f, g) = \inf \{U(P; f, g)\};$$

here the supremum and the infimum are taken over all partitions P of J. Show that $L(f, g) \leq U(f, g)$.

(f) Prove that f is integrable with respect to the increasing function g if and only if the lower and upper integrals introduced in (e) are equal. In this case the common value of these integrals equals

$$\int_a^b f \, dg.$$

(g) If f_1 and f_2 are bounded on J, then the lower and upper integrals of $f_1 + f_2$ satisfy

$$L(f_1 + f_2, g) \geq L(f_1, g) + L(f_2, g),$$

$$U(f_1 + f_2, g) \leq U(f_1, g) + U(f_2, g).$$

Show that strict inequality can hold in these relations.

22.β. This project develops the well-known Wallis† product formula. Throughout it we shall let

$$S_n = \int_0^{\pi/2} (\sin x)^n \, dx.$$

(a) If $n > 2$, then $S_n = [(n - 1)/n]S_{n-2}$. (Hint: integrate by parts.)

(b) Establish the formulas

$$S_{2n} = \frac{1 \cdot 3 \cdot 5 \cdots (2n - 1)}{2 \cdot 4 \cdot 6 \cdots (2n)} \frac{\pi}{2},$$

$$S_{2n+1} = \frac{2 \cdot 4 \cdots (2n)}{1 \cdot 3 \cdot 5 \cdots (2n + 1)}.$$

(c) Show that the sequence (S_n) is monotone decreasing. (Hint: $0 \leq \sin x \leq 1$.)

(d) Let W_n be defined by

$$W_n = \frac{2 \cdot 2 \cdot 4 \cdot 4 \cdot 6 \cdot 6 \cdots (2n)(2n)}{1 \cdot 3 \cdot 3 \cdot 5 \cdot 5 \cdot 7 \cdots (2n - 1)(2n + 1)}$$

Prove that $\lim(W_n) = \pi/2$. (This is Wallis's product.)

(e) Prove that

$$\lim \left(\frac{(n!)^2 2^{2n}}{(2n)! \sqrt{n}} \right) = \sqrt{\pi}.$$

---

† JOHN WALLIS (1616–1703), the Savilian professor of geometry at Oxford for sixty years, was a precurser of Newton. He helped to lay the groundwork for the development of calculus.

22.γ. This project develops the important Stirling† formula, which estimates the magnitude of $n!$

(a) By comparing the area under the hyperbola $y = 1/x$ and the area of a trapezoid inscribed in it, show that

$$\frac{2}{2n + 1} < \log\left(1 + \frac{1}{n}\right).$$

From this, show that

$$e < (1 + 1/n)^{n+1/2}.$$

(b) Show that

$$\int_1^n \log x \, dx = n \log n - n + 1 = \log (n/e)^n + 1.$$

Consider the figure F made up of rectangles with bases $[1, \frac{3}{2}]$, $[n - \frac{1}{2}, n]$ and heights 2, $\log n$, respectively, and with trapezoids with bases $[k - \frac{1}{2}, k + \frac{1}{2}]$ $k = 2, 3, \ldots, n - 1$, and with slant heights passing through the points $(k, \log k)$. Show that the area of F is

$$1 + \log 2 + \cdots + \log (n - 1) + \tfrac{1}{2} \log n = 1 + \log (n!) - \log \sqrt{n}.$$

(c) Comparing the two areas in part (b), show that

$$u_n = \frac{(n/e)^n \sqrt{n}}{n!} < 1, \qquad n \in \mathbf{N}.$$

(d) Show that the sequence (u_n) is monotone increasing. (Hint: consider u_{n+1}/u_n.)

(e) By considering $u_n{}^2/u_{2n}$ and making use of the result of part (e) of the preceding project, show that $\lim (u_n) = (2\pi)^{-1/2}$.

(f) Obtain Stirling's formula

$$\lim \left(\frac{(n/e)^n \sqrt{2\pi n}}{n!}\right) = 1.$$

Section 23   The Main Theorems of Integral Calculus

As in the preceding section, $J = [a, b]$ denotes a compact interval of the real line and f and g denote bounded real-valued functions defined on J. In this section we shall be primarily concerned with the Riemann integral where the integrator function is $g(x) = x$, but there are a few results which we shall establish for the Riemann-Stieltjes integral.

† JAMES STIRLING (1692–1770) was an English mathematician of the Newtonian school. The formula attributed to Stirling was actually established earlier by ABRAHAM DE MOIVRE (1667–1754), a French Huguenot who settled in London and was a friend of Newton's.

23.1   FIRST MEAN VALUE THEOREM. *If g is increasing on $J = [a, b]$ and f is continuous on J to $\mathbf{R}$, then there exists a number c in J such that*

$$(23.1) \qquad \int_a^b f \, dg = f(c) \int_a^b dg = f(c)\{g(b) - g(a)\}.$$

PROOF.   It follows from the Integrability Theorem 22.8 that f is integrable with respect to g. If $m = \inf \{f(x) : x \in J\}$ and $M = \sup \{f(x) : x \in J\}$, it was seen in Lemma 22.10 that

$$m\{g(b) - g(a)\} \leq \int_a^b f \, dg \leq M\{g(b) - g(a)\}.$$

If $g(b) = g(a)$, then the relation (23.1) is trivial; if $g(b) > g(a)$, then it follows from Bolzano's Intermediate Value Theorem 16.4 that there exists a number c in J such that

$$f(c) = \left\{ \int_a^b f \, dg \right\} \bigg/ \left\{ g(b) - g(a) \right\}.$$

Q.E.D.

23.2   DIFFERENTIATION THEOREM. *Suppose that f is continuous on J and that g is increasing on J and has a derivative at a point c in J. Then the function F, defined for x in J by*

$$(23.2) \qquad\qquad F(x) = \int_a^x f \, dg,$$

has a derivative at c and $F'(c) = f(c)g'(c)$.

PROOF.   If $h > 0$ is such that $c + h$ belongs to J, then it follows from Theorem 22.6 and the preceding result that

$$F(c + h) - F(c) = \int_a^{c+h} f \, dg - \int_a^c f \, dg$$

$$= \int_c^{c+h} f \, dg = f(c_1)\{g(c + h) - g(c)\},$$

for some c_1 with $c \leq c_1 \leq c + h$. A similar relation holds if $h < 0$. Since f is continuous and g has a derivative at c, then $F'(c)$ exists and equals $f(c)g'(c)$.

Q.E.D.

Specializing this theorem to the Riemann case, we obtain the result which provides the basis for the familiar method of evaluating integrals in calculus.

23.3 FUNDAMENTAL THEOREM OF INTEGRAL CALCULUS. *Let f be continuous on $J = [a, b]$. A function F on J satisfies*

(23.3) $$F(x) - F(a) = \int_a^x f \quad for \quad x \in J,$$

if and only if $F' = f$ on J.

PROOF. If relation (23.3) holds and $c \in J$, then it is seen from the preceding theorem that $F'(c) = f(c)$.

Conversely, let F_a be defined for x in J by

$$F_a(x) = \int_a^x f.$$

The preceding theorem asserts that $F_a' = f$ on J. If F is such that $F' = f$, then it follows from the Mean Value Theorem 19.6 (in particular, Consequence 19.10(ii)) that there exists a constant C such that

$$F(x) = F_a(x) + C, \qquad x \in J.$$

Since $F_a(a) = 0$, then $C = F(a)$ whence it follows that

$$F(x) - F(a) = \int_a^x f$$

whenever $F' = f$ on J.

Q.E.D.

NOTE. If F is a function defined on J such that $F' = f$ on J, then we sometimes say that F is an **indefinite integral**, an **anti-derivative**, or a **primitive** of f. In this terminology, the Differentiation Theorem 23.2 asserts that every continuous function has a primitive. Sometimes the Fundamental Theorem of Integral Calculus is formulated in ways differing from that given in 23.3, but it always includes the assertion that, under suitable hypotheses, the Riemann integral of f can be calculated by evaluating any primitive of f at the end points of the interval of integration. We have given the above formulation, which yields a necessary and sufficient condition for a function to be a primitive of a continuous function. A somewhat more general result, not requiring the continuity of the integrand, will be found in Exercise 23.E.

It should *not* be supposed that the Fundamental Theorem asserts that if the derivative f of a function F exists at every point of J, then f is integrable and (23.3) holds. In fact, it may happen that f is not Riemann integrable (see Exercise 23.F). Similarly, a function f may be Riemann integrable but not have a primitive (see Exercise 23.G).

Modification of the Integral

When the integrator function g has a continuous derivative, it is possible and often convenient to replace the Riemann-Stieltjes integral by a Riemann integral. We now establish the validity of this reduction.

23.4   THEOREM.   *If the derivative $g' = h$ exists and is continuous on J and if f is integrable with respect to g, then the product fh is Riemann integrable and*

(23.4)
$$\int_a^b f \, dg = \int_a^b fh.$$

PROOF.   The hypothesis implies that $h = g'$ is uniformly continuous on J. If $\epsilon > 0$, let $P = (x_0, x_1, \ldots, x_n)$ be a partition of J such that if ξ_k and ζ_k belong to $[x_{k-1}, x_k]$ then $|h(\xi_k) - h(\zeta_k)| < \epsilon$. We consider the difference of the Riemann-Stieltjes sum $S(P; f, g)$ and the Riemann sum $S(P; fh)$, using the same intermediate points ξ_k. In doing so we have a sum of terms of the form

$$f(\xi_k)\{g(x_k) - g(x_{k-1})\} - f(\xi_k)h(\xi_k)\{x_k - x_{k-1}\}.$$

If we apply the Mean Value Theorem 19.6 to g, we can write this difference in the form

$$f(\xi_k)\{h(\zeta_k) - h(\xi_k)\}(x_k - x_{k-1}),$$

where ζ_k is some point in the interval $[x_{k-1}, x_k]$. Since this term is dominated by $\epsilon \, \|f\| \, (x_k - x_{k-1})$, we conclude that

(23.5)
$$|S(P; f, g) - S(P; fh)| < \epsilon \, \|f\| \, (b - a),$$

provided the partition P is sufficiently fine. Since the integral on the left side of (23.4) exists and is the limit of the Riemann-Stieltjes sums $S(P; f, g)$, we infer that the integral on the right side of (23.4) also exists and that the equality holds.

Q.E.D.

As a consequence, we obtain the following variant of the First Mean Value Theorem 23.1, here stated for Riemann integrals.

23.5   FIRST MEAN VALUE THEOREM.   *If f and h are continuous on J and h is non-negative, then there exists a point c in J such that*

(23.6)
$$\int_a^b f(x) \, h(x) \, dx = f(c) \int_a^b h(x) \, dx.$$

PROOF.   Let g be defined by

$$g(x) = \int_a^x h(t) \, dt \quad \text{for} \quad x \in J.$$

Since $h(x) \geq 0$, it is seen that g is increasing and it follows from the Differentiation Theorem 23.2 that $g' = h$. By Theorem 23.4, we conclude that

$$\int_a^b f \, dg = \int_a^b fh,$$

and from the First Mean Value Theorem 23.1, we infer that for some c in J, then

$$\int_a^b f \, dg = f(c) \int_a^b h.$$

Q.E.D.

As a second application of Theorem 23.4 we shall reformulate Theorem 22.7, which is concerned with integration by parts, in a more traditional form. The proof will be left to the reader.

23.6 INTEGRATION BY PARTS. *If f and g have continuous derivatives on $[a, b]$, then*

$$\int_a^b fg' = f(b)g(b) - f(a)g(a) - \int_a^b f'g.$$

The next result is often useful.

23.7 SECOND MEAN VALUE THEOREM. (a) *If f is increasing and g is continuous on $J = [a, b]$, then there exists a point c in J such that*

$$(23.7) \qquad \int_a^b f \, dg = f(a) \int_a^c dg + f(b) \int_c^b dg.$$

(b) *If f is increasing and h is continuous on J, then there exists a point c in J such that*

$$(23.8) \qquad \int_a^b fh = f(a) \int_a^c h + f(b) \int_c^b h.$$

(c) *If f is non-negative and increasing and h is continuous on J, then there exists a point c in J such that*

$$\int_a^b fh = f(b) \int_c^b h.$$

PROOF. The hypotheses, together with the Integrability Theorem 22.8 imply that g is integrable with respect to f on J. Furthermore, by the First Mean Value Theorem 23.1,

$$\int_a^b g \, df = g(c)\{f(b) - f(a)\}.$$

After using Theorem 22.7 concerning integration by parts, we conclude that f is integrable with respect to g and

$$
\begin{aligned}
\int_a^b f\,dg &= \{f(b)g(b) - f(a)g(a)\} - g(c)\{f(b) - f(a)\} \\
&= f(a)\{g(c) - g(a)\} + f(b)\{g(b) - g(c)\} \\
&= f(a)\int_a^c dg + f(b)\int_c^b dg,
\end{aligned}
$$

which establishes part (a). To prove (b) let g be defined on J by

$$
g(x) = \int_a^x h,
$$

so that $g' = h$. The conclusion then follows from part (a) by using Theorem 23.4. To prove (c) define F to be equal to f for x in $(a, b]$ and define $F(a) = 0$. We now apply part (b) to F.

Q.E.D.

Part (c) of the preceding theorem is frequently called the Bonnet† form of the Second Mean Value Theorem. It is evident that there is a corresponding result for a decreasing function.

Change of Variable

We shall now establish a theorem justifying the familiar formula relating to the "change of variable" in a Riemann integral.

23.8   CHANGE OF VARIABLE THEOREM.   *Let φ be defined on an interval $[\alpha, \beta]$ to $\mathbf{R}$ with a continuous derivative and suppose that $a = \varphi(\alpha) < b = \varphi(\beta)$. If f is continuous on the range of φ, then*

$$
(23.9) \qquad \int_a^b f(x)\,dx = \int_\alpha^\beta f[\varphi(t)]\varphi'(t)\,dt.
$$

PROOF.   Both integrals in (23.9) exist. Let F be defined by

$$
F(\xi) = \int_a^\xi f(x)\,dx \quad \text{for} \quad a \le \xi \le b,
$$

and consider the function H defined by

$$
H(t) = F[\varphi(t)] \quad \text{for} \quad \alpha \le t \le \beta.
$$

† OSSIAN BONNET (1819–1892) is primarily known for his work in differential geometry.

Observe that $H(\alpha) = F(a) = 0$. Differentiating with respect to t and using the fact that $F' = f$, we obtain

$$H'(t) = F'[\varphi(t)]\varphi'(t) = f[\varphi(t)]\varphi'(t).$$

Applying the Fundamental Theorem, we infer that

$$\int_a^b f(x)\, dx = F(b) = H(\beta) = \int_\alpha^\beta f[\varphi(t)]\varphi'(t)\, dt.$$

Q.E.D.

Integrals Depending on a Parameter

It is often important to consider integrals in which the integrands depend on a parameter. In such cases one desires to have conditions assuring the continuity, the differentiability, and the integrability of the resulting function. The next few results are useful in this connection.

Let D be the rectangle in $\mathbf{R} \times \mathbf{R}$ given by

$$D = \{(x, t) : a \le x \le b, c \le t \le d\},$$

and suppose that f is continuous on D to $\mathbf{R}$. Then it is easily seen (cf. Exercise 16.E) that, for each fixed t in $[c, d]$, the function which sends x into $f(x, t)$ is continuous on $[a, b]$ and, therefore, Riemann integrable. We define F for t in $[c, d]$ by the formula

$$(23.10) \qquad\qquad F(t) = \int_a^b f(x, t)\, dx.$$

It will first be proved that F is continuous.

23.9 THEOREM. *If f is continuous on D to $\mathbf{R}$ and if F is defined by (23.10), then F is continuous on $[c, d]$ to $\mathbf{R}$.*

PROOF. The Uniform Continuity Theorem 16.12 implies that if $\epsilon > 0$, then there exists a $\delta(\epsilon) > 0$ such that if t and t_0 belong to $[c, d]$ and $|t - t_0| < \delta(\epsilon)$, then

$$|f(x, t) - f(x, t_0)| < \epsilon,$$

for all x in $[a, b]$. It follows from Lemma 22.10 that

$$|F(t) - F(t_0)| = \left| \int_a^b \{f(x, t) - f(x, t_0)\}\, dx \right|$$

$$\le \int_a^b |f(x, t) - f(x, t_0)|\, dx < \epsilon(b - a),$$

which establishes the continuity of F.

Q.E.D.

23.10 THEOREM. *If f and its partial derivative f_t are continuous on D to R, then the function F defined by (23.10) has a derivative on $[c, d]$ and*

$$(23.11) \qquad F'(t) = \int_a^b f_t(x, t) \, dx.$$

PROOF. From the uniform continuity of f_t on D we infer that if $\epsilon > 0$, then there is a $\delta(\epsilon) > 0$ such that if $|t - t_0| < \delta(\epsilon)$, then

$$|f_t(x, t) - f_t(x, t_0)| < \epsilon$$

for all x in $[a, b]$. Let t, t_0 satisfy this condition and apply the Mean Value Theorem to obtain a t_1 (which may depend on x and lies between t and t_0) such that

$$f(x, t) - f(x, t_0) = (t - t_0) f_t(x, t_1).$$

Combining these two relations, we infer that if $0 < |t - t_0| < \delta(\epsilon)$, then

$$\left| \frac{f(x, t) - f(x, t_0)}{t - t_0} - f_t(x, t_0) \right| < \epsilon,$$

for all x in $[a, b]$. By applying Lemma 22.10, we obtain the estimate

$$\left| \frac{F(t) - F(t_0)}{t - t_0} - \int_a^b f_t(x, t_0) \, dx \right|$$
$$\leq \int_a^b \left| \frac{f(x, t) - f(x, t_0)}{t - t_0} - f_t(x, t_0) \right| dx < \epsilon(b - a),$$

which establishes the differentiability of F.

Q.E.D.

Sometimes the parameter t enters in the limits of integration as well as in the integrand. The next result considers this possibility.

23.11 LEIBNIZ'S FORMULA. *Suppose that f and f_t are continuous on D to R and that α and β are functions which are differentiable on the interval $[c, d]$ and have values in $[a, b]$. If φ is defined on $[c, d]$ by*

$$(23.12) \qquad \varphi(t) = \int_{\alpha(t)}^{\beta(t)} f(x, t) \, dx,$$

then φ has a derivative for each t in $[c, d]$ which is given by

$$(23.13) \qquad \varphi'(t) = f[\beta(t), t]\beta'(t) - f[\alpha(t), t]\alpha'(t) + \int_{\alpha(t)}^{\beta(t)} f_t(x, t) \, dx.$$

PROOF. Let H be defined for (u, v, t) by

$$H(u, v, t) = \int_v^u f(x, t)\, dx,$$

when u, v belong to $[a, b]$ and t belongs to $[c, d]$. The function φ defined on (23.12) is the composition given by $\varphi(t) = H[\beta(t), \alpha(t), t]$. Applying the Chain Rule 20.9, we have

$$\varphi'(t) = H_u[\beta(t), \alpha(t), t]\beta'(t) + H_v[\beta(t), \alpha(t), t]\alpha'(t) + H_t[\beta(t), \alpha(t), t].$$

According to the Differentiation Theorem 23.2,

$$H_u(u, v, t) = f(u, t), \qquad H_v(u, v, t) = -f(v, t),$$

and from the preceding theorem, we have

$$H_t(u, v, t) = \int_v^u f_t(x, t)\, dx.$$

If we substitute $u = \beta(t)$ and $v = \alpha(t)$, then we obtain the formula (23.13).

Q.E.D.

If f is continuous on D to $\mathbf{R}$ and if F is defined by formula (23.11), then it was proved in Theorem 23.9 that F is continuous and hence Riemann integrable on the interval $[c, d]$. We now show that this hypothesis of continuity is sufficient to insure that we may *interchange the order of integration*. In formulas, this may be expressed as

$$(23.14) \qquad \int_c^d \left\{ \int_a^b f(x, t)\, dx \right\} dt = \int_a^b \left\{ \int_c^d f(x, t)\, dt \right\} dx.$$

23.12 INTERCHANGE THEOREM. *If f is continuous on D with values in $\mathbf{R}$, then formula (23.14) is valid.*

PROOF. Theorem 23.9 and the Integrability Theorem 22.8 imply that both of the iterated integrals appearing in (23.14) exist; it remains only to establish their equality. Since f is uniformly continuous on D, if $\epsilon > 0$ there exists a $\delta(\epsilon) > 0$ such that if $|x - x'| < \delta(\epsilon)$ and $|t - t'| < \delta(\epsilon)$, then $|f(x, t) - f(x', t')| < \epsilon$. Let n be chosen so large that $(b - a)/n < \delta(\epsilon)$ and $(d - c)/n < \delta(\epsilon)$ and divide D into n^2 equal rectangles by dividing $[a, b]$ and $[c, d]$ each into n equal parts. For $j = 0, 1, \ldots, n$, we let

$$x_j = a + (b - a)j/n, \qquad t_j = c + (d - c)j/n.$$

We can write the integral on the left of (23.14) in the form of the sum

$$\sum_{k=1}^{n} \sum_{j=1}^{n} \int_{t_{k-1}}^{t_k} \left\{ \int_{x_{j-1}}^{x_j} f(x, t) \, dx \right\} dt.$$

Applying the First Mean Value Theorem 23.1 twice, we infer that there exists a number x_j' in $[x_{j-1}, x_j]$ and a number t_k' in $[t_{k-1}, t_k]$ such that

$$\int_{t_{k-1}}^{t_k} \left\{ \int_{x_{j-1}}^{x_j} f(x, t) \, dx \right\} dt = f(x_j', t_k')(x_j - x_{j-1})(t_k - t_{k-1}).$$

Hence we have

$$\int_c^d \left\{ \int_a^b f(x, t) \, dx \right\} dt = \sum_{k=1}^{n} \sum_{j=1}^{n} f(x_j', t_k')(x_j - x_{j-1})(t_k - t_{k-1}).$$

The same line of reasoning, applied to the integral on the right of (23.14), yields the existence of numbers x_j'' in $[x_{j-1}, x_j]$ and t_k'' in $[t_{k-1}, t_k]$ such that

$$\int_a^b \left\{ \int_c^d f(x, t) \, dt \right\} dx = \sum_{k=1}^{n} \sum_{j=1}^{n} f(x_j'', t_k'')(x_j - x_{j-1})(t_k - t_{k-1}).$$

Since both x_j' and x_j'' belong to $[x_{j-1}, x_j]$ and t_k', t_k'' belong to $[t_{k-1}, t_k]$, we conclude from the uniform continuity of f that the two double sums, and therefore the two iterated integrals, differ by at most $\epsilon(b - a)(d - c)$. Since ϵ is an arbitrary positive number, the equality of these integrals is confirmed.

Q.E.D.

Integral Form for the Remainder

The reader will recall Taylor's Theorem 19.9, which enables one to calculate the value $f(b)$ in terms of the values $f(a), f'(a), \ldots, f^{(n-1)}(a)$ and a remainder term which involves $f^{(n)}$ evaluated at a point between a and b. For many applications it is more convenient to be able to express the remainder term as an integral involving $f^{(n)}$.

23.13 TAYLOR'S THEOREM. *Suppose that f and its derivatives f', $f'', \ldots, f^{(n)}$ are continuous on $[a, b]$ to* R. *Then*

$$f(b) = f(a) + \frac{f'(a)}{1!}(b - a) + \cdots + \frac{f^{(n-1)}(a)}{(n-1)!}(b - a)^{n-1} + R_n,$$

where the remainder is given by

$$(23.15) \qquad R_n = \frac{1}{(n-1)!} \int_a^b (b - t)^{n-1} f^{(n)}(t) \, dt.$$

PROOF. Integrate R_n by parts to obtain

$$R_n = \frac{1}{(n-1)!} \left\{ (b-t)^{n-1} f^{(n-1)}(t) \bigg|_{t=a}^{t=b} \right.$$

$$\left. + (n-1) \int_a^b (b-t)^{n-2} f^{(n-1)}(t) \, dt \right\}$$

$$= - \frac{f^{(n-1)}(a)}{(n-1)!} (b-a)^{n-1} + \frac{1}{(n-2)!} \int_a^b (b-t)^{n-2} f^{(n-1)}(t) \, dt.$$

Continuing to integrate by parts in this way, we obtain the stated formula.

Q.E.D.

Instead of the formula (23.15), it is often convenient to make the change of variable $t = (1-s)a + sb$, for s in $[0, 1]$, and to obtain the formula

$$(23.16) \quad R_n = \frac{(b-a)^{n-1}}{(n-1)!} \int_0^1 (1-s)^{n-1} f^{(n)}[a + (b-a)s] \, ds.$$

This form of the remainder can be extended to the case where f has domain in $\mathbf{R}^p$ and range in $\mathbf{R}^q$.

Exercises

23.A. Does the First Mean Value Theorem hold if f is not assumed to be continuous?

23.B. Show that the Differentiation Theorem 23.2 holds if it is assumed that f is integrable on J with respect to an increasing function g, that f is continuous at c, and that g is differentiable at c.

23.C. Suppose that f is integrable with respect to function g on $J = [a, b]$ and let F be defined for $x \in J$ by

$$F(x) = \int_a^x f \, dg.$$

Prove that (a) if g is continuous at c, then F is continuous at c, and (b) if g is increasing and f is non-negative, then F is increasing.

23.D. Give an example of a Riemann integrable function f on J such that the function F, defined for $x \in J$ by

$$F(x) = \int_a^x f,$$

does not have a derivative at some points of J. Can you find an integrable function f such that F is not continuous on J?

23.E. If f is Riemann integrable on $J = [a, b]$ and if $F' = f$ on J, then

$$F(b) - F(a) = \int_a^b f.$$

Hint: if $P = (x_0, x_1, \ldots, x_n)$ is a partition of J, write

$$F(b) - F(a) = \sum_{j=1}^n \{F(x_j) - F(x_{j-1})\}.$$

23.F. Let F be defined by

$$F(x) = x^2 \sin (1/x^2), \qquad 0 < x \leq 1,$$
$$= 0, \qquad\qquad x = 0.$$

Then F has a derivative at every point of $\mathbf{I}$. However F' is not integrable on $\mathbf{I}$ and so F is not the integral of its derivative.

23.G. Let f be defined by

$$f(x) = 0, \qquad 0 \leq x \leq 1,$$
$$= 1, \qquad 1 < x \leq 2.$$

Then f is Riemann integrable on $[0, 2]$, but it is not the derivative of any function. For a more dramatic example, consider the function in Example 22.3(h), which cannot be a derivative by Exercise 19.N.

23.H. [A function f on $J = [a, b]$ to $\mathbf{R}$ is **piecewise continuous** on J if (i) it is continuous on J except for at most a finite number of points; (ii) if $c \in (a, b)$ is a point of discontinuity of f, then the right- and left-hand (deleted) limits $f(c + 0)$ and $f(c - 0)$ of f at c exist; and (iii) at $x = a$ the right-hand limit of f exists and at $x = b$ the left-hand limit of f exists.] Show that a piecewise continuous function is Riemann integrable and that the value of the integral does not depend on the values of f at the points of discontinuity.

23.I. If f is piecewise continuous on $J = [a, b]$, then

$$F(x) = \int_a^x f$$

is continuous on J. Moreover, $F'(x)$ exists and equals $f(x)$ except for at most a finite number of points in J. Show that F' may exist at a point where f is discontinuous.

23.J. In the First Mean Value Theorem 23.5, assume that h is Riemann integrable (instead of that h is continuous). Show that the conclusion holds.

23.K. Use the Fundamental Theorem 23.3 to show that if a sequence (f_n) of functions converges on J to a function f and if the derivatives (f_n') are continuous and converge uniformly on J to a function g, then f' exists and equals g. (This result is less general than Theorem 19.12, but it is easier to establish.)

23.L. Let f be continuous on $I = [0, 1]$, let $f_0 = f$, and let f_{n+1} be defined by

$$f_{n+1}(x) = \int_0^x f_n(t)\,dt \quad \text{for} \quad n \in \mathbf{N},\, x \in \mathbf{I}.$$

By induction, show that

$$|f_n(x)| \le \frac{M}{n!} x^n \le \frac{M}{n!},$$

where $M = \sup\{|f(x)| : x \in \mathbf{I}\}$. It follows that the sequence (f_n) converges uniformly on $\mathbf{I}$ to the zero function.

23.M. Let $\{r_1, r_2, \ldots, r_n, \ldots\}$ be an enumeration of the rational numbers in $\mathbf{I}$. Let f_n be defined to be 1 if $x \in \{r_1, \ldots, r_n\}$ and to be 0 otherwise. Then f_n is Riemann integrable on $\mathbf{I}$ and the sequence (f_n) converges monotonely to the Dirichlet discontinuous function f (which equals 1 on $\mathbf{I} \cap \mathbf{Q}$ and equals 0 on $\mathbf{I} \backslash \mathbf{Q}$). Hence the monotone limit of a sequence of Riemann integrable functions does not need to be Riemann integrable.

23.N. Let f be a non-negative continuous function on $J = [a, b]$ and let $M = \sup\{f(x) : x \in J\}$. Prove that if M_n is defined by

$$M_n = \left\{ \int_a^b [f(x)]^n\,dx \right\}^{1/n} \quad \text{for} \quad n \in \mathbf{N},$$

then $M = \lim\,(M_n)$.

23.O. If f is integrable with respect to g on $J = [a, b]$, if φ is continuous and strictly increasing on $[c, d]$, and if $\varphi(c) = a$, $\varphi(d) = b$, then $f \circ \varphi$ is integrable with respect to $g \circ \varphi$ and

$$\int_a^b f\,dg = \int_c^d f \circ \varphi \; l(g \circ \varphi).$$

23.P. If $J_1 = [a, b]$, $J_2 = [c, d]$, and if f is continuous on $J_1 \times J_2$ to $\mathbf{R}$ and g is Riemann integrable on J_1, then the function F, defined on J_2 by

$$F(t) = \int_a^b f(x, t) g(x)\,dx,$$

is continuous on J_2.

23.Q. Let g be an increasing function on $J_1 = [a, b]$ to $\mathbf{R}$ and for each fixed t in $J_2 = [c, d]$, suppose that the integral

$$F(t) = \int_a^b f(x, t)\,dg(x)$$

exists. If the partial derivative f_t is continuous on $J_1 \times J_2$, then the derivative F' exists on J_2 and is given by

$$F'(t) = \int_a^b f_t(x, t)\,dg(x).$$

23.R. Let $J_1 = [a, b]$ and $J_2 = [c, d]$. Assume that the real valued function g is monotone on J_1, that h is monotone on J_2, and that f is continuous on $J_1 \times J_2$. Define G on J_2 and H on J_1 by

$$G(t) = \int_a^b f(x, t) \, dg(x), \qquad H(x) = \int_c^d f(x, t) \, dh(t).$$

Show that G is integrable with respect to h on J_2, that H is integrable with respect to g on J_1 and that

$$\int_c^d G(t) \, dh(t) = \int_a^b H(x) \, dg(x).$$

We can write this last equation in the form,

$$\int_c^d \left\{ \int_a^b f(x, t) \, dg(x) \right\} dh(t) = \int_a^b \left\{ \int_c^d f(x, t) \, dh(t) \right\} dg(x).$$

23.S. Show that, if the nth derivative $f^{(n)}$ is continuous on $[a, b]$, then the Integral Form of Taylor's Theorem 23.13 and the First Mean Value Theorem 23.5 can be used to obtain the Lagrange form of the remainder given in 19.9.

23.T. Let f be continuous on $I = [0, 1]$ to R and define f_n on I to R by

$$f_0(x) = f(x), \quad f_{n+1}(x) = \frac{1}{n!} \int_0^x (x - t)^n f_n(t) \, dt.$$

Show that the nth derivative of f_n exists and equals f. By induction, show that the number of changes in sign of f on I is not ess than the number of changes of sign in the ordered set

$$f_0(1), f_1(1), \ldots, f_n(1).$$

23.U. Let f, J_1, and J_2 be as in Exercise 23.R. If φ is in $C_R(J_1)$ (that is, φ is a continuous function on J_1 to R), let $T(\varphi)$ be the function defined on J_2 by the formula

$$T(\varphi)(t) = \int_a^b f(x, t)\varphi(x) \, dx.$$

Show that T is a **linear transformation** of $C_R(J_1)$ into $C_R(J_2)$ in the sense that if φ, ψ belong to $C_R(J_1)$, then

(a) $T(\varphi)$ belongs to $C_R(J_2)$,

(b) $T(\varphi + \psi) = T(\varphi) + T(\psi)$,

(c) $T(c\varphi) = cT(\varphi)$ for $c \in R$.

If $M = \sup \{|f(x, t)| : (x, t) \in J_1 \times J_2\}$, then T is **bounded** in the sense that

(d) $\|T(\varphi)\|_{J_2} \leq M\|\varphi\|_{J_1}$ for $\varphi \in C_R(J_1)$.

23.V. Continuing the notation of the preceding exercise, show that if $r > 0$, then T sends the collection

$$B_r = \{\varphi \in C_{\mathbf{R}}(J_1) : \|\varphi\|_{J_1} \le r\}$$

into an equicontinuous set of functions in $C_{\mathbf{R}}(J_2)$ (see Definition 17.14). Therefore, if (φ_n) is any sequence of functions in B_r, there is a subsequence (φ_{n_k}) such that the sequence $(T(\varphi_{n_k}))$ converges uniformly on J_2.

23.W. Let J_1 and J_2 be as before and let f be continuous on $\mathbf{R} \times J_2$ into $\mathbf{R}$. If φ is in $C_{\mathbf{R}}(J_1)$, let $S(\varphi)$ be the function defined on J_2 by the formula

$$S(\varphi)(t) = \int_a^b f[\varphi(x), t]\, dx.$$

Show that $S(\varphi)$ belongs to $C_{\mathbf{R}}(J_2)$, but that, in general, S is not a linear transformation in the sense of Exercise 23.U. However, show that S sends the collection B_r of Exercise 23.V into an equicontinuous set of functions in $C_{\mathbf{R}}(J_2)$. Also, if (φ_n) is any sequence in B_r, there is a subsequence such that $(S(\varphi_{n_k}))$ converges uniformly on J_2. (This result is important in the theory of non-linear integral equations.)

Projects

23.α. The purpose of this project is to develop the logarithm by using an integral as its definition. Let $P = \{x \in \mathbf{R} : x > 0\}$.

(a) If $x \in P$, define $L(x)$ to be

$$L(x) = \int_1^x \frac{1}{t}\, dt.$$

Hence $L(1) = 0$. Prove that L is differentiable and that $L'(x) = 1/x$.

(b) Show that $L(x) < 0$ for $0 < x < 1$ and $L(x) > 0$ for $x > 1$. In fact,

$$1 - 1/x < L(x) < x - 1 \qquad \text{for} \qquad x > 0.$$

(c) Prove that $L(xy) = L(x) + L(y)$ for x, y in P. Hence $L(1/x) = -L(x)$ for x in P. (Hint: if $y \in P$, let L_1 be defined on P by $L_1(x) = L(xy)$ and show that $L_1' = L'$.)

(d) Show that if $n \in \mathbf{N}$, then

$$\frac{1}{2} + \frac{1}{3} + \cdots + \frac{1}{n} < L(n) < 1 + \frac{1}{2} + \cdots + \frac{1}{n-1}.$$

(e) Prove that L is a one-one function mapping P onto all of $\mathbf{R}$. Letting e denote the unique number such that $L(e) = 1$, and using the fact that $L'(1) = 1$, show that

$$e = \lim\left(\left(1 + \frac{1}{n}\right)^n\right).$$

(f) Let r be any positive rational number, then

$$\lim_{x \to +\infty} \frac{L(x)}{x^r} = 0.$$

(g) Observe that

$$L(1 + x) = \int_1^{1+x} \frac{dt}{t} = \int_0^x \frac{dt}{1 + t}.$$

Write $(1 + t)^{-1}$ as a finite geometric series to obtain

$$L(1 + x) = \sum_{k=1}^{n-1} \frac{(-1)^{k-1}}{k} x^k + R_n(x).$$

Show that $|R_n(x)| \leq 1/(n + 1)$ for $0 \leq x \leq 1$ and

$$|R_n(x)| \leq \frac{|x|^{n+1}}{(n + 1)(1 + x)}$$

for $-1 < x < 0$.

23.β. This project develops the trigonometric functions starting with an integral.

(a) Let A be defined for x in $\mathbf{R}$ by

$$A(x) = \int_0^x \frac{dt}{1 + t^2}.$$

Then A is an odd function $\big(\text{that is, } A(-x) = -A(x)\big)$, it is strictly increasing, and it is bounded by 2. Define π by the formula

$$\pi/2 = \sup \{A(x) : x \in \mathbf{R}\}.$$

(b) Let T be the inverse of A, so that T is a strictly increasing function with domain $(-\pi/2, \pi/2)$ and range $\mathbf{R}$. Show that T has a derivative and that

$$T' = 1 + T^2.$$

(c) Define C and S on $(-\pi/2, \pi/2)$ by the formulas

$$C = \frac{1}{(1 + T^2)^{1/2}}, \qquad S = \frac{T}{(1 + T^2)^{1/2}}.$$

Hence C is even and S is odd on $(-\pi/2, \pi/2)$. Show that $C(0) = 1$ and $S(0) = 0$ and $C(x) \to 0$ and $S(x) \to 1$ as $x \to \pi/2$.

(d) Prove that $C'(x) = -S(x)$ and $S'(x) = C(x)$ for x in $(-\pi/2, \pi/2)$. Therefore, both C and S satisfy the differential equation

$$h'' + h = 0$$

on the interval $(-\pi/2, \pi/2)$.

(e) Define $C(\pi/2) = 0$ and $S(\pi/2) = 0$ and define C, S, T outside the interval $(-\pi/2, \pi/2)$ by the equations

$$C(x + \pi) = -C(x), S(x + \pi) = -S(x),$$
$$T(x + \pi) = T(x).$$

If this is done successively, then C and S are defined for all $\mathbf{R}$ and have period 2π. Similarly, T is defined except at odd multiples of $\pi/2$ and has period π.

(f) Show that the functions C and S, as defined on $\mathbf{R}$ in the preceding part, are differentiable at every point of $\mathbf{R}$ and that they continue to satisfy the relations

$$C' = -S, \qquad S' = C$$

everywhere on $\mathbf{R}$.

Section 24 Integration in Cartesian Spaces

In the preceding two sections, we have discussed the integral of a bounded real-valued function defined on a compact interval J in $\mathbf{R}$. A reader with an eye for generalizations will have noticed that a considerable part of what was done in those sections can be carried out when the *values* of the functions lie in a Cartesian space $\mathbf{R}^q$. Once the possibility of such generalizations has been recognized, it is not difficult to carry out the modifications necessary to obtain an integration theory for functions on J to $\mathbf{R}^q$.

It is also natural to ask whether we can obtain an integration theory for functions whose domain is a subset of the space $\mathbf{R}^p$. The reader will recall that this was done for real-valued functions defined in $\mathbf{R}^2$ and $\mathbf{R}^3$ in calculus courses, where one considered "double" and "triple" integrals. In this section we shall present an exposition of the Riemann integral of a function defined on a suitable compact subset of $\mathbf{R}^p$. Most of the results permit the values to be in $\mathbf{R}^q$, although some of the later theorems are given only for $q = 1$.

Content in a Cartesian Space

We shall preface our discussion of the integral by a few remarks concerning content in $\mathbf{R}^p$. Recall that a closed interval J in $\mathbf{R}^p$ is the Cartesian product of p real intervals:

$$(24.1) \qquad J = [a_1, b_1] \times \cdots \times [a_p, b_p].$$

If the sides of J all have equal lengths; that is, if

$$b_1 - a_1 = b_2 - a_2 = \cdots = b_p - a_p,$$

then we shall sometimes refer to J as a *cube*.

We define the *content* of an interval J to be the product

(24.2) $$A(J) = (b_1 - a_1) \cdots (b_p - a_p).$$

If $p = 1$, the usual term for content is length; if $p = 2$, it is area; if $p = 3$, it is volume. We shall employ the word "content," because it is free from special connotations that these other words may have.

It will be observed that if $a_k = b_k$ for some $k = 1, \ldots, p$, then the interval J has content $A(J) = 0$. This does not mean that J is empty, but merely that it has no thickness in the kth dimension. Although the intersection of two intervals is always an interval, the union of two intervals need not be an interval.

If a set in R^p can be expressed as the union of a finite collection of non-overlapping intervals, then we define the content of the set to be the sum of the contents of the intervals. It is geometrically clear that this definition is not dependent on the particular collection of intervals selected. It is sometimes desirable to have the notion of content for a larger class of subsets of R^p than those that can be expressed as the union of a finite number of intervals. It is natural to proceed in extending the notion of content to more general subsets by approximating them by finite unions of intervals; for example, by inscribing and circumscribing the subset by finite unions of intervals and taking the supremum and infimum, respectively, over all such finite unions. Such a procedure is not difficult, but we shall not carry it out as it is not necessary for our purposes. Instead, we shall use the integral to define the content of more general sets. However, we do need to have the notion of zero content in order to develop our theory of integration.

24.1 DEFINITION. A subset Z of R^p has **zero content** if, for each positive number ϵ, there is a finite set $\{J_1, J_2, \ldots, J_n\}$ of closed intervals whose union contains Z such that

$$A(J_1) + A(J_2) + \cdots + A(J_n) < \epsilon.$$

24.2 EXAMPLES. (a) Any finite subset of R^p evidently has zero content, for we can enclose each of the points in an interval of arbitrarily small content.

(b) A set whose elements are the terms of a convergent sequence in R^p has zero content. To see this, let $Z = (z_n)$ converge to the point z and let $\epsilon > 0$. Let J_0 be a closed interval with center at z such that $0 < A(J_0) < \epsilon/2$. Since $z = \lim(z_n)$, all but a finite number of the points in Z are contained in an open interval contained in J_0 and this finite number of points is contained in a finite number of closed intervals with total content less that $\epsilon/2$.

(c) In R^2, the segment $S = \{(\xi, 0) : 0 \leq \xi \leq 1\}$ has zero content. In fact, if $\epsilon > 0$, the single interval

$$J_\epsilon = [0, 1] \times [-\epsilon/2, \epsilon/2]$$

has content ϵ and contains S.

(d) In the space R^2, the diamond-shaped set $S = \{(\xi, \eta) : |\xi| + |\eta| = 1\}$ is seen to have zero content. For, if we introduce intervals (here squares) with diagonals along S and vertices at the points $|\xi| = |\eta| = k/n$, where $k = 0, 1, \ldots, n$, then we easily see that we can enclose S in $4n$ closed

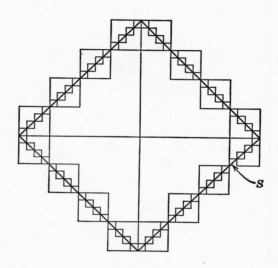

Figure 24.1.

intervals, each having content $1/n^2$. (See Figure 24.1.) Hence the total content of these intervals is $4/n$ which can be made arbitrarily small.

(e) The circle $S = \{(\xi, \eta) : \xi^2 + \eta^2 = 1\}$ in R^2 is seen to have zero content. This can be proved by means of a modification of the argument in (d).

(f) Let f be a continuous function on $J = [a, b]$ to R. Then the graph of f; that is, the set

$$G = \{(\xi, f(\xi)) \in R^2 : \xi \in J\},$$

has zero content in R^2. This assertion can be proved by modifying the argument in (d).

(g) The subset S of R^2 which consists of all points (ξ, η) where both ξ and η are rational numbers satisfying $0 \leq \xi \leq 1$, $0 \leq \eta \leq 1$ does not have zero content. Although this set is countable, any finite union of intervals which contains S must also contain the interval $[0, 1] \times [0, 1]$, which has content equal to 1.

(h) The union of a finite number of sets with zero content has zero content.

(i) In contrast to (f), we shall show that there are "continuous curves" in $\mathbf{R}^2$ which have positive content. We shall show that there exist continuous functions f, g defined on $\mathbf{I}$ to $\mathbf{R}$ such that the set

$$S = \{(f(t), g(t)) : t \in \mathbf{I}\}$$

has positive content. To establish this, it is enough to prove that the set S can contain the set $\mathbf{I} \times \mathbf{I}$ in $\mathbf{R}^2$. Such a curve is called a **space-filling curve** or a **Peano curve**. We shall outline here the construction (due to I. J. Schoenberg†) of a Peano curve, but leave the details as exercises.

Let φ be a continuous function on $\mathbf{R}$ to $\mathbf{R}$ which is even, has period 2, and is such that

$$\begin{aligned}
\varphi(t) &= 0, & 0 \leq t \leq \tfrac{1}{3}, \\
&= 3t - 1, & \tfrac{1}{3} < t < \tfrac{2}{3}, \\
&= 1, & \tfrac{2}{3} \leq t \leq 1.
\end{aligned}$$

(See Figure 24.2.) We define f_n and g_n for $n \in \mathbf{N}$ by

$$f_1(t) = \left(\frac{1}{2}\right)\varphi(t), \qquad f_n(t) = f_{n-1}(t) + \left(\frac{1}{2^n}\right)\varphi(3^{2n-2}t),$$

$$g_1(t) = \left(\frac{1}{2}\right)\varphi(3t), \qquad g_n(t) = g_{n-1}(t) + \left(\frac{1}{2^n}\right)\varphi(3^{2n-1}t).$$

Since $\|\varphi\| = 1$, it is readily seen that the sequences (f_n) and (g_n) converge uniformly on $\mathbf{I}$ to functions f and g, which are therefore continuous.

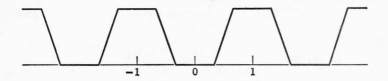

Figure 24.2.

† Isaac J. Schoenberg (1903–   ) was born in Roumania and educated there and in Germany. Long at the University of Pennsylvania, he has worked in number theory, real and complex analysis, and the calculus of variations.

To see that every point (x^*, y^*) with $0 \leq x^* \leq 1$, $0 \leq y^* \leq 1$, belongs to the graph S of this curve, write x and y in their binary expansions:

$$x^* = 0.\alpha_1\alpha_2\alpha_3 \ldots, \qquad y^* = 0.\beta_1\beta_2\beta_3 \ldots,$$

where α_n, β_m are either 0 or 1. Let t^* be the real number whose ternary (base 3) expansion is

$$t^* = 0.(2\alpha_1)(2\beta_1)(2\alpha_2)(2\beta_2) \ldots$$

We leave it to the reader to show that $f(t^*) = x^*$ and $g(t^*) = y^*$.

Definition of the Integral

We shall now define the integral. In what follows, unless there is explicit mention to the contrary, we shall let D be a compact subset of $\mathbf{R}^p$ and consider a function f with domain D and with values in $\mathbf{R}^q$. We shall assume that f is bounded and shall define f to be the zero vector θ outside of D. This extension will be denoted by the same letter f.

Since D is bounded, there exists an interval I_f in $\mathbf{R}^p$ which contains D. Let the interval I_f be represented as a Cartesian product of p real intervals as given in equation (24.1) with $a_k < b_k$. For each $k = 1, \ldots, p$, let P_k be a partition of $[a_k, b_k]$ into a finite number of closed real intervals. This induces a **partition** P of I_f into a finite number of closed intervals in $\mathbf{R}^p$. In the space $\mathbf{R}^2$ the geometrical picture is indicated in Figure 24.3, where $[a_1, b_1]$ has been partitioned into four subintervals, resulting in a partitioning of $I_f = [a_1, b_1] \times [a_2, b_2]$ into $20(= 4 \times 5)$ closed intervals (here rectangles). If P and Q are partitions of I_f, we say that P is a **refinement** of Q if each subinterval in P is contained in some subinterval in Q. Alternatively, noting that a partition is determined by the vertices of its intervals, P is a refinement of Q if and only if all of the vertices contained in Q are also contained in P.

24.3 DEFINITION. A **Riemann sum** $S(P; f)$ corresponding to the partition $P = \{J_1, \ldots, J_n\}$ of I_f is given by

$$(24.3) \qquad S(P; f) = \sum_{k=1}^{n} f(x_k) A(J_k),$$

where x_k is any point in the subinterval J_k, $k = 1, \ldots, n$. An element L of $\mathbf{R}^q$ is defined to be the **Riemann integral** of f if, for every positive real number ϵ there is a partition P_ϵ of I_f such that if P is a refinement of P_ϵ and $S(P; f)$ is any Riemann sum corresponding to P, then

$$(24.4) \qquad |S(P; f) - L| < \epsilon.$$

In case this integral exists, we say that f is **integrable over** D.

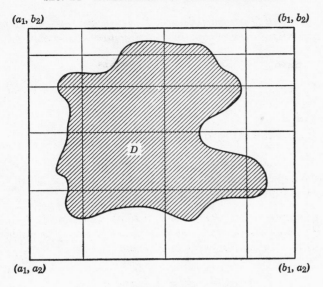

Figure 24.3.

It is routine to show that the value L of the integral of f is unique when it exists. It is also straightforward to show that the existence and the value of the integral does not depend on the interval I_f enclosing the original domain D of f. Therefore, we shall ordinarily denote the value of the integral by the symbol

$$\int_D f,$$

displaying only the function f and its domain. Sometimes, when $p = 2$, we denote the integral by one of the symbols

$$(24.5) \qquad \iint_D f, \quad \text{or} \quad \iint_D f(x, y)\, dx\, dy;$$

when $p = 3$, we may employ one of the symbols

$$(24.6) \qquad \iiint_D f, \quad \text{or} \quad \iiint_D f(x, y, z)\, dx\, dy\, dz.$$

There is a convenient Cauchy Criterion for integrability.

24.4 CAUCHY CRITERION. *The function f is integrable on D if and only if for every positive number ϵ there is a partition Q_ϵ of the interval I_f*

such that if P and Q are partitions of I_f which are refinements of Q_ϵ and $S(P;f)$ and $S(Q;f)$ are corresponding Riemann sums, then

(24.7) $$|S(P;f) - S(Q;f)| < \epsilon.$$

Since the details are entirely similar to the proof of Theorem 22.4, we shall omit them.

Properties of the Integral

We shall now state some of the expected properties of the integral. It should be kept in mind that the value of the integral lies in the space R^q where the function has its range.

24.5 THEOREM. *Let f and g be functions with domain D in R^p and range in R^q which are integrable over D and let a, b be real numbers. Then the function af + bg is integrable over D and*

(24.8) $$\int_D (af + bg) = a \int_D f + b \int_D g.$$

PROOF. This result follows directly from the observation that the Riemann sums for a partition P of I_f satisfy the relation

$$S(P; af + bg) = aS(P;f) + bS(P;g),$$

when the same intermediate points are used.

Q.E.D.

24.6 LEMMA. *If f is a non-negative function which is integrable over D, then*

(24.9) $$\int_D f \geq 0.$$

PROOF. Note that $S(P;f) \geq 0$ for any partition P of I_f.

Q.E.D.

24.7 LEMMA. *Let f be a bounded function on D to R^q and suppose that D has content zero. Then f is integrable over D and*

(24.10) $$\int_D f = \theta.$$

PROOF. If $\epsilon > 0$, let P_ϵ be a partition of I_f which is fine enough so that those subintervals of P_ϵ which contain points of D have total content less than ϵ. If P is a refinement of P_ϵ, then those subintervals of P which contain points of D will also have total content less than ϵ. If M is a bound for f, then $|S(P;f)| < M\epsilon$, whence we obtain formula (24.10).

Q.E.D.

24.8 **Lemma.** *Let f be integrable over D, let E be a subset of D which has zero content, and suppose that $f(x) = g(x)$ for all x in $D\backslash E$. Then g is integrable over D and*

$$(24.11) \qquad \int_D f = \int_D g.$$

PROOF. The hypotheses imply that the difference $h = f - g$ equals θ except on E. According to the preceding lemma, h is integrable and the value of its integral is θ. Applying Theorem 24.5, we infer that $g = f - h$ is integrable and

$$\int_D g = \int_D (f - h) = \int_D f - \int_D h = \int_D f.$$

Q.E.D

Existence of the Integral

It is to be expected that if f is continuous on an interval J, then f is integrable over J. We shall establish a stronger result that permits the function to have discontinuities on a set with zero content.

24.9 FIRST INTEGRABILITY THEOREM. *Suppose that f is defined on an interval J in $\mathbf{R}^p$ and has values in $\mathbf{R}^q$. If f is continuous except on a subset E of J which has zero content, then f is integrable over J.*

PROOF. Let M be a bound for f on J and let ϵ be a positive number. Then there exists a partition P_ϵ of J with the property that the subintervals in P_ϵ which contain points of E have total content less than ϵ. (See Figure 24.4.) The union C of the subintervals of P_ϵ which do not contain points of E is a compact subset of $\mathbf{R}^p$ on which f is continuous. According to the Uniform Continuity Theorem 16.12, f is uniformly continuous on the set C. Replacing P_ϵ by a refinement, if necessary, we may suppose that if J_k is a subinterval of P_ϵ which is contained in C, and if x, y are any points of J_k, then $|f(x) - f(y)| < \epsilon$.

Now suppose that P and Q are refinements of the partition P_ϵ. If $S'(P;f)$ and $S'(Q;f)$ denote the portion of the Riemann sums extended over the subintervals contained in C, then

$$|S'(P;f) - S'(Q;f)| < \epsilon A(J).$$

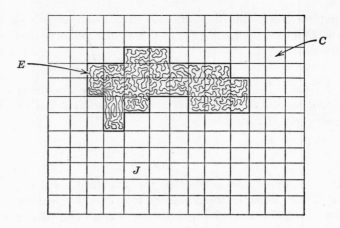

Figure 24.4.

Similarly, if $S''(P;f)$ and $S''(Q;f)$ denote the remaining portion of the Riemann sums, then

$$|S''(P;f) - S''(Q;f)| \le |S''(P;f)| + |S''(Q;f)| < 2M\epsilon.$$

It therefore follows that

$$|S(P;f) - S(Q;f)| < \epsilon\{A(J) + 2M\},$$

whence f is integrable over J.

Q.E.D.

The theorem just established yields the integrability of f over an *interval*, provided the stated continuity condition is satisfied. We wish to obtain a theorem which will imply the integrability of a function over a subset more general than an interval. In order to obtain such a result, the notion of the boundary of a subset is needed.

24.10 DEFINITION. If D is a subset of $\mathbf{R}^p$, then a point x of $\mathbf{R}^p$ is said to be a **boundary point** of D if every neighborhood of x contains points both of D and its complement $\mathfrak{C}(D)$. The **boundary** of D is the subset of $\mathbf{R}^p$ consisting of all of the boundary points of D.

We generally expect the boundary of a set to be small, but this is because we are accustomed to thinking about rectangles, circles, and such forms. Example 24.2(g) shows that a countable subset in $\mathbf{R}^2$ can have its boundary equal to $I \times I$.

24.11 SECOND INTEGRABILITY THEOREM. *Let D be a compact subset of $\mathbf{R}^p$ and let f be continuous with domain D and range in $\mathbf{R}^q$. If the boundary of D has zero content, then f is integrable over D.*

PROOF.   As usual, let I_f be a closed interval containing D and extend f to all of $\mathbf{R}^p$ by setting $f(x) = \theta$ for x outside D. The extended function is continuous at every point of I_f except, possibly, at the boundary of D. Since the boundary has zero content, the First Integrability Theorem implies that f is integrable over I_f and hence over D.

Q.E.D.

We shall now define the content of a subset of $\mathbf{R}^p$ whose boundary has zero content. It turns out (see Exercise 24.N) that we obtain the same result as if we used the approximation procedure mentioned before Definition 24.1.

24.12   DEFINITION.   If a bounded subset D of $\mathbf{R}^p$ is such that its boundary B has zero content, we say that the set D has **content** and define the **content** $A(D)$ of D to be the integral over the compact set $D \cup B$ of the function identically equal to the real number 1.

24.13   LEMMA.   *Let D be a bounded subset of $\mathbf{R}^p$ which has content and let B be the boundary of D, then the compact set $D \cup B$ has content and $A(D) = A(D \cup B)$.*

PROOF.   It is readily established that the set B contains the boundary of the set $D \cup B$. Hence $D \cup B$ has content and its value $A(D \cup B)$ is obtained in the same way as the value of $A(D)$.

Q.E.D.

We have already introduced, in Definition 24.1, the concept of a set having zero content and it behooves us to relate this notion with Definition 24.12. Suppose that a set D has zero content in the sense of Definition 24.1. Thus, if $\epsilon > 0$, we can enclose D in the union of a finite number of closed intervals with total content less than ϵ. It is evident that this union also contains the boundary B of D; hence B and $D \cup B$ have zero content. Therefore, D has content in the sense of Definition 24.12 and $A(D)$ is given by the integral of 1 over $D \cup B$. By Lemma 24.7 it follows that $A(D) = 0$. Conversely, suppose the set D has content and $A(D) = 0$. If $\epsilon > 0$, there is a partition P_ϵ of an interval containing D such that any Riemann sum corresponding to P_ϵ for the function defined by

$$f_D(x) = 1, \quad x \in D \cup B,$$
$$= 0, \quad \text{otherwise,}$$

is such that $0 \leq S(P_\epsilon; f_D) < \epsilon$. Taking the "intermediate" points to be in $D \cup B$ when possible, we infer that $D \cup B$ is enclosed in a finite number of intervals in P_ϵ with total content less than ϵ. This proves that D has zero content in the sense of Definition 24.1. We conclude, therefore, that *a set D has zero content if and only if it has content and $A(D) = 0$.* This justifies the simultaneous use of Definitions 24.1 and 24.12.

24.14 LEMMA. *If D_1 and D_2 have content, then their union and intersection also have content and*

$$(24.12) \qquad A(D_1) + A(D_2) = A(D_1 \cup D_2) + A(D_1 \cap D_2).$$

In particular, if $A(D_1 \cap D_2) = 0$, then

$$(24.13) \qquad A(D_1 \cup D_2) = A(D_1) + A(D_2).$$

PROOF. By hypothesis, the boundaries B_1 and B_2 of the sets D_1 and D_2 have zero content. Since it is readily established that the boundaries of $D_1 \cap D_2$ and $D_1 \cup D_2$ are contained in $B_1 \cup B_2$, we infer from 24.2(h) that the sets $D_1 \cap D_2$ and $D_1 \cup D_2$ have content. In view of Lemma 24.13, we shall suppose that D_1 and D_2 are closed sets; hence $D_1 \cap D_2$ and $D_1 \cup D_2$ are also closed. Let f_1, f_2, f_i and f_u be the functions which are equal to 1 on $D_1, D_2, D_1 \cap D_2$ and $D_1 \cup D_2$, respectively, and equal to 0 elsewhere. Observe that each of these functions is integrable and

$$f_1 + f_2 = f_i + f_u.$$

Integrating over an interval J containing $D_1 \cup D_2$ and using Theorem 24.5, we have

$$A(D_1) + A(D_2) = \int_J f_1 + \int_J f_2 = \int_J (f_1 + f_2)$$

$$= \int_J (f_i + f_u) = \int_J f_i + \int_J f_u = A(D_1 \cap D_2) + A(D_1 \cup D_2).$$

Q.E.D.

We now show that the integral is additive with respect to the set over which the integral is extended.

24.15 THEOREM. *Let D be a compact set in $\mathbf{R}^p$ which has content and let D_1 and D_2 be closed subsets of D with content such that $D = D_1 \cup D_2$ and such that $D_1 \cap D_2$ has zero content. If g is integrable over D with values in $\mathbf{R}^q$, then g is integrable over D_1 and D_2 and*

$$(24.14) \qquad \int_D g = \int_{D_1} g + \int_{D_2} g.$$

PROOF. Define g_1 and g_2 by

$$\begin{aligned} g_1(x) &= g(x), & x \in D_1 & \qquad & g_2(x) &= g(x), & x \in D_2, \\ &= \theta, & x \notin D_1 & \qquad & &= \theta, & x \notin D_2. \end{aligned}$$

Since D_1 has content, it may be shown as in the proof of Theorem 22.6(b), that g_1 is integrable over the sets D and D_1 and that

$$\int_D g_1 = \int_{D_1} g_1 = \int_{D_1} g.$$

Similarly g_2 is integrable over the sets D and D_2 and

$$\int_D g_2 = \int_{D_2} g_2 = \int_{D_2} g.$$

Moreover, except for x in the set $D_1 \cap D_2$, which has zero content, then $g(x) = g_1(x) + g_2(x)$. By Lemma 24.8 and Theorem 24.5, it follows that

$$\int_D g = \int_D (g_1 + g_2) = \int_D g_1 + \int_D g_2.$$

Combining this with the equations written above, we obtain (24.14).

Q.E.D.

The following result is often useful to estimate the magnitude of an integral. Since the proof is relatively straightforward, it will be left as an exercise.

24.16 THEOREM. *Let D be a compact subset of $\mathbf{R}^p$ which has content. Let f be integrable over D and such that $|f(x)| \leq M$ for x in D. Then*

$$(24.15) \qquad \left| \int_D f \right| \leq M A(D).$$

In particular, if f is real-valued and $m \leq f(x) \leq M$ for x in D, then

$$(24.16) \qquad m A(D) \leq \int_D f \leq M A(D).$$

As a consequence of this result, we obtain the following theorem, which is an extension of the First Mean Value Theorem 23.1.

24.17 MEAN VALUE THEOREM. *If D is a compact and connected subset of $\mathbf{R}^p$ with content and if f is continuous on D and has values in $\mathbf{R}$, then there is a point p in D such that*

$$(24.17) \qquad \int_D f = f(p) A(D).$$

PROOF.   The conclusion is immediate if $A(D) = 0$, so we shall consider the contrary case. Let $m = \inf \{f(x) : x \in D\}$ and $M = \sup \{f(x) : x \in D\}$; according to the preceding theorem,

$$m \leq \frac{1}{A(D)} \int_D f \leq M.$$

Since D is connected, it follows from Bolzano's Intermediate Value Theorem 16.4 that there is a point p in D such that

$$f(p) = \frac{1}{A(D)} \int_D f,$$

proving the assertion.

Q.E.D.

The Integral as an Iterated Integral

It is desirable to know that if f is integrable over a subset D of $\mathbf{R}^p$ and has values in $\mathbf{R}$, then the integral

$$\int_D f$$

can be calculated in terms of a p-fold iterated integral

$$\int \left\{ \ldots \left\{ \int \left\{ \int f(\xi_1, \xi_2, \ldots, \xi_p) \, d\xi_1 \right\} d\xi_2 \right\} \ldots \right\} d\xi_p.$$

This is the method of evaluating double and triple integrals by means of iterated integrals that is familiar to the reader from elementary calculus. We intend to give a justification of this procedure of calculation, but for the sake of simplicity, we shall consider the case where $p = 2$ only. It will be clear that the results extend to higher dimension and that only notational complications are involved. First we shall treat the case where the domain D is an interval in $\mathbf{R}^2$.

24.18   THEOREM.   *If f is a continuous function defined on the set*

$$D = \{ (\xi, \eta) : a \leq \xi \leq b, c \leq \eta \leq d \},$$

and with values in $\mathbf{R}$, *then*

(24.18)
$$\int_D f = \int_c^d \left\{ \int_a^b f(\xi, \eta) \, d\xi \right\} d\eta,$$

$$= \int_a^b \left\{ \int_c^d f(\xi, \eta) \, d\eta \right\} d\xi.$$

PROOF.   It was seen in the Interchange Theorem 23.12 that the two iterated integrals are equal. Therefore, it remains only to show that the integral of f over D is given by the first iterated integral.

Let F be defined for η in $[c, d]$ by

$$F(\eta) = \int_a^b f(\xi, \eta) \, d\xi.$$

Let $c = \eta_0 \leq \eta_1 \leq \cdots \leq \eta_r = d$ be a partition of the interval $[c, d]$; let $a = \xi_0 \leq \xi_1 \leq \cdots \leq \xi_s = b$ be a partition of $[a, b]$; and let P denote the partition of D obtained by using the rectangles

$$[\eta_{j-1}, \eta_j] \times [\xi_{k-1}, \xi_k].$$

Let η_j^* be any point in $[\eta_{j-1}, \eta_j]$ and observe that

$$F(\eta_j^*) = \int_a^b f(\xi, \eta_j^*) \, d\xi = \sum_{k=1}^s \left\{ \int_{\xi_{k-1}}^{\xi_k} f(\xi, \eta_j^*) \, d\xi \right\}.$$

According to the First Mean Value Theorem 23.1, for each value of j and k there exists a point ξ_{jk}^* in the interval $[\xi_{k-1}, \xi_k]$ such that

$$F(\eta_j^*) = \sum_{k=1}^s f(\xi_{jk}^*, \eta_j^*)(\xi_k - \xi_{k-1}).$$

Multiply by $(\eta_j - \eta_{j-1})$ and sum to obtain

$$\sum_{j=1}^r F(\eta_j^*)(\eta_j - \eta_{j-1}) = \sum_{j=1}^r \sum_{k=1}^s f(\xi_{jk}^*, \eta_j^*)(\xi_k - \xi_{k-1})(\eta_j - \eta_{j-1}).$$

The expression on the left side of this formula is an arbitrary Riemann sum for the integral

$$\int_c^d F(\eta) \, d\eta,$$

which is equal to the first iterated integral in (24.18). We have shown that this Riemann sum is equal to a particular (two-dimensional) Riemann sum corresponding to the partition P. Since f is integrable over D, the equality of these integrals is established.

Q.E.D.

A modification is the proof of the preceding theorem yields the following, slightly stronger, result.

24.19 THEOREM. *Let f be integrable over the rectangle D with values in $\mathbf{R}$ and suppose that, for each value of η in $[c, d]$, the integral*

(24.19) $$F(\eta) = \int_a^b f(\xi, \eta) \, d\xi$$

exists. Then F is integrable on $[c, d]$ and

$$\int_D f = \int_c^d F(\eta) \, d\eta = \int_c^d \left\{ \int_a^b f(\xi, \eta) \, d\xi \right\} d\eta.$$

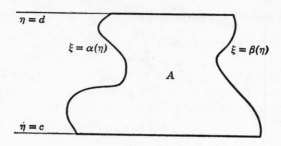

Figure 24.5.

As a consequence of this theorem, we obtain a result which is often used in evaluating integrals over sets which are bounded by continuous curves. For the sake of convenience, we shall state the result in the case where the set has line segments as its boundary on the top and bottom and continuous curves as its lateral boundaries. (See Figure 24.5.) It is plain that a similar result holds in the case that the top and bottom boundaries are curves. A more complicated set is handled by decomposing it into the union of subsets of one of these two types.

24.20 COROLLARY. *Let A be the set in* $\mathbf{R}^2$ *given by*

$$A = \{ (\xi, \eta) : \alpha(\eta) \leq \xi \leq \beta(\eta), c \leq \eta \leq d \},$$

where α and β are continuous functions on [c, d] *with values in the interval* [a, b]. *If f is continuous on A and has values in* R, *then f is integrable on A and*

$$\int_A f = \int_c^d \left\{ \int_{\alpha(\eta)}^{\beta(\eta)} f(\xi, \eta) \, d\xi \right\} d\eta.$$

PROOF. We suppose that f is defined to be zero outside the set A. Employing the observation in Example 24.2(f), it is easily seen that the boundary of A has zero content, whence it follows from the Second Integrability Theorem 24.11 that f is integrable over A. Moreover, for each fixed η, the integral (24.19) exists and equals

$$\int_{\alpha(\eta)}^{\beta(\eta)} f(\xi, \eta) \, d\xi.$$

Hence the conclusion follows from the preceding theorem, applied to $D = [a, b] \times [c, d]$.

Q.E.D.

Transformation of Integrals

We shall conclude this section with an important theorem which is a generalization to $\mathbf{R}^p$ of the Change of Variable Theorem 23.8. The latter result asserts that if φ is defined and has a continuous derivative on $[\alpha, \beta]$ and if f is continuous on the range of φ, then

$$\int_{\varphi(\alpha)}^{\varphi(\beta)} f = \int_\alpha^\beta (f \circ \varphi)\varphi'.$$

The result we shall establish concerns a function φ defined on an open subset G of $\mathbf{R}^p$ with values in $\mathbf{R}^p$. We shall assume that φ is in Class C' on G in the sense of Definition 21.1 and that its Jacobian determinant

(24.20)
$$J_\varphi(x) = \det \begin{vmatrix} \dfrac{\partial \varphi_1}{\partial \xi_1}(x) & \cdots & \dfrac{\partial \varphi_1}{\partial \xi_p}(x) \\ \cdots \cdots \cdots \cdots \\ \dfrac{\partial \varphi_p}{\partial \xi_1}(x) & \cdots & \dfrac{\partial \varphi_p}{\partial \xi_p}(x) \end{vmatrix}$$

does not vanish on G. It will be shown that if D is a compact subset of G which has content, and if f is continuous on $\varphi(D)$ to $\mathbf{R}$, then $\varphi(D)$ has content and

(24.21)
$$\int_{\varphi(D)} f = \int_D (f \circ \varphi)|J_\varphi|.$$

It will be observed that the hypotheses are somewhat more restrictive in the case $p > 1$; for example, we assume that $J_\varphi(x) \neq 0$ for all $x \in G$; hence the function φ is one-one. This hypothesis was not made in the case of Theorem 23.8.

In order to establish this result, it is convenient to break it up into several steps. First, we shall limit ourselves to the case where the function f is identically equal to 1 and relate the content of the set D with the content of the set $\varphi(D)$. In carrying this out it is convenient first to consider the case where φ is a linear function. In this case the Jacobian determinant of φ is constant and equals the determinant of the matrix corresponding to φ. (Recall that an interval in which the sides have equal length is called a cube.)

24.21 LEMMA. *If φ is a linear transformation of $\mathbf{R}^p$ into $\mathbf{R}^p$ and if K is a cube in $\mathbf{R}^p$, then the set $\varphi(K)$ has content and $A[\varphi(K)] = |J_\varphi|A(K)$.*

PROOF. A linear transformation will map a cube K into a subset of $\mathbf{R}^p$ which is bounded by $(p - 1)$-dimensional planes; that is: sets of points $x = (\xi_1, \ldots, \xi_p)$ satisfying conditions of the form

(24.22)
$$a_1\xi_1 + \cdots + a_p\xi_p = c.$$

It is easily seen from this that the boundary of $\varphi(K)$ can be enclosed in the union of a finite number of rectangles whose total content is arbitrarily small. Hence $\varphi(K)$ has content.

It is a little difficult to give an entirely satisfactory proof of the remainder of this lemma, since we have not defined what is meant by the determinant of a $p \times p$ matrix. One possible definition of the absolute value of the determinant of a linear function is as the content of the figure into which the unit cube

$$I^p = I \times \cdots \times I$$

is transformed. If this definition is adopted, then the case of a general cube K is readily obtained from the result for I^p.

If the reader prefers another definition for the determinant of a matrix, he can verify this result by noting that it holds in the case where φ has the elementary form of multiplication of one coordinate:

$$\varphi_1(\xi_1, \ldots, \xi_k, \ldots, \xi_p) = (\xi_1, \ldots, c\xi_k, \ldots, \xi_p),$$

addition of one coordinate with another:

$$\varphi_2(\xi_1, \ldots, \xi_k, \ldots, \xi_p) = (\xi_1, \ldots, \xi_j + \xi_k, \ldots, \xi_p),$$

or interchanging two coordinates:

$$\varphi_3(\xi_1, \ldots, \xi_j, \ldots, \xi_k, \ldots, \xi_p) = (\xi_1, \ldots, \xi_k, \ldots, \xi_j, \ldots, \xi_p).$$

Moreover, it can be proved that every linear transformation can be obtained as the composition of a finite number of elementary linear transformations of these types. Since the determinant of the composition of linear transformations is the product of their determinants, the validity of this result for these elementary transformations implies its validity for general linear transformations.

Q.E.D.

24.22 LEMMA. *Let φ belong to Class C' on an open set G in $\mathbf{R}^p$ to $\mathbf{R}^p$. If D is a compact subset of G which has content zero, then $\varphi(D)$ has content zero.*

PROOF. Let $\epsilon > 0$ and enclose D in a finite number of balls $\{B_j\}$ lying inside G such that the total content of the balls is less than ϵ. Since φ is in Class C' and D is compact, there exists a constant M such that $|D\varphi(x)(z)| \leq M |z|$ for all $x \in D$ and $z \in \mathbf{R}^p$. Therefore, if x and y are points in the same ball B_j, then $|\varphi(x) - \varphi(y)| \leq M |x - y|$. If the radius of B_j is r_j, then the set $\varphi(B_j)$ is contained in a ball with radius Mr_j. Therefore, $\varphi(D)$ is contained in a finite number of balls with total content less than $M^p\epsilon$.

Q.E.D.

24.23 LEMMA. *Let φ belong to Class C' on an open set G in $\mathbf{R}^p$ to $\mathbf{R}^p$ and suppose that its Jacobian J_φ does not vanish on G. If D is a compact subset of G which has content, then $\varphi(D)$ is a compact set with content.*

PROOF. Since J_φ does not vanish on G, it follows from the Inversion Theorem 21.11 that φ is one-one on G and maps each open subset of G into an open set. Consequently, if B is the set of boundary points of D, then $\varphi(B)$ is the set of boundary points of $\varphi(D)$. Since B has content zero, it follows from the preceding lemma that $\varphi(B)$ has content zero. Hence $\varphi(D)$ has content.

Q.E.D.

We need to relate the content of a cube K with the content of its image $\varphi(K)$. In order to do this, it is convenient to impose an additional condition that will simplify the calculation and which will be removed later.

24.24 LEMMA. *Let K be a cube in $\mathbf{R}^p$ with the origin as center and let ψ belong to Class C' on K to $\mathbf{R}^p$. Suppose that the Jacobian J_ψ does not vanish on K and that*

$$(24.23) \qquad |\psi(x) - x| \leq \alpha\,|x| \quad for \quad x \in K,$$

where α satisfies $0 < \alpha < 1/\sqrt{p}$. Then

$$(24.24) \qquad (1 - \alpha\,\sqrt{p})^p \leq \frac{A[\psi(K)]}{A(K)} \leq (1 + \alpha\,\sqrt{p})^p.$$

PROOF. In view of the hypotheses, ψ maps the boundary of K into the boundary of $\psi(K)$. Hence, in order to find how $\psi(K)$ is situated, it is enough to locate where ψ sends the boundary of K. If the sides of the cube K have length $2r$, and if x is on the boundary of K, then it is seen from Theorem 7.11 that $r \leq |x| \leq r\,\sqrt{p}$. Inequality (24.23) asserts that $\psi(x)$ is within distance $\alpha\,|x| \leq \alpha r\,\sqrt{p}$ of the point x. Hence, if x is on the boundary of K, then $\psi(x)$ lies outside a cube with side length $2(1 - \alpha\,\sqrt{p})r$ and inside a cube with side length $2(1 + \alpha\,\sqrt{p})r$. The relation (24.24) follows from these inclusions.

Q.E.D.

We now return to the transformation φ and shall show that the absolute value of the Jacobian $|J_\varphi(x)|$ approximates the ratio

$$\frac{A[\varphi(K)]}{A(K)}$$

for sufficiently small cubes K with center x.

24.25 THE JACOBIAN THEOREM. *Suppose that φ is in Class C' on an open set G and that J_φ does not vanish on G. If D is a compact subset of G and $\epsilon > 0$, there exists $\gamma > 0$ such that if K is a cube with center x in D and side length less than 2γ, then*

$$(24.25) \qquad |J_\varphi(x)|(1 - \epsilon)^p \leq \frac{A[\varphi(K)]}{A(K)} \leq |J_\varphi(x)|(1 + \epsilon)^p.$$

PROOF. Let $x \in G$, then the Jacobian of the linear function $D\varphi(x)$ is equal to $J_\varphi(x)$. Since $J_\varphi(x) \neq 0$, then $D\varphi(x)$ has an inverse function λ_x whose Jacobian is the reciprocal of $J_\varphi(x)$. Moreover, since the entries in the matrix representation of λ_x are continuous functions of x, it follows from Theorem 15.11 and the compactness of D that there exists a constant M such that $|\lambda_x(z)| \leq M |z|$ for $x \in D$ and $z \in \mathbf{R}^p$.

It is also a consequence of the fact that φ is in Class C' on the compact set D that if $\epsilon > 0$, then there exists $\delta > 0$ such that if $x \in D$ and $|z| < \delta$, then

$$|\varphi(x + z) - \varphi(x) - D\varphi(x)(z)| \leq \frac{\epsilon}{M \sqrt{p}} |z|.$$

We now fix x and define ψ for $|z| < \delta$ by

$$\psi(z) = \lambda_x[\varphi(x + z) - \varphi(x)].$$

Since $\lambda_x[D\varphi(x)(w)] = w$ for all $w \in \mathbf{R}^p$, the above inequality yields

$$|\psi(z) - z| \leq \frac{\epsilon}{\sqrt{p}} |z| \quad \text{for} \quad |z| < \delta.$$

According to the preceding lemma with $\alpha = \epsilon/\sqrt{p}$, we conclude that if K is a cube with center x and contained in the ball with radius δ, then

$$(1 - \epsilon)^p \leq \frac{A[\psi(K)]}{A(K)} \leq (1 + \epsilon)^p.$$

It follows from the definition of ψ and from Lemma 24.21 that $A[\psi(K)]$ equals the product of $A(\varphi(K))$ with the absolute value of the Jacobian of λ_x. Hence

$$A(\psi(K)) = \frac{A[\varphi(K)]}{|J_\varphi(x)|}.$$

Combining the last two formulas, we obtain the relation (24.23).

Q.E.D.

We are now prepared to establish the basic theorem on the transformation of integrals.

24.26 TRANSFORMATION OF INTEGRALS THEOREM. *Suppose that* φ *is in Class* C' *on an open subset* G *of* $\mathbf{R}^p$ *with values in* $\mathbf{R}^p$ *and that the Jacobian* J_φ *does not vanish on* G. *If* D *is a compact subset of* G *which has content and if* f *is continuous on* $\varphi(D)$ *to* $\mathbf{R}$, *then* $\varphi(D)$ *has content and*

$$(24.26) \qquad \int_{\varphi(D)} f = \int_D (f \circ \varphi)|J_\varphi|.$$

PROOF. Since J_φ is continuous and non-zero, we shall assume that it is everywhere positive. Furthermore, we shall suppose that f is non-negative, since we can break it into the difference of two non-negative continuous functions. It was seen in Lemma 24.23 that $\varphi(D)$ has content. Since f is continuous on $\varphi(D)$, and $f \circ \varphi$ and J_φ are continuous on D, then both of the integrals appearing in (24.26) exist.

To show that they are equal, let $\epsilon > 0$ and select a partition of D into non-overlapping cubes K_j with centers x_j such that if y_j is any point in K_j, then

$$(24.27) \qquad \left| \int_D (f \circ \varphi)J_\varphi - \sum (f \circ \varphi)(y_j)J_\varphi(x_j)A(K_j) \right| < \epsilon.$$

It follows from the existence of the integral and the uniform continuity of $f \circ \varphi$ on D that this can be done (cf. Exercise 24.G). Moreover, applying the Jacobian Theorem 24.25, we may assume that each K_j is so small that relation (24.25) holds.

Since any two of the sets $\{K_j\}$ intersect in at most a face which has content zero, it follows from Theorem 24.15 that

$$\int_{\varphi(D)} f = \sum_j \int_{\varphi(K_j)} f.$$

Since K_j is compact and connected, the set $\varphi(K_j)$ is compact and connected. Applying the Mean Value Theorem 24.17, we infer that there exists a point p_j in $\varphi(K_j)$ such that

$$\int_{\varphi(K_j)} f = f(p_j)A[\varphi(K_j)].$$

Because φ is one-one, there exists a unique point $x_j{}^*$ in K_j such that $p_j = \varphi(x_j{}^*)$, whence $f(p_j) = (f \circ \varphi)(x_j{}^*)$. Therefore, we have

$$\int_{\varphi(D)} f = \sum_j (f \circ \varphi)(x_j{}^*)A[\varphi(K_j)].$$

In view of the relation

$$J_\varphi(x_j)A(K_j)(1 - \epsilon)^p \leq A[\varphi(K_j)] \leq J_\varphi(x_j)A(K_j)(1 + \epsilon)^p,$$

we find, on multiplying by the non-negative number $(f \circ \varphi)(x_j{}^*)$ and summing over j, that the integral

$$(24.28) \qquad \qquad \int_{\varphi(D)} f$$

lies between $(1 - \epsilon)^p$ and $(1 + \epsilon)^p$ times the sum

$$\sum (f \circ \varphi)(x_j{}^*)J_\varphi(x_j)A(K_j).$$

However, this sum was seen in (24.27) to be within ϵ of the integral

$$(24.29) \qquad \qquad \int_D (f \circ \varphi)J_\varphi.$$

Since ϵ is arbitrary, it follows that the two integrals in (24.28) and (24.29) are equal.

Q.E.D.

It will be seen, in Exercise 24.X, that the conclusion still holds if J_φ vanishes on a set which has content zero.

Exercises

24.A. If f is a continuous function on I to R, show that the graph G of f; that is,

$$G = \{(\xi, f(\xi)) \in R^2 : \xi \in I\},$$

has zero content in R^2.

24.B. Show that the sequences (f_n) and (g_n) in Example 24.2(i) are uniformly convergent on I. Also show that every point (x^*, y^*) in $I \times I$ is in the graph S of the curve

$$x = f(t), \qquad y = g(t), \qquad t \in I.$$

24.C. Show that the integral of a function f on an interval $J \subseteq R^p$ to R^q is uniquely determined, when it exists.

24.D. Let f be a function defined on $D \subseteq R^p$ with values in R^q. Let I_1 and I_2 be intervals in R^p containing D and let f_1 and f_2 be the functions obtained by setting $f(x) = \theta$ for $x \notin D_j$. Prove that f_1 is integrable over I_1 if and only if f_2 is integrable over I_2, in which case

$$\int f_1 = \int f_2.$$

(Hint: reduce to the case $I_1 \subseteq I_2$.)

24.E. Establish the Cauchy Criterion 24.4.

24.F. Let f be defined on an interval $J \subseteq \mathbf{R}^p$ to $\mathbf{R}^q$ and let $e_j, j = 1, \ldots, q$, be the vectors in $\mathbf{R}^q$ given by

$$e_1 = (1, 0, \ldots, 0), \qquad e_2 = (0, 1, \ldots, 0), \qquad \ldots, \qquad e_q = (0, 0, \ldots, 1).$$

Prove that f is integrable over J to $\mathbf{R}^q$, if and only if each $f_j = f \cdot e_j$ is integrable over J to $\mathbf{R}$.

24.G. If f, g are continuous over an interval J to $\mathbf{R}$ and if $\epsilon > 0$, then there exists a partition $P_\epsilon = \{J_k\}$ of J such that if ξ_k and η_k are any points in J_k, then

$$\left| \int_J fg - \sum_k f(\xi_k) g(\eta_k) A(J_k) \right| < \epsilon.$$

24.H. If B is the boundary of a subset D of $\mathbf{R}^p$, then B contains the boundary of $D \cup B$. Can this inclusion be proper?

24.I. Show that the boundaries of the sets $D_1 \cap D_2$ and $D_1 \cup D_2$ are contained in $B_1 \cup B_2$, where B_j is the boundary of D_j.

24.J. Is it true that the boundary of the intersection $D_1 \cap D_2$ is contained in $B_1 \cap B_2$?

24.K. Prove Theorem 24.16.

24.L. Show that the Mean Value Theorem 24.17 may fail if D is not connected.

24.M. Let D be a subset of $\mathbf{R}^p$ which has content and let f be integrable over D with values in $\mathbf{R}^q$. If D_1 is a compact subset of D with content, then f is integrable over D_1.

24.N. A **figure** in $\mathbf{R}^p$ is the union of a finite number of non-overlapping intervals in $\mathbf{R}^p$. If D is a non-empty bounded subset of $\mathbf{R}^p$, let D^* be the collection of all figures which contain D and let D_* be the collection of all figures which are contained in D. Define

$$A^*(D) = \inf \{A(F) : F \in D^*\},$$

$$A_*(D) = \sup \{A(F) : F \in D_*\}.$$

Prove that $A_*(D) \leq A^*(D)$ and that D has zero content if and only if $A^*(D) = 0$. Also show that D has content if and only if $A_*(D) = A^*(D)$ in which case the content $A(D)$ is equal to this common value.

24.O. In the notation of the preceding exercise, show that if D_1 and D_2 are disjoint subsets of $\mathbf{R}^p$, then

$$A^*(D_1 \cup D_2) \leq A^*(D_1) + A^*(D_2).$$

Give examples to show that (i) equality can hold in this relation, and (ii) strict inequality can hold. In fact, show there exist disjoint sets D_1 and D_2 such that

$$0 \neq A^*(D_1) = A^*(D_2) = A^*(D_1 \cup D_2).$$

24.P. Let f be defined on a subset A of $\mathbf{R}^p$ with values in $\mathbf{R}$. Suppose that x, y and the line segment

$$\{x + t(y - x) : t \in \mathbf{I}\}$$

joining x to y belong to A and that all of the partial derivatives of f of order $\leq n$ exist and are continuous on this line segment. Establish Taylor's Theorem

$$f(y) = f(x) + Df(x)(y - x) + \frac{1}{2!} D^2f(x)(y - x)^2$$

$$+ \cdots + \frac{1}{(n - 1)!} D^{n-1}f(x)(y - x)^{n-1} + r_n,$$

where the element r_n in $\mathbf{R}^q$ is given by the Integral Formula

$$r_n = \frac{1}{(n - 1)!} \int_0^1 (1 - t)^{n-1} D^n f(x + t(y - x))(y - x)^n \, dt.$$

24.Q. Let f be defined on a subset A of $\mathbf{R}$ with values in $\mathbf{R}^q$. Suppose that the line segment joining two points x, y belongs to A and that f is in Class C' at every point of this segment. Show that

$$f(y) = f(x) + \int_0^1 Df(x + t(y - x))(y - x) \, dt.$$

and use this result to give another proof of the Approximation Lemma 21.4. [Hint: if $w \in \mathbf{R}^q$ and if F is defined on $\mathbf{I}$ to $\mathbf{R}$ by $F(t) = f(x + t(y - x)) \cdot w$, then $F'(t) = Df(x + t(y - x))(y - x) \cdot w$.]

24.R. Let f be a real-valued continuous function on an interval J in $\mathbf{R}^2$ containing $\theta = (0, 0)$ as an interior point. If (x, y) is in J, let F be defined on J to $\mathbf{R}$ by

$$F(x, y) = \int_0^x \left\{ \int_0^y f(x, y) dy \right\} dx.$$

Show that

$$\frac{\partial^2 F}{\partial y \, \partial x}(x, y) = \frac{\partial^2 F}{\partial x \, \partial y}(x, y) = f(x, y).$$

24.S. Let D be the compact subset of $\mathbf{R}^2$ given by

$$D = \{ (\xi, \eta) \in \mathbf{R}^2 : 1 \leq |\xi| + |\eta| \leq 3 \}.$$

Break D into subsets to which Corollary 24.20 and the related result with ξ and η interchanged apply. Show that the area ($=$ content) of D is 16. Also introduce the transformation

$$x = \xi + \eta, \qquad y = \xi - \eta$$

and use Theorem 24.25 or 24.26 to evaluate this area.

24.T. Let φ be a continuous, one-one, increasing function on $\{ \xi \in \mathbf{R} : \xi \geq 0 \}$ to $\mathbf{R}$ with $\varphi(0) = 0$ and let ψ be its inverse function. Hence ψ is also continuous, one-one, increasing on $\{ \eta \in \mathbf{R} : \eta \geq 0 \}$ to $\mathbf{R}$ and $\psi(0) = 0$. Let α, β be non-negative real numbers and compare the area of the interval $[0, \alpha] \times [0, \beta]$ with the areas bounded by the coordinate axes and the curves φ, ψ to obtain Young's Inequality

$$\alpha\beta \leq \int_0^\alpha \varphi + \int_0^\beta \psi.$$

(Note the special case $\varphi(\xi) = \xi$.) Let p, q be real numbers exceeding 1 and satisfying $(1/p) + (1/q) = 1$. Hence $p/q = p - 1$ and $q/p = q - 1$. If $\varphi\,(\xi) = \xi^{p/q}$ and $\psi(\eta) = \eta^{q/p}$, use Young's Inequality to establish the inequality

$$\alpha\beta \leq \alpha^p/p + \beta^q/q.$$

If a_j and b_j, $j = 1, \ldots, n$, are real numbers, and if

$$A = \left\{ \sum_{j=1}^n |a_j|^p \right\}^{1/p}, \quad B = \left\{ \sum_{j=1}^n |b_j|^q \right\}^{1/q},$$

then let $\alpha_j = |a_j|/A$ and $\beta_j = |b_j|/B$. Employ the above inequality and derive Hölder's Inequality

$$\sum_{j=1}^n |a_j b_j| \leq AB,$$

which was obtained in Exercise 21.X. (For $p = q = 2$, this reduces to the C.-B.-S. Inequality.)

24.U. Let D be the set in $\mathbf{R}^2$ given by

$$D = \{ (x, y) \in \mathbf{R}^2 : 1 \leq x \leq 3, x^2 \leq y \leq x^2 + 1 \}.$$

Show that the area of D is given by the integral

$$\int_1^3 \left\{ \int_{x^2}^{x^2+1} dy \right\} dx = 2.$$

Introduce the transformation

$$\xi = x, \quad \eta = y - x^2,$$

and calculate the area of D. Justify each step.

24.V. Using Theorem 24.26, determine the area of the region bounded by the hyperbolas

$$xy = 1, \quad xy = 2$$

and the parabolas

$$y = x^2, \quad y = x^2 + 1.$$

24.W. Let f be a real-valued continuous function. Introducing the change of variables $x = \xi + \eta$, $y = \xi - \eta$, show that

$$\int_0^1 \left\{ \int_0^x f(x, y)\,dy \right\} dx = 2 \int_0^{1/2} \left\{ \int_\eta^{1-\eta} f(\xi + \eta, \xi - \eta)\,d\xi \right\} d\eta.$$

24.X. Suppose that φ is in Class C' on an open set $G \subseteq \mathbf{R}^p$ to $\mathbf{R}^p$ and that the Jacobian J_φ vanishes on a set E with content zero. Suppose that D is a compact subset of G, which has content, and f is continuous on $\varphi(D)$ to $\mathbf{R}$. Show that $\varphi(D)$ has content and

$$\int_{\varphi(D)} f = \int_D (f \circ \varphi)|J_\varphi|.$$

(Hint: by Lemma 24.22, $\varphi(E)$ has content zero. If $\epsilon > 0$, we enclose E in the union of a finite number of open balls whose union U has total content less than ϵ. Apply Theorem 24.26 to $D \backslash U$.)

24.Y. (a) If φ is the transformation of the (r, θ)-plane into the (x, y)-plane given by

$$x = r \cos \theta, \qquad y = r \sin \theta,$$

show that $J_\varphi = r$. If D is a compact subset of $\mathbf{R}^2$ and if D_p is the subset of the (r, θ)-plane with

$$r \geq 0, \qquad 0 \leq \theta \leq 2\pi,$$

such that $\varphi(D_p) = D$, then

$$\iint_D f(x, y)dx\, dy = \iint_{D_p} f(r \cos \theta, \sin \theta)\, r\, dr\, d\theta.$$

(b) Similarly, if ψ is the transformation of the (r, θ, φ)-space into $(x, y, z\text{-})$ space given by

$$x = r \cos \theta \sin \varphi, \qquad y = r \sin \theta \sin \varphi, \qquad z = r \cos \varphi,$$

then $J_\psi = r^2 \sin \varphi$. If D is a compact subset of $\mathbf{R}^3$ and if D_s is the subset of the (r, θ, φ)-space with

$$r \geq 0, \qquad 0 \leq \theta \leq 2\pi, \qquad 0 \leq \varphi \leq \pi,$$

such that $\psi(D_s) = D$, then

$$\iiint_D f(x, y, z)dx\, dy\, dz = \iiint_{D_s} f(r \cos \theta \sin \varphi, r \sin \theta \sin \varphi,$$

$$r \cos \varphi)\, r^2 \sin \varphi\, dr\, d\theta\, d\varphi.$$

24.Z. Show that if $p = 2k$ is even, then the content ω_p of the closed unit ball $\{x \in \mathbf{R}^p : |x| \leq 1\}$ is $\pi^k/k!$. Show that if $p = 2k - 1$ is odd, then the content ω_p of the closed unit ball is

$$\pi^k \frac{4^k k!}{(2k)!}.$$

Hence it follows that $\lim(\omega_p) = 0$; that is, the content of the unit ball in $\mathbf{R}^p$ converges to zero as $p \to \infty$. (Hint: use induction and the fact that

$$\omega_{p+1} = 2\omega_p \int_0^1 (1 - r^2)^{p/2}\, dr.)$$

In terms of the Gamma function, we have

$$\omega_n = \pi^{n/2}/\Gamma((n + 2)/2).$$

Section 25   Improper and Infinite Integrals

In the preceding three sections we have had two standing assumptions: we required the functions to be bounded and we required the domain of integration to be compact. If either of these hypotheses is dropped, the foregoing integration theory does not apply without some change. Since there are a number of important applications where it is desirable to permit one or both of these new phenomena, we shall indicate here the changes that are to be made. Most of the applications pertain to the case of real-valued functions and we shall restrict our attention to this case.

Unbounded Functions

Let $J = [a, b]$ be an interval in $\mathbf{R}$ and let f be a real-valued function which is defined at least for x satisfying $a < x \leq b$. If f is Riemann integrable on the interval $[c, b]$ for each c satisfying $a < c \leq b$, let

(25.1)
$$I_c = \int_c^b f.$$

We shall define the improper integral of f over $J = [a, b]$ to be the limit of I_c as $c \to a$.

25.1 DEFINITION. Suppose that the Riemann integral in (25.1) exists for each c in $(a, b]$. Suppose that there exists a real number I such that for every $\epsilon > 0$ there is a $\delta(\epsilon) > 0$ such that if $a < c < a + \delta(\epsilon)$ then $|I_c - I| < \epsilon$. In this case we say that I is the improper integral of f over $J = [a, b]$ and we sometimes denote the value I of this improper integral by

(25.2)
$$\int_{a+}^b f \quad \text{or by} \quad \int_{a+}^b f(x)\, dx,$$

although it is more usual not to write the plus signs in the lower limit.

25.2 EXAMPLES.   (a) Suppose the function f is defined on $(a, b]$ and is bounded on this interval. If f is Riemann integrable on every interval $[c, b]$ with $a < c \leq b$, then it is easily seen (Exercise 25.A) that the improper integral (25.2) exists. Thus the function $f(x) = \sin (1/x)$ has an improper integral on the interval $[0, 1]$.

(b) If $f(x) = 1/x$ for x in $(0, 1]$ and if c is in $(0, 1]$ then it follows from the Fundamental Theorem 23.3 and the fact that f is the derivative of the logarithm that

$$I_c = \int_c^1 f = \log (1) - \log (c) = - \log (c).$$

Since $\log (c)$ becomes unbounded as $c \rightarrow 0$, the improper integral of f on $[0, 1]$ does not exist.

(c) Let $f(x) = x^\alpha$ for x in $(0, 1]$. If $\alpha < 0$, the function is continuous but not bounded on $(0, 1]$. If $\alpha \neq -1$, then f is the derivative of

$$g(x) = \frac{1}{\alpha + 1} x^{\alpha+1}.$$

It follows from the Fundamental Theorem 23.3 that

$$\int_c^1 x^\alpha \, dx = \frac{1}{\alpha + 1} (1 - c^{\alpha+1}).$$

If α satisfies $-1 < \alpha < 0$, then $c^{\alpha+1} \rightarrow 0$ as $c \rightarrow 0$, and f has an improper integral. On the other hand, if $\alpha < -1$, then $c^{\alpha+1}$ does not have a (finite) limit as $c \rightarrow 0$, and hence f does not have an improper integral.

The preceding discussion pertained to a function which is not defined or not bounded at the left end point of the interval. It is obvious how to treat analogous behavior at the right end point. Somewhat more interesting is the case where the function is not defined or not bounded at an interior point of the interval. Suppose that p is an interior point of $[a, b]$ and that f is defined at every point of $[a, b]$ except perhaps p. If both of the improper integrals

$$\int_a^{p-} f, \quad \int_{p+}^b f$$

exist, then we define the improper integral of f over $[a, b]$ to be their sum. In the limit notation, we define the improper integral of f over $[a, b]$ to be

(25.3) $$\lim_{\epsilon \rightarrow 0+} \int_a^{p-\epsilon} f(x) \, dx + \lim_{\delta \rightarrow 0+} \int_{p+\delta}^b f(x) \, dx.$$

It is clear that if those two limits exist, then the single limit

$$(25.4) \qquad \lim_{\epsilon \to 0+} \left\{ \int_a^{p-\epsilon} f(x)\, dx + \int_{p+\epsilon}^b f(x)\, dx \right\}$$

also exists and has the same value. However, the existence of the limit (25.4) does not imply the existence of (25.3). For example, if f is defined for $x \in [-1, 1]$, $x \neq 0$, by $f(x) = 1/x^3$, then it is easily seen that

$$\int_{-1}^{-\epsilon} \left(\frac{1}{x^3}\right) dx + \int_{\epsilon}^1 \left(\frac{1}{x^3}\right) dx = \left(\frac{-1}{2}\right)\left(\frac{1}{\epsilon^2} - 1\right) + \left(\frac{-1}{2}\right)\left(1 - \frac{1}{\epsilon^2}\right) = 0$$

for all ϵ satisfying $0 < \epsilon < 1$. However, we have seen in Example 25.2 (c) that if $\alpha = -3$, then the improper integrals

$$\int_{-1}^{0-} \frac{1}{x^3}\, dx, \qquad \int_{0+}^1 \frac{1}{x^3}\, dx$$

do not exist.

The preceding comments show that the limit in (25.4) may exist without the limit in (25.3) existing. We defined the improper integral (which is sometimes called the Cauchy integral) of f to be given by (25.3). The limit in (25.4) is also of interest and is called the Cauchy principal value of the integral and denoted by

$$(\text{CPV}) \int_a^b f(x)\, dx.$$

It is clear that a function which has a finite number of points where it is not defined or bounded can be treated by breaking the interval into subintervals with these points as end points.

Infinite Integrals

It is important to extend the integral to certain functions which are defined on unbounded sets. For example, if f is defined on $\{x \in R : x \geq a\}$ to R and is Riemann integrable over $[a, c]$ for every $c > a$, we let I_c be the partial integral given by

$$(25.5) \qquad I_c = \int_a^c f.$$

We shall now define the "infinite integral" of f for $x \geq a$ to be the limit of I_c as c increases.

25.3 DEFINITION. If f is Riemann integrable over $[a, c]$ for each $c > a$, let I_c be the partial integral given by (25.5). A real number I is said to be the **infinite integral** of f over $\{x:x \geq a\}$ if for every $\epsilon > 0$, there exists a real number $M(\epsilon)$ such that if $c > M(\epsilon)$ then $|I - I_c| < \epsilon$. In this case we denote I by

$$(25.6) \qquad \int_a^{+\infty} f \quad \text{or} \quad \int_a^{+\infty} f(x)\,dx.$$

It should be remarked that infinite integrals are sometimes called "improper integrals of the first kind." We prefer the present terminology, which is due to Hardy,† for it is both simpler and parallel to the terminology used in connection with infinite series.

25.4 EXAMPLES. (a) If $f(x) = 1/x$ for $x > a > 0$, then the partial integrals are

$$I_c = \int_a^c \frac{1}{x}\,dx = \log(c) - \log(a).$$

Since $\log(c)$ becomes unbounded as $c \to +\infty$, the infinite integral of f does not exist.

(b) Let $f(x) = x^\alpha$ for $x \geq a > 0$ and $\alpha \neq -1$. Then

$$I_c = \int_a^c x^\alpha\,dx = \frac{1}{\alpha + 1}(c^{\alpha+1} - a^{\alpha+1}).$$

If $\alpha > -1$, then $\alpha + 1 > 0$ and the infinite integral does not exist. However, if $\alpha < -1$, then

$$\int_a^{+\infty} x^\alpha\,dx = -\frac{a^{\alpha+1}}{\alpha + 1}.$$

(c) Let $f(x) = e^{-x}$ for $x \geq 0$. Then

$$\int_0^c e^{-x}\,dx = -(e^{-c} - 1);$$

hence the infinite integral of f over $\{x:x \geq 0\}$ exists and equals 1.

It is also possible to consider the integral of a function defined on all of **R**. In this case we require that f be Riemann integrable over every interval in **R** and consider the limits

$$(25.7a) \qquad \int_{-\infty}^a f(x)\,dx = \lim_{b \to -\infty} \int_b^a f(x)\,dx,$$

$$(25.7b) \qquad \int_a^{+\infty} f(x)\,dx = \lim_{c \to +\infty} \int_a^c f(x)\,dx.$$

---

† GEOFFREY H. HARDY (1877–1947) was professor at Cambridge and long-time dean of British mathematics. He made frequent and deep contributions to mathematical analysis.

It is easily seen that if both of these limits exist for one value of a, then they both exist for all values of a. In this case we define the infinite integral of f over R to be the sum of these two infinite integrals:

$$(25.8) \qquad \int_{-\infty}^{+\infty} f(x) \, dx = \lim_{b \to -\infty} \int_{b}^{a} f(x) \, dx + \lim_{c \to +\infty} \int_{a}^{c} f(x) \, dx.$$

As in the case of the improper integral, the existence of both of the limits in (25.8) implies the existence of the limit

$$(25.9) \qquad \lim_{c \to +\infty} \left\{ \int_{-c}^{a} f(x) \, dx + \int_{a}^{c} f(x) \, dx \right\},$$

and the equality of (25.8) and (25.9). The limit in (25.9), when it exists, is often called the **Cauchy principal value** of the infinite integral over R and is denoted by

$$(25.10) \qquad (\text{CPV}) \int_{-\infty}^{+\infty} f(x) \, dx.$$

However, the existence of the Cauchy principal value does not imply the existence of the infinite integral (25.8). This is seen by considering $f(x) = x$, whence

$$\int_{-c}^{c} x \, dx = \tfrac{1}{2}(c^2 - c^2) = 0$$

for all c. Thus the Cauchy principal value of the infinite integral for $f(x) = x$ exists and equals 0, but the infinite integral of this function does not exist, since neither of the infinite integrals in (25.7) exists.

Existence of the Infinite Integral

We now obtain a few conditions for the existence of the infinite integral over the set $\{x : x \geq a\}$. These results can also be applied to give conditions for the infinite integral over R, since the latter involves consideration of infinite integrals over the sets $\{x : x \leq a\}$ and $\{x : x \geq a\}$. First we state the Cauchy Criterion.

25.5 CAUCHY CRITERION. *Suppose that f is integrable over $[a, c]$ for all $c \geq a$. Then the infinite integral*

$$\int_{a}^{+\infty} f$$

exists if and only if for every $\epsilon > 0$ there exists a $K(\epsilon)$ such that if $b \geq c \geq K(\epsilon)$, then

$$(25.11) \qquad \left| \int_{c}^{b} f \right| < \epsilon.$$

PROOF. The necessity of the condition is established in the usual manner. Suppose that the condition is satisfied and let I_n be the partial integral defined for $n \in \mathbf{N}$ by

$$I_n = \int_a^{a+n} f.$$

It is seen that (I_n) is a Cauchy sequence of real numbers. If $I = \lim (I_n)$ and $\epsilon > 0$, then there exists $N(\epsilon)$ such that if $n \geq N(\epsilon)$, then $|I - I_n| < \epsilon$. Let $M(\epsilon) = \sup \{K(\epsilon), a + N(\epsilon)\}$ and let $c \geq M(\epsilon)$; then the partial integral I_c is given by

$$I_c = \int_a^c f = \int_a^{a+N(\epsilon)} f + \int_{a+N(\epsilon)}^c f,$$

whence it follows that $|I - I_c| < 2\epsilon$.

Q.E.D.

In the important case where $f(x) \geq 0$ for all $x \geq a$, the next result provides a useful test.

25.6 THEOREM. *Suppose that $f(x) \geq 0$ for all $x \geq a$ and that f is integrable over $[a, c]$ for all $c \geq a$. Then the infinite integral of f exists if and only if the set $\{I_c : c \geq a\}$ is bounded. In this case*

$$\int_a^{+\infty} f = \sup \left\{ \int_a^c f : c \geq a \right\}.$$

PROOF. If $a \leq c \leq b$, then the hypothesis that $f(x) \geq 0$ implies that $I_c \leq I_b$ so I_c is a monotone increasing function of c. Therefore, the existence of $\lim I_c$ is equivalent to the boundedness of $\{I_c : c \geq a\}$.

Q.E.D.

25.7 COMPARISON TEST. *Suppose that f and g are integrable over $[a, c]$ for all $c \geq a$ and that $0 \leq f(x) \leq g(x)$ for all $x \geq a$. If the infinite integral of g exists, then the infinite integral of f exists and*

$$0 \leq \int_a^{+\infty} f \leq \int_a^{+\infty} g.$$

PROOF. If $c \geq a$, then

$$\int_a^c f \leq \int_a^c g.$$

If the set of partial integrals of g is bounded, then the set of partial integrals of f is also bounded.

Q.E.D.

25.8   LIMIT COMPARISON TEST.   *Suppose that f and g are non-negative and integrable over [a, c] for all c ≥ a and that*

$$(25.12) \qquad \lim_{x \to +\infty} \frac{f(x)}{g(x)} \neq 0.$$

Then both or neither of the infinite integrals $\int_a^{+\infty} f,\ \int_a^{+\infty} g$ *exist.*

PROOF.   In view of the relation (25.12) we infer that there exist positive numbers $A < B$ and $K \geq a$ such that

$$Ag(x) \leq f(x) \leq Bg(x) \qquad \text{for } x \geq K.$$

The Comparison Test 25.7 and this relation show that both or neither of the infinite integrals

$$\int_K^{+\infty} f, \quad \int_K^{+\infty} g$$

exist. Since both f and g are integrable on $[a, K]$, the statement follows.
                                                                    Q.E.D.

25.9   DIRICHLET'S TEST.   *Suppose that f is continuous for x ≥ a, that the partial integrals*

$$I_c = \int_a^c f, \qquad c \geq a,$$

are bounded, and that φ is monotone decreasing to zero as x → + ∞. Then the infinite integral $\int_a^{+\infty} f\varphi$ *exists.*

PROOF.   Let A be a bound for the set $\{|I_c| : c \geq a\}$. If $\epsilon > 0$, let $K(\epsilon)$ be such that if $x \geq K(\epsilon)$, then $0 \leq \varphi(x) \leq \epsilon/2A$. If $b \geq c \geq K(\epsilon)$, then it follows from Bonnet's form of the Second Mean Value Theorem 23.7(c) that there exists a number ξ in $[c, b]$ such that

$$\int_c^b f\varphi = \varphi(c) \int_c^\xi f.$$

In view of the estimate

$$\left| \int_c^\xi f \right| = \left| I_\xi - I_c \right| \leq 2A,$$

it follows that

$$\left| \int_c^b f\varphi \right| < \epsilon$$

when $b \geq c$ both exceed $K(\epsilon)$. We can then apply the Cauchy Criterion 25.5.

Q.E.D.

25.10 EXAMPLES. (a) If $f(x) = 1/(1 + x^2)$ and $g(x) = 1/x^2$ for $x \geq a > 0$, then $0 \leq f(x) \leq g(x)$. Since we have already seen in Example 25.4(b) that the infinite integral

$$\int_1^{+\infty} \frac{1}{x^2}\, dx$$

exists, it follows from the Comparison Test 25.7 that the infinite integral

$$\int_1^{+\infty} \frac{1}{1 + x^2}\, dx$$

also exists. (This could be shown directly by noting that

$$\int_1^c \frac{1}{1 + x^2}\, dx = \text{Arc tan } (c) - \text{Arc tan } (1)$$

and that Arc tan $(c) \to \pi/2$ as $c \to +\infty$.)

(b) If $h(x) = e^{-x^2}$ and $g(x) = e^{-x}$ then $0 \leq h(x) \leq g(x)$ for $x \geq 1$. It was seen in Example 25.4(c) that the infinite integral $\int_0^{+\infty} e^{-x}\, dx$ exists, whence it follows from the Comparison Test 25.7 that the infinite integral

$$I = \int_0^{+\infty} e^{-x^2}\, dx$$

also exists. This time, a direct evaluation of the partial integrals is not possible, using elementary functions. However, there is an elegant artifice that can be used to evaluate this important integral. Let I_c denote the partial integral

$$I_c = \int_0^c e^{-x^2}\, dx,$$

and consider the positive continuous function $f(x, y) = e^{-(x^2+y^2)}$ on the first quadrant of the (x, y) plane. It follows from Theorem 24.18 that the integral of f over the square $S_c = [0, c] \times [0, c]$ can be evaluated as an iterated integral

$$\int_{S_c} e^{-(x^2+y^2)} = \int_0^c \left\{ \int_0^c e^{-x^2} e^{-y^2}\, dx \right\} dy.$$

It is clear that this iterated integral equals

$$I_c^2 = \left\{ \int_0^c e^{-x^2}\, dx \right\} \left\{ \int_0^c e^{-y}\, dy \right\}.$$

We now let $R_c = \{(x, y) : 0 \leq x, 0 \leq y, x^2 + y^2 \leq c^2\}$ and note that the sector R_c is contained in the square S_c and contains the square $S_{c/2}$. Since f is positive, its integral over R_c lies between its integral over $S_{c/2}$ and S_c. Therefore, it follows that

$$(I_{c/2})^2 < \int_{R_c} f < (I_c)^2.$$

If we change to polar coordinates it is easy to evaluate this middle integral. In fact,

$$\int_{R_c} f = \int_0^{\pi/2} \left\{ \int_0^c e^{-r^2} r\, dr \right\} d\theta = \frac{\pi}{2} \left(-\frac{1}{2} \right) e^{-r^2} \Big|_{r=0}^{r=c} = \frac{\pi}{4}\,(1 - e^{-c^2}).$$

In view of the inequalities above,

$$\sup_c\, (I_c)^2 = \sup_c \int_{R_c} f = \frac{\pi}{4},$$

and it follows from Theorem 25.6 that

(24.13) $$\int_0^{+\infty} e^{-x^2}\, dx = \sup_c I_c = \frac{1}{2}\, \sqrt{\pi}.$$

(c) Let $p > 0$ and consider the existence of the infinite integral

$$\int_1^{+\infty} \frac{\sin (x)}{x^p}\, dx.$$

If $p > 1$, then the integrand is dominated by $1/x^p$, which was seen in Example 25.4(b) to be convergent. In this case the Comparison Test implies that the infinite integral converges. If $0 < p \leq 1$, this argument fails; however, if we set $f(x) = \sin (x)$ and $\varphi(x) = 1/x^p$, then Dirichlet's Test 25.9 shows that the infinite integral exists.

(d) Let $f(x) = \sin (x^2)$ for $x \geq 0$ and consider the **Fresnel**† **Integral**

$$\int_0^{+\infty} \sin (x^2)\, dx.$$

It is clear that the integral over $[0, 1]$ exists, so we shall examine only

† AUGUSTIN FRESNEL (1788–1827), a French mathematical physicist, helped to reestablish the undulatory theory of light which was introduced earlier by Huygens.

the integral over $\{x : x \geq 1\}$. If we make the substitution $t = x^2$ and apply the Change of Variable Theorem 23.8, we obtain

$$\int_1^c \sin (x^2)\, dx = \frac{1}{2} \int_1^{c^2} \frac{\sin (t)}{\sqrt{t}}\, dt.$$

The preceding example shows that the integral on the right converges when $c \to + \infty$; hence it follows that the infinite integral

$$\int_1^{+\infty} \sin (x^2)\, dx$$

exists. (It should be observed that the integrand does not converge to 0 as $x \to + \infty$.)

(e) Suppose that $\alpha \geq 1$ and let $\Gamma(\alpha)$ be defined by the integral

(25.14) $$\Gamma(\alpha) = \int_0^{+\infty} e^{-x} x^{\alpha-1}\, dx.$$

In order to see that this infinite integral exists, consider the function $g(x) = 1/x^2$ for $x \geq 1$. Since

$$\lim_{x \to +\infty} \frac{e^{-x} x^{\alpha-1}}{x^{-2}} = \lim_{x \to +\infty} \frac{x^{\alpha+1}}{e^x} = 0,$$

it follows that if $\epsilon > 0$ then there exists $K(\epsilon)$ such that

$$0 < e^{-x} x^{\alpha-1} \leq \epsilon\, x^{-2} \quad \text{for} \quad x \geq K(\epsilon).$$

Since the infinite integral $\int_K^{+\infty} x^{-2}\, dx$ exists, we infer that the integral (25.14) also converges. The important function defined for $\alpha \geq 1$ by formula (25.14) is called the Gamma function. It will be quickly seen that if $\alpha < 1$, then the integrand $e^{-x} x^{\alpha-1}$ becomes unbounded near $x = 0$. However, if α satisfies $0 < \alpha < 1$, then we have seen in Example 25.2(c) that the function $x^{\alpha-1}$ has an improper integral over the interval $[0, 1]$. Since $0 < e^{-x} \leq 1$ for all $x \geq 0$, it is readily established that the improper integral

$$\int_{0+}^1 e^{-x} x^{\alpha-1}\, dx$$

exists when $0 < \alpha < 1$. Hence we can extend the definition of the Gamma function to be given for all $\alpha > 0$ by an integral of the form of (25.14) provided it is interpreted as a sum

$$\int_{0+}^a e^{-x} x^{\alpha-1}\, dx + \int_a^{+\infty} e^{-x} x^{\alpha-1}\, dx$$

of an improper integral and an infinite integral.

Absolute and Uniform Convergence

If f is Riemann integrable on $[a, c]$ for every $c \geq a$, then it follows that $|f|$, the absolute value of f, is also Riemann integrable on $[a, c]$ for $c \geq a$. Since the inequality

$$- |f(x)| \leq f(x) \leq |f(x)|$$

holds, it follows from the Comparison Test 25.7 that if the infinite integral

$$(25.15) \qquad\qquad \int_a^{+\infty} |f(x)| \, dx$$

exists, then the infinite integral

$$(25.16) \qquad\qquad \int_a^{+\infty} f(x) \, dx$$

also exists and is bounded in absolute value by (25.15).

25.11 DEFINITION. If the infinite integral (25.15) exists, then we say that f is absolutely integrable over $\{x : x \geq a\}$, or that the infinite integral (25.16) is **absolutely convergent**.

We have remarked that if f is absolutely integrable over $\{x : x \geq a\}$, then the infinite integral (25.16) exists. The converse is not true, however, as may be seen by considering the integral

$$\int_\pi^{+\infty} \frac{\sin (x)}{x} \, dx.$$

The convergence of this integral was established in Example 25.10(c). However, it is easily seen that in each interval $[k\pi, (k + 1)\pi]$, $k \in \mathbf{N}$, there is a subinterval of length $b > 0$ on which

$$|\sin (x)| \geq \tfrac{1}{2}.$$

(In fact, we can take $b = 2\pi/3$.) Therefore, we have

$$\int_\pi^{k\pi} \left| \frac{\sin(x)}{x} \right| dx \geq \int_\pi^{2\pi} + \cdots + \int_\pi^{k\pi} \geq \frac{b}{2} \left\{ \frac{1}{2\pi} + \frac{1}{3\pi} + \cdots + \frac{1}{k\pi} \right\},$$

whence it follows that the function $f(x) = \sin(x)/x$ is not absolutely integrable over $\{x : x \geq \pi\}$.

In many applications it is important to consider infinite integrals in which the integrand depends on a parameter. In order to handle this situation easily, the notion of uniform convergence of the integral relative to the parameter is of prime importance. We shall first treat the case that the parameter belongs to an interval $J = [\alpha, \beta]$.

25.12 DEFINITION. Let f be a real-valued function, defined for (x, t) satisfying $x \geq a$ and $\alpha \leq t \leq \beta$. Suppose that for each t in $J = [\alpha, \beta]$ the infinite integral

$$(25.17) \qquad F(t) = \int_a^{+\infty} f(x, t) \, dx$$

exists. We say that this convergence is uniform on J if for every $\epsilon > 0$ there exists a number $M(\epsilon)$ such that if $c \geq M(\epsilon)$ and $t \in J$, then

$$\left| F(t) - \int_a^c f(x, t) \, dx \right| < \epsilon.$$

The distinction between ordinary convergence of the infinite integrals given in (25.17) and uniform convergence is that $M(\epsilon)$ can be chosen to be independent of the value of t in J. We leave it to the reader to write out the definition of uniform convergence of the infinite integrals when the parameter t belongs to the set $\{t : t \geq \alpha\}$ or to the set N.

It is useful to have some tests for uniform convergence of the infinite integral.

25.13 CAUCHY CRITERION. *Suppose that for each $t \in J$, the infinite integral (25.17) exists. Then the convergence is uniform on J if and only if for each $\epsilon > 0$ there is a number $K(\epsilon)$ such that if $b \geq c \geq K(\epsilon)$ and $t \in J$, then*

$$(25.18) \qquad \left| \int_c^b f(x, t) \, dx \right| < \epsilon.$$

We leave the proof as an exercise.

25.14 WEIERSTRASS M-TEST. *Suppose that f is Riemann integrable over $[a, c]$ for all $c \geq a$ and all $t \in J$. Suppose that there exists a positive function M defined for $x \geq a$ and such that*

$$|f(x, t)| \leq M(x) \quad \text{for} \quad x \geq a, t \in J,$$

and such that the infinite integral $\int_a^{+\infty} M(x) \, dx$ exists. Then, for each $t \in J$, the integral

$$F(t) = \int_a^{+\infty} f(x, t) \, dx$$

is (absolutely) convergent and the convergence is uniform on J.

PROOF.   The convergence of

$$\int_a^{+\infty} |f(x, t)|\, dx \quad \text{for} \quad t \in J,$$

is an immediate consequence of the Comparison Test and the hypotheses. Therefore, the integral yielding $F(t)$ is absolutely convergent for $t \in J$. If we use the Cauchy Criterion together with the estimate

$$\left| \int_c^b f(x, t)\, dx \right| \le \int_c^b \left| f(x, t) \right| dx \le \int_c^b M(x)\, dx,$$

we can readily establish the uniform convergence on J.

Q.E.D.

The Weierstrass M-test is useful when the convergence is absolute as well as uniform, but it is not quite delicate enough to handle the case of non-absolute uniform convergence. For this, we turn to an analogue of Dirichlet's Test 25.9.

25.15 DIRICHLET'S TEST.   *Let f be continuous in (x, t) for $x \ge a$ and t in J and suppose that there exists a constant A such that*

$$\left| \int_a^c f(x, t)\, dx \right| \le A \quad \text{for} \quad c \ge a, \quad t \in J.$$

Suppose that for each $t \in J$, the function $\varphi(x, t)$ is monotone decreasing for $x \ge a$ and converges to 0 as $x \to +\infty$ uniformly for $t \in J$. Then the integral

$$F(t) = \int_a^{+\infty} f(x, t)\varphi(x, t)\, dx$$

converges uniformly on J.

PROOF.   Let $\epsilon > 0$ and choose $K(\epsilon)$ such that if $x \ge K(\epsilon)$ and $t \in J$, then $\varphi(x, t) < \epsilon/2A$. If $b \ge c \ge K(\epsilon)$, then it follows from Bonnet's form of the Second Mean Value Theorem 23.7(c) that, for each $t \in J$, there exists a number $\xi(t)$ in $[c, b]$ such that

$$\int_c^b f(x, t)\varphi(x, t)\, dx = \varphi(c, t) \int_c^{\xi(t)} f(x, t)\, dx.$$

Therefore, if $b \ge c \ge K(\epsilon)$ and $t \in J$, we have

$$\left| \int_c^b f(x, t)\varphi(x, t)\, dx \right| \le \varphi(c, t)2A < \epsilon,$$

so the uniformity of the convergence follows from the Cauchy Criterion 25.13.

Q.E.D.

25.16 EXAMPLES.   (a) If f is given by

$$f(x, t) = \frac{\cos (tx)}{1 + x^2}, \qquad x \geq 0, \qquad t \in \mathbf{R},$$

and if we define M by $M(x) = (1 + x^2)^{-1}$, then $|f(x, t)| \leq M(x)$. Since the infinite integral

$$\int_0^{+\infty} M(x)\, dx$$

exists, it follows from the Weierstrass M-test that the infinite integral

$$\int_0^{+\infty} \frac{\cos (tx)}{1 + x^2}\, dx$$

converges uniformly for $t \in \mathbf{R}$.

(b) Let $f(x, t) = e^{-x}x^t$ for $x \geq 0$, $t \geq 0$. It is seen that the integral

$$\int_0^{+\infty} e^{-x}x^t\, dx$$

converges uniformly for t in an interval $[0, \beta]$ for any $\beta > 0$. However, it does not converge uniformly on $\{t \in \mathbf{R} : t \geq 0\}$ (See Exercise 25.K).

(c) If $f(x, t) = e^{-tx} \sin (x)$ for $x \geq 0$ and $t \geq \gamma > 0$, then

$$|f(x, t)| \leq e^{-tx} \leq e^{-\gamma x}.$$

If we set $M(x) = e^{-\gamma x}$, then the Weierstrass M-test implies that the integral

$$\int_0^{+\infty} e^{-tx} \sin (x)\, dx$$

converges uniformly for $t \geq \gamma > 0$ and an elementary calculation shows that it converges to $(1 + t^2)^{-1}$. (Note that if $t = 0$, then the integral no longer converges.)

(d) Consider the infinite integral

$$\int_0^{+\infty} e^{-tx} \frac{\sin (x)}{x}\, dx \quad \text{for} \quad t \geq 0,$$

where we interpret the integrand to be 1 for $x = 0$. Since the integrand is dominated by 1, it suffices to show that the integral over $\epsilon \leq x$ converges uniformly for $t \geq 0$. The Weierstrass M-test does not apply to this integrand. However, if we take $f(x, t) = \sin (x)$ and $\varphi(x, t) = e^{-tx}/x$, then the hypotheses of Dirichlet's Test are satisfied.

Infinite Integrals Depending on a Parameter

Suppose that f is a continuous function of (x, t) defined for $x \geq a$ and for t in $J = [\alpha, \beta]$. Furthermore, suppose that the infinite integral

$$(25.19) \qquad F(t) = \int_a^{+\infty} f(x, t)\, dx$$

exists for each $t \in J$. We shall now show that if this convergence is uniform, then F is continuous on J and its integral can be calculated by interchanging the order of integration. A similar result will be established for the derivative.

25.17 THEOREM. *Suppose that f is continuous in (x, t) for $x \geq a$ and t in $J = [\alpha, \beta]$ and that the convergence in (25.19) is uniform on J. Then F is continuous on J.*

PROOF.   If $n \in \mathbf{N}$, let F_n be defined on J by

$$F_n(t) = \int_a^{a+n} f(x, t)\, dx.$$

It follows from Theorem 23.9 that F_n is continuous on J. Since the sequence (F_n) converges to F uniformly on J, it follows from Theorem 17.1 that F is continuous on J.

Q.E.D.

25.18 THEOREM. *Under the hypotheses of the preceding theorem, then*

$$\int_\alpha^\beta F(t)\, dt = \int_a^{+\infty} \left\{ \int_\alpha^\beta f(x, t)\, dt \right\} dx,$$

which can be written in the form

$$(25.20) \qquad \int_\alpha^\beta \left\{ \int_a^{+\infty} f(x, t)\, dx \right\} dt = \int_a^{+\infty} \left\{ \int_\alpha^\beta f(x, t)\, dt \right\} dx.$$

PROOF.   If F_n is defined as in the preceding proof, then it follows from Theorem 23.12 that

$$\int_\alpha^\beta F_n(t)\, dt = \int_a^{a+n} \left\{ \int_\alpha^\beta f(x, t)\, dt \right\} dx.$$

Since (F_n) converges to F uniformly on J, then Theorem 22.12 implies that

$$\int_\alpha^\beta F(t)\, dt = \lim_n \int_\alpha^\beta F_n(t)\, dt.$$

Combining the last two relations, we obtain (25.20).

Q.E.D.

25.19   THEOREM.   *Suppose that f and its partial derivative f_t are continuous in (x, t) for $x \geq a$ and t in $J = [\alpha, \beta]$. Suppose that (25.19) exists for all $t \in J$ and that*

$$G(t) = \int_a^{+\infty} f_t(x, t)\, dx$$

is uniformly convergent on J. Then F is differentiable on J and $F' = G$. In symbols:

$$\frac{d}{dt} \int_a^{+\infty} f(x, t)\, dx = \int_a^{+\infty} \frac{\partial f}{\partial t}(x, t)\, dx.$$

PROOF.   If F_n is defined for $t \in J$ to be

$$F_n(t) = \int_a^{a+n} f(x, t)\, dx,$$

then it follows from Theorem 23.10 that F_n is differentiable and that

$$F_n'(t) = \int_a^{a+n} f_t(x, t)\, dx.$$

By hypothesis, the sequence (F_n) converges on J to F and the sequence (F_n') converges uniformly on J to G. It follows from Theorem 19.12 that F is differentiable on J and that $F' = G$.

Q.E.D.

25.20   EXAMPLES.   (a) We observe that if $t > 0$, then

$$\frac{1}{t} = \int_0^{+\infty} e^{-tx}\, dx$$

and that the convergence is uniform for $t \geq t_0 > 0$. If we integrate both sides of this relation with respect to t over an interval $[\alpha, \beta]$ where $0 < \alpha < \beta$, and use Theorem 25.18, we obtain the formula

$$\log (\beta/\alpha) = \int_\alpha^\beta \frac{1}{t}\, dt = \int_0^{+\infty} \left\{ \int_\alpha^\beta e^{-tx}\, dt \right\} dx$$

$$= \int_0^{+\infty} \frac{e^{-\alpha x} - e^{-\beta x}}{x}\, dx.$$

(Observe that the last integrand can be defined to be continuous at $x = 0$.)

(b) Instead of integrating with respect to t, we differentiate and formally obtain

$$\frac{1}{t^2} = \int_0^{+\infty} x e^{-tx}\, dx.$$

Since this latter integral converges uniformly with respect to t, provided $t \geq t_0 > 0$, the formula holds for $t > 0$. By induction we obtain

$$\frac{n!}{t^{n+1}} = \int_0^{+\infty} x^n e^{-tx}\, dx.$$

Referring to the definition of the Gamma function, given in Example 25.10(e), we see that

$$\Gamma(n+1) = n!$$

(c) If $\alpha > 1$ is a real number and $x > 0$, then $x^{\alpha-1} = e^{(\alpha-1)\log(x)}$. Hence $f(\alpha) = x^{\alpha-1}$ is a continuous function of (α, x). Moreover, it is seen that there exists a neighborhood of α on which the integral

$$\Gamma(\alpha) = \int_0^{+\infty} x^{\alpha-1} e^{-x}\, dx$$

is uniformly convergent. It follows from Theorem 25.17 that the Gamma function is continuous at least for $\alpha > 1$. (If $0 < \alpha \leq 1$, the same conclusion can be drawn, but the fact that the integral is improper at $x = 0$ must be considered.)

(d) Let $t \geq 0$ and $u \geq 0$ and let F be defined by

$$F(u) = \int_0^{+\infty} e^{-tx} \frac{\sin(ux)}{x}\, dx.$$

If $t > 0$, then this integral is uniformly convergent for $u \geq 0$ and so is the integral

$$F'(u) = \int_0^{+\infty} e^{-tx} \cos(ux)\, dx.$$

Moreover, integration by parts shows that

$$\int_0^A e^{-tx} \cos(ux)\, dx = \left[\frac{e^{-tx}[u \sin(ux) - t \cos(ux)]}{t^2 + u^2} \right]_{x=0}^{x=A},$$

and as $A \to +\infty$ we obtain the formula

$$F'(u) = \int_0^{+\infty} e^{-tx} \cos(ux)\, dx = \frac{t}{t^2 + u^2}, \quad u \geq 0.$$

Therefore, there exists a constant C such that

$$F(u) = \text{Arc tan}\,(u/t) + C \quad \text{for} \quad u \geq 0.$$

In order to evaluate the constant C, we use the fact that $F(0) = 0$ and Arc tan $(0) = 0$ and infer that $C = 0$. Hence, if $t > 0$ and $u \geq 0$, then

$$\text{Arc tan } (u/t) = \int_0^{+\infty} e^{-tx} \frac{\sin (ux)}{x} \, dx.$$

(e) Now hold $u > 0$ fixed in the last formula and observe, as in Example 25.16(d) that the integral converges uniformly for $t \geq 0$ so that the limit is continuous for $t \geq 0$. Letting $t \to 0+$, we obtain the important formula

(25.21) $$\frac{\pi}{2} = \int_0^{+\infty} \frac{\sin (ux)}{x} \, dx, \qquad u > 0.$$

Infinite Integrals of Sequences

Let (f_n) be a sequence of real-valued functions which are defined for $x \geq a$. We shall suppose that the infinite integrals

$$\int_a^{+\infty} f_n$$

all exist and that the limit

$$f(x) = \lim \, (f_n(x))$$

exists for each $x \geq a$. We would like to be able to conclude that the infinite integral of f exists and that

(25.22) $$\int_a^{+\infty} f = \lim \int_a^{+\infty} f_n.$$

In Theorem 22.12 it was proved that if a sequence (f_n) of Riemann integrable functions converges uniformly on an interval $[a, c]$ to a function f, then f is Riemann integrable and the integral of f is the limit of the integrals of the f_n. The corresponding result is not necessarily true for infinite integrals; it will be seen in Exercise 25.T that the limit function need not possess an infinite integral. Moreover, even if the infinite integral does exist and both sides of (25.22) have a meaning, the equality may fail (cf. Exercise 25.U). Similarly, the obvious extension of the Bounded Convergence Theorem 22.14 may fail for infinite integrals. However, there are two important and useful results which give conditions under which equation (25.22) holds. In proving them we shall make use of the Bounded Convergence Theorem 22.14. The first result is a special case of a celebrated theorem due to Lebesgue. (Since we are dealing with infinite Riemann integrals, we need to add the hypothesis that the limit function is integrable. In the more general Lebesgue theory of integration, this additional hypothesis is not required.)

25.21 **DOMINATED CONVERGENCE THEOREM.** *Suppose that* (f_n) *is a sequence of real-valued functions, that* $f(x) = \lim \left(f_n(x) \right)$ *for all* $x \geq a$, *and that* f *and* f_n, $n \in \mathbf{N}$, *are Riemann integrable over* $[a, c]$ *for all* $c > a$. *Suppose that there exists a function* M *which has an integral over* $x \geq a$ *and that*

$$|f_n(x)| \leq M(x) \quad \text{for } x \geq a, \quad n \in \mathbf{N}.$$

Then f *has an integral over* $x \geq a$ *and*

(25.22)
$$\int_a^{+\infty} f = \lim \int_a^{+\infty} f_n.$$

PROOF. It follows from the Comparison Test 25.7 that the infinite integrals

$$\int_a^{+\infty} f, \qquad \int_a^{+\infty} f_n, \qquad n \in \mathbf{N},$$

exist. If $\epsilon > 0$, let K be chosen such that

$$\int_K^{+\infty} M < \epsilon,$$

from which it follows that

$$\left| \int_K^{+\infty} f \right| < \epsilon \quad \text{and} \quad \left| \int_K^{+\infty} f_n \right| < \epsilon, \qquad n \in \mathbf{N}.$$

Since $f(x) = \lim \left(f_n(x) \right)$ for all $x \in [a, K]$ it follows from the Bounded Convergence Theorem 22.14 that

$$\int_a^K f = \lim_n \int_a^K f_n.$$

Therefore, we have

$$\left| \int_a^{+\infty} f - \int_a^{+\infty} f_n \right| \leq \left| \int_a^K f - \int_a^K f_n \right| + 2\epsilon,$$

which is less than 3ϵ for sufficiently large n.

Q.E.D.

25.22 MONOTONE CONVERGENCE THEOREM. *Suppose that* (f_n) *is a bounded sequence of real-valued functions on* $\{x : x \geq a\}$ *which is monotone increasing in the sense that* $f_n(x) \leq f_{n+1}(x)$ *for* $n \in \mathbf{N}$ *and* $x \geq a$, *and such that each* f_n *has an integral over* $\{x : x \geq a\}$. *Then the limit function* f *has an integral over* $\{x : x \geq a\}$ *if and only if the set* $\left\{ \int_a^{+\infty} f_n : n \in \mathbf{N} \right\}$ *is bounded. In this case*

$$\int_a^{+\infty} f = \sup_n \left\{ \int_a^{+\infty} f_n \right\} = \lim_n \int_a^{+\infty} f_n.$$

PROOF.   It is no loss of generality to assume that $f_n(x) \geq 0$. Since the sequence (f_n) is monotone increasing, we infer from the Comparison Test 25.7, that the sequence $\left(\int_a^{+\infty} f_n : n \in \mathbf{N} \right)$ is also monotone increasing. If f has an integral over $\{x : x \geq a\}$, then the Dominated Convergence Theorem (with $M = f$) shows that

$$\int_a^{+\infty} f = \lim_n \int_a^{+\infty} f_n.$$

Conversely, suppose that the set of infinite integrals is bounded and let S be the supremum of this set. If $c > a$, then the Monotone Convergence Theorem 22.15 implies that

$$\int_a^c f = \lim_n \int_a^c f_n = \sup_n \left\{ \int_a^c f_n \right\}.$$

Since $f_n \geq 0$, it follows that

$$\int_a^c f_n \leq \int_a^{+\infty} f_n \leq S,$$

and hence that

$$\int_a^c f \leq S.$$

By Theorem 25.6 the infinite integral of f exists and, since

$$\int_a^{+\infty} f = \sup_c \int_a^c f = \sup_c \left\{ \sup_n \int_a^c f_n \right\}$$
$$= \sup_n \left\{ \sup_c \int_a^c f_n \right\} = \sup_n \int_a^{+\infty} f_n,$$

the stated relation holds.

                                                                    Q.E.D.

Iterated Infinite Integrals

In Theorem 25.18 we obtained a result which justifies the interchange of the order of integration over the region $\{(x, t) : a \leq x, \alpha \leq t \leq \beta\}$. It is also desirable to be able to interchange the order of integration of an iterated infinite integral. That is, we wish to establish the equality

$$(25.23) \qquad \int_{\alpha}^{+\infty} \left\{ \int_{b}^{+\infty} f(x, t) \, dx \right\} dt = \int_{a}^{+\infty} \left\{ \int_{\alpha}^{+\infty} f(x, t) \, dt \right\} dx,$$

under suitable hypotheses. It turns out that a simple condition can be given which will also imply absolute convergence of the integrals. However, in order to treat iterated infinite integrals which are not necessarily absolutely convergent, a more complicated set of conditions is required.

25.23 Theorem. *Suppose that f is a non-negative function defined for (x, t) satisfying $x \geq a$, $t \geq \alpha$. Suppose that*

$$(25.24) \qquad \int_{\alpha}^{+\infty} \left\{ \int_{a}^{b} f(x, t) \, dx \right\} dt = \int_{a}^{b} \left\{ \int_{\alpha}^{+\infty} f(x, t) \, dt \right\} dx$$

for each $b \geq a$ and that

$$(25.25) \qquad \int_{\alpha}^{\beta} \left\{ \int_{a}^{+\infty} f(x, t) \, dx \right\} dt = \int_{a}^{+\infty} \left\{ \int_{\alpha}^{\beta} f(x, t) \, dt \right\} dx$$

for each $\beta \geq \alpha$. Then, if one of the iterated integrals in equation (25.23) *exists, the other also exists and they are equal.*

PROOF. Suppose that the integral on the left side of (25.23) exists. Since f is non-negative,

$$\int_{a}^{b} f(x, t) \, dx \leq \int_{a}^{+\infty} f(x, t) \, dx$$

for each $b \geq a$ and $t \geq \alpha$. Therefore, it follows from the Comparison Test 25.7, that

$$\int_{\alpha}^{+\infty} \left\{ \int_{a}^{b} f(x, t) \, dx \right\} dt \leq \int_{\alpha}^{+\infty} \left\{ \int_{a}^{+\infty} f(x, t) \, dx \right\} dt.$$

Employing relation (25.24), we conclude that

$$\int_{a}^{b} \left\{ \int_{\alpha}^{+\infty} f(x, t) \, dt \right\} dx \leq \int_{\alpha}^{+\infty} \left\{ \int_{a}^{+\infty} f(x, t) \, dx \right\} dt.$$

for each $b \geq a$. An application of Theorem 25.6 shows that we can take the limit as $b \to +\infty$, so the other iterated integral exists and

$$\int_{a}^{+\infty} \left\{ \int_{\alpha}^{+\infty} f(x, t) \, dt \right\} dx \leq \int_{\alpha}^{+\infty} \left\{ \int_{a}^{+\infty} f(x, t) \, dx \right\} dt.$$

If we repeat this argument and apply equation (25.25), we obtain the reverse inequality. Therefore, the equality must hold and we obtain (25.23).

Q.E.D.

25.24 Corollary. *Suppose that f is defined for (x, t) with x $\geq$ α, t $\geq$ α, and that equations (25.24) and (25.25) hold. If the iterated integral*

$$\int_{\alpha}^{+\infty} \left\{ \int_{a}^{+\infty} |f(x, t)| dx \right\} dt$$

exists, then both of the integrals in (25.23) exist and are equal.

PROOF. Break f into positive and negative parts in the following manner. Let f_1 and f_2 be defined by

$$f_1 = \tfrac{1}{2}(|f| + f), \qquad f_2 = \tfrac{1}{2}(|f| - f),$$

then f_1 and f_2 are non-negative and $f = f_1 - f_2$. It is readily seen that equations (25.24) and (25.25) hold with f replaced by $|f|$, and hence by f_1 and f_2. Since $0 \leq f_1 \leq |f|$ and $0 \leq f_2 \leq |f|$, the Comparison Test assures that the iterated integrals of f_1, f_2 exist. Hence the theorem can be applied to f_1, f_2. Since $f = f_1 - f_2$, the conclusion is obtained.

Q.E.D.

25.25 Theorem. *Suppose that f is continuous for x $\geq$ a, t $\geq$ α, and that there exist non-negative functions M and N such that the infinite integrals*

$$\int_{a}^{+\infty} M, \qquad \int_{\alpha}^{+\infty} N$$

exist. If the inequality

(25.26) $$|f(x, t)| \leq M(x)N(t)$$

holds, then the iterated integrals in (25.23) both exist and are equal.

PROOF. Since N is bounded on each interval $[\alpha, \beta]$, it follows from the inequality (25.26) and the Weierstrass M-test 25.14 that the integral

$$\int_{a}^{+\infty} f(x, t) \, dx$$

exists uniformly for t in $[\alpha, \beta]$. By applying Theorem 25.18, we observe that the formula (25.25) holds for each $\beta \geq \alpha$. Similarly, (25.24) holds for each $b \geq a$. Moreover, the Comparison Test implies that the iterated limits exist. Therefore, this equality follows from Theorem 25.23.

Q.E.D.

All of these results deal with the case that the iterated integrals are absolutely convergent. We now present a result which treats the case of non-absolute convergence.

25.26 THEOREM. *Suppose that the real-valued function f is continuous in (x, t) for $x \geq a$ and $t \geq \alpha$ and that the infinite integrals*

$$(25.27) \qquad \int_a^{+\infty} f(x, t) \, dx, \qquad \int_\alpha^{+\infty} f(x, t) \, dt$$

converge uniformly for $t \geq \alpha$ and $x \geq a$, respectively. In addition, let F be defined by

$$F(x, \beta) = \int_\alpha^\beta f(x, t) \, dt$$

and suppose that the infinite integral

$$(25.28) \qquad \int_a^{+\infty} F(x, \beta) \, dx$$

converges uniformly for $\beta \geq \alpha$. Then both iterated infinite integrals exist and are equal.

PROOF. Since the infinite integral (25.28) is uniformly convergent for $\beta \geq \alpha$, if $\epsilon > 0$ there exists a number $A_\epsilon \geq a$ such that if $A \geq A_\epsilon$, then

$$(25.29) \qquad \left| \int_a^A F(x, \beta) \, dx - \int_a^{+\infty} F(x, \beta) \, dx \right| < \epsilon$$

for all $\beta \geq \alpha$. Also we observe that

$$(25.30) \qquad \int_a^A F(x, \beta) \, dx = \int_a^A \left\{ \int_\alpha^\beta f(x, t) \, dt \right\} dx$$

$$= \int_\alpha^\beta \left\{ \int_a^A f(x, t) \, dx \right\} dt.$$

From Theorem 25.18 and the uniform convergence of the second integral in (25.27), we infer that

$$\lim_{\beta \to +\infty} \int_a^A F(x, \beta) \, dx = \int_a^A \left\{ \int_\alpha^{+\infty} f(x, t) \, dt \right\} dx.$$

Hence there exists a number $B \geq \alpha$ such that if $\beta_2 \geq \beta_1 \geq B$, then

$$(25.31) \qquad \left| \int_a^A F(x, \beta_2) \, dx - \int_a^A F(x, \beta_1) \, dx \right| < \epsilon.$$

By combining (25.29) and (25.31), it is seen that if $\beta_2 \geq \beta_1 \geq B$, then

$$\left| \int_a^{+\infty} F(x, \beta_2) \, dx - \int_a^{+\infty} F(x, \beta_1) \, dx \right| < 3\epsilon,$$

whence it follows that the limit of $\int_a^{+\infty} F(x, \beta) \, dx$ exists as $\beta \to +\infty$.

After applying Theorem 25.18 to the uniform convergence of the first integral in (25.27) and using (25.30), we have

$$\lim_{\beta \to +\infty} \int_a^{+\infty} F(x, \beta) \, dx = \lim_{\beta \to +\infty} \int_a^{+\infty} \left\{ \int_\alpha^\beta f(x, t) \, dt \right\} dx$$

$$= \lim_{\beta \to +\infty} \int_\alpha^\beta \left\{ \int_a^{+\infty} f(x, t) \, dx \right\} dt = \int_\alpha^{+\infty} \left\{ \int_a^{+\infty} f(x, t) \, dx \right\} dt.$$

Since both terms on the left side of (25.29) have limits as $\beta \to +\infty$ we conclude, on passing to the limit, that

$$\left| \int_a^A \left\{ \int_\alpha^{+\infty} f(x, t) \, dt \right\} dx - \int_\alpha^{+\infty} \left\{ \int_a^{+\infty} f(x, t) \, dx \right\} dt \right| \leq \epsilon.$$

If we let $A \to +\infty$, we obtain the equality of the iterated improper integrals.

Q.E.D.

The theorems given above justifying the interchange of the order of integration are often useful, but they still leave ample room for ingenuity. Frequently they are used in conjunction with the Dominated or Monotone Convergence Theorems 25.21 and 25.22.

25.27 EXAMPLES. (a) If $f(x, t) = e^{-(x+t)} \sin (xt)$, then we can take $M(x) = e^{-x}$ and $N(t) = e^{-t}$ and apply Theorem 25.25 to infer that

$$\int_0^{+\infty} \left\{ \int_0^{+\infty} e^{-(x+t)} \sin (xt) \, dx \right\} dt = \int_0^{+\infty} \left\{ \int_0^{+\infty} e^{-(x+t)} \sin (xt) \, dt \right\} dx.$$

(b) If $g(x, t) = e^{-xt}$, for $x \geq 0$ and $t \geq 0$, then we are in trouble on the lines $x = 0$ and $t = 0$. However, if $a > 0$, $\alpha > 0$, and $x \geq a$ and $t \geq \alpha$, then we observe that

$$e^{-xt} = e^{-(xt)/2} e^{-(xt)/2} \leq e^{-\alpha x/2} e^{-at/2},$$

If we set $M(x) = e^{-\alpha x/2}$ and $N(t) = e^{-at/2}$, then Theorem 25.25 implies that

$$\int_\alpha^{+\infty} \left\{ \int_a^{+\infty} e^{-xt} \, dx \right\} dt = \int_a^{+\infty} \left\{ \int_\alpha^{+\infty} e^{-xt} \, dt \right\} dx.$$

(c) Consider the function

$$f(x, y) = xe^{-x^2(1+y^2)}$$

for $x \geq a > 0$ and $y \geq 0$. If we put $M(x) = xe^{-x^2}$ and $N(y) = e^{-a^2 y^2}$, then we can invert the order of integration over $a \leq x$ and $0 \leq y$. Since we have

$$\int_a^{+\infty} xe^{-(1+y^2)x^2} \, dx = \frac{-e^{-(1+y^2)x^2}}{2(1+y^2)}\Big|_{x=a}^{x \to +\infty}$$

$$= \frac{e^{-a^2(1+y^2)}}{2(1+y^2)},$$

it follows that

$$\frac{e^{-a^2}}{2} \int_0^{+\infty} \frac{e^{-a^2 y^2}}{1+y^2} \, dy = \int_a^{+\infty} e^{-x^2} \left\{ \int_0^{+\infty} xe^{-x^2 y^2} \, dy \right\} dx.$$

If we introduce the change of variable $t = xy$, we find that

$$\int_0^{+\infty} xe^{-x^2 y^2} \, dy = \int_0^{+\infty} e^{-t^2} \, dt = I.$$

It follows that

$$\int_0^{+\infty} \frac{e^{-a^2 y^2}}{1+y^2} \, dy = 2e^{a^2} I \int_a^{+\infty} e^{-x^2} \, dx.$$

If we let $a \to 0$, the expression on the right side converges to $2I^2$. On the left hand side, we observe that the integrand is dominated by the integrable function $(1+y^2)^{-1}$. Applying the Dominated Convergence Theorem, we have

$$\frac{\pi}{2} = \int_0^{+\infty} \frac{dy}{1+y^2} = \lim_{a \to 0} \int_0^{+\infty} \frac{e^{-a^2 y^2}}{1+y^2} \, dy = 2I^2.$$

Therefore $I^2 = \pi/4$, which yields a new derivation of the formula

$$\int_0^{+\infty} e^{-x^2} \, dx = \frac{\sqrt{\pi}}{2}.$$

(d) If we integrate by parts twice, we obtain the formula

$$(25.32) \quad \int_a^{+\infty} e^{-xy} \sin(x) \, dx = \frac{e^{-ay}}{1+y^2} \cos(a) + \frac{ye^{-ay}}{1+y^2} \sin(a).$$

If $x \geq a > 0$ and $y \geq \alpha > 0$, we can argue as in Example (b) to show that

$$
\int_\alpha^{+\infty} \frac{e^{-ay} \cos (a)}{1 + y^2}\, dy + \int_\alpha^{+\infty} \frac{y e^{-ay} \sin (a)}{1 + y^2}\, dy
$$

$$
= \int_a^{+\infty} \left\{ \int_\alpha^{+\infty} e^{-xy} \sin (x)\, dy \right\} dx
$$

$$
= \int_a^{+\infty} \frac{e^{-\alpha x} \sin (x)}{x}\, dx.
$$

We want to take the limit as $a \to 0$. In the last integral this can evidently be done, and we obtain

$$
\int_0^{+\infty} \frac{e^{-\alpha x} \sin (x)}{x}\, dx.
$$

In view of the fact that $e^{-ay} \cos (a)$ is dominated by 1 for $y \geq 0$, and the integral

$$
\int_\alpha^{+\infty} \frac{1}{1 + y^2}\, dy
$$

exists, we can use the Dominated Convergence Theorem 25.21 to conclude that

$$
\lim_{a \to 0} \int_\alpha^{+\infty} \frac{e^{-ay} \cos (a)}{1 + y^2}\, dy = \int_\alpha^{+\infty} \frac{dy}{1 + y^2}\, \cdot
$$

The second integral is a bit more troublesome as the same type of estimate shows that

$$
\left| \frac{y e^{-ay} \sin (a)}{1 + y^2} \right| \leq \frac{y}{1 + y^2},
$$

and the dominant function is not integrable; hence we must do better. Since $u \leq e^u$ and $|\sin (u)| \leq u$ for $u \geq 0$, we infer that $|e^{-ay} \sin (a)| \leq 1/y$, whence we obtain the sharper estimate

$$
\left| \frac{y e^{-ay} \sin (a)}{1 + y^2} \right| \leq \frac{1}{1 + y^2}\, \cdot
$$

We can now employ the Dominated Convergence Theorem to take the limit under the integral sign, to obtain

$$
\lim_{a \to 0} \int_\alpha^{+\infty} \frac{y e^{-ay} \sin (a)}{1 + y^2}\, dy = 0.
$$

We have arrived at the formula

$$
\frac{\pi}{2} - \text{Arc tan} (\alpha) = \int_\alpha^{+\infty} \frac{dy}{1 + y^2} = \int_0^{+\infty} \frac{e^{-\alpha x} \sin (x)}{x}\, dx.
$$

We now want to take the limit as $\alpha \to 0$. This time we cannot use the Dominated Convergence Theorem, since $\int_0^{+\infty} x^{-1} \sin(x)\, dx$ is not absolutely convergent. Although the convergence of $e^{-\alpha x}$ to 1 as $\alpha \to 0$ is monotone, the fact that $\sin(x)$ takes both signs implies that the convergence of the entire integrand is not monotone. Fortunately, we have already seen in Example 25.16(d) that the convergence of the integral is uniform for $\alpha \geq 0$. According to Theorem 25.17, the integral is continuous for $\alpha \geq 0$ and hence we once more obtain the formula

$$\int_0^{+\infty} \frac{\sin(x)}{x}\, dx = \frac{\pi}{2}$$

Exercises

25.A. Suppose that f is a bounded real-valued function on $J = [a, b]$ and that f is integrable over $[c, b]$ for all $c > a$. Prove that the improper integral of f over J exists.

25.B. Suppose that f is integrable over $[c, b]$ for all $c > a$ and that the improper integral $\int_{a+}^{b} |f|$ exists. Shows that the improper integral $\int_{a+}^{b} f$ exists, but that the converse may not be true.

25.C. Suppose that f and g are integrable on $[c, b]$ for all $c > a$. If $|f(x)| \leq g(x)$ for $x \in J = [a, b]$ and if g has an improper integral on J, then so does f.

25.D. Discuss the convergence or the divergence of the following improper integrals:

(a) $\int_0^1 \dfrac{dx}{(x + x^2)^{1/2}}$,

(b) $\int_0^1 \dfrac{dx}{(x - x^2)^{1/2}}$,

(c) $\int_0^1 \dfrac{x\, dx}{(1 - x^3)}$,

(d) $\int_0^1 \dfrac{\log(x)}{\sqrt{x}}\, dx$,

(e) $\int_0^1 \dfrac{\log(x)}{1 - x^2}\, dx$,

(f) $\int_0^1 \dfrac{x\, dx}{(1 - x^3)^{1/2}}$.

25.E. Determine the values of p and q for which the following integrals converge:

(a) $\int_0^1 x^p (1 - x)^q\, dx$,

(b) $\int_0^{\pi/2} x^p [\sin(x)]^q\, dx$,

(c) $\int_1^2 [\log(x)]^p\, dx$,

(d) $\int_0^1 x^p [-\log(x)]^q\, dx$,

25.F. Discuss the convergence or the divergence of the following integrals. Which are absolutely convergent?

(a) $\int_1^{+\infty} \dfrac{dx}{x(1 + \sqrt{x})}$,

(b) $\int_1^{+\infty} \dfrac{x + 2}{x^2 + 1}\, dx$,

(c) $\int_1^{+\infty} \dfrac{\sin(1/x)}{x}\, dx$,

(d) $\int_1^{+\infty} \dfrac{\cos(x)}{\sqrt{x}}\, dx$,

(e) $\int_0^{+\infty} \dfrac{x\sin(x)}{1 + x^2}\, dx$,

(f) $\int_0^{+\infty} \dfrac{\sin(x)\sin(2x)}{x}\, dx$.

25.G. For what values of p and q are the following integrals convergent? For what values are they absolutely convergent?

(a) $\int_1^{+\infty} \dfrac{x^p}{1 + x^q}\, dx$,

(b) $\int_1^{+\infty} \dfrac{\sin(x)}{x^q}\, dx$,

(c) $\int_1^{+\infty} \dfrac{\sin(x^p)}{x}\, dx$,

(d) $\int_1^{+\infty} \dfrac{1 - \cos(x)}{x^q}\, dx$.

25.H. If f is integrable on any interval $[0, c]$ for $c > 0$, show that the infinite integral $\int_0^{+\infty} f$ exists if and only if the infinite integral $\int_5^{+\infty} f$ exists.

25.I. Give an example where the infinite integral $\int_0^{+\infty} f$ exists but where f is not bounded on the set $\{x : x \ge 0\}$.

25.J. If f is monotone and the infinite integral $\int_0^{+\infty} f$ exists, then $xf(x) \to 0$ as $x \to +\infty$.

25.K. Show that the integral $\int_0^{+\infty} x^t e^{-x}\, dx$ converges uniformly for t in an interval $[0, \beta]$ but that it does not converge uniformly for $t \ge 0$.

25.L. Show that the integral

$$\int_0^{+\infty} \frac{\sin(tx)}{x}\, dx$$

is uniformly convergent for $t \ge 1$, but that it is not absolutely convergent for any of these values of t.

25.M. For what values of t do the following infinite integrals converge uniformly?

(a) $\int_0^{+\infty} \dfrac{dx}{x^2 + t^2}$,

(b) $\int_0^{+\infty} \dfrac{dx}{x^2 + t}$,

(c) $\displaystyle\int_0^{+\infty} e^{-x}\cos(tx)\,dx,$ (d) $\displaystyle\int_0^{+\infty} x^n e^{-x^2}\cos(tx)\,dx,$

(e) $\displaystyle\int_0^{+\infty} e^{-x^2-t^2/x^2}\,dx,$ (f) $\displaystyle\int_0^{+\infty} \frac{t}{x^2} e^{-x^2-t^2/x^2}\,dx.$

25.N. Use formula (25.13) to show that $\Gamma(\tfrac{1}{2}) = \sqrt{\pi}$.

25.O. Use formula (25.13) to show that $\displaystyle\int_0^{+\infty} e^{-tx^2}\,dx = \tfrac{1}{2}\sqrt{\pi/t}$ for $t > 0$. Justify the differentiation and show that

$$\int_0^{+\infty} x^{2n} e^{-x^2}\,dx = \frac{1\cdot 3\cdots(2n-1)}{2^{n+1}}\sqrt{\pi}.$$

25.P. Establish the existence of the integral $\displaystyle\int_0^{+\infty} \frac{1-e^{-x^2}}{x^2}\,dx$. (Note that the integrand can be defined to be continuous at $x = 0$.) Evaluate this integral by

(a) replacing e^{-x^2} by e^{-tx^2} and differentiating with respect to t;

(b) integrating $\displaystyle\int_1^{+\infty} e^{-tx^2}\,dx$ with respect to t. Justify all of the steps.

25.Q. Let F be given for $t \in \mathbf{R}$ by

$$F(t) = \int_0^{+\infty} e^{-x^2}\cos(tx)\,dx.$$

Differentiate with respect to t and integrate by parts to prove that $F'(t) = (-1/2)t\,F(t)$. Then find $F(t)$ and, after a change of variable, establish the formula

$$\int_0^{+\infty} e^{-cx^2}\cos(tx)\,dx = \frac{1}{2}\sqrt{\frac{\pi}{c}}\,e^{-t^2/4c}, \qquad c > 0.$$

25.R. Let G be defined for $t > 0$ by

$$G(t) = \int_0^{+\infty} e^{-x^2-t^2/x^2}\,dx.$$

Differentiate and change variables to show that $G'(t) = -2G(t)$. Then find $G(t)$ and, after a change of variables, establish the formula

$$\int_0^{+\infty} e^{-x^2-t^2/x^2}\,dx = \frac{\sqrt{\pi}}{2}\,e^{-2|t|}.$$

25.S. Use formula (25.21), elementary trigonometric formulas, and manipulations to show that

(a) $\dfrac{2}{\pi} \displaystyle\int_0^{+\infty} \dfrac{\sin(ax)}{x}\, dx = 1, \qquad a > 0,$

$\qquad\qquad\qquad\qquad\quad\ = 0, \qquad a = 0,$

$\qquad\qquad\qquad\qquad\quad\ = -1, \qquad a < 0.$

(b) $\dfrac{2}{\pi} \displaystyle\int_0^{+\infty} \dfrac{\sin(x)\cos(ax)}{x}\, dx = 1, \qquad |a| < 1,$

$\qquad\qquad\qquad\qquad\qquad\quad\ = \tfrac{1}{2}, \qquad |a| = 1,$

$\qquad\qquad\qquad\qquad\qquad\quad\ = 0, \qquad |a| > 1.$

(c) $\dfrac{2}{\pi} \displaystyle\int_0^{+\infty} \dfrac{\sin(x)\sin(ax)}{x}\, dx = -1, \qquad a < -1,$

$\qquad\qquad\qquad\qquad\qquad\quad\ = a, \qquad -1 \le a \le +1,$

$\qquad\qquad\qquad\qquad\qquad\quad\ = +1, \qquad a > +1.$

(d) $\dfrac{2}{\pi} \displaystyle\int \left[\dfrac{\sin(x)}{x}\right]^2 dx = 1.$

25.T. For $n \in \mathbf{N}$ let f_n be defined by

$$f_n(x) = 1/x, \qquad 1 \le x \le n,$$
$$= 0, \qquad x > n.$$

Each f_n has an integral for $x \ge 1$ and the sequence (f_n) is bounded, monotone increasing, and converges uniformly to a continuous function which is not integrable over $\{x \in \mathbf{R} : x \ge 1\}$.

25.U. Let g_n be defined by

$$g_n(x) = 1/n, \qquad 0 \le x \le n^2,$$
$$= 0, \qquad x > n^2.$$

Each g_n has an integral over $x \ge 0$ and the sequence (g_n) is bounded and converges to a function g which has an integral over $x \ge 0$, but it is *not* true that

$$\lim \int_0^{+\infty} g_n = \int_0^{+\infty} g.$$

Is the convergence monotone?

25.V. If $f(x, t) = (x - t)/(x + t)^3$, show that

$$\int_1^A \left\{ \int_1^{+\infty} f(x, t)dx \right\} dt > 0 \quad \text{for each} \quad A \ge 1;$$

$$\int_1^B \left\{ \int_1^{+\infty} f(x, t)dt \right\} dx < 0 \quad \text{for each} \quad B \ge 1.$$

Hence, show that

$$\int_1^{+\infty} \left\{ \int_1^{+\infty} f(x, t)\, dx \right\} dt \ne \int_1^{+\infty} \left\{ \int_1^{+\infty} f(x, t)dt \right\} dx.$$

25.W. Using an argument similar to that in Example 25.27(c) and formulas from Exercises 25.Q and 25.R, show that

$$\int_0^{+\infty} \frac{\cos(ty)}{1 + y^2} \, dy = \frac{\pi}{2} e^{-|t|}.$$

25.X. By considering the iterated integrals of $e^{-(a+y)x} \sin(y)$ over the quadrant $x \geq 0$, $y \geq 0$, establish the formula

$$\int_0^{+\infty} \frac{e^{-ax}}{1 + x^2} \, dx = \int_0^{+\infty} \frac{\sin(y)}{a + y} \, dy, \qquad a > 0.$$

Projects

25.α. This project treats the **Gamma function**, which was introduced in Example 25.10(e). Recall that Γ is defined for x in $P = \{x \in \mathbf{R} : x > 0\}$ by the integral

$$\Gamma(x) = \int_{0+}^{+\infty} e^{-t} t^{x-1} \, dt.$$

We have already seen that this integral converges for $x \in P$ and that $\Gamma(\frac{1}{2}) = \sqrt{\pi}$.

(a) Show that Γ is continuous on P.

(b) Prove that $\Gamma(x + 1) = x\Gamma(x)$ for $x \in P$. (Hint: integrate by parts on the interval $[\epsilon, c]$.)

(c) Show that $\Gamma(n + 1) = n!$ for $n \in \mathbf{N}$.

(d) Show that $\lim\limits_{x \to 0+} x\Gamma(x) = 1$. Hence it follows that Γ is not bounded to the right of $x = 0$.

(e) Show that Γ is differentiable on P and that the second derivative is always positive. (Hence Γ is a convex function on P.)

(f) By changing the variable t, show that

$$\Gamma(x) = 2 \int_{0+}^{+\infty} e^{-s^2} s^{2x-1} \, ds = u^x \int_{0+}^{+\infty} e^{-us} s^{x-1} \, ds.$$

25.β. We introduce the **Beta function** of Euler. Let $B(x, y)$ be defined for x, y in $P = \{x \in \mathbf{R} : x > 0\}$ by

$$B(x, y) = \int_{0+}^{1-} t^{x-1} (1 - t)^{y-1} \, dt.$$

If $x \geq 1$ and $y \geq 1$, this integral is proper, but if $0 < x < 1$ or $0 < y < 1$, the integral is improper.

(a) Establish the convergence of the integral for x, y in P.

(b) Prove that $B(x, y) = B(y, x)$.

(c) Show that if x, y belong to P, then

$$B(x, y) = 2 \int_{0+}^{+\infty} (\sin t)^{2x-1} (\cos t)^{2y-1} dt$$

and

$$B(x, y) = \int_{0+}^{+\infty} \frac{u^{x-1}}{(1 + u)^{x+y}} du.$$

(d) By integrating the non-negative function

$$f(t, u) = e^{-t^2-u^2} t^{2x-1} u^{2y-1}$$

over $\{(t, u): t^2 + u^2 = R^2, t \geq 0, u \geq 0\}$ and comparing this integral with the integral over inscribed and circumscribed squares (as in Example 25.10(b)), derive the important formula

$$B(x, y) = \frac{\Gamma(x)\Gamma(y)}{\Gamma(x + y)}.$$

(e) Establish the integration formulas

$$\int_0^{\pi/2} (\sin x)^{2n} dx = \frac{\sqrt{\pi}\,\Gamma(n + \frac{1}{2})}{2\Gamma(n + 1)} = \frac{1 \cdot 3 \cdot 5 \cdots (2n - 1)}{2 \cdot 4 \cdot 6 \cdots (2n)} \frac{\pi}{2},$$

$$\int_0^{\pi/2} (\sin x)^{2n+1} dx = \frac{\sqrt{\pi}\,\Gamma(n + 1)}{2\,\Gamma(n + \frac{3}{2})} = \frac{2 \cdot 4 \cdot 6 \cdots (2n)}{1 \cdot 3 \cdot 5 \cdot 7 \cdots (2n + 1)}.$$

25.γ. This and the next project present a few of the properties of the Laplace† transform, which is important both for theoretical and applied mathematics. To simplify the discussion, we shall restrict our attention to continuous functions f defined on $\{t \in \mathbf{R} : t \geq 0\}$ to $\mathbf{R}$. The **Laplace transform** of f is the function $\hat{f}$ defined at the real number s by the formula

$$\hat{f}(s) = \int_0^{+\infty} e^{-st} f(t) \, dt,$$

whenever this integral converges. Sometimes we denote $\hat{f}$ by $\mathfrak{L}(f)$.

(a) Suppose there exists a real number c such that $|f(t)| \leq e^{ct}$ for sufficiently large t. Then the integral defining the Laplace transform $\hat{f}$ converges for $s > c$. Moreover, it converges uniformly for $s \geq c + \delta$ if $\delta > 0$.

(b) If f satisfies the boundedness condition in part (a), then $\hat{f}$ is continuous and has a derivative for $s > c$ given by the formula

$$\hat{f}'(s) = \int_0^{+\infty} e^{-st} (-t)f(t) \, dt.$$

---

† PIERRE-SIMON LAPLACE (1749–1827), the son of a Norman farmer, became professor at the Military School in Paris and was elected to the Academy of Sciences. He is famous for his work on celestial mechanics and probability.

[Thus the derivative of the Laplace transform of f is the Laplace transform of the function $g(t) = -tf(t)$.]

(c) By induction, show that under the boundedness condition in (a), then $\hat{f}$ has derivatives of all orders for $s > c$ and that

$$\hat{f}^{(n)}(s) = \int_0^{+\infty} e^{-st}\, (-t)^n f(t)\, dt.$$

(d) Suppose f and g are continuous functions whose Laplace transforms $\hat{f}$ and $\hat{g}$ converge for $s > s_0$, and if a and b are real numbers then the function $af + bg$ has a Laplace transform converging for $s > s_0$ and which equals $a\hat{f} + b\hat{g}$.

(e) If $a > 0$ and $g(t) = f(at)$, then $\hat{g}$ converges for $s > as_0$ and

$$\hat{g}(s) = \frac{1}{a}\hat{f}\left(\frac{s}{a}\right).$$

Similarly, if $h(t) = \dfrac{1}{a} f\left(\dfrac{t}{a}\right)$, then $\hat{h}$ converges for $s > s_0/a$ and

$$\hat{h}(s) = \hat{f}\,(as).$$

(f) Suppose that the Laplace transform $\hat{f}$ of f exists for $s > s_0$ and let f be defined for $t < 0$ to be equal to 0. If $b > 0$ and if $g(t) = f(t - b)$, then $\hat{g}$ converges for $s > s_0$ and

$$\hat{g}(s) = e^{-bs}\,\hat{f}(s).$$

Similarly, if $h(t) = e^{bt}f(t)$ for any real b, then $\hat{h}$ converges for $s > s_0 + b$ and

$$\hat{h}(s) = \hat{f}(s - b).$$

25.δ. This project continues the preceding one and makes use of its results.

(a) Establish the following short table of Laplace transforms.

$f(t)$	$\hat{f}(s)$	Interval of Convergence
1	$1/s$	$s > 0,$
t^n	$n!/s^{n+1}$	$s > 0,$
e^{at}	$(s-a)^{-1}$	$s > a,$
$t^n e^{at}$	$n!/(s-a)^{n+1}$	$s > a,$
$\sin at$	$\dfrac{a}{s^2 + a^2}$	all $s,$
$\cos at$	$\dfrac{s}{s^2 + a^2}$	all $s,$
$\sinh at$	$\dfrac{a}{s^2 - a^2}$	$s > a,$
$\cosh at$	$\dfrac{s}{s^2 - a^2}$	$s > a,$
$\dfrac{\sin t}{t}$	$\operatorname{Arc\,tan}(1/s)$	$s > 0.$

(b) Suppose that f and f' are continuous for $t \geq 0$, that $\hat{f}$ converges for $s > s_0$ and that $e^{-st}f(t) \to 0$ as $t \to +\infty$ for all $s > s_0$. Then the Laplace transform of f' exists for $s > s_0$ and

$$\hat{f'}(s) = s\hat{f}(s) - f(0).$$

(Hint: integrate by parts.)

(c) Suppose that f, f' and f'' are continuous for $t \geq 0$ and that $\hat{f}$ converges for $s > s_0$. In addition, suppose that $e^{-st}f(t)$ and $e^{-st}f'(t)$ approach 0 as $t \to +\infty$ for all $s > s_0$. Then the Laplace transform of f'' exists for $s > s_0$ and

$$\hat{f''}(s) = s^2\hat{f}(s) - sf(0) - f'(0).$$

(d) When all or part of an integrand is seen to be a Laplace transform, the integral can sometimes be evaluated by changing the order of integration. Use this method to evaluate the integral

$$\int_0^{+\infty} \frac{\sin s}{s}\, ds = \frac{\pi}{2}.$$

(e) It is desired to solve the differential equation

$$y'(t) + 2y(t) = 3\sin t, \qquad y(0) = 1.$$

Assume that this equation has a solution y such that the Laplace transforms of y and y' exists for sufficiently large s. In this case the transform of y must satisfy the equation

$$s\hat{y}(s) - y(0) + 2\hat{y}(s) = 4/(s-1), \qquad s > 1,$$

from which it follows that

$$\hat{y}(s) = \frac{s+3}{(s+2)(s-1)}.$$

Use partial fractions and the table in (a) to obtain $y(t) = (\tfrac{4}{3})e^t - (\tfrac{1}{3})e^{-2t}$, which can be directly verified to be a solution.

(f) Find the solution of the equation

$$y'' + y' = 0, \qquad y(0) = a, \qquad y'(0) = b,$$

by using the Laplace transform.

(g) Show that a linear homogeneous differential equation with constant coefficients can be solved by using the Laplace transform and the technique of decomposing a rational function into partial fractions.

VII

Infinite Series

This chapter is concerned with establishing the most important theorems in the theory of infinite series. Although a few peripheral results are included here, our attention is directed to the basic propositions. The reader is referred to more extensive treatises for advanced results and applications.

In the first section we shall present the main theorems concerning the convergence of infinite series in R^p. We shall obtain some results of a general nature which serve to establish the convergence of series and justify certain manipulations with series.

In Section 27 we shall give some familiar "tests" for the convergence of series. In addition to guaranteeing the convergence of the series to which the tests are applicable, each of these tests yields a quantitative estimate concerning the *rapidity* of the convergence.

The final section discusses series of functions, with special attention being paid to power series. Although this discussion is not lengthy, it presents the results that are of greatest utility in real analysis.

Section 26   Convergence of Infinite Series

In elementary texts, an infinite series is sometimes "defined" to be "an expression of the form

(26.1) $$x_1 + x_2 + \cdots + x_n + \cdots.$$"

This "definition" lacks clarity, however, since there is no particular value that we can attach a priori to this array of symbols which calls for an infinite number of additions to be performed. Although there are other definitions that are suitable, we shall take an infinite series to be the same as the sequence of partial sums.

26.1 Definition. If $X = (x_n)$ is a sequence in $\mathbf{R}^p$, then the **infinite series** (or simply the **series**) generated by X is the sequence $S = (s_k)$ defined by

$$s_1 = x_1,$$
$$s_2 = s_1 + x_2 (= x_1 + x_2),$$
$$\cdot \ \cdot \ \cdot \ \cdot \ \cdot \ \cdot \ \cdot \ \cdot \ \cdot \ \cdot \ \cdot \ \cdot$$
$$s_k = s_{k-1} + x_k (= x_1 + x_2 + \cdots + x_k),$$
$$\cdot \ \cdot \ \cdot \ \cdot \ \cdot \ \cdot \ \cdot \ \cdot \ \cdot \ \cdot \ \cdot \ \cdot$$

If S converges, we refer to $\lim S$ as the **sum** of the infinite series. The elements x_n are called the **terms** and the elements s_k are called the **partial sums** of this infinite series.

It is conventional to use the expression (26.1) or one of the symbols

$$(26.2) \qquad \sum (x_n), \qquad \sum_{n=1}^{\infty} (x_n), \qquad \sum_{n=1}^{\infty} x_n$$

both to denote the infinite series generated by the sequence $X = (x_n)$ and also to denote $\lim S$ in the case that this infinite series is convergent. In actual practice, the double use of these notations does not lead to confusion, provided it is understood that the convergence of the series must be established.

The reader should guard against confusing the words "sequence" and "series." In non-mathematical language, these words are interchangeable; in mathematics, however, they are not synonyms. According to our definition, an infinite series is a sequence S obtained from a given sequence X according to a special procedure that was stated above. There are many other ways of generating new sequences and attaching "sums" to the given sequence X. The reader should consult books on **divergent series, asymptotic series,** and the **summability** of series for examples of such theories.

A final word on notational matters. Although we generally index the elements of the series by natural numbers, it is sometimes more convenient to start with $n = 0$, with $n = 5$, or with $n = k$. When such is the case, we shall denote the resulting series or their sums by notations such as

$$\sum_{n=0}^{\infty} x_n, \qquad \sum_{n=5}^{\infty} x_n, \qquad \sum_{n=k}^{\infty} x_n.$$

In Definition 11.2, we defined the sum and difference of two sequences X, Y in $\mathbf{R}^p$. Similarly, if c is a real number and if w is an element in $\mathbf{R}^p$, we defined the sequences $cX = (cx_n)$ and $(w \cdot x_n)$ in $\mathbf{R}^p$ and $\mathbf{R}$, respectively. We now examine the series generated by these sequences.

26.2 THEOREM. (a) *If the series $\sum (x_n)$ and $\sum (y_n)$ converge, then the series $\sum (x_n + y_n)$ converges and the sums are related by the formula*

$$\sum (x_n + y_n) = \sum (x_n) + \sum (y_n).$$

A similar result holds for the series generated by $X - Y$.

(b) *If the series $\sum (x_n)$ is convergent, c is a real number, and w is a fixed element of $\mathbf{R}^p$, then the series $\sum (cx_n)$ and $\sum (w \cdot x_n)$ converge and*

$$\sum (cx_n) = c \sum (x_n), \quad \sum (w \cdot x_n) = w \cdot \sum (x_n).$$

PROOF.   This result follows directly from Theorem 11.14 and Definition 26.1.

Q.E.D.

It might be expected that if the sequences $X = (x_n)$ and $Y = (y_n)$ generate convergent series, then the sequence $X \cdot Y = (x_n \cdot y_n)$ also generates a convergent series. That this is not always true may be seen by taking $X = Y = ((-1)^n / \sqrt{n})$ in $\mathbf{R}$.

We now present a very simple necessary condition for convergence of a series. It is far from sufficient, however.

26.3 LEMMA. *If $\sum (x_n)$ converges in $\mathbf{R}^p$, then $\lim (x_n) = \theta$.*

PROOF.   By definition, the convergence of $\sum (x_n)$ means that $\lim (s_k)$ exists. But, since

$$x_k = s_k - s_{k-1},$$

then $\lim (x_k) = \lim (s_k) - \lim (s_{k-1}) = \theta$.

Q.E.D.

The next result, although limited in scope, is of great importance.

26.4 THEOREM. *Let (x_n) be a sequence of non-negative real numbers. Then $\sum (x_n)$ converges if and only if the sequence $S = (s_k)$ of partial sums is bounded. In this case,*

$$\sum x_n = \lim (s_k) = \sup \{s_k\}.$$

PROOF.   Since $x_n \geq 0$, the sequence of partial sums is monotone increasing:

$$s_1 \leq s_2 \leq \cdots \leq s_k \leq \cdots$$

According to the Monotone Convergence Theorem 12.1, the sequence S converges if and only if it is bounded.

Q.E.D.

Since the following Cauchy Criterion is precisely a reformulation of Theorem 12.10, we shall omit its proof.

26.5 CAUCHY CRITERION FOR SERIES. *The series $\sum (x_n)$ in $\mathbf{R}^p$ converges if and only if for each positive number ϵ there is a natural number $M(\epsilon)$ such that if $m \geq n \geq M(\epsilon)$, then*

(26.3) $|s_m - s_n| = |x_{n+1} + x_{n+2} + \cdots + x_m| < \epsilon.$

The notion of absolute convergence is often of great importance in treating series, as we shall show later.

26.6 DEFINITION. Let $X = (x_n)$ be a sequence in $\mathbf{R}^p$. We say that the series $\sum (x_n)$ is **absolutely convergent** if the series $\sum (|x_n|)$ is convergent in $\mathbf{R}$. A series is said to be **conditionally convergent** if it is convergent but not absolutely convergent.

It is stressed that for series whose elements are non-negative real numbers, there is no distinction between ordinary convergence and absolute convergence. However, for other series there is a difference.

26.7 THEOREM. *If a series in $\mathbf{R}^p$ is absolutely convergent, then it is convergent.*

PROOF. By hypothesis, the series $\sum (|x_n|)$ converges. Therefore, it follows from the necessity of the Cauchy Criterion 26.5 that given $\epsilon > 0$ there is a natural number $M(\epsilon)$ such that if $m \geq n \geq M(\epsilon)$, then

$$|x_{n+1}| + |x_{n+2}| + \cdots + |x_m| < \epsilon.$$

According to the Triangle Inequality, the left-hand side of this relation dominates

$$|x_{n+1} + x_{n+2} + \cdots + x_m|.$$

We apply the sufficiency of the Cauchy Criterion to conclude that the $\sum (x_n)$ must converge.

Q.E.D.

26.8 EXAMPLES. (a) We consider the real sequence $X = (a^n)$, which generates the geometric series

(26.4) $a + a^2 + \cdots + a^n + \cdots$

A necessary condition for convergence is that $\lim (a^n) = 0$, which requires that $|a| < 1$. If $m \geq n$, then

(26.5) $a^{n+1} + a^{n+2} + \cdots + a^m = \dfrac{a^{n+1} - a^{m+1}}{1 - a},$

as can be verified by multiplying both sides by $1 - a$ and noticing the telescoping on the left side. Hence the partial sums satisfy

$$|s_m - s_n| = |a^{n+1} + \cdots + a^m| \leq \frac{|a^{n+1}| + |a^{m+1}|}{|1 - a|}, \quad m \geq n.$$

If $|a| < 1$, then $|a^{n+1}| \to 0$ so the Cauchy Criterion implies that the geometric series (26.4) converges if and only if $|a| < 1$. Letting $n = 0$ in (26.5) and passing to the limit with respect to m we find that (26.4) converges to the limit $a/(1 - a)$ when $|a| < 1$.

(b) Consider the harmonic series $\sum (1/n)$, which is well-known to diverge. Since $\lim (1/n) = 0$, we cannot use Lemma 26.3 to establish this divergence, but must carry out a more delicate argument, which we shall base on Theorem 26.4. We shall show that a subsequence of the partial sums is not bounded. In fact, if $k_1 = 2$, then

$$s_{k_1} = \frac{1}{1} + \frac{1}{2},$$

and if $k_2 = 2^2$, then

$$s_{k_2} = \frac{1}{1} + \frac{1}{2} + \frac{1}{3} + \frac{1}{4} = s_{k_1} + \frac{1}{3} + \frac{1}{4} > s_{k_1} + 2\left(\frac{1}{4}\right) = 1 + \frac{2}{2}.$$

By mathematical induction, we establish that if $k_r = 2^r$, then

$$s_{k_r} > s_{k_{r-1}} + 2^{r-1}\left(\frac{1}{2^r}\right) = s_{k_{r-1}} + \frac{1}{2} = 1 + \frac{r}{2}.$$

Therefore, the subsequence (s_{k_r}) is not bounded and the harmonic series does not converge.

(c) We now treat the p-series $\sum (1/n^p)$ where $0 < p \leq 1$ and use the elementary inequality $n^p \leq n$, for $n \in \mathbf{N}$. From this it follows that, when $0 < p \leq 1$, then

$$\frac{1}{n} \leq \frac{1}{n^p}, \qquad n \in \mathbf{N}.$$

Since the partial sums of the harmonic series are not bounded, this inequality shows that the partial sums of $\sum (1/n^p)$ are not bounded for $0 < p \leq 1$. Hence the series diverges for these values of p.

(d) Consider the p-series for $p > 1$. Since the partial sums are monotone, it is sufficient to show that some subsequence remains bounded in order to establish the convergence of the series. If $k_1 = 2^1 - 1 = 1$, then $s_{k_1} = 1$. If $k_2 = 2^2 - 1 = 3$, we have

$$s_{k_2} = \frac{1}{1} + \left(\frac{1}{2^p} + \frac{2}{3^p}\right) < 1 + \frac{2}{2^p} = 1 + \frac{1}{2^{p-1}},$$

and if $k_3 = 2^3 - 1$, we have

$$s_{k_3} = s_{k_2} + \left(\frac{1}{4^p} + \frac{1}{5^p} + \frac{1}{6^p} + \frac{1}{7^p}\right) < s_{k_2} + \frac{4}{4^p} < 1 + \frac{1}{2^{p-1}} + \frac{1}{4^{p-1}},$$

let $a = 1/2^{p-1}$; since $p > 1$, it is seen that $0 < a < 1$. By mathematical induction, we find that if $k_r = 2^r - 1$, then

$$0 < s_{k_r} < 1 + a + a^2 + \cdots + a^{r-1}.$$

Hence the number $1/(1 - a)$ is an upper bound for the partial sums of the p-series when $1 < p$. From Theorem 26.4 it follows that for such values of p, the p-series converges.

(e) Consider the series $\sum (1/(n^2 + n))$. By using partial fractions, we can write

$$\frac{1}{k^2 + k} = \frac{1}{k(k + 1)} = \frac{1}{k} - \frac{1}{k + 1}.$$

This expression shows that the partial sums are telescoping and hence

$$s_n = \frac{1}{1 \cdot 2} + \frac{1}{2 \cdot 3} + \cdots + \frac{1}{n(n + 1)} = \frac{1}{1} - \frac{1}{n + 1}.$$

It follows that the sequence (s_n) is convergent to 1.

Rearrangements of Series

Loosely speaking, a rearrangement of a series is another series which is obtained from the given one by using all of the terms exactly once, but scrambling the order in which the terms are taken. For example, the harmonic series

$$\frac{1}{1} + \frac{1}{2} + \frac{1}{3} + \cdots + \frac{1}{n} + \cdots$$

has rearrangements

$$\frac{1}{2} + \frac{1}{1} + \frac{1}{4} + \frac{1}{3} + \cdots + \frac{1}{2n} + \frac{1}{2n - 1} + \cdots,$$

$$\frac{1}{1} + \frac{1}{2} + \frac{1}{4} + \frac{1}{3} + \frac{1}{5} + \frac{1}{7} + \cdots$$

The first rearrangement is obtained by interchanging the first and second terms, the third and fourth terms, and so forth. The second rearrangement is obtained from the harmonic series by taking one "odd term," two "even terms," three "odd terms," and so on. It is evident that there are infinitely many other possible rearrangements of the harmonic series.

26.9 **DEFINITION.** A series $\sum (y_m)$ in R^p is a **rearrangement** of a series $\sum (x_n)$ if there exists a one-one function f of N onto all of N such that $y_m = x_{f(m)}$ for all $m \in N$.

There is a remarkable observation due to Riemann, that if $\sum (x_n)$ is a series in R which is conditionally convergent (that is, it is convergent but not absolutely convergent) and if c is an arbitrary real number, then there exists a rearrangement of $\sum (x_n)$ which converges to c. The idea of the proof of this assertion is very elementary: we take positive terms until we obtain a partial sum exceeding c, then we take negative terms from the given series until we obtain a partial sum of terms less than c, etc. Since $\lim (x_n) = 0$, it is not difficult to see that a rearrangement which converges to c can be constructed.

In our manipulations with series, we generally find it convenient to be sure that rearrangements will not affect the convergence or the value of the limit.

26.10 REARRANGEMENT THEOREM. *Let $\sum (x_n)$ be an absolutely convergent series in R^p. Then any rearrangement of $\sum (x_n)$ converges absolutely to the same value.*

PROOF.   Let $\sum (y_m)$ be a rearrangement of $\sum (x_n)$. Let K be an upper bound for the partial sums of the series $\sum (|x_n|)$; if $t_r = y_1 + y_2 + \cdots + y_r$ is a partial sum of $\sum (y_m)$, then we have $|t_r| \leq K$. It follows that the series $\sum (y_m)$ is absolutely convergent to an element y of R^p. Let $x = \sum (x_n)$; we wish to show that $x = y$. If $\epsilon > 0$, let $N(\epsilon)$ be such that if $m \geq n \geq N(\epsilon)$, then $|x - s_n| < \epsilon$ and

$$\sum_{k=n+1}^{m} |x_k| < \epsilon.$$

Choose a partial sum t_r of $\sum (y_m)$ such that $|y - t_r| < \epsilon$ and such that each $x_1, x_2, \ldots, x_n$ occurs in t_r. After having done this, choose $m > n$ so large that every y_k appearing in t_r also appears in s_m. Therefore,

$$|x - y| \leq |x - s_m| + |s_m - t_r| + |t_r - y| < \epsilon + \sum_{n+1}^{m} |x_k| + \epsilon < 3\epsilon.$$

Since ϵ is any positive real number, we infer that $x = y$.

Q.E.D.

Double Series

Sometimes it is necessary to consider infinite sums depending on two integral indices. The theory of such double series is developed by reducing them to double sequences; thus all of the results in Section 14 dealing with double sequences can be interpreted for double series. However, we shall not draw from the results of Section 14; instead, we shall restrict our attention to absolutely convergent double series, since those are the type of double series that arise most often.

Suppose that to every pair (i, j) in $N \times N$ one has an element x_{ij} in R^p. One defines the (m, n)th partial sum s_{mn} to be

$$s_{mn} = \sum_{j=1}^{n} \sum_{i=1}^{m} x_{ij}.$$

By analogy with Definition 26.1, we shall say that the double series $\sum (x_{ij})$ converges to an element x in R^p if for every $\epsilon > 0$ there exists a natural number $M(\epsilon)$ such that if $m \geq M(\epsilon)$ and $n \geq M(\epsilon)$ then

$$|x - s_{mn}| < \epsilon.$$

By analogy with Definition 26.6, we shall say that the double series $\sum (x_{ij})$ is absolutely convergent if the double series $\sum (|x_{ij}|)$ in R is convergent.

It is an exercise to show that if a double series is absolutely convergent, then it is convergent. Moreover, a double series is absolutely convergent if and only if the set

$$(26.6) \qquad \left\{ \sum_{j=1}^{n} \sum_{i=1}^{m} |x_{ij}| : m, n \in N \right\}$$

is a bounded set of real numbers.

We wish to relate double series with iterated series, but we shall discuss only absolutely convergent series. The next result is very elementary, but it gives a useful criterion for the absolute convergence of the double series.

26.11 LEMMA. *Suppose that the iterated series $\sum_{j=1}^{\infty} \sum_{i=1}^{\infty} (|x_{ij}|)$ converges. Then the double series $\sum (x_{ij})$ is absolutely convergent.*

PROOF. By hypothesis each series $\sum_{i=1}^{\infty} (|x_{ij}|)$ converges to a nonnegative real number a_j, $j \in N$. Moreover, the series $\sum (a_j)$ converges to a real number A. It is clear that A is an upper bound for the set (26.6).
Q.E.D.

26.12 THEOREM. *Suppose that the double series $\sum (x_{ij})$ converges absolutely to x in R^p. Then both of the iterated series*

$$(26.7) \qquad \sum_{j=1}^{\infty} \sum_{i=1}^{\infty} x_{ij}, \qquad \sum_{i=1}^{\infty} \sum_{j=1}^{\infty} x_{ij}$$

also converge to x.

PROOF. By hypothesis there exists a positive real number A which is an upper bound for the set in (26.6). If n is fixed, we observe that

$$\sum_{i=1}^{m} |x_{in}| \leq \sum_{j=1}^{n} \sum_{i=1}^{m} |x_{ij}| \leq A,$$

for each m in N. It thus follows that, for each $n \in N$, the single series $\sum_{i=1}^{\infty} (x_{in})$ is absolutely convergent to an element y_n in R^p.

If $\epsilon > 0$, let $M(\epsilon)$ be such that if $m, n \geq M(\epsilon)$, then

(26.8) $$|s_{mn} - x| < \epsilon.$$

In view of the relation

$$s_{mn} = \sum_{i=1}^{m} x_{i1} + \sum_{i=1}^{m} x_{i2} + \cdots + \sum_{i=1}^{m} x_{in},$$

we infer that

$$\lim_{m} (s_{mn}) = \sum_{i=1}^{\infty} x_{i1} + \sum_{i=1}^{\infty} x_{i2} + \cdots + \sum_{i=1}^{\infty} x_{in}$$

$$= y_1 + y_2 + \cdots + y_n.$$

If we pass to the limit in (26.8) with respect to m, we obtain the relation

$$\left| \sum_{j=1}^{n} y_j - x \right| \leq \epsilon$$

when $n \geq M(\epsilon)$. This proves that the first iterated sum in (26.7) exists and equals x. An analogous proof applies to the second iterated sum.

Q.E.D.

There is one additional method of summing double series that we shall consider, namely along the diagonals $i + j = n$.

26.13 THEOREM. *Suppose that the double series $\sum (x_{ij})$ converges absolutely to x in $\mathbf{R}^p$. If we define*

$$t_k = \sum_{i+j=k} x_{ij} = x_{1,\,k-1} + x_{2,\,k-2} + \cdots + x_{k-1,\,1},$$

then the series $\sum (t_k)$ converges absolutely to x.

PROOF. Let A be the supremum of the set in (26.6). We observe that

$$\sum_{k=1}^{n} |t_k| \leq \sum_{j=1}^{n} \sum_{i=1}^{n} |x_{ij}| \leq A.$$

Hence the series $\sum (t_k)$ is absolutely convergent; it remains to show that it converges to x. Let $\epsilon > 0$ and let M be such that

$$A - \epsilon < \sum_{j=1}^{M} \sum_{i=1}^{M} |x_{ij}| \leq A.$$

If $m, n \geq M$, then it follows that $|s_{mn} - s_{MM}|$ is no greater than the sum $\sum (|x_{ij}|)$ extended over all pairs (i, j) satisfying either $M < i \leq m$ or $M < j \leq n$. Hence $|s_{mn} - s_{MM}| < \epsilon$, when $m, n \geq M$. It follows from this that

$$|x - s_{MM}| \leq \epsilon.$$

A similar argument shows that if $n \geq 2M$, then

$$\left| \sum_{k=1}^{n} t_k - s_{MM} \right| < \epsilon,$$

whence it follows that $x = \sum t_k$.

Q.E.D.

Cauchy Multiplication

In the process of multiplying two power series and collecting the terms according to the powers, there arises very naturally a new method of generating a series from two given ones. In this connection it is notationally useful to have the terms of the series indexed by $0, 1, 2, \ldots$.

26.14 DEFINITION. If $\sum_{i=0}^{\infty} (y_i)$ and $\sum_{j=0}^{\infty} (z_j)$ are infinite series in $\mathbf{R}^p$, their **Cauchy product** is the series $\sum_{k=0}^{\infty} (x_k)$, where

$$x_k = y_0 \cdot z_k + y_1 \cdot z_{k-1} + \cdots + y_k \cdot z_0.$$

Here the dot denotes the inner product in $\mathbf{R}^p$. In like manner we can define the Cauchy product of a series in $\mathbf{R}$ and a series in $\mathbf{R}^p$.

It is perhaps a bit surprising that the Cauchy product of two convergent series may fail to converge. However, it is seen that the series

$$\sum_{n=0}^{\infty} \frac{(-1)^n}{\sqrt{n+1}}$$

is convergent, but the nth term of the Cauchy product of this series with itself is

$$(-1)^n \left[\frac{1}{\sqrt{1}\sqrt{n+1}} + \frac{1}{\sqrt{2}\sqrt{n}} + \cdots + \frac{1}{\sqrt{n+1}\sqrt{1}} \right].$$

Since there are $n + 1$ terms in the bracket and each term exceeds $1/(n + 2)$, the terms in the Cauchy product do not converge to zero. Hence this Cauchy product cannot converge.

26.15 THEOREM. *If the series*

$$\sum_{i=0}^{\infty} y_i, \quad \sum_{j=0}^{\infty} z_j$$

converge absolutely to y, z in $\mathbf{R}^p$, then their Cauchy product converges absolutely to $y \cdot z$.

PROOF. If $i, j = 0, 1, 2, \ldots$, let $x_{ij} = y_i \cdot z_j$. The hypotheses imply that the iterated series

$$\sum_{j=0}^{\infty} \sum_{i=0}^{\infty} |x_{ij}|$$

converges. By Lemma 26.11, the double series $\sum (x_{ij})$ is absolutely convergent to a real number x. By applying Theorems 26.12 and 26.13, we infer that both of the series

$$\sum_{j=0}^{\infty} \sum_{i=0}^{\infty} x_{ij}, \qquad \sum_{k=0}^{\infty} \sum_{i+j=k} x_{ij}$$

converge to x. It is readily checked that the iterated series converges to $y \cdot z$ and that the diagonal series is the Cauchy product of $\sum (y_i)$ and $\sum (z_j)$.

Q.E.D.

In the case $p = 1$, it was proved by Mertens[†] that the absolute convergence of one of the series is sufficient to imply the convergence of the Cauchy product. In addition, Cesàro showed that the arithmetic means of the partial sums of the Cauchy product converge to yz. (See Exercises 26.W, X.)

Exercises

26.A. Let $\sum (a_n)$ be a given series and let $\sum (b_n)$ be one in which the terms are the same as those in $\sum (a_n)$, except those for which $a_n = 0$ have been omitted. Show that $\sum (a_n)$ converges to a number A if and only if $\sum (b_n)$ converges to A.

26.B. Show that the convergence of a series is not affected by changing a finite number of its terms. (Of course, the sum may well be changed.)

26.C. Show that grouping the terms of a convergent series by introducing parentheses containing a finite number terms does not destroy the convergence or the value of the limit. However, grouping terms in a divergent series can produce convergence.

26.D. Show that if a convergent series of real numbers contains only a finite number of negative terms, then it is absolutely convergent.

26.E. Show that if a series of real numbers is conditionally convergent, then the series of positive terms is divergent and the series of negative terms is divergent.

26.F. By using partial fractions, show that

(a) $\displaystyle \sum_{n=0}^{\infty} \frac{1}{(\alpha + n)(\alpha + n + 1)} = \frac{1}{\alpha}$ if $\alpha > 0$,

(b) $\displaystyle \sum_{n=1}^{\infty} \frac{1}{n(n + 1)(n + 2)} = \frac{1}{2}.$

[†] FRANZ (C. J.) MERTENS (1840–1927) studied at Berlin and taught at Cracow and Vienna. He contributed primarily to geometry, number theory, and algebra.

26.G. If $\sum (a_n)$ is a convergent series of real numbers, then is $\sum (a_n^2)$ always convergent? If $a_n \geq 0$, then is it true that $\sum (\sqrt{a_n})$ is always convergent?

26.H. If $\sum (a_n)$ is convergent and $a_n \geq 0$, then is $\sum (\sqrt{a_n a_{n+1}})$ convergent?

26.I. Let $\sum (a_n)$ be a series of positive real numbers and let b_n, $n \in \mathbf{N}$, be defined to be

$$b_n = \frac{a_1 + a_2 + \cdots + a_n}{n}.$$

Show that $\sum (b_n)$ always diverges.

26.J. Let $\sum (a_n)$ be convergent and let c_n, $n \in \mathbf{N}$, be defined to be the weighted means

$$c_n = \frac{a_1 + 2a_2 + \cdots + na_n}{n(n+1)}.$$

Then $\sum (c_n)$ converges and equals $\sum (a_n)$.

26.K. Let $\sum (a_n)$ be a series of monotone decreasing positive numbers. Prove that $\sum_{n=1}^{\infty} (a_n)$ converges if and only if the series

$$\sum_{n=1}^{\infty} 2^n a_{2^n}$$

converges. This result is often called the **Cauchy Condensation Test**. (Hint: group the terms into blocks as in Examples 26.8(b, d).)

26.L. Use the Cauchy Condensation Test to discuss the convergence of the p-series $\sum (1/n^p)$.

26.M. Use the Cauchy Condensation Test to show that the series

$$\sum \frac{1}{n \log n}, \qquad \sum \frac{1}{n (\log n)(\log \log n)},$$

$$\sum \frac{1}{n (\log n)(\log \log n)(\log \log \log n)}$$

are divergent.

26.N. Show that if $c > 1$, the series

$$\sum \frac{1}{n (\log n)^c}, \qquad \sum \frac{1}{n (\log n)(\log \log n)^c}$$

are convergent.

26.O. Suppose that (a_n) is a monotone decreasing sequence of positive numbers. Show that if the series $\sum (a_n)$ converges, then $\lim (na_n) = 0$. Is the converse true?

26.P. If $\lim (a_n) = 0$, then $\sum (a_n)$ and $\sum (a_n + 2a_{n+1})$ are both convergent or both divergent.

26.Q. Let $\sum (a_{mn})$ be the double series given by

$$
\begin{aligned}
a_{mn} &= +1, & \text{if} \quad m - n = 1, \\
&= -1, & \text{if} \quad m - n = -1, \\
&= 0, & \text{otherwise.}
\end{aligned}
$$

Show that both iterated sums exist, but are unequal, and the double sum does not exist. However, if (s_{mn}) denote the partial sums, then $\lim(s_{nn})$ exists.

26.R. Show that if the double and the iterated series of $\sum (a_{mn})$ exist, then they are all equal. Show that the existence of the double series does not imply the existence of the iterated series; in fact the existence of the double series does not even imply that $\lim_{n}(a_{mn}) = 0$ for each m.

26.S. Show that if $p > 1$ and $q > 1$, then the double series
$$\sum \left(\frac{1}{m^p n^q}\right) \quad \text{and} \quad \sum \left(\frac{1}{(m^2 + n^2)^p}\right)$$
are convergent.

26.T. By separating $\sum (1/n^2)$ into odd and even parts, show that
$$\sum_{n=1}^{\infty} \frac{1}{n^2} = 4 \sum_{n=1}^{\infty} \frac{1}{(2n)^2} = \frac{4}{3} \sum_{n=1}^{\infty} \frac{1}{(2n-1)^2}.$$

26.U. If $|a| < 1$ and $|b| < 1$, prove that the series $a + b + a^2 + b^2 + a^3 + b^3 + \cdots$ converges. What is the limit?

26.V. If $\sum (a_n{}^2)$ and $\sum (b_n{}^2)$ are convergent, then $\sum (a_n b_n)$ is absolutely convergent and
$$\sum a_n b_n \leq \{\sum a_n{}^2\}^{1/2} \{\sum b_n{}^2\}^{1/2}.$$
In addition, $\sum (a_n + b_n)^2$ converges and
$$\{\sum (a_n + b_n)^2\}^{1/2} \leq \{\sum a_n{}^2\}^{1/2} + \{\sum b_n{}^2\}^{1/2}.$$

26.W. Prove Mertens' Theorem: If $\sum (a_n)$ converges absolutely to A and $\sum (b_n)$ converges to B, then their Cauchy product converges to AB. (Hint: Let the partial sums be denoted by A_n, B_n, C_n, respectively. Show that $\lim(C_{2n} - A_n B_n) = 0$ and $\lim(C_{2n+1} - A_n B_n) = 0$.)

26.X. Prove Cesàro's Theorem: Let $\sum (a_n)$ converge to A and $\sum (b_n)$ converge to B, and let $\sum (c_n)$ be their Cauchy product. If (C_n) is the sequence of partial sums of $\sum (c_n)$, then
$$\frac{1}{n} (C_1 + C_2 + \cdots + C_n) \to AB.$$
(Hint: write $C_1 + \cdots + C_n = A_1 B_n + \cdots + A_n B_1$; break this sum into three parts; and use the fact that $A_n \to A$ and $B_n \to B$.)

Section 27   Tests for Convergence

In the preceding section we obtained some results concerning the manipulation of infinite series, especially in the important case where the series are absolutely convergent. However, except for the Cauchy Criterion and the fact that the terms of a convergent series converge to zero, we did not establish any necessary or sufficient conditions for convergence of infinite series.

We shall now give some results which can be used to establish the convergence or divergence of infinite series. In view of its importance, we shall pay special attention to absolute convergence. Since the absolute convergence of the series $\sum (x_n)$ in R^p is equivalent with the convergence of the series $\sum (|x_n|)$ of non-negative elements of R, it is clear that results establishing the convergence of non-negative real series have particular interest.

Our first test shows that if the terms of a non-negative real series are dominated by the corresponding terms of a convergent series, then the first series is convergent. It yields a test for absolute convergence that the reader should formulate.

27.1 COMPARISON TEST. *Let* $X = (x_n)$ *and* $Y = (y_n)$ *be non-negative real sequences and suppose that for some natural number* K,

$$(27.1) \qquad x_n \leq y_n \quad for \quad n \geq K.$$

Then the convergence of $\sum (y_n)$ *implies the convergence of* $\sum (x_n)$.

PROOF. If $m \geq n \geq \sup \{K, M(\epsilon)\}$, then

$$x_{n+1} + \cdots + x_m \leq y_{n+1} + \cdots + y_m < \epsilon,$$

from which the assertion is evident.

Q.E.D.

27.2 LIMIT COMPARISON TEST. *Suppose that* $X = (x_n)$ *and* $Y = (y_n)$ *are non-negative real sequences.*

(a) *If the relation*

$$(27.2) \qquad \lim (x_n/y_n) \neq 0$$

holds, then $\sum (x_n)$ *is convergent if and only if* $\sum (y_n)$ *is convergent.*

(b) *If the limit in* (27.2) *is zero and* $\sum (y_n)$ *is convergent, then* $\sum (x_n)$ *is convergent.*

PROOF. It follows from (27.2) that for some real number $c > 1$ and some natural number K, then

$$(1/c)y_n \leq x_n \leq cy_n \quad for \quad n \geq K.$$

If we apply the Comparison Test 27.1 twice, we obtain the assertion in part (a). The details of the proof of (b) are similar and will be omitted.

Q.E.D.

We now give an important test due to Cauchy.

27.3 ROOT TEST. (a) *If* $X = (x_n)$ *is a sequence in* R^p *and there exists a non-negative number* $r < 1$ *and a natural number* K *such that*

$$(27.3) \qquad |x_n|^{1/n} \leq r \quad for \quad n \geq K,$$

then the series $\sum (x_n)$ *is absolutely convergent.*

(b) *If there exists a number $r > 1$ and a natural number K such that*

(27.4) $$|x_n|^{1/n} \geq r \quad for \quad n \geq K,$$

then the series $\sum(x_n)$ is divergent.

PROOF. (a) If (27.3) holds, then we have $|x_n| \leq r^n$. Now for $0 \leq r < 1$, the series $\sum(r^n)$ is convergent, as was seen in Example 26.8(a). Hence it follows from the Comparison Test that $\sum(x_n)$ is absolutely convergent.

(b) If (24.4) holds, then $|x_n| \geq r^n$. However, since $r \geq 1$, it is false that $\lim(|x_n|) = 0$.

Q.E.D.

In addition to establishing the convergence of $\sum(x_n)$, the root test can be used to obtain an estimate of the rapidity of convergence. This estimate is useful in numerical computations and in some theoretical estimates as well.

27.4 COROLLARY. *If r satisfies $0 < r < 1$ and if the sequence $X = (x_n)$ satisfies (27.3), then the partial sums s_n, $n \geq K$, approximate the sum $s = \sum(x_n)$ according to the estimate*

(27.5) $$|s - s_n| \leq \frac{r^{n+1}}{1 - r} \quad for \quad n \geq K.$$

PROOF. If $m \geq n \geq K$, we have

$$|s_m - s_n| = |x_{n+1} + \cdots + x_m| \leq |x_{n+1}| + \cdots + |x_m|$$
$$\leq r^{n+1} + \cdots + r^m < \frac{r^{n+1}}{1 - r}.$$

Now take the limit with respect to m to obtain (27.5).

Q.E.D.

It is often convenient to make use of the following variant of the root test.

27.5 COROLLARY. *Let $X = (x_n)$ be a sequence in $\mathbf{R}^p$ and set*

(27.6) $$r = \lim(|x_n|^{1/n}),$$

whenever this limit exists. Then $\sum(x_n)$ is absolutely convergent when $r < 1$ and is divergent when $r > 1$.

PROOF. It follows that if the limit in (27.6) exists and is less than 1, then there is a real number r_1 with $r < r_1 < 1$ and a natural number K such that

$$|x_n|^{1/n} \leq r_1 \quad for \quad n \geq K.$$

In this case the series is absolutely convergent. If this limit exceeds 1, then there is a real number $r_2 > 1$ and a natural number K such that

$$|x_n|^{1/n} \geq r_2 \quad \text{for} \quad n \geq K,$$

in which case series is divergent.

Q.E.D.

This corollary can be generalized by using the limit superior instead of the limit. We leave the details as an exercise. The next test is due to D'Alembert.†

27.6 Ratio Test. (a) *If* $X = (x_n)$ *is a sequence of non-zero elements of* $\mathbf{R}^p$ *and there is a positive number* $r < 1$ *and a natural number* K *such that*

$$(27.7) \qquad\qquad \frac{|x_{n+1}|}{|x_n|} \leq r \quad for \quad n \geq K,$$

then the series $\sum (x_n)$ *is absolutely convergent.*

(b) *If there exists a number* $r > 1$ *and a natural number* K *such that*

$$(27.8) \qquad\qquad \frac{|x_{n+1}|}{|x_n|} \geq r \quad for \quad n \geq K,$$

then the series $\sum (x_n)$ *is divergent.*

PROOF. (a) If (27.7) holds, then an elementary induction argument shows that $|x_{K+m}| \leq r^m |x_K|$ for $m \geq 1$. It follows that for $n \geq K$ the terms of $\sum (x_n)$ are dominated by a fixed multiple of the terms of the geometric series $\sum (r^n)$ with $0 \leq r < 1$. From the Comparison Test 27.1, we infer that $\sum (x_n)$ is absolutely convergent.

(b) If (27.8) holds, then an elementary induction argument shows that $|x_{K+m}| \geq r^m |x_K|$ for $m \geq 1$. Since $r \geq 1$, it is impossible to have $\lim (|x_n|) = 0$, so the series cannot converge.

Q.E.D.

27.7 Corollary. *If* r *satisfies* $0 \leq r < 1$ *and if the sequence* $X = (x_n)$ *satisfies* (27.7) *for* $n \geq K$, *then the partial sums approximate the sum* $s = \sum (x_n)$ *according to the estimate*

$$(27.9) \qquad\qquad |s - s_n| \leq \frac{r}{1 - r} |x_n| \quad for \quad n \geq K.$$

---

† JEAN LE ROND D'ALEMBERT (1717–1783) was a son of the Chevalier Destouches. He became the secretary of the French Academy and the leading mathematician of the Encyclopedists. He contributed to dynamics and differential equations.

PROOF. The relation (27.7) implies that $|x_{n+k}| \le r^k |x_n|$ when $n \ge K$. Therefore, if $m \ge n \ge K$, we have

$$|s_m - s_n| = |x_{n+1} + \cdots + x_m| \le |x_{n+1}| + \cdots + |x_m|$$
$$\le (r + r^2 + \cdots + r^{m-n}) |x_n| < \frac{r}{1-r} |x_n|.$$

Again we take the limit with respect to m to obtain (27.9).

Q.E.D.

27.8 COROLLARY. *Let $X = (x_n)$ be a sequence in $\mathbf{R}^p$ and set*

(27.10)
$$r = \lim \left(\frac{|x_{n+1}|}{|x_n|} \right),$$

whenever the limit exists. Then the series $\sum (x_n)$ is absolutely convergent when $r < 1$ and divergent when $r > 1$.

PROOF. Suppose that the limit exists and $r < 1$. If r_1 satisfies $r < r_1 < 1$, then there is a natural number K such that

$$\frac{|x_{n+1}|}{|x_n|} < r_1 \quad \text{for} \quad n \ge K.$$

In this case Theorem 27.6 establishes the absolute convergence of the series. If $r > 1$, and if r_2 satisfies $1 < r_2 < r$, then there is a natural number K such that

$$\frac{|x_{n+1}|}{|x_n|} > r_2 \quad \text{for} \quad n \ge K,$$

and in this case there is divergence.

Q.E.D.

Although the Root Test is stronger than the Ratio Test, it is sometimes easier to apply the latter. If $r = 1$, both of these tests fail and either convergence or divergence may take place. (See Example 27.13(d)). For some purposes it is useful to have a more delicate form of the Ratio Test for the case when $r = 1$. The next result, which is attributed to Raabe†, is usually adequate.

27.9 RAABE'S TEST. (a) *If $X = (x_n)$ is a sequence of non-zero elements of $\mathbf{R}^p$ and there is a real number $a > 1$ and a natural number K such that*

(27.11)
$$\frac{|x_{n+1}|}{|x_n|} \le 1 - \frac{a}{n} \quad \text{for} \quad n \ge K,$$

then the series $\sum (x_n)$ is absolutely convergent.

---

† JOSEPH L. RAABE (1801–1859) was born in Galacia and taught at Zürich. He worked in both geometry and analysis.

(b) *If there is a real number $a \leq 1$ and a natural number K such that*

(27.12) $$\frac{|x_{n+1}|}{|x_n|} \geq 1 - \frac{a}{n} \quad \text{for} \quad n \geq K,$$

then the series $\sum (x_n)$ is not absolutely convergent.

PROOF. (a) Assuming that relation (27.11) holds, we have

$$k\,|x_{k+1}| \leq (k-1)\,|x_k| - (a-1)\,|x_k| \quad \text{for} \quad k \geq K.$$

Since $a > 1$, then $a - 1 > 0$ and

(27.13) $$(k-1)\,|x_k| - k\,|x_{k+1}| \geq (a-1)\,|x_k| > 0 \quad \text{for} \quad k \geq K,$$

from which it follows that the sequence $(k\,|x_{k+1}|)$ is decreasing for $k \geq K$. On adding the relation (27.13) for $k = K, \ldots, n$ and noting that the left side telescopes, we find that

$$(K-1)\,|x_K| - n\,|x_{n+1}| \geq (a-1)(|x_K| + \cdots + |x_n|).$$

This shows that the partial sums of $\sum (|x_n|)$ are bounded and establishes the absolute convergence of $\sum (x_n)$.

(b) If the relation (27.12) holds for $n \geq K$ then, since $a \leq 1$,

$$n\,|x_{n+1}| \geq (n-a)\,|x_n| \geq (n-1)\,|x_n|.$$

Therefore, the sequence $(n\,|x_{n+1}|)$ is increasing for $n \geq K$, and there exists a positive number c such that

$$|x_{n+1}| > c/n, \quad n \geq K.$$

Since the harmonic series $\sum (1/n)$ diverges, then $\sum (x_n)$ cannot be absolutely convergent.

Q.E.D.

We can also use Raabe's Test to obtain information on the rapidity of the convergence.

27.10 COROLLARY. *If $a > 1$ and if the sequence $X = (x_n)$ satisfies (27.11), then the partial sums approximate the sum s of $\sum (x_k)$ according to the estimate*

(27.14) $$|s - s_n| \leq \frac{n}{a-1}\,|x_{n+1}| \quad \text{for} \quad n \geq K.$$

PROOF. Let $m \geq n \geq K$ and add the inequalities obtained from (27.13) for $k = n+1, \ldots, m$ to obtain

$$n\,|x_{n+1}| - m\,|x_{m+1}| \geq (a-1)(|x_{n+1}| + \cdots + |x_m|).$$

Hence we have

$$|s_m - s_n| \leq |x_{n+1}| + \cdots + |x_m| \leq \frac{n}{a-1} |x_{n+1}|;$$

taking the limit with respect to m, we obtain (27.14).

Q.E.D.

In the application of Raabe's Test, it may be convenient to use the following less sharp limiting form.

27.11 COROLLARY. (a) *Let* $X = (x_n)$ *be a sequence of non-zero elements of* R^p *and set*

$$(27.15) \qquad a = \lim \left(n \left(1 - \frac{|x_{n+1}|}{|x_n|} \right) \right),$$

whenever this limit exists. Then $\sum (x_n)$ *is absolutely convergent when* $a > 1$ *and is not absolutely convergent when* $a < 1$.

PROOF. Suppose the limit (27.15) exists and satisfies $a > 1$. If a_1 is any number with $a > a_1 > 1$, then there exists a natural number K such that

$$a_1 < n \left(1 - \frac{|x_{n+1}|}{|x_n|} \right) \quad \text{for} \quad n \geq K.$$

Therefore, it follows that

$$\frac{|x_{n+1}|}{|x_n|} < 1 - \frac{a_1}{n} \quad \text{for} \quad n \geq K$$

and Theorem 27.9 assures the absolute convergence of the series. The case where $a < 1$ is handled similarly and will be omitted.

Q.E.D.

We now present a powerful test, due to Maclaurin†, for a series of positive numbers.

27.12 INTEGRAL TEST. *Let* f *be a positive, non-increasing continuous function on* $\{t : t \geq 1\}$. *Then the series* $\sum (f(n))$ *converges if and only if the infinite integral*

$$\int_1^{+\infty} f(t) \, dt = \lim_n \left(\int_1^n f(t) \, dt \right)$$

exists. In the case of convergence, the partial sum $s_n = \sum_{k=1}^n (f(k))$ *and the sum* s *of* $\sum_{k=1}^{\infty} (f(k))$ *satisfy the estimate*

$$(27.16) \qquad \int_{n+1}^{+\infty} f(t) \, dt \leq s - s_n \leq \int_n^{+\infty} f(t) \, dt.$$

† COLIN MACLAURIN (1698–1746) was a student of Newton's and professor at Edinburgh. He was the leading British mathematician of his time and contributed both to geometry and mathematical physics.

PROOF. Since f is positive, continuous, and non-increasing on the interval $[k - 1, k]$, it follows that

$$(27.17) \qquad f(k) \leq \int_{k-1}^{k} f(t)\, dt \leq f(k - 1).$$

By summing this inequality for $k = 2, 3, \ldots, n$, we obtain the relation

$$s_n - f(1) \leq \int_{1}^{n} f(t)\, dt \leq s_{n-1},$$

which shows that both or neither of the limits

$$\lim (s_n), \qquad \lim \left(\int_{1}^{n} f(t)\, dt \right)$$

exist. If they exist, we obtain on summing relation (27.17) for $k = n + 1, \ldots, m$, that

$$s_m - s_n \leq \int_{n}^{m} f(t)\, dt \leq s_{m-1} - s_{n-1},$$

whence it follows that

$$\int_{n+1}^{m+1} f(t)\, dt \leq s_m - s_n \leq \int_{n}^{m} f(t)\, dt.$$

If we take the limit with respect to m in this last inequality, we obtain (27.16).

Q.E.D.

We shall show how the results in Theorems 27.1–27.12 can be applied to the p-series, which were introduced in Example 26.8(c).

27.13 EXAMPLES. (a) First we shall apply the Comparison Test. Knowing that the harmonic series $\sum (1/n)$ diverges, it is seen that if $p \leq 1$, then $n^p \leq n$ and hence

$$\frac{1}{n} \leq \frac{1}{n^p}.$$

After using the Comparison Test 27.1, we conclude that the p-series $\sum (1/n^p)$ diverges for $p \leq 1$.

(b) Now consider the case $p = 2$; that is, the series $\sum (1/n^2)$. We compare the series with the convergent series $\sum \left(\dfrac{1}{n(n + 1)} \right)$ of Example 26.8(e). Since the relation

$$\frac{1}{n(n + 1)} < \frac{1}{n^2}$$

holds and the terms on the left form a convergent series, we cannot apply the Comparison Theorem directly. However, we could apply this theorem if we compared the nth term of $\sum \left(\dfrac{1}{n(n+1)} \right)$ with the $(n+1)$st term of $\sum (1/n^2)$. Instead, we choose to apply the Limit Comparison Test 27.2 and note that

$$\frac{1}{n(n+1)} \div \frac{1}{n^2} = \frac{n^2}{n(n+1)} = \frac{n}{n+1} \, .$$

Since the limit of this quotient is 1 and $\sum \left(\dfrac{1}{n(n+1)} \right)$ converges, then so does the series $\sum (1/n^2)$.

(c) Now consider the case $p \geq 2$. If we note that $n^p \geq n^2$ for $p \geq 2$, then

$$\frac{1}{n^p} \leq \frac{1}{n^2} \, ,$$

a direct application of the Comparison Test assures that $\sum (1/n^p)$ converges for $p \geq 2$. Alternatively, we could apply the Limit Comparison Test and note that

$$\frac{1}{n^p} \div \frac{1}{n^2} = \frac{n^2}{n^p} = \frac{1}{n^{p-2}} \, .$$

If $p > 2$, this expression converges to 0, whence it follows from Corollary 27.2(b) that the series $\sum (1/n^p)$ converges for $p \geq 2$.

By using the Comparison Test, we cannot gain any information concerning the p-series for $1 < p < 2$ unless we can find a series whose convergence character is known and which can be compared to the series in this range.

(d) We demonstrate the Root and the Ratio Tests as applied to the p-series. Note that

$$\left(\frac{1}{n^p} \right)^{1/n} = (n^{-p})^{1/n} = (n^{1/n})^{-p}.$$

Now it is known (see Exercise 11.P) that the sequence $(n^{1/n})$ converges to 1. Hence we have

$$\lim \left(\left(\frac{1}{n^p} \right)^{1/n} \right) = 1,$$

so that the Root Test (in the form of Corollary 27.5) does not apply.

In the same way, since

$$\frac{1}{(n+1)^p} \div \frac{1}{n^p} = \frac{n^p}{(n+1)^p} = \frac{1}{(1+1/n)^p},$$

and since the sequence $((1 + 1/n)^p)$ converges to 1, the Ratio Test (in the form of Corollary 27.8) does not apply.

(e) In desperation, we apply Raabe's Test to the p-series for integral values of p. First, we attempt to use Corollary 27.11. Observe that

$$n\left(1 - \frac{(n+1)^{-p}}{n^{-p}}\right) = n\left(1 - \frac{n^p}{(n+1)^p}\right)$$

$$= n\left(1 - \frac{(n+1-1)^p}{(n+1)^p}\right) = n\left(1 - \left(1 - \frac{1}{n+1}\right)^p\right).$$

If p is an integer, then we can use the Binomial Theorem to obtain an estimate for the last term. In fact,

$$n\left(1 - \left(1 - \frac{1}{n+1}\right)^p\right) = n\left(1 - 1 + \frac{p}{n+1} - \frac{p(p-1)}{2(n+1)^2} + \cdots\right).$$

If we take the limit with respect to n, we obtain p. Hence this corollary to Raabe's Test shows that the series converges for integral values of $p \geq 2$ (and, if the Binomial Theorem is known for non-integral values of p, this could be improved). The case $p = 1$ is not settled by Corollary 27.11, but it can be treated by Theorem 27.9. In fact,

$$\frac{1}{n+1} \div \frac{1}{n} = \frac{1}{n+1/n} \geq 1 - \frac{1}{n},$$

and so Raabe's Test shows that we have divergence for $p = 1$,

(f) Finally, we apply the Integral Test to the p-series. Let $f(t) = t^{-p}$ and recall that

$$\int_1^n \frac{1}{t}\, dt = \log(n) - \log(1),$$

$$\int_1^n \frac{1}{t^p}\, dt = \frac{1}{1-p}(n^{1-p} - 1) \quad \text{for} \quad p \neq 1.$$

From these relations we see that the p-series converges if $p > 1$ and diverges if $p \leq 1$.

Conditional Convergence

The tests given in Theorems 27.1–27.12 all have the character that they guarantee that, if certain hypotheses are fulfilled, then the series

$\sum (x_n)$ is absolutely convergent. Now it is known that absolute convergence implies ordinary convergence, but it is readily seen from an examination of special series, such as

$$\sum \frac{(-1)^n}{n}, \qquad \sum \frac{(-1)^n}{\sqrt{n}},$$

that convergence may take place even though absolute convergence fails. It is desired, therefore, to have a test which yields information about ordinary convergence. There are many such tests which apply to special types of series. Perhaps the ones with most general applicability are those due to Abel† and Dirichlet.

To establish these tests, we need a lemma which is sometimes called the partial summation formula, since it corresponds to the familiar integration by parts formula. In most applications, the sequences X and Y are both sequences in R, but the results hold when X and Y are sequences in $\mathbb{R}^p$ and the inner product is used or when one of X and Y is a real sequence and the other is in $\mathbb{R}^p$.

27.14 ABEL'S LEMMA. *Let $X = (x_n)$ and $Y = (y_n)$ be sequences and let the partial sums of $\sum (y_n)$ be denoted by (s_k). If $m \geq n$, then*

$$(27.18) \qquad \sum_{j=n}^{m} x_j y_j = (x_{m+1} s_n - x_n s_{n-1}) + \sum_{j=n}^{m} (x_j - x_{j+1}) s_j.$$

PROOF.   A proof of this result may be given by noting that $y_j = s_j - s_{j-1}$ and by matching the terms on each side of the equality. We shall leave the details to the reader.

Q.E.D.

We apply Abel's Lemma to conclude that the series $\sum (x_n y_n)$ is convergent in a case where both of the series $\sum (x_n)$ and $\sum (y_n)$ may be divergent.

27.15 DIRICHLET'S TEST. *Suppose the partial sums of $\sum (y_n)$ are bounded. (a) If the sequence $X = (x_n)$ converges to zero, and if*

$$(27.19) \qquad \sum |x_n - x_{n+1}|$$

is convergent, then the series $\sum (x_n y_n)$ is convergent.

(b) In particular, if $X = (x_n)$ is a decreasing sequence of positive real numbers which converges to zero, then the series $\sum (x_n y_n)$ is convergent.

† NIELS HENRIK ABEL (1802–1829) was the son of a poor Norwegian minister. When only twenty-two he proved the impossibility of solving the general quintic equation by radicals. This self-taught genius also did outstanding work on series and elliptic functions before his early death of tuberculosis.

PROOF. (a) Suppose that $|s_j| < B$ for all j. Using (27.18), we have the estimate

$$(27.20) \qquad \left| \sum_{j=n}^{m} x_j y_j \right| \leq \{ |x_{m+1}| + |x_n| + \sum_{j=n}^{m} |x_j - x_{j+1}| \} B.$$

If $\lim (x_n) = 0$, the first two terms on the right side can be made arbitrarily small by taking m and n sufficiently large. Also if the series (27.19) converges, then the Cauchy Criterion assures that the final term on this side can be made less than ϵ by taking $m \geq n \geq M(\epsilon)$. Hence the Cauchy Criterion implies that the series $\sum (x_n y_n)$ is convergent.

(b) If $x_1 \geq x_2 \geq \ldots$, then the series in (27.19) is telescoping and convergent.

Q.E.D.

27.16 COROLLARY. *In part* (b), *we have the error estimate*

$$\left| \sum_{j=1}^{\infty} x_j y_j - \sum_{j=1}^{n} x_j y_j \right| \leq 2|x_{n+1}|B,$$

where B is an upper bound for the partial sums of $\sum (y_j)$.

PROOF. This is readily obtained from relation (27.20).

Q.E.D.

The next test strengthens the hypothesis on $\sum (y_n)$, but it relaxes the one on the real sequence (x_n).

27.17 ABEL'S TEST. *Suppose that the series $\sum (y_n)$ is convergent in R^p and that $X = (x_n)$ is a convergent monotone sequence in R. Then the series $\sum (x_n y_n)$ is convergent.*

PROOF. To be explicit, we shall suppose that $X = (x_n)$ is an increasing sequence and converges to x. Since the partial sums s_k of $\sum (y_n)$ converge to an element s in R^p, given $\epsilon > 0$ there is a $N(\epsilon)$ such that if $m \geq n \geq N(\epsilon)$, then

$$|x_{m+1} s_m - x_n s_{n-1}| \leq |x_{m+1} s_m - xs| + |xs - x_n s_{n-1}| < 2\epsilon.$$

In addition, if B is a bound for $\{ |s_k| : k \in N \}$ then

$$\left| \sum_{j=n}^{m} (x_j - x_{j+1}) s_j \right| \leq |x_n - x_{m+1}| B.$$

By using these two estimates and Abel's Lemma, we conclude that the series $\sum (x_n y_n)$ is convergent in R^p.

Q.E.D.

If we use the same type of argument, we can establish the following error estimate.

27.18 COROLLARY. *With the notation of the preceding proof, we have the estimate*

$$\left| \sum_{j=1}^{\infty} x_j y_j - \sum_{j=1}^{n} x_j y_j \right| \leq |x|\, |s - s_n| + 2B|x - x_{n+1}|.$$

There is a particularly important class of conditionally convergent real series, namely those whose terms are alternately positive and negative.

27.19 DEFINITION. A sequence $X = (x_n)$ of non-zero real numbers is **alternating** if the terms $(-1)^n x_n$, $n = 1, 2, \ldots$, are all positive (or all negative) real numbers. If a sequence $X = (x_n)$ is alternating, we say that the series $\sum (x_n)$ it generates is an **alternating series.**

It is useful to set $x_n = (-1)^n z_n$ and require that $z_n > 0$ (or $z_n < 0$) for all $n = 1, 2, \ldots$. The convergence of alternating series is easily treated when the next result, proved by Leibniz, can be applied.

27.20 ALTERNATING SERIES TEST. *Let $Z = (z_n)$ be a non-increasing sequence of positive numbers with $\lim (z_n) = 0$. Then the alternating series $\sum ((-1)^n z_n)$ is convergent. Moreover, if s is the sum of this series and s_n is the nth partial sum, then we have the estimate*

$$(27.21) \qquad\qquad\qquad |s - s_n| \leq z_{n+1}$$

for the rapidity of convergence.

PROOF. This follows immediately from Dirichlet's Test 27.15(b) if we take $y_n = (-1)^n$, but the error estimate given in Corollary 27.16 is not as sharp as (27.21). We can also proceed directly and show by mathematical induction that if $m \geq n$, then

$$|s_m - s_n| = |z_{n+1} - z_{n+2} + \cdots + (-1)^{m-n-1} z_m| \leq |z_{n+1}|.$$

This yields both the convergence and the estimate (27.21).

Q.E.D.

27.21 EXAMPLES. (a) The series $\sum ((-1)^n/n)$, which is sometimes called the **alternating harmonic series**, is not absolutely convergent. However, it follows from the Alternating Series Test that it is convergent.

(b) Similarly, the series $\sum \left(\dfrac{(-1)^n}{\sqrt{n}} \right)$ is convergent, but not absolutely convergent.

(c) Let x be any real number which is different from $2\pi k$, where k is a positive or negative integer. Then, since

$$2 \cos (kx) \sin (x/2) = \sin (k - \tfrac{1}{2})x - \sin (k + \tfrac{1}{2})x,$$

it follows that

$$2 \sin (x/2) [\cos (x) + \cdots + \cos (nx)] = \sin (\tfrac{1}{2})x - \sin (n + \tfrac{1}{2})x,$$

so that

$$\cos x + \cdots + \cos nx = \frac{\sin (\tfrac{1}{2})x - \sin ((n + \tfrac{1}{2})x)}{2 \sin (x/2)}.$$

Therefore, we have the bound

$$|\cos x + \cdots + \cos nx| \le \frac{1}{|\sin (x/2)|}$$

for the partial sums of the series $\sum (\cos nx)$. Dirichlet's Test shows that even though the series $\sum (\cos nx)$ does not converge, the series

$$\sum \frac{\cos nx}{n}$$

does converge for $x \ne 2k\pi$, $k \in Z$.

(d) Let $x \ne 2k\pi$, $k \in Z$. Since

$$2 \sin (kx) \sin (\tfrac{1}{2})x = \cos (k - \tfrac{1}{2})x - \cos (k + \tfrac{1}{2})x,$$

it follows that

$$2 \sin (\tfrac{1}{2})x [\sin x + \cdots + \sin nx] = \cos (\tfrac{1}{2})x - \cos (n + \tfrac{1}{2})x.$$

Therefore, we have the bound

$$|\sin x + \cdots + \sin nx| \le \frac{1}{|\sin (x/2)|}$$

for the partial sums of the series $\sum (\sin nx)$. As before, Dirichlet's Test yields the convergence of the series

$$\sum \left(\frac{\sin nx}{n} \right)$$

when x is not an integral multiple of 2π.

(e) Let $Y = (y_n)$ be the sequence in R^2 whose elements are

$$y_1 = (1, 0), y_2 = (0, 1), y_3 = (-1, 0),$$
$$y_4 = (0, -1), \ldots, y_{n+4} = y_n, \ldots.$$

It is readily seen that the series $\sum (y_n)$ does not converge, but its partial sums s_k are bounded; in fact, we have $|s_k| \le \sqrt{2}$. Dirichlet's Test shows that the series $\sum \left(\frac{1}{n} y_n \right)$ is convergent in R^2.

Exercises

27.A. Suppose that $\sum (a_n)$ is a convergent series of real numbers. Either prove that $\sum (b_n)$ converges or give a counter-example, when we define b_n by

(a) a_n/n,

(b) $\sqrt{a_n}/n$ $(a_n \geq 0)$,

(c) $a_n \sin n$,

(d) $\sqrt{a_n}/n$ $(a_n \geq 0)$,

(e) $n^{1/n} a_n$,

(f) $a_n/(1 + |a_n|)$.

27.B. Establish the convergence or the divergence of the series whose nth term is given by

(a) $\dfrac{1}{(n+1)(n+2)}$,

(b) $\dfrac{n}{(n+1)(n+2)}$,

(c) $2^{-1/n}$,

(d) $n/2^n$,

(e) $[n(n+1)]^{-1/2}$,

(f) $[n^2(n+1)]^{-1/2}$,

(g) $n!/n^n$,

(h) $(-1)^n n/(n+1)$.

27.C. For each of the series in Exercise 27.B which converge, estimate the remainder if only four terms are taken. If we wish to determine the sum within $1/1000$, how many terms should we take?

27.D. Discuss the convergence or the divergence of the series with nth term (for sufficiently large n) given by

(a) $[\log n]^{-p}$,

(b) $[\log n]^{-n}$,

(c) $[\log n]^{-\log n}$,

(d) $[\log n]^{-\log \log n}$,

(e) $[n \log n]^{-1}$,

(f) $[n(\log n)(\log \log n)^2]^{-1}$.

27.E. Discuss the convergence or the divergence of the series with nth term

(a) $2^n e^{-n}$,

(b) $n^n e^{-n}$,

(c) $e^{-\log n}$,

(d) $(\log n) e^{-\sqrt{n}}$,

(e) $n! e^{-n}$,

(f) $n! e^{-n^2}$.

27.F. Show that the series

$$\frac{1}{1^2} + \frac{1}{2^3} + \frac{1}{3^2} + \frac{1}{4^3} + \cdots$$

is convergent, but that both the Ratio and the Root Tests fail.

27.G. If a and b are positive numbers, then

$$\sum \frac{1}{(an+b)^p}$$

converges if $p > 1$ and diverges if $p \leq 1$.

27.H. If p and q are positive numbers, then

$$\sum (-1)^n \frac{(\log n)^p}{n^q}$$

is a convergent series.

27.I. Discuss the series whose nth term is

(a) $(-1)^n \dfrac{n^n}{(n+1)^{n+1}}$,

(b) $\dfrac{n^n}{(n+1)^{n+1}}$,

(c) $(-1)^n \dfrac{(n+1)^n}{n^n}$,

(d) $\dfrac{(n+1)^n}{n^{n+1}}$.

27.J. Discuss the series whose nth term is

(a) $\dfrac{n!}{3 \cdot 5 \cdot 7 \cdots (2n+1)}$,

(b) $\dfrac{(n!)^2}{(2n)!}$,

(c) $\dfrac{2 \cdot 4 \cdots (2n)}{3 \cdot 5 \cdots (2n+1)}$,

(d) $\dfrac{2 \cdot 4 \cdots (2n)}{5 \cdot 7 \cdots (2n+3)}$.

27.K. The series given by

$$\left(\frac{1}{2}\right)^p + \left(\frac{1 \cdot 3}{2 \cdot 4}\right)^p + \left(\frac{1 \cdot 3 \cdot 5}{2 \cdot 4 \cdot 6}\right)^p + \cdots$$

converges for $p > 2$ and diverges for $p \leq 2$.

27.L. Let $X = (x_n)$ be a sequence in $\mathbf{R}^p$ and let r be given by

$$r = \lim \sup \, (|x_n|^{1/n}).$$

Then $\sum (x_n)$ is absolutely convergent if $r < 1$ and divergent if $r > 1$. [The limit superior $u = \lim \sup (b_n)$ of a bounded sequence of real numbers was defined in Section 14. It is the unique number u with the properties that (i) if $u < v$ then $b_n \leq v$ for all sufficiently large $n \in \mathbf{N}$, and (ii) if $w < u$, then $w \leq b_n$ for infinitely many $n \in \mathbf{N}$.]

27.M. Let $X = (x_n)$ be a sequence of non-zero elements of $\mathbf{R}^p$ and let r be given by

$$r = \lim \sup \left(\frac{|x_{n+1}|}{|x_n|}\right).$$

Show that if $r < 1$, then the series $\sum (x_n)$ is absolutely convergent and if $r > 1$, then the series is divergent.

27.N. Let $X = (x_n)$ be a sequence of non-zero elements in $\mathbf{R}^p$ and let a be given by

$$a = \lim \sup \left(n\left(1 - \frac{|x_{n+1}|}{|x_n|}\right)\right).$$

If $a > 1$ the series $\sum (x_n)$ is absolutely convergent, and if $a < 1$ the series is not absolutely convergent.

27.O. If p, q are positive, then the series

$$\sum \frac{(p+1) \cdots (p+2)(p+n)}{(q+1) \cdots (q+2)(q+n)}$$

converges for $2 > p + 1$ and diverges for $q \leq p + 1$.

27.P. Let $a_n > 0$ and let r be given by

$$r = \lim \sup \left(- \frac{\log a_n}{\log n}\right).$$

Show that $\sum (a_n)$ converges if $r > 1$ and diverges if $r < 1$.

27.Q. Suppose that none of the numbers a, b, c is a negative integer or zero. Prove that the **hypergeometric series**

$$\frac{ab}{1!c} + \frac{a(a+1)b(b+1)}{2!\,c(c+1)} + \frac{a(a+1)(a+2)b(b+1)(b+2)}{3!\,c(c+1)(c+2)} + \cdots$$

is absolutely convergent for $c > a + b$ and divergent for $c \le a + b$.

27.R. Consider the series

$$1 - \frac{1}{2} - \frac{1}{3} + \frac{1}{4} + \frac{1}{5} - \frac{1}{6} - \frac{1}{7} + + - - \cdots,$$

where the signs come in groups of two. Does it converge?

27.S. Let a_n be real (but not necessarily positive) and let $p < q$. If the series $\sum (a_n n^{-p})$ is convergent, then $\sum (a_n n^{-q})$ is also convergent.

27.T. For $n \in \mathbf{N}$, let c_n be defined by

$$c_n = \sum_{k=1}^{n} (1/k) - \log n,$$

Show that (c_n) is a monotone decreasing sequence of positive numbers. The limit C of this sequence is called **Euler's constant** (and is approximately equal to 0.577). Show that if we put $b_n = 1 - 1/2 + 1/3 - \cdots - 1/2n$, then the sequence (b_n) converges to $\log 2$. (Hint: $b_n = c_{2n} - c_n + \log 2$.) Show that the series

$$1 + \frac{1}{2} - \frac{1}{3} + \frac{1}{4} + \frac{1}{5} - \frac{1}{6} + + - \cdots$$

diverges.

27.U. Let $a_n > 0$ and suppose that $\sum (a_n)$ converges. Construct a convergent series $\sum (b_n)$ with $b_n > 0$ such that $\lim (a_n/b_n) = 0$; hence $\sum (b_n)$ converges less rapidly than $\sum (a_n)$. (Hint: let (A_n) be the partial sums of $\sum (a_n)$ and A its limit. Define $r_0 = A, r_n = A - A_n$ and $b_n = \sqrt{r_{n-1}} - \sqrt{r_n}$.)

27.V. Let $a_n > 0$ and suppose that $\sum (a_n)$ diverges. Construct a divergent series $\sum (b_n)$ with $b_n > 0$ such that $\lim (b_n/a_n) = 0$; hence $\sum (b_n)$ diverges less rapidly than $\sum (a_n)$. (Hint: Let $b_1 = \sqrt{a_1}$ and $b_n = \sqrt{a_{n-1}} - \sqrt{a_n}, n > 1$.)

27.W. If the quotient a_{n+1}/a_n has the form $P(n)/Q(n)$ where P, Q are polynomials in n of degree at most n^k, and if the highest term in $Q(n) - P(n)$ equals An^{k-1}, then the series $\sum (a_n)$ converges for $A > 1$ and diverges for $A \le 1$.

27.X. Let $\{n_1, n_2, \ldots\}$ denote the collection of natural numbers that do not use the digit 6 in their decimal expansion. Show that the series $\sum (1/n_k)$ converges to a number less than 90. If $\{m_1, m_2, \ldots\}$ is the collection that ends in 6, then $\sum (1/m_k)$ diverges.

Project

27.α. Although infinite products do not occur as frequently as infinite series, they are of importance in many investigations and applications. For simplicity, we shall restrict attention here to infinite products with positive terms a_n. If

$A = (a_n)$ is a sequence of positive real numbers, then the **infinite product, or the sequence of partial products,** generated by A is the sequence $P = (p_n)$ defined by

$$p_1 = a_1, \; p_2 = p_1 a_2 \; (= a_1 a_2), \ldots,$$
$$p_n = p_{n-1} a_n \; (= a_1 a_2 \cdots a_{n-1} a_n), \ldots.$$

If the sequence P is convergent *to a non-zero number*, then we call $\lim P$ the **product** of the infinite product generated by A. In this case we say that the infinite product is **convergent** and write either

$$\prod_{n=1}^{\infty} a_n \quad \text{or} \quad a_1 a_2 a_3 \cdots a_n \cdots$$

to denote both P and $\lim P$.

(*Note:* the requirement that $\lim P \neq 0$ is not essential but is conventional, since it insures that certain properties of finite products carry over to infinite products.)

(a) Show that a necessary condition for the convergence of the infinite product is that $\lim (a_n) = 1$.

(b) Prove that a necessary and sufficient condition for the convergence of the infinite product

$$\prod_{n=1}^{\infty} a_n, \qquad a_n > 0,$$

is the convergence of the infinite series

$$\sum_{n=1}^{\infty} \log(a_n).$$

(c) Infinite products often have terms of the form $a_n = 1 + u_n$. In keeping with our standing restriction, we suppose $u_n > -1$ for all $n \in \mathbf{N}$. If $u_n \geq 0$, show that a necessary and sufficient condition for the convergence of the infinite product is the convergence of the infinite series

$$\sum_{n=1}^{\infty} u_n.$$

(Hint: use the Limit Comparison Test 27.2.)

(d) Let $u_n > -1$. Show that if the infinite series

$$\sum_{n=1}^{\infty} u_n$$

is absolutely convergent, then the infinite product

$$\prod_{n=1}^{\infty} (1 + u_n)$$

is convergent.

(e) Suppose that $u_n > -1$ and that the series $\sum (u_n)$ is convergent. Then a necessary and sufficient condition for the convergence of the infinite product $\Pi (1 + u_n)$ is the convergence of the infinite series

$$\sum_{n=1}^{\infty} u_n^2.$$

(Hint: use Taylor's Theorem and show that there exist positive constants A and B such that if $|u| < \frac{1}{2}$, then $Au^2 \leq u - \log (1 + u) \leq Bu^2$.)

Section 28   Series of Functions

Because of their frequent appearance and importance, we shall conclude this chapter with a discussion of infinite series of functions. Since the convergence of an infinite series is handled by examining the sequence of partial sums, questions concerning series of functions are answered by examining corresponding questions for sequences of functions. For this reason, a portion of the present section is merely a translation of facts already established for sequences of functions into series terminology. This is the case, for example, for the portion of the section dealing with series of general functions. However, in the second part of the section, where we discuss power series, some new features arise merely because of the special character of the functions involved.

28.1 DEFINITION. If (f_n) is a sequence of functions defined on a subset D of $\mathbf{R}^p$ with values in $\mathbf{R}^q$, the sequence of partial sums (s_n) of the infinite series $\sum (f_n)$ is defined for x in D by

$$s_1(x) = f_1(x),$$
$$s_2(x) = s_1(x) + f_2(x) \qquad [= f_1(x) + f_2(x)],$$
$$\cdots \cdots \cdots \cdots \cdots \cdots \cdots \cdots$$
$$s_{n+1}(x) = s_n(x) + f_{n+1}(x) \qquad [= f_1(x) + \cdots + f_n(x) + f_{n+1}(x)],$$
$$\cdots \cdots \cdots \cdots \cdots \cdots \cdots \cdots$$

In case the sequence (s_n) converges on D to a function f, we say that the infinite series of functions $\sum (f_n)$ converges to f on D. We shall often write

$$\sum (f_n), \qquad \sum_{n=1}^{\infty} (f_n), \qquad \text{or} \qquad \sum_{n=1}^{\infty} f_n$$

to denote either the series or the limit function, when it exists.

If the series $\sum (|f_n(x)|)$ converges for each x in D, then we say that $\sum (f_n)$ is absolutely convergent on D. If the sequence (s_n) is uniformly convergent on D to f, then we say that $\sum (f_n)$ is **uniformly convergent on D**, or that it **converges to f uniformly on D**.

One of the main reasons for the interest in uniformly convergent series of functions is the validity of the following results which give conditions justifying the change of order of the summation and other limiting operations.

28.2 THEOREM. *If f_n is continuous on $D \subseteq \mathbf{R}^p$ to $\mathbf{R}^q$ for each $n \in \mathbf{N}$ and if $\sum (f_n)$ converges to f uniformly on D, then f is continuous on D.*

This is a direct translation of Theorem 17.1 for series. The next result is a translation of Theorem 22.12.

28.3 THEOREM. *Suppose that the real-valued functions f_n are Riemann-Stieltjes integrable with respect to g on the interval $J = [a, b]$ for each $n \in \mathbf{N}$. If the series $\sum (f_n)$ converges to f uniformly on D, then f is Riemann-Stieltjes integrable with respect to g and*

$$(28.1) \qquad \int_a^b f \, dg = \sum_{n=1}^{\infty} \int_a^b f_n \, dg.$$

We now recast the Monotone Convergence Theorem 22.14 into series form.

28.4 THEOREM. *If the f_n are non-negative Riemann integrable functions on $J = [a, b]$ and if their sum $f = \sum (f_n)$ is Riemann integrable, then*

$$(28.2) \qquad \int_a^b f = \sum_{n=1}^{\infty} \int_a^b f_n.$$

Next we turn to the corresponding theorem pertaining to differentiation. Here we assume the uniform convergence of the series obtained after term-by-term differentiation of the given series. This result is an immediate consequence of Theorem 19.12.

28.5 THEOREM. *For each $n \in \mathbf{N}$, let f_n be a real-valued function on $J = [a, b]$ which has a derivative f_n' on J. Suppose that the infinite series $\sum (f_n)$ converges for at least one point of J and that the series of derivatives $\sum (f_n')$ converges uniformly on J. Then there exists a real-valued function f on J such that $\sum (f_n)$ converges uniformly on J to f. In addition, f has a derivative on J and*

$$(28.3) \qquad f' = \sum f_n'.$$

Tests for Uniform Convergence

Since we have stated some consequences of uniform convergence of series, we shall now present a few tests which can be used to establish uniform convergence.

28.6   CAUCHY CRITERION. *Let* (f_n) *be a sequence of functions on* $D \subseteq \mathbf{R}^p$ *to* $\mathbf{R}^q$. *The infinite series* $\sum (f_n)$ *is uniformly convergent on* D *if and only if for every* $\epsilon > 0$ *there exists an* $M(\epsilon)$ *such that if* $m \geq n \geq M(\epsilon)$, *then*

$$(28.4) \qquad ||f_n + f_{n+1} + \cdots + f_m||_D < \epsilon.$$

Here we have used the D-norm, which was introduced in Definition 13.7. The proof of this result is immediate from 13.11, which is the corresponding Cauchy Criterion for the uniform convergence of sequences.

28.7   WEIERSTRASS M-TEST. *Let* (M_n) *be a sequence of non-negative real numbers such that* $||f_n||_D \leq M_n$ *for each* $n \in \mathbf{N}$. *If the infinite series* $\sum (M_n)$ *is convergent, then* $\sum (f_n)$ *is uniformly convergent on* D.

PROOF.   If $m \geq n$, we have the relation

$$||f_n + \cdots + f_m||_D \leq ||f_n||_D + \cdots + ||f_m||_D \leq M_n + \cdots + M_m.$$

The assertion follows from the Cauchy Criteria 26.5 and 28.6 and the convergence of $\sum (M_n)$.

Q.E.D.

The next two results are very useful in establishing uniform convergence, even when the convergence is not absolute. Their proofs are obtained by modifying the proofs of 27.15 and 27.16 and will be left as exercises.

28.8   DIRICHLET'S TEST. *Let* (f_n) *be a sequence of functions on* $D \subseteq \mathbf{R}^p$ *to* $\mathbf{R}^q$ *such that the partial sums*

$$s_n = \sum_{j=1}^{n} f_j, \qquad n \in \mathbf{N},$$

are all bounded in D-*norm. Let* (φ_n) *be a decreasing sequence of functions on* D *to* $\mathbf{R}$ *which converges uniformly on* D *to zero. Then the series* $\sum (\varphi_n f_n)$ *converges uniformly on* D.

28.9   ABEL'S TEST. *Let* $\sum (f_n)$ *be a series of functions on* $D \subseteq \mathbf{R}^p$ *to* $\mathbf{R}^q$ *which is uniformly convergent on* D. *Let* (φ_n) *be a bounded and monotone sequence of real-valued functions on* D. *Then the series* $\sum (\varphi_n f_n)$ *converges uniformly on* D.

28.10   EXAMPLES.   (a) Consider the series $\sum_{n=1}^{\infty} (x^n/n^2)$. If $|x| \leq 1$, then $|x^n/n^2| \leq 1/n^2$. Since the series $\sum (1/n^2)$ is convergent, it follows from the Weierstrass M-test that the given series is uniformly convergent on the interval $[-1, 1]$.

(b) The series obtained after term-by-term differentiation of the series in (a) is $\sum_{n=1}^{\infty} (x^{n-1}/n)$. The Weierstrass M-test does not apply on the interval $[-1, 1]$ so we cannot apply Theorem 28.5. In fact, it is clear that this series of derivatives is not convergent for $x = 1$. However, if $0 < r < 1$, then the geometric series $\sum (r^{n-1})$ converges. Since

$$\left| \frac{x^{n-1}}{n} \right| \leq r^{n-1}$$

for $|x| \leq r$, it follows from the M-test that the differentiated series is uniformly convergent on the interval $[-r, r]$.

(c) A direct application of the M-test (with $M_n = 1/n^2$) shows that

$$\sum_{n=1}^{\infty} \left(\frac{\sin (nx)}{n^2} \right) \text{ is uniformly convergent for all } x \text{ in } \mathbf{R}.$$

(d) Since the harmonic series $\sum (1/n)$ diverges, we cannot apply the M-test to

$$(28.5) \qquad\qquad \sum_{n=1}^{\infty} \frac{\sin (nx)}{n}.$$

However, it follows from the discussion in Example 26.21 (d) that if the interval $J = [a, b]$ is contained in the open interval $(0, 2\pi)$, then the partial sums $s_n(x) = \sum_{k=1}^{n} (\sin (kx))$ are uniformly bounded on J. Since the sequence $(1/n)$ decreases to zero, Dirichlet's Test 28.8 implies that the series (28.5) is uniformly convergent on J.

(e) Consider $\sum_{n=1}^{\infty} \left(\frac{(-1)^n}{n} e^{-nx} \right)$ on the interval $\mathbf{I} = [0, 1]$. Since the norm of the nth term on $\mathbf{I}$ is $1/n$, we cannot apply the Weierstrass Test. Dirichlet's Test can be applied if we can show that the partial sums of $\sum ((-1)^n e^{-nx})$ are bounded. Alternatively, Abel's Test applies since $\sum ((-1)^n/n))$ is convergent and the bounded sequence (e^{-nx}) is monotone decreasing on $\mathbf{I}$ (but not uniformly convergent to zero).

Power Series

We shall now turn to a discussion of power series. This is an important class of series of functions and enjoys properties that are not valid for general series of functions.

28.11 DEFINITION. A series of real functions $\sum (f_n)$ is said to be a **power series** around $x = c$ if the function f_n has the form

$$f_n(x) = a_n(x - c)^n,$$

where a_n and c belong to $\mathbf{R}$ and where $n = 0, 1, 2, \ldots$

For the sake of simplicity of our notation, we shall treat only the case where $c = 0$. This is no loss of generality, however, since the translation $x' = x - c$ reduces a power series around c to a power series around 0. Thus whenever we refer to a power series, we shall mean a series of the form

$$(28.6) \qquad \sum_{n=0}^{\infty} a_n x^n = a_0 + a_1 x + \cdots + a_n x^n + \cdots.$$

Even though the functions appearing in (28.6) are defined over all of R, it is not to be expected that the series (28.6) will converge for all x in R. For example, by using the Ratio Test 26.8, we can show that the series

$$\sum_{n=0}^{\infty} n! x^n, \qquad \sum_{n=0}^{\infty} x^n, \qquad \sum_{n=0}^{\infty} x^n / n!,$$

converge for x in the sets

$$\{0\}, \quad \{x \in \mathbf{R} : |x| < 1\}, \quad \mathbf{R},$$

respectively. Thus the set on which a power series converges may be small, medium, or large. However, an arbitrary subset of R cannot be the precise set on which a power series converges, as we shall show.

If (b_n) is a bounded sequence of non-negative real numbers, then we define the limit superior of (b_n) to be the infimum of those numbers v such that $b_n \leq v$ for all sufficiently large $n \in \mathbf{N}$. This infimum is uniquely determined and is denoted by

$$\lim \sup (b_n).$$

Some other characterizations and properties of the limit superior of a sequence were given in Section 14, but the only thing we need to know is (i) that if $v > \lim \sup (b_n)$, then $b_n \leq v$ for all sufficiently large $n \in \mathbf{N}$, and (ii) that if $w < \lim \sup (b_n)$, then $w \leq b_n$ for infinitely many $n \in \mathbf{N}$.

28.12   DEFINITION.   Let $\sum (a_n x^n)$ be a power series. If the sequence $(|a_n|^{1/n})$ is bounded, we set $\rho = \lim \sup (|a_n|^{1/n})$; if this sequence is not bounded we set $\rho = +\infty$. We define the radius of convergence of $\sum (a_n x^n)$ to be given by

$$\begin{aligned} R &= 0, && \text{if} \quad \rho = +\infty, \\ &= 1/\rho, && \text{if} \quad 0 < \rho < +\infty, \\ &= +\infty, && \text{if} \quad \rho = 0. \end{aligned}$$

The interval of convergence is the open interval $(-R, R)$.

We shall now justify the term "radius of convergence."

28.13   CAUCHY-HADAMARD† THEOREM. *If R is the radius of convergence of the power series $\sum (a_n x^n)$, then the series is absolutely convergent if $|x| < R$ and divergent if $|x| > R$.*

PROOF. We shall treat only the case where $0 < R < +\infty$, leaving the cases $R = 0$, $R = +\infty$, as exercises. If $0 < |x| < R$, then there exists a positive number $c < 1$ such that $|x| < cR$. Therefore $\rho < c/|x|$ and so it follows that if n is sufficiently large, then

$$|a_n|^{1/n} \leq \frac{c}{|x|}.$$

This is equivalent to the statement that

(28.7) $|a_n x^n| \leq c^n$

for all sufficiently large n. Since $c < 1$, the absolute convergence of $\sum (a_n x^n)$ follows from the Comparison Test 27.1.

If $|x| > R = 1/\rho$, then there are infinitely many $n \in \mathbf{N}$ for which

$$|a_n|^{1/n} > \frac{1}{|x|}.$$

Therefore, $|a_n x^n| > 1$ for infinitely many n, so that the sequence $(a_n x^n)$ does not converge to zero.

Q.E.D.

It will be noted that the Cauchy-Hadamard Theorem makes no statement as to whether the power series converges when $|x| = R$. Indeed, anything can happen, as the examples

(28.8) $\sum x^n, \qquad \sum \frac{1}{n} x^n, \qquad \sum \frac{1}{n^2} x^n,$

show. Since $\lim (n^{1/n}) = 1$ (cf. Exercise 11.P), each of these power series has radius of convergence equal to 1. The first power series converges at neither of the points $x = -1$ and $x = +1$; the second series converges at $x = -1$ but diverges at $x = +1$; and the third power series converges at both $x = -1$ and $x = +1$. (Find a power series with $R = 1$ which converges at $x = +1$ but diverges at $x = -1$.)

---

† JACQUES HADAMARD (1865–1963), long-time dean of French mathematicians, was admitted to the École Polytechnique with the highest score attained during its first century. He was Henri Poincaré's successor in the Academy of Sciences and proved the Prime Number Theorem in 1896, although this theorem had been conjectured by Gauss many years before. Hadamard made other contributions to number theory, complex analysis, partial differential equations, and even psychology.

It is an exercise to show that the radius of convergence of $\sum (a_n x^n)$ is also given by

$$(28.9) \qquad\qquad \lim \left(\frac{|a_n|}{|a_{n+1}|} \right),$$

provided this limit exists. Frequently, it is more convenient to use (28.9) than Definition 28.12.

The argument used in the proof of the Cauchy-Hadamard Theorem yields the uniform convergence of the power series on any fixed compact subset in the interval of convergence $(-R, R)$.

28.14 THEOREM. *Let R be the radius of convergence of $\sum (a_n x^n)$ and let K be a compact subset of the interval of convergence $(-R, R)$. Then the power series converges uniformly on K.*

PROOF.   The compactness of $K \subseteq (-R, R)$ implies that there exists a positive constant $c < 1$ such that $|x| < c R$ for all $x \in K$. (Why?) By the argument in 28.13, we infer that for sufficiently large n, the estimate (28.7) holds for all $x \in K$. Since $c < 1$, the uniform convergence of $\sum (a_n x^n)$ on K is a direct consequence of the Weierstrass M-test with $M_n = c^n$.

Q.E.D.

28.15 THEOREM. *The limit of a power series is continuous on the interval of convergence. A power series can be integrated term-by-term over any compact interval contained in the interval of convergence.*

PROOF.   If $|x_0| < R$, then the preceding result asserts that $\sum (a_n x^n)$ converges uniformly on any compact neighborhood of x_0 contained in $(-R, R)$. The continuity at x_0 then follows from Theorem 28.2. Similarly, the term-by-term integration is justified by Theorem 28.3.

Q.E.D.

We now show that a power series can be differentiated term-by-term. Unlike the situation for general series, we do not need to assume that the differentiated series is uniformly convergent. Hence this result is stronger than the corresponding result for the differentiation of infinite series.

28.16 DIFFERENTIATION THEOREM. *A power series can be differentiated term-by-term within the interval of convergence. In fact, if*

$$f(x) = \sum_{n=0}^{\infty} (a_n x^n), \quad then \quad f'(x) = \sum_{n=1}^{\infty} (n a_n x^{n-1}).$$

Both series have the same radius of convergence.

PROOF. Since $\lim (n^{1/n}) = 1$, the sequence $(|na_n|^{1/n})$ is bounded if and only if the sequence $(|a_n|^{1/n})$ is bounded. Moreover, it is easily seen that

$$\limsup (|na_n|^{1/n}) = \limsup (|a_n|^{1/n}).$$

Therefore, the radius of convergence of the two series is the same, so the formally differentiated series is uniformly convergent on each compact subset of the interval of convergence. We can then apply Theorem 28.5 to conclude that the formally differentiated series converges to the derivative of the given series.

Q.E.D.

It is to be observed that the theorem makes no assertion about the end points of the interval of convergence. If a series is convergent at an end point, then the differentiated series may or may not be convergent at this point. For example, the series $\sum_{n=0}^{\infty} (x^n/n^2)$ converges at both end points $x = -1$ and $x = +1$. However, the differentiated series

$$\sum_{n=1}^{\infty} \frac{x^{n-1}}{n} = \sum_{m=0}^{\infty} \frac{x^m}{m + 1}$$

converges at $x = -1$ but diverges at $x = +1$.

By repeated application of the preceding result, we conclude that if k is any natural number, then the power series $\sum_{n=0}^{\infty} (a_n x^n)$ can be differentiated term-by-term k times to obtain

$$(28.10) \qquad \sum_{n=k}^{\infty} \frac{n!}{(n - k)!} a_n x^{n-k}.$$

Moreover, this series converges absolutely to $f^{(k)}$ for $|x| < R$ and uniformly over any compact subset of the interval of convergence.

If we substitute $x = 0$ in (28.10), we obtain the important formula

$$(28.11) \qquad f^{(k)}(0) = k! \, a_k.$$

28.17 UNIQUENESS THEOREM. *If* $\sum (a_n x^n)$ *and* $\sum (b_n x^n)$ *converge on some interval* $(-r, r)$, $r > 0$, *to the same function* f, *then*

$$a_n = b_n \quad \text{for all} \quad n \in \mathbf{N}.$$

PROOF. Our preceding remarks show that $n! \, a_n = f^{(n)}(0) = n! \, b_n$ for $n \in \mathbf{N}$.

Q.E.D.

There are a number of results concerning various algebraic combinations of power series, but those involving substitution and inversion are more naturally proved by using arguments from complex analysis. For this reason we shall not go into these questions but content ourselves with one result in this direction. Fortunately, it is one of the most useful.

28.18 MULTIPLICATION THEOREM. *If f and g are given on the interval* $(-r, r)$ *by the power series*

$$f(x) = \sum_{n=0}^{\infty} a_n x^n, \qquad g(x) = \sum_{n=0}^{\infty} b_n x^n,$$

then their product is given on this interval by the series $\sum (c_n x^n)$, *where the coefficients* (c_n) *are*

$$c_n = \sum_{k=0}^{n} a_k b_{n-k} \quad for \quad n = 0, 1, 2, \ldots..$$

PROOF. We have seen in 28.13 that if $|x| < r$, then the series giving $f(x)$ and $g(x)$ are absolutely convergent. If we apply Theorem 26.15, we obtain the desired conclusion.

Q.E.D.

The Multiplication Theorem asserts that the radius of convergence of the product is at least r. It can be larger, however, as is easily shown.

We have seen that, in order for a function f to be given by a power series on an interval $(-r, r)$, $r > 0$, it is necessary that all of the derivatives of f exist on this interval. It might be suspected that this condition is also sufficient; however, things are not quite so simple. For example, the function f, given by

$$(28.12) \qquad f(x) = e^{-1/x^2}, \qquad x \neq 0,$$
$$= 0, \qquad x = 0,$$

can be shown (see Exercise 28.N) to possess derivatives of all orders and that $f^{(n)}(0) = 0$ for $n = 0, 1, 2, \ldots$ If f can be given on an interval $(-r, r)$ by a power series around $x = 0$, then it follows from the Uniqueness Theorem 28.17 that the series must vanish identically, contrary to the fact that $f(x) \neq 0$ for $x \neq 0$.

Nevertheless, there are some useful sufficient conditions that can be given in order to guarantee that f can be given by a power series. As an example, we observe that it follows from Taylor's Theorem 19.9 that if there exists a constant $B > 0$ such that

$$(28.13) \qquad |f^{(n)}(x)| \leq B$$

for all $|x| < r$ and $n = 0, 1, 2, \ldots$, then the power series

$$\sum_{n=0}^{\infty} \frac{f^{(n)}(0)}{n!} x^n$$

converges to $f(x)$ for $|x| < r$. Similar (but less stringent) conditions on the magnitude of the derivatives can be given which yield the same conclusion.

As an example, we present an elegant and useful result due to Serge Bernstein concerning the one-sided expansion of a function in a power series.

28.19 BERNSTEĬN'S THEOREM. *Let f be defined and possess derivatives of all orders on an interval $[0, r]$ and suppose that f and all of its derivatives are non-negative on the interval $[0, r]$. If $0 \leq x < r$, then $f(x)$ is given by the expansion*

$$f(x) = \sum_{n=0}^{\infty} \frac{f^{(n)}(0)}{n!} x^n.$$

PROOF. We shall make use of the integral form for the remainder in Taylor's Theorem given by the relation (23.16). If $0 \leq x \leq r$, then

(28.14) $$f(x) = \sum_{k=0}^{n-1} \frac{f^{(k)}(0)}{k!} x^k + R_n,$$

where we have the formula

$$R_n = \frac{x^{n-1}}{(n-1)!} \int_0^1 (1 - s)^{n-1} f^{(n)}(sx) \, ds.$$

Since all the terms in the sum in (28.14) are non-negative,

(28.15) $$f(r) \geq \frac{r^{n-1}}{(n-1)!} \int_0^1 (1 - s)^{n-1} f^{(n)}(sr) \, ds.$$

Since $f^{(n+1)}$ is non-negative, $f^{(n)}$ is increasing on $[0, r]$; therefore, if x is in this interval, then

(28.16) $$R_n \leq \frac{x^{n-1}}{(n-1)!} \int_0^1 (1 - s)^{n-1} f(sr) \, ds.$$

By combining (28.15) and (28.16), we have

$$R_n \leq \left(\frac{x}{r}\right)^{n-1} f(r).$$

Hence, if $0 \leq x < r$, then $\lim (R_n) = 0$.

Q.E.D.

We have seen in Theorem 28.14 that a power series converges uniformly on every compact subset of its interval of convergence. However, there is no *a priori* reason to believe that this result can be extended to the end points of the interval of convergence. However, there is a remarkable theorem of the great Abel that, if convergence does take place at one of the end points, then the series converges uniformly out to this end point. We shall present two proofs of this result: the first one is a direct application of Abel's Test 28.9 and is over too soon; the second one is, perhaps, more interesting.

In order to simplify our notation, we shall suppose that the radius of convergence of the series is equal to 1. This is no loss of generality and can always be attained by letting $x' = x/R$, which is merely a change of scale.

28.20   ABEL'S THEOREM.   *Suppose that the power series $\sum_{n=0}^{\infty} (a_n x^n)$ converges to $f(x)$ for $|x| < 1$ and that $\sum_{n=0}^{\infty} (a_n)$ converges to A. Then the power series converges uniformly in $I = [0, 1]$ and*

$$(28.17) \qquad\qquad \lim_{x \to 1-} f(x) = A.$$

FIRST PROOF.   Abel's Test 28.9, with $f_n(x) = a_n$ and $\varphi_n(x) = x^n$, applies to give the uniform convergence of $\sum (a_n x^n)$ on I. Hence the limit is continuous on I; since it agrees with $f(x)$ for $0 \le x < 1$, the limit relation (28.17) follows.

SECOND PROOF.   The function $g(x) = (1 - x)^{-1}$ is given for $|x| < 1$ by the geometric series

$$\sum_{n=0}^{\infty} x^n.$$

According to the Multiplication Theorem 28.18, the product of f and g is given for $|x| < 1$ by

$$f(x)g(x) = \sum_{n=0}^{\infty} c_n x^n,$$

where the coefficient c_n is

$$c_n = \sum_{k=0}^{n} a_k.$$

By hypothesis $A = \lim (c_n)$. It is clear that if $0 \le x < 1$, then

$$f(x) - A = (1 - x)\{f(x)g(x) - Ag(x)\}.$$

It follows from this that

$$(28.18) \qquad f(x) - A = (1 - x)\left\{ \sum_{n=0}^{\infty} c_n x^n - \sum_{n=0}^{\infty} A x^n \right\}$$

$$= (1 - x) \sum_{n=0}^{\infty} (c_n - A)x^n.$$

If $\epsilon > 0$, let N be such that if $n \geq N$, then $|c_n - A| < \epsilon$. Furthermore, choose x so close to 1 that

$$(1 - x) \left| \sum_{n=0}^{N} (c_n - A)x^n \right| < \epsilon.$$

It follows from (28.18) that if x is sufficiently near 1, then

$$|f(x) - A| \leq (1 - x) \left| \sum_{n=0}^{N} (c_n - A)x^n \right| + (1 - x) \sum_{N+1}^{\infty} |c_n - A| x^n$$

$$< \epsilon + (1 - x) \frac{\epsilon x^{N+1}}{1 - x} < 2\epsilon.$$

This establishes formula (28.17).

Q.E.D.

One of the most interesting things about this result is that it suggest a method of attaching a limit to series which may not be convergent. Thus, if $\sum_{n=1}^{\infty} (b_n)$ is an infinite series, we can form the corresponding power series $\sum (b_n x^n)$. If the b_n do not increase too rapidly, this power series converges to a function $B(x)$ for $|x| < 1$. If $B(x) \to \beta$ as $x \to 1 -$, we say that the series $\sum (b_n)$ is **Abel summable** to β. This type of summation is similar to (but more powerful than) the Cesàro method of arithmetic means mentioned in Section 14 and has deep and interesting consequences. The content of Abel's Theorem 28.20 is similar to Theorem 14.8; it asserts that if a series is already convergent, then it is Abel summable to the same limit. The converse is not true, however, for the series $\sum_{n=0}^{\infty} (-1)^n$ is not convergent but since

$$\frac{1}{1 + x} = \sum_{n=0}^{\infty} (-1)^n x^n,$$

it follows that $\sum (-1)^n$ is Abel summable to $\frac{1}{2}$.

It sometimes happens that if a series is known to be Abel summable, and if certain other conditions are satisfied, then it can be proved that the series is actually convergent. Theorems of this nature are called **Tauberian** theorems and are often very deep and difficult to prove. They are also useful because they enable one to go from a weaker type of convergence to a stronger type, provided certain additional hypotheses are satisfied.

Our final theorem is the first result of this type and was proved by A. Tauber† in 1897. It provides a partial converse to Abel's Theorem.

---

† ALFRED TAUBER (1866-circa 1947) was a professor at Vienna. He contributed primarily to analysis.

28.21 TAUBER'S THEOREM. *Suppose that the power series* $\sum (a_n x^n)$ *converges to* $f(x)$ *for* $|x| < 1$ *and that* $\lim (n a_n) = 0$. *If* $\lim f(x) = A$ *as* $x \to 1-$, *then the series* $\sum (a_n)$ *converges to* A.

PROOF. It is desired to estimate differences such as $\sum_{}^{N} (a_n) - A$. To do this, we write

$$(28.20) \quad \sum_{n=0}^{N} a_n - A = \left\{ \sum_{n=0}^{N} a_n - f(x) \right\} + \{ f(x) - A \}$$

$$= \sum_{n=0}^{N} a_n (1 - x^n) - \sum_{N+1}^{\infty} a_n x^n + \{ f(x) - A \}.$$

Since $0 \le x < 1$, we have $1 - x^n = (1 - x)(1 + x + \cdots + x^{n-1}) < n(1 - x)$, so we can dominate the first term on the right side by the expression $(1 - x) \sum_{n=0}^{N} n a_n$.

By hypothesis $\lim (n a_n) = 0$; hence Theorem 14.8 implies that

$$\lim \left(\frac{1}{m+1} \sum_{n=0}^{m} n a_n \right) = 0.$$

In addition, we have the relation $A = \lim f(x)$.

Now let $\epsilon > 0$ be given and choose a fixed natural number N which is so large that

(i) $\left| \sum_{n=0}^{N} n a_n \right| < (N + 1)\epsilon$;

(ii) $|a_n| < \dfrac{\epsilon}{N + 1}$ for all $n \ge N$;

(iii) $|f(x_0) - A| < \epsilon$ for $x_0 = 1 - \dfrac{1}{N + 1}$.

We shall assess the magnitude of (28.20) for this value of N and x_0. From (i), (ii), (iii) and the fact that $(1 - x_0)(N + 1) = 1$, we derive the estimate

$$\left| \sum_{n=0}^{N} a_n - A \right| \le (1 - x_0)(N + 1)\epsilon + \frac{\epsilon}{N + 1} \frac{x_0^{N+1}}{1 - x_0} + \epsilon < 3\epsilon.$$

Since this can be done for each $\epsilon > 0$, the convergence of $\sum (a_n)$ to A is established.

Q.E.D.

Exercises

28.A. Discuss the convergence and the uniform convergence of the series $\sum (f_n)$, where $f_n(x)$ is given by

(a) $(x^2 + n^2)^{-1}$,   (b) $(nx)^{-2}$, $x \neq 0$,

(c) $\sin (x/n^2)$,   (d) $(x^n + 1)^{-1}$, $x \geq 0$,

(e) $x^n(x^n + 1)^{-1}$, $x \geq 0$,   (f) $(-1)^n(n + x)^{-1}$, $x \geq 0$.

28.B. If $\sum (a_n)$ is an absolutely convergent series, then the series $\sum (a_n \sin nx)$ is absolutely and uniformly convergent.

28.C. Let (c_n) be a decreasing sequence of positive numbers. If $\sum (c_n \sin nx)$ is uniformly convergent, then $\lim (nc_n) = 0$.

28.D. Give the details of the proof of Dirichlet's Test 28.8.

28.E. Give the details of the proof of Abel's Test 28.9.

28.F. Discuss the cases $R = 0$, $R = +\infty$ in the Cauchy-Hadamard Theorem 28.13.

28.G. Show that the radius of convergence R of the power series $\sum (a_n x^n)$ is given by

$$\lim \left(\frac{|a_n|}{|a_{n+1}|} \right)$$

whenever this limit exists. Give an example of a power series where this limit does not exist.

28.H. Determine the radius of convergence of the series $\sum (a_n x^n)$, where a_n is given by

(a) $1/n^n$,   (b) $n^\alpha/n!$,

(c) $n^n/n!$,   (d) $(\log n)^{-1}$, $n \geq 2$,

(e) $(n!)^2/(2n)!$,   (f) $n^{-\sqrt{n}}$.

28.I. If $a_n = 1$ when n is the square of a natural number and $a_n = 0$ otherwise, find the radius of convergence of $\sum (a_n x^n)$. If $b_n = 1$ when $n = m!$ for $m \in \mathbf{N}$ and $b_n = 0$ otherwise, find the radius of convergence of $\sum (b_n x^n)$.

28.J. Prove in detail that

$$\lim \sup (|na_n|^{1/n}) = \lim \sup (|a_n|^{1/n}).$$

28.K. If $0 < p \leq |a_n| \leq q$ for all $n \in \mathbf{N}$, find the radius of convergence of $\sum (a_n x^n)$.

28.L. Let $f(x) = \sum (a_n x^n)$ for $|x| < R$. If $f(x) = f(-x)$ for all $|x| < R$, show that $a_n = 0$ for all odd n.

28.M. Prove that if f is defined for $|x| < r$ and if there exists a constant B such that $|f^{(n)}(x)| \leq B$ for all $|x| < r$ and $n \in \mathbf{N}$, then the Taylor series expansion

$$\sum_{n=0}^{\infty} \frac{f^{(n)}(0)}{n!} x^n$$

converges to $f(x)$ for $|x| < r$.

28.N. Prove by induction that the function given in formula (28.12) has derivatives of all orders at every point and that all of these derivatives vanish at $x = 0$. Hence this function is not given by its Taylor expansion about $x = 0$.

28.O. Given an example of a function which is equal to its Taylor series expansion about $x = 0$ for $x \geq 0$, but which is not equal to this expansion for $x < 0$.

28.P. The argument outlined in Exercise 19.S shows that the Lagrange form of the remainder can be used to justify the general Binomial Expansion

$$(1 + x)^m = \sum_{n=0}^{\infty} \binom{m}{n} x^n$$

when x is in the interval $0 \leq x < 1$. Similarly Exercise 19.T validates this expansion for $-1 < x \leq 0$, but the argument is based on the Cauchy form of the remainder and is somewhat more involved. To obtain an alternative proof of this second case, apply Bernstein's Theorem to $g(x) = (1 - x)^m$ for $0 \leq x < 1$.

28.Q. Consider the Binomial Expansion at the end points $x = \pm 1$. Show that if $x = -1$, then the series converges absolutely for $m \geq 0$ and diverges for $m < 0$. At $x = +1$, the series converges absolutely for $m \geq 0$, converges conditionally for $-1 < m < 0$, and diverges for $m \leq -1$.

28.R. Let $f(x) = \tan(x)$ for $|x| < \pi/2$. Use the fact that f is odd and Bernstein's Theorem to show that f is given on this interval by its Taylor series expansion about $x = 0$.

28.S. Use Abel's Theorem to prove that if $f(x) = \sum (a_n x^n)$ for $|x| < R$, then

$$\int_0^R f(x)\, dx = \sum_{n=0}^{\infty} \frac{a_n}{n+1} R^{n+1},$$

provided that the series on the right side is convergent even though the original series may not converge at $x = R$. Hence it follows that

$$\log(2) = \sum_{n=1}^{\infty} \frac{(-1)^{n+1}}{n}, \qquad \frac{\pi}{4} = \sum_{n=0}^{\infty} \frac{(-1)^n}{2n+1}.$$

28.T. By using Abel's Theorem, prove that if the series $\sum (a_n)$ and $\sum (b_n)$ converge and if their Cauchy product $\sum (c_n)$ converges, then we have $\sum (c_n) = \sum (a_n) \cdot \sum (b_n)$.

28.U. Suppose that $a_n \geq 0$ and that $f(x) = \sum (a_n x^n)$ has radius of convergence 1. If $\sum (a_n)$ diverges, prove that $f(x) \to +\infty$ as $x \to 1-$. Use this result to prove the elementary Tauberian theorem: If $a_n \geq 0$ and if

$$A = \lim_{x \to 1-} \sum a_n x^n,$$

then $\sum (a_n)$ converges to A.

28.V. Let $\sum_{n=0}^{\infty}(p_n)$ be a divergent series of positive numbers such that the radius of convergence of $\sum (p_n x^n)$ is 1. Prove Appell's† Theorem: If $s = \lim (a_n/p_n)$, then the radius of convergence of $\sum (a_n x^n)$ is also 1 and

$$\lim_{x \to 1-} \frac{\sum a_n x^n}{\sum p_n x^n} = s.$$

† PAUL APPELL (1855–1930) was a student of Hermite at the Sorbonne. He did research in complex analysis.

(Hint: it is sufficient to treat the case $s = 0$. Also use the fact that $\lim\limits_{x \to 1-} [\sum (p_n x^n)]^{-1} = 0$.)

28.W. Apply Appell's Theorem with $p(x) = \sum_{n=0}^{\infty} (x^n)$ to obtain Abel's Theorem.

28.X. If (a_n) is a sequence of real numbers and $a_0 = 0$, let $s_n = a_1 + \cdots + a_n$ and let $\sigma_n = (s_1 + \cdots + s_n)/n$. Prove Frobenius'[†] Theorem: If $s = \lim (\sigma_n)$ then

$$s = \lim_{x \to 1-} \sum_{n=0}^{\infty} a_n x^n.$$

REMARK. In the terminology of summability theory, this result says that if a sequence (a_n) is Cesàro summable to s, then it is also Abel summable to s. (Hint: apply Appell's Theorem to $p(x) = (1 - x)^{-2} = \sum_{n=0}^{\infty} (nx^{n-1})$ and note that $\sum (n \cdot \sigma_n x^n) = p(x) \sum (a_n x^n)$.)

Projects

28.α. The theory of power series presented in the text extends to complex power series.

(a) In view of the observations in Section 10, all of the definitions and theorems that are meaningful and valid for series in $\mathbf{R}^2$ are also valid for series with elements in $\mathbf{C}$. In particular the results pertaining to absolute convergence extend readily.

(b) Examine the results of Section 26 pertaining to rearrangements and the Cauchy product to see if they extend to $\mathbf{C}$.

(c) Show that the Comparison, Root, and Ratio Tests of Section 27 extend to $\mathbf{C}$.

(d) Let R be the radius of convergence of a complex power series

$$\sum_{n=0}^{\infty} a_n z^n.$$

Prove that the series converges absolutely for $|z| < R$ and uniformly on any compact subset of $\{z \in \mathbf{C} : |z| < R\}$.

(e) Let f and g be functions defined for $D = \{z \in \mathbf{C} : |z| < r\}$ with values in $\mathbf{C}$ which are the limits on D of two power series. Show that if f and g agree on $D \cap \mathbf{R}$, then they agree on all of D.

(f) Show that two power series in $\mathbf{C}$ can be multiplied together within their common circle of convergence.

28.β. In this project we define the exponential function in terms of power series. In doing so, we shall define it for complex numbers as well as real.

(a) Let E be defined for $z \in \mathbf{C}$ by the series

$$E(z) = \sum_{n=0}^{\infty} \frac{z^n}{n!}.$$

† GEORG FROBENIUS (1849–1917) was professor at Berlin. He is known for his work both in algebra and analysis.

Show that the series is absolutely convergent for all $z \in \mathbf{C}$ and that it is uniformly convergent on any bounded subset of $\mathbf{C}$.

(b) Prove that E is a continuous function on $\mathbf{C}$ to $\mathbf{C}$, that $E(0) = 1$, and that

$$E(z + w) = E(z)E(w)$$

for z, w in $\mathbf{C}$. (Hint: the Binomial Theorem for $(z + w)^n$ holds when $z, w \in \mathbf{C}$ and $n \in \mathbf{N}$.)

(c) If x and y are real numbers, define E_1 and E_2 by $E_1(x) = E(x)$, $E_2(y) = E(iy)$; hence $E(x + iy) = E_1(x)E_2(y)$. Show that E_1 takes on only real values but that E_2 has some non-real values. Define C and S on $\mathbf{R}$ to $\mathbf{R}$ by

$$C(y) = \operatorname{Re} E_2(y), \qquad S(y) = \operatorname{Im} E_2(y)$$

for $y \in \mathbf{R}$, and show that

$$C(y_1 + y_2) = C(y_1)C(y_2) - S(y_1)S(y_2),$$

$$S(y_1 + y_2) = S(y_1)C(y_2) + C(y_1)S(y_2).$$

(d) Prove that C and S, as defined in (c), have the series expansions

$$C(y) = \sum_{n=0}^{\infty} \frac{(-1)^n y^{2n}}{(2n)!} \cdot \qquad S(y) = \sum_{n=0}^{\infty} \frac{(-1)^n y^{2n+1}}{(2n+1)!} \cdot$$

(e) Show that $C' = -S$ and $S' = C$. Hence $[C^2 + S^2]' = 2\,CC' + 2\,SS' = 0$ which implies that $C^2 + S^2$ is identically equal to 1. In particular, this implies that both C and S are bounded in absolute value by 1.

(f) Infer that the function E_2 on $\mathbf{R}$ to $\mathbf{C}$ satisfies $E_2(0) = 1$, $E_2(y_1 + y_2) = E_2(y_1)E_2(y_2)$. Hence $E_2(-y) = 1/E_2(y)$ and $|E_2(y)| = 1$ for all y in $\mathbf{R}$.

References

The following list includes books that were cited in the text and some additional references that will be useful for further study.

Anderson, K. W., and D. W. Hall, *Sets, Sequences, and Mappings*, John Wiley and Sons, New York, 1963.

Apostol, T. M., *Mathematical Analysis*, Addison-Wesley, Reading, Mass., 1957.

Boas, R. P., Jr., *A Primer of Real Functions*, Carus Monograph Number 13, Mathematical Association of America, 1960.

Bohr, H., *Almost Periodic Functions*, H. Cohn, translator, Chelsea, New York, 1947.

Buck, R. C., *Advanced Calculus*, McGraw-Hill, New York, 1956.

Dienes, P., *The Taylor Series*, Oxford University Press, London, 1931. (Reprinted by Dover, New York, 1957.)

Dieudonné, J., *Foundations of Modern Analysis*, Academic Press, New York, 1960.

Dunford, N., and J. T. Schwartz, *Linear Operators, Part I*, Interscience, New York, 1958.

Goffman, C., *Real Functions*, Rinehart, New York, 1953.

Graves, L. M., *Theory of Functions of Real Variables*, Second Edition, McGraw-Hill, New York, 1956.

Hall, D. W., and G. L. Spencer II, *Elementary Topology*, John Wiley and Sons, New York, 1955.

Halmos, P. R., *Naïve Set Theory*, D. Van Nostrand, Princeton, 1960.

Hamilton, N. T., and J. Landin, *Set Theory*, Allyn-Bacon, Boston, 1961.

Hardy, G. H., *A Course of Pure Mathematics*, Ninth Edition, Cambridge University Press, Cambridge, 1947.

Hardy, G. H., *Divergent Series*, Oxford University Press, London, 1949.

Hardy, G. H., J. E. Littlewood, and G. Pólya, *Inequalities*, Second Edition Cambridge University Press, Cambridge, 1959.

Kazarinoff, N. D., *Analytic Inequalities*, Holt, Rinehart and Winston, New York 1961.

Kelley, J. L., *General Topology*, D. Van Nostrand, New York, 1955.

Knopp, K., *Theory and Application of Infinite Series*, R. C. Young, translator, Hafner, New York, 1951.

Landau, E., *Foundations of Analysis*, F. Steinhardt, translator, Chelsea, New York, 1951.

422

Lefschetz, S., *Introduction to Topology*, Princeton University Press, Princeton, 1949.

McShane, E. J., *A theory of limits*. (An article published in *Studies in Modern Analysis*, vol. 1, R. C. Buck, editor, Mathematical Association of America, 1962.)

Royden, H. L., *Real Analysis*, Macmillan, New York, 1963.

Rudin, W., *Principles of Mathematical Analysis*, McGraw-Hill, New York, 1953.

Schwartz, J., *The formula for change in variables in a multiple integral*, American *Mathematical Monthly*, vol. 61 (1954), pp. 81–85.

Sierpiński, W., *Cardinal and Ordinal Numbers*, Monografie Matematyczne, vol. 34, Warsaw, 1958.

Stone, M. H., *The generalized Weierstrass approximation theorem*, *Mathematics Magazine*, vol. 21 (1947–1948), pp. 167–184, 237–254. (Reprinted in *Studies in Modern Analysis*, vol. 1, R. C. Buck, editor, Mathematical Association of America, 1962.)

Suppes, P., *Axiomatic Set Theory*, D. Van Nostrand, Princeton, 1961.

Timan, A. F., *Theory of Approximation of Functions of a Real Variable*, J. Berry, translator, Pergamon, Oxford, 1963.

Titchmarsh, E. C., *The Theory of Functions*, Second Edition, Oxford University Press, London, 1939.

Wilder, R. L., *The Foundations of Mathematics*, John Wiley and Sons, New York, 1952.

Hints for Selected Exercises

The reader is urged not to look at these hints unless he is stymied. Most of the exercises call for proofs, and there is no single way that is correct; even if the reader has given a totally different argument, his may be entirely correct. However, in order to help the reader learn the material and to develop his technical skill, some hints and a few solutions are offered. It will be observed that more detail is presented for the early material.

Section 1

1.B. By definition $A \cap B \subseteq A$. If $A \subseteq B$, then $A \cap B \supseteq A$ so that $A \cap B = A$. Conversely, if $A \cap B = A$, then $A \cap B \supseteq A$ whence it follows that $B \supseteq A$.

1.C, D. The symmetric difference of A and B is the union of $\{x : x \in A$ and $x \notin B\}$ and $\{x : x \notin A$ and $x \in B\}$.

1.G. If x belongs to $E \cap \bigcup A_j$, then $x \in E$ and $x \in \bigcup A_j$. Therefore, $x \in E$ and $x \in A_j$ for at least one j. This implies that $x \in E \cap A_j$ for at least one j, so that

$$E \cap \bigcup A_j \subseteq \bigcup (E \cap A_j).$$

The opposite inclusion is proved by reversing these steps. The other equality is handled similarly.

1.J. If $x \in \mathcal{C}(\bigcap \{A_j : j \in J\})$, then $x \notin \bigcap \{A_j : j \in J\}$. This implies that there exists a $k \in J$ such that $x \notin A_k$. Therefore, $x \in \mathcal{C}(A_k)$, and hence $x \in \bigcup \{\mathcal{C}(A_j) : j \in J\}$. This proves that $\mathcal{C}(\bigcap A_j) \subseteq \bigcup \mathcal{C}(A_j)$. The opposite inclusion is proved by reversing these steps. The other equality is similar.

Section 2

2.A. If (a, c) and (a, c') belong to $g \circ f$, then there exist b, b' in B such that $(a, b), (a, b')$ belong to f and $(b, c), (b', c')$ belong to g. Since f is a function, $b = b'$; since g is a function, $c = c'$.

2.B. No. Both $(0, 1)$ and $(0, -1)$ belong to C.

2.D. Let $f(x) = 2x$, $g(x) = 3x$.

2.E. If $(b, a), (b, a')$ belong to f^{-1}, then $(a, b), (a', b)$ belong to f. Since f is one-one, then $a = a'$. Hence f^{-1} is a function.

2.G. If $f(x_1) = f(x_2)$ then $x_1 = g \circ f(x_1) = g \circ f(x_2) = x_2$. Hence f is one-one. If $x = g \circ f(x)$ for all x in $\mathfrak{D}(f)$, then $\mathfrak{R}(f) \subseteq \mathfrak{D}(g)$.

2.H. Apply Exercise 2.G twice.

Section 3

3.A. Let $f_1(n) = n/2$, $n \in E$; $f_2(n) = (n + 1)/2$, $n \in O$.

3.B. Let $f(n) = n + 1$, $n \in \mathbf{N}$.

3.C. If A is infinite and $B = \{b_n : n \in \mathbf{N}\}$ is a subset of A, then the function defined by

$$f(x) = b_{n+1}, \qquad x = b_n \in B,$$
$$= x, \qquad x \in A \backslash B,$$

is one-one and maps A onto $A \backslash \{b_1\}$.

3.D. See Theorem 3.1.

3.E. Let $A_n = \{n\}$, $n \in \mathbf{N}$. Then each set A_n has a single point, but $\mathbf{N} = \mathbf{U}\{A_n : n \in \mathbf{N}\}$ is infinite.

3.F. If f is a one-one map of A onto B and g is a one-one map of B onto C, then $g \circ f$ is a one-one map of A onto C.

Section 4

4.A. According to (A4), $e \neq \theta$.

4.C. No, since inverses do not always exist.

4.G. Since $a^2 = 0$, the element a does not have an inverse, so G_4 is not a field.

Section 5

5.A. If a field F has n elements, then at least two of the elements ke, $k = 0$, $1, \ldots, n$, must be equal. Hence there exists a natural number p such that $pe = 0$.

5.B. Since $a^2 \geq 0$ and $b^2 \geq 0$, then $a^2 + b^2 = 0$ implies that $a^2 = b^2 = 0$.

5.C. Apply Theorem 5.5(a).

5.F. If $c = 1 + a$ with $a > 0$, then $c^n = (1 + a)^n \geq 1 + na \geq 1 + a = c$.

5.H. Observe that $1 < 2^1 = 2$. If $k < 2^k$ for $k \geq 1$, then $k + 1 \leq 2k < 2 \cdot 2^k = 2^{k+1}$. Therefore, $n < 2^n$ for all $n \in \mathbf{N}$.

5.I. Note that $b^n - a^n = (b - a)(b^{n-1} + \cdots + a^{n-1}) = (b - a)p$, where $p > 0$.

5.K. If $p(t) = t$, then $p(t) - n > 0$ and hence $p(t) > n$ for all $n \in \mathbf{N}$.

5.L. It was seen in Exercise 5.H that $n < 2^n$, whence $1/2^n < 1/n$ for $n \in \mathbf{N}$.

5.Q. If $x \neq y$ are common points of the intervals $I_n = \{a_n, b_n\}$, $n \in \mathbf{N}$, then since $|x - y| > 0$ there exists an M such that

$$\frac{1}{2^M} < |x - y|.$$

Now $a_M \le x \le b_M$ and $a_M \le y \le b_M$, from which

$$\frac{1}{2^M} = b_M - a_M \ge |x - y|.$$

Section 6

6.A. If $x > 0$, the Archimedean property implies that there is a natural number m such that $0 < 1/m < x$.

6.C. If $A = \{x_1\}$, then $x_1 = \inf A = \sup A$. If $A = \{x_1, \ldots, x_n, x_{n+1}\}$ and if $u = \sup \{x_1, \ldots, x_n\}$, then $\sup \{u, x_{n+1}\}$ is the supremum of A.

6.E. Let $S = \{x \in \mathbf{Q} : x^2 < 2\}$, then $\sup S$ is irrational. For, if $x^2 < 2$, then for sufficiently large n, $[x(1 + 1/n)]^2 < 2$.

6.H. Let $A_n = \{1/n\}$; then $\mathbf{U}\{A_n : n \in \mathbf{N}\}$ is bounded. If $B_n = \{n\}$, then $\mathbf{U}\{B_n : n \in \mathbf{N}\} = \mathbf{N}$ is not bounded.

6.J. Let $x \in F$ and let $A = \{n \in \mathbf{N} : n < x\}$. If $A = \emptyset$, then every natural number n satisfies $x \le n$. If $A \ne \emptyset$, then by hypothesis, there exists $y = \sup A$. Since $y - \frac{1}{2} < \sup A$, there exists $n \in A$ such that $y - \frac{1}{2} \le n$. Therefore $n + 1$ does not belong to A.

6.K. If $m \ge n$, then $I_m \subseteq I_n$ and hence $a_m \le b_n$. Therefore, b_n is an upper bound for the set $\{a_m\}$, so that $a = \sup \{a_m\} \le b_n$. Since this inequality holds for each $n \in \mathbf{N}$, then a is a lower bound for the set $\{b_n\}$, and $a \le b = \inf \{b_n\}$. If c satisfies $a \le c \le b$, then $a_n \le c \le b_n$ from which $c \in I_n$ for each $n \in \mathbf{N}$. Conversely, if $c \in I_n$ for each $n \in \mathbf{N}$, then $a_n \le c \le b_n$ for each $n \in \mathbf{N}$. Therefore $a = \sup \{a_n\} \le c$ and $c \le \inf \{b_n\} = b$.

6.L. Clearly A and B are non-void and $A \cup B = \mathbf{Q}$. If $y \in A \cap B$ then $y > 0$ and both $y^2 < 2$ and $y^2 > 2$, a contradiction showing that $A \cap B = \emptyset$. Observe that if $x \in A$, then $x(1 + 1/n) \in A$ for sufficiently large n. Hence if $c \in \mathbf{Q}$ is such that $a \le c$ for all $a \in A$, then, according to the observation just made, we must have $c \notin A$, so that $c \in B$. A similar argument shows that if $c \in \mathbf{Q}$ is such that $c \le b$ for all $b \in B$, then $c \in A$. But $A \cap B = \emptyset$.

6.M. Every element in F_1 has a ternary expansion whose first digit is either 0 or 2. The points in the four subintervals of F_2 have ternary expansions beginning

$$0.00 \ldots, \qquad 0.02 \ldots, \qquad 0.20 \ldots, \qquad 0.22 \ldots.$$

and so forth.

6.N. The "right-hand" end points of F are the elements with ternary expansion consisting of all 2's after a certain place. There are denumerably many such elements. If $x \in F$ and is not a "right-hand" end point, then let y be the point in $[0, 1)$ whose binary expansion is obtained by replacing the 2's in the ternary expansion of x by 1's. Show that this gives a one-one correspondence of this part of F and all of $[0, 1)$.

6.O. If n is sufficiently large, then $1/3^n < b - a$.

6.P. The length can be made as close to 1 as desired by removing intervals of positive length at each stage of the construction.

6.Q. If F contains a non-empty interval $[a, b]$, then $a = b$. Hence the union of a countable collection of subintervals of F is a countable subset of F.

6.S. If $S = \sup \{f(x, y) : (x, y) \in X \times Y\}$, then since $f(x, y) \leq S$ for all x in X and y in Y, it follows that $f_1(x) \leq S$ for all x in X; hence $\sup \{f_1(x) : x \in X\} \leq S$. Conversely, if $\epsilon > 0$ there exists (x_0, y_0) such that $S - \epsilon < f(x_0, y_0)$. Hence $S - \epsilon < f_1(x_0)$, and therefore $S - \epsilon < \sup \{f_1(x) : x \in X\}$.

6.U. Since $f(x) \leq \sup \{f(z) : z \in X\}$, it follows that

$$f(x) + g(x) \leq \sup \{f(z) : z \in X\} + \sup \{g(z) : z \in X\}$$

so that $\sup \{f(x) + g(x) : x \in X\} \leq \sup \{f(z) : z \in X\} + \sup \{g(z) : z \in X\}$. Similarly, if $x \in X$, then

$$\inf \{f(z) : z \in X\} \leq f(x),$$

whence it follows that

$$\inf \{f(z) : z \in X\} + g(x) \leq f(x) + g(x).$$

If we note that $\sup \{c + g(x) : x \in X\} = c + \sup \{g(x) : x \in X\}$, it follows from the preceding inequality (with $c = \inf f$) that

$$\inf f + \sup g \leq \sup (f + g).$$

The other assertions are proved in the same way (or follow from these inequalities).

Section 7

7.A. Add $-z$ to both sides of $w + z = z$ to conclude that $w = \theta$.

7.B. Direct calculation. To see that the Parallelogram Identity is not satisfied, take $x = (1, 0)$ and $y = (0, 1)$ in $\mathbf{R}^2$.

7.D. S_1 is the interior of the square with vertices $(0, \pm 1)$, $(\pm 1, 0)$. S_2 is the interior of the circle with center at origin and radius 1. S_∞ is the interior of the square with vertices $(1, \pm 1)$, $(\pm 1, 1)$.

7.E. Take $a = 1/\sqrt{p}$, $b = 1$.

7.F. Take $a = 1/p$, $b = 1$.

7.G. $|x \cdot y| \leq \Sigma |\xi_j||\eta_j| \leq \{\Sigma |\xi_j|\} \sup |\eta_j| \leq |x|_1 |y|_1$. But $|x \cdot y| \leq p|x|_\infty |y|_\infty$, and if $x = y = (1, 1, \ldots, 1)$, then equality is attained.

7.H. The stated relation implies that

$$|x|^2 + 2x \cdot y + |y|^2 = |x + y|^2 = (|x| + |y|)^2 = |x|^2 + 2|x||y| + |y|^2.$$

Hence $x \cdot y = |x||y|$ and the condition for equality in 7.6 applies, provided x and y are non-zero.

7.I. If $x = cy$ or $y = cx$ with $c \geq 0$ then

$$|x + y|_\infty = |x|_\infty + |y|_\infty.$$

Conversely, we always have $|x + y|_\infty \leq |x|_\infty + |y|_\infty$, but when equality holds we cannot conclude that x and y are proportional.

7.J. Since $|x + y|^2 = |x|^2 + 2x \cdot y + |y|^2$, the stated relation holds if and only if $x \cdot y = 0$.

7.K. A set K is convex if and only if it contains the line segment joining any two points in K. If $x, y \in K_1$, then $|tx + (1 - t)y| \leq t|x| + (1 - t)|y| \leq t + (1 - t) = 1$ so $tx + (1 - t)y \in K_1$ for $0 \leq t \leq 1$. The points $(\pm 1, 0)$ belong to K_4, but their midpoint $(0, 0)$ does not belong to K_4.

7.L. If x, y belong to $\bigcap K_\alpha$, then $x, y \in K_\alpha$ for all α. Hence $tx + (1 - t)y \in K_\alpha$ for all α; whence it follows that $\bigcap K_\alpha$ is convex. Consider the union of two disjoint intervals.

7.M. Every point $|x| = 1$ is an extreme point of K_1. There are no extreme points in K_2. Every point on the three bounding lines is an extreme point of K_3.

Section 8

8.A. If $x \in G$, let $r = \inf\{x, 1 - x\}$. Then, if $|y - x| < r$, we have $x - r < y < x + r$ whence

$$0 \leq x - r < y < x + r \leq 1,$$

so that $y \in G$. If $z = 0$, then there does *not* exist a positive real number r such that every point y in $\mathbf{R}$ satisfying $|y| < r$ belongs to F. Similarly for $z = 1$.

8.B. If $x = (\xi, \eta) \in G$, take $r = 1 - |x|$. If $x \in H$, take $r = \inf\{|x|, 1 - |x|\}$. If $z = (1, 0)$, then for any $r > 0$, there is a point y in $\mathcal{C}(F)$ such that $|y - z| < r$.

8.E. If $z = 0$, then for any $r > 0$, there is a point y in $\mathcal{C}(A)$ such that $|y - z| < r$. Hence A is not open. If $w = 1$, then for any $r > 0$, there is a point u in A such that $|u - w| < r$. Hence $\mathcal{C}(A)$ is not open so that A is not closed.

8.H. Let $F_n = \{x \in \mathbf{R}^p : |x| \leq 1 - 1/n\}$ for $n \in \mathbf{N}$.

8.I. Let G be open in $\mathbf{R}^p$ and let A be the subset of G consisting of the elements of G whose coordinates are all rational numbers. By Theorem 3.2, the set A is countable. For each x in A there is a smallest natural number n_x such that if $n \geq n_x$ then the set $F_{x,n} = \{y \in \mathbf{R}^p : |y - x| \leq 1/n\}$ is contained in G. Show that G equals $\bigcup \{F_{x,n} : x \in A, n = n_x\}$.

8.J. Take complements of sets in 8.I. Alternatively, if F is closed in $\mathbf{R}^p$, let $G_n = \{y \in \mathbf{R}^p : |y - x| > 1/n$ for all $x \in F\}$ for $n \in \mathbf{N}$. Show that G_n is open and that $F = \bigcap \{G_n : n \in \mathbf{N}\}$.

8.K. If $A^- = \bigcap \{F : F$ closed and $F \supseteq A\}$, then A^- is closed, by Theorem 8.6(c). A^- is the intersection of sets containing A, so $A \subseteq A^-$. It follows that $A^- \subseteq (A^-)^-$. Since A^- is closed and $(A^-)^-$ is the intersection of *all* closed sets containing A^-, it follows that $(A^-)^- \subseteq A^-$, whence $A^- = (A^-)^-$. If F is closed and $A \cup B \subseteq F$, then $A \subseteq F$ and $B \subseteq F$, $A^- \subseteq F$ and $B^- \subseteq F$ so that $A^- \cup B^- \subseteq F$. Therefore, $A^- \cup B^- \subseteq (A \cup B)^-$. Conversely $A \subseteq A^-$ and $B \subseteq B^-$, whence it follows that $A \cup B \subseteq A^- \cup B^-$. Since the latter set is closed it follows that $(A \cup B)^- \subseteq A^- \cup B^-$. Clearly $\emptyset \subseteq \emptyset^-$, and since $\emptyset$ is closed, it follows that $\emptyset^- \subseteq \emptyset$.

8.L. True for closed sets, false in general.

8.M. Either argue by analogy with 8.K or use the fact that the complement of closed sets is open.

8.N. Let $p = 1$, and let $A = \mathbf{Q}$.

8.P. Argue as in Exercise 8.I, but use open balls $G_{x,n} = \{y \in \mathbf{R}^p : |y - x| < 1/n\}$, $x \in A$, $n \geq n_x$, instead of the closed balls $F_{x,n}$.

8.R. If $A \times B$ is closed in $\mathbf{R}^2$ and $x = (\xi_1, \xi_2)$ does not belong to $A \times B$, then there exists $r > 0$ such that $\{y \in \mathbf{R}^2 : |y - x| < r\}$ is disjoint from $A \times B$. Therefore, if $G = \{\eta \in \mathbf{R} : |\eta - \xi_1| < r\}$, then $G \cap A = \emptyset$. Hence A is closed in $\mathbf{R}$. Conversely, if A, B are closed and $x = (\xi_1, \xi_2) \in A \times B$, then there exists $s > 0$ such that $\{\eta_i \in \mathbf{R} : |\eta_i - \xi_i| < s\}$ is disjoint from A, B, respectively. Hence the set $\{y \in \mathbf{R}^2 : |x - y| < s\}$ does not intersect $A \times B$.

8.S. If r is a positive rational number, and if y is a point in $\mathbf{R}^p$ with rational coordinates such that the ball $\{x \in \mathbf{R}^p : |x - y| < r\}$ intersects A, then choose one point in this intersection. Doing this for each r, y, we obtain C.

8.T. If x is a cluster point of A and U is a neighborhood of x containing only a finite number of points of A, then there exists a neighborhood of x which contains no points of A except, perhaps, the point x.

8.V. If G is open and $y \in G$, then some neighborhood V of y is contained in G, so y cannot be a boundary point. If G is not open, there exists a point $x \in G$, every neighborhood of which contains a point of $\mathcal{C}(G)$. Hence, if G is not open, it contains at least one boundary point.

8.X. Suppose that A, B are open sets in R^2 which form a disconnection for $C_1 \times C_2$. Let $A_1 = \{x \in \mathbf{R} : (x, y) \in A \text{ for some } y \in \mathbf{R}\}$ and let $B_1 = \{x \in \mathbf{R} : (x, y) \in B \text{ for some } y \in \mathbf{R}\}$. Then A_1 and B_1 are non-void open sets in $\mathbf{R}$ (why?) and their union contains C_1. Since C_1 is connected, there exists an element $u_1 \in A_1 \cap B_1$ belonging to C_1. Now let $A_2 = \{y \in \mathbf{R} : (u_1, y) \in A\}$, and $B_2 = \{y \in \mathbf{R} : (u_1, y) \in B\}$. Again, A_2 and B_2 are non-void open subsets of $\mathbf{R}$ and their union contains C_2. Since C_2 is connected, there exists an element u_2 in $A_2 \cap B_2$ belonging to C_2. Since $u_1 \in A_1$ and $u_2 \in A_2$, then $(u_1, u_2) \in A$; similarly $(u_1, u_2) \in B$, which contradicts the supposition that $A \cap B = \emptyset$.

8.Y. No line segment can lie in A and terminate at the origin.

Section 9

9.A. Let $G_n = \{(x, y) : x^2 + y^2 < 1 - 1/n\}$ for $n \in \mathbf{N}$.

9.B. Let $G_n = \{(x, y) : x^2 + y^2 < n^2\}$ for $n \in \mathbf{N}$.

9.C. Let $\mathcal{G} = \{G_\alpha\}$ be an open covering for F and let $G = \mathcal{C}(F)$, so that G is open in $\mathbf{R}^p$. If $\mathcal{G}_1 = \mathcal{G} \cup \{G\}$, then $\mathcal{G}_1$ is an open covering for K; hence K has a finite subcovering $\{G, G_\alpha, G_\beta, \ldots, G_\omega\}$. Then $\{G_\alpha, G_\beta, \ldots, G_\omega\}$ forms a subcovering of $\mathcal{G}$ for the set F.

9.D. Observe that if G is open in $\mathbf{R}$, then there exists an open subset G_1 of $\mathbf{R}^2$ such that $G = G_1 \cap \mathbf{R}$. Alternatively, use the Heine-Borel Theorem.

9.E. Let $\mathcal{G} = \{G_\alpha\}$ be an open covering of the closed unit interval J in $\mathbf{R}^2$. Consider those real numbers x such that the square $[0, x] \times [0, x]$ is contained in the union of a finite number of sets in g and let x^* be their supremum.

9.G. Let $x_n \in F_n$, $n \in \mathbf{N}$. If there are only a finite number of points in $\{x_n : n \in \mathbf{N}\}$, then at least one of them occurs infinitely often and is a common point.

If there are infinitely many points in the bounded set $\{x_n\}$, then there is a cluster point x. Since $x_m \in F_n$ for $m \geq n$ and since F_n is closed, then $x \in F_n$ for all $n \in \mathbf{N}$.

9.H. If $d(x, F) = 0$, then x is a cluster point of the closed set F.

9.J. No. Let $F = \{y \in \mathbf{R}^p : |y - x| = r\}$, then every point of F has the same distance to x.

9.K. Let G be an open set and let $x \in \mathbf{R}^p$. If $H = \{y - x : y \in G\}$, then H is an open set in $\mathbf{R}^p$.

9.L. Apply 8.3(b) and 8.18.

9.M. Follow the argument in 9.7, except use open intervals instead of open balls.

9.N. If the point (x_0, y_0) lies on the line $ax + by = c$, then the point $(x_0 + at, y_0 + bt)$, $t \neq 0$, does not lie on this line and the distance between these points is $|t|(a^2 + b^2)^{1/2}$.

9.O. Yes. Let $A = \mathbf{Q} \cap \mathbf{I}$.

9.P. Not necessarily.

9.Q. Suppose that $\mathbf{Q} = \bigcap \{G_n : n \in \mathbf{N}\}$, where G_n is open in $\mathbf{R}$. The complement F_n of G_n is a closed set which does not contain any non-empty open subset, by Theorem 5.16. Hence the set of irrationals is the union of a countable family of closed sets not one of which contains a non-empty open set but this contradicts Corollary 9.10.

9.S. If F is a closed set containing the dense set D, then it follows from Theorem 8.10 that F must contain every cluster point of D and hence $F = \mathbf{R}^p$, so that $D^- = \mathbf{R}^p$. If D is not dense in $\mathbf{R}^p$, let x be a point in $\mathbf{R}^p$ which is not a cluster point of D, and let V be an open neighborhood of x which contains no point of D except (perhaps) x. Then $H = \mathcal{C}(V) \cup \{x\}$ is a closed set containing D such that $H \neq \mathbf{R}^p$.

9.T. Of course, the entire space $\mathbf{R}^p$ is open and dense in $\mathbf{R}^p$. Alternatively, let $p = 1$ and take $G = \mathbf{R} \setminus \mathbf{Z}$, then G is open and dense in $\mathbf{R}$. The only dense *closed* subset of $\mathbf{R}^p$ is $\mathbf{R}^p$.

9.U. By Exercise 8.K, $(A \cup B)^- = A^- \cup B^-$ so it follows that the union of any subset with a subset which is dense, is also dense. According to Exercise 9.R, an open set is dense in $\mathbf{R}^p$ if and only if its complement does not contain a non-void open set in $\mathbf{R}^p$. Apply Baire's Theorem (or the first two steps in its proof), to find that the closed set $\mathcal{C}(D_1 \cap D_2) = \mathcal{C}(D_1) \cup \mathcal{C}(D_2)$ cannot contain a non-void open subset of $\mathbf{R}^p$.

9.V. The set $D_1 \cup D_2$ is dense, but it may happen that $D_1 \cap D_2$ is not dense.

9.W. As in the second part of Exercise 9.U, we consider the complements $\mathcal{C}(D_n)$. The result follows from Baire's Theorem.

Section 10

10.A. Examine the geometrical position of $iz = (-y, x)$ in terms of $z = (x, y)$.

10.B. Note that $cz = (x \cos \theta - y \sin \theta, \ x \sin \theta + y \cos \theta)$, and this corresponds to a counter-clockwise rotation of θ radians about the origin.

10.C. The circle $|z - c| = r$ is mapped into the circle $|w - (ac + b)| = |a|r$. We can write $z = a^{-1}w - a^{-1}b$ and calculate $x = \operatorname{Re} z$, $y = \operatorname{Im} z$ in terms of

$u = \operatorname{Re} w$, $v = \operatorname{Im} w$. Doing so we easily see that the equation $ax + by = c$ transforms into an equation of the form $Au + Bv = C$.

10.D. A circle is left fixed by g if and only if its center lies on the real axis. The only lines left fixed by g are the real and the imaginary axis.

10.E. Circles passing through the origin are sent into lines by h. All lines not passing through the origin are sent into circles passing through the origin; all lines passing through the origin are sent into lines passing through the origin.

10.F. Every point of $\mathbf{C}$, except the origin, is the image under g of two elements of $\mathbf{C}$. If $\operatorname{Re} g(z) = k$, then $x^2 - y^2 = k$. If $\operatorname{Im} g(z) = k$, then $2xy = k$. If $|g(z)| = k$, then $k \geq 0$ and $|z| = \sqrt{k}$.

Section 11

11.A. Consider $z_n = y_n - x_n$ and apply Example 11.13(c) and Theorem 11.14(a).

11.C. (a) Converges to 1. (b) Diverges. (f) Diverges.

11.D. Let $Y = -X$.

11.F. If X converges to x, then Y converges to $|x|$. If Y converges to 0, then X converges to 0. If $\lim Y \neq 0$, it does not follow that X converges.

11.G. Consider two cases: $x = 0$ and $x > 0$.

11.H. Yes.

⌐11.I. Use the hint in Exercise 11.G.

11.L. Consider $(1/n)$ and (n).

11.M, N, O. Apply the preceding exercises.

11.P. Apply Exercise 11.H.

11.T. Show that $\lim (1/\sqrt[n]{n!}) = 0$ by comparing $n!$ with $(n/2)^{n/2}$.

11.U. Observe that $a \leq x_n \leq a\, 2^{1/n}$.

Section 12

12.A. Either multiply by -1 and use Theorem 12.1, or argue as in the proof of 12.1.

12.B. By induction $1 < x_n < 2$ for $n \geq 2$. Since $x_{n+1} - x_n = (x_n - x_{n-1}) \cdot (x_n x_{n-1})^{-1}$, then (x_n) is monotone.

12.D. The sequence (a^n) is decreasing.

12.E. If (x_n) does not have an increasing subsequence, each x_n is exceeded by at most a finite number of x_m with $m > n$. Let $k_1 = 1$ and take $k_2 > k_1$ such that if $m \geq k_2$, then $x_m \leq x_{k_1}$. Choose $k_3 > k_2$ such that if $m \geq k_3$, then $x_m \leq x_{k_2}$; etc.

12.H. The sequence (x_n) is increasing and $x_n \leq n/(n + 1) < 1$.

12.I. Yes.

12.L. If $\epsilon > 0$ there exists $K = K(\epsilon)$ such that $(L - \epsilon)x_n < x_{n+1} < (L + \epsilon)x_n$ for $n \geq K$. By an argument similar to the one in Exercise 11.J, there exist A, B with the stated property.

12.N. Yes.

12.P. Note that $(x_n{}^2)$ is a subsequence of $((1 + 1/n)^n)$ and that (y_n) is increasing. Either argue as in Example 12.3(d) to show that (y_n) is bounded or consider $(y_{2k}{}^{1/2})$.

12.Q. The sequence (a_n) is increasing and (b_n) is decreasing. Moreover, $a_n \leq b_n$ for all $n \in \mathbf{N}$.

12.V. Let $y_n \in F$ be such that $|x - y_n| < d + 1/n$. If $y = \lim (y_{n_k})$, then $|x - y| = d$.

12.X. The set K is bounded. To show that it is closed, let z be a cluster point of K. Use Exercise 12.T to obtain $z = \lim (x_n + y_n)$ and use the Bolzano-Weierstrass Theorem 12.4 twice.

Section 13

13.A. All.

13.C. If $x \in \mathbf{Z}$, the limit is 1; if $x \notin \mathbf{Z}$, the limit is 0.

13.E. If $x = 0$, the limit is 1; if $x \neq 0$, the limit is 0.

13.G. If $x > 0$ and $0 < \epsilon < \pi/2$, then $\tan (\pi/2 - \epsilon) > 0$. Therefore $nx \geq \tan (\pi/2 - \epsilon)$ for all $n \geq n_x$, from which

$$\pi/2 - \epsilon \leq f_n(x) \leq \pi/2.$$

13.H. If $x > 0$, then $e^{-x} < 1$.

13.J. Not necessarily.

13.M. Consider the sequence $(1/n)$ or note that $\|f_n\| > \frac{1}{2}$.

13.P. Let $y = nx$ and estimate $\|f_n\|$.

Section 14

14.A. (a) $\lim \inf(x_n) = -1$; $\lim \sup(x_n) = 1$. (b) $0, 2$. (c) The sequence is neither bounded below nor above.

14.B. See the first part of the proof of Lemma 14.5.

14.C. Let $y = \lim \inf (x_n)$. Let n_1 be such that $x_{n_1} < y + 1$; let $n_2 > n_1$ be such that $x_{n_2} < y + \frac{1}{2}$, etc.

14.D. (i) If $x^* = \lim \sup (x_n)$ and $\epsilon > 0$, then there are only a finite number of $n \in \mathbf{N}$ such that $x^* + \epsilon < x_n$. However, by the definition of x^*, there must be an infinite number of $n \in \mathbf{N}$ such that $x^* - \epsilon < x_n$. Hence 14.3(a) implies 14.3(b). (ii) If x^* satisfies the condition in 14.3(b), then for m sufficiently large we have $v_m \leq x^* + \epsilon$. Hence inf $\{v_m\} \leq x^* + \epsilon$ and so inf $\{v_m\} \leq x^*$. Since there are infinitely many $n \in \mathbf{N}$ with $x^* - \epsilon < x_n$, then $x^* - \epsilon \leq v_m$ for all m. Hence $x^* - \epsilon \leq$ inf $\{v_m\}$ for arbitrary $\epsilon > 0$ and so $x^* \leq$ inf $\{v_m\}$. Therefore 14.3(b) implies 14.3(c). (iii) Since (v_m) is a monotone decreasing sequence, then inf $\{v_m\} = \lim (v_m)$, so 14.3(c) implies 14.3(d). (iv) If $X' = (x_{n_k})$ is a convergent subsequence of $X = (x_n)$, then since $n_k \geq k$, we have $x_{n_k} \leq v_k$ and hence $\lim X' \leq \lim (v_k) - x^*$. Conversely, there exists a natural number n, such that $v_1 - 1 <$

$x_{n_1} \leq v_1$. Inductively, choose $n_{k+1} > n_k$ such that $v_{n_k} - \dfrac{1}{k+1} < x_{n_{k+1}} \leq v_{n_k}$.

Since (v_n) converges to x^*, it follows that $x^* = \lim (x_{n_k})$. Therefore, 14.3(d) implies 14.3(e). (v) Finally, if $w = \sup V$ and if $\epsilon > 0$, then there can be at most a finite number of $n \in \mathbf{N}$ with $w + \epsilon \leq x_n$. Therefore, $\limsup (x_n) \leq w + \epsilon$ for all $\epsilon > 0$, whence $\limsup (x_n) \leq w$. Conversely, if $\epsilon > 0$, then there are an infinite number of $n \in \mathbf{N}$ such that $w - \epsilon \leq x_n$. Hence $w - \epsilon \leq \limsup (x_n)$ for $\epsilon > 0$, and therefore $w \leq \limsup (x_n)$.

14.F. If $v < \liminf (x_n)$ and $u < \liminf (y_n)$, then there are only a finite number of $n \in \mathbf{N}$ such that $v > x_n$ and a finite number of $m \in \mathbf{N}$ such that $u > y_m$. Hence there can be only a finite number of $n \in \mathbf{N}$ such that $v + u > x_k + y_k$, so it follows that $v + u \leq \liminf (x_n + y_n)$. As an alternate proof, we let $X_1 = (-1)X$, $Y_1 = (-1)Y$ and use part (b') and (d) of Theorem 14.4.

14.G (i) Note that $v_m(x + y) = \sup \{x_n + y_n : n \geq m\} \leq \sup \{x_n : n \geq m\} + \sup \{y_n : n \geq m\} = v_m(x) + v_m(y)$, so

$$(x + y)^* = \inf \{v_m(x + y) : m \in \mathbf{N}\} \leq v_m(x) + v_m(y) \leq v_p(x) + v_p(y)$$

for $p \leq m$. Hence $(x + y)^* \leq v_p(x) + y^*$ for all $p \in \mathbf{N}$ and so $(x + y)^* \leq x^* + y^*$.

(ii) Since $v_m(x + y) \leq v_m(x) + v_m(y)$ and since the sequences v_m are convergent, we have, using Theorem 11.14,

$$(x + y)^* = \lim \left((v_m(x + y)\right) \leq \lim \left(v_m(x) + v_m(y)\right)$$
$$= \lim \left(v_m(x)\right) + \lim \left(v_m(y)\right) = x^* + y^*.$$

(iii) There is a subsequence of $X + Y$ converging to $\limsup (X + Y)$, say $(x_{n_k} + y_{n_k})$. If the subsequence (x_{n_k}) does converge, then so does (y_{n_k}) and hence $\limsup (X + Y) \leq \limsup X + \limsup Y$. If the subsequence (x_{n_k}) does not converge, then, by the Bolzano-Weierstrass Theorem 12.4, some further subsequence of (x_{n_k}) and (y_{n_k}) will converge to limits which are no greater than $\limsup X$ and $\limsup Y$, respectively.

14.H. Recall Exercise 11.J.

14.I. (e) $2\sqrt{n}\,[\sqrt{n+1} - \sqrt{n}] = \dfrac{2\sqrt{n}}{\sqrt{n+1} + \sqrt{n}}.$

14.K. (a) If $X_1 = (x_n)$ and $X_2 = (u_n)$ satisfy

$$|x_n| \leq K_1|y_n|, \qquad |u_n| \leq K_2|y_n|$$

for $n \geq n_0$, then $|x_n \pm u_n| \leq (K_1 + K_2)|y_n|$ for $n \geq n_0$.

14.M. If $j < n + 1$, then $x_j \leq x_{n+1}$ and $x_j(1 + 1/n) \leq x_j + (1/n)x_{n+1}$. Adding, we get $\sigma_n \leq \sigma_{n+1}$.

14.R. Yes. If X is increasing and not convergent, then X is not bounded. Show that (σ_n) is not bounded.

14.T. (a) None of the three limits exist. (b, c) All three are equal. (d) The iterated limits are different and the double limit does not exist. (e) The double limit and one iterated limit exist and are equal. (f) The iterated limits are equal, but the double limit does not exist.

14.U. Let $x_{mn} = n$ if $m = 1$ and let $x_{mn} = 0$ if $m > 1$.

14.W. In (b, c, e).

14.X. Let $x = \sup \{x_{mn} : m, n \in \mathbf{N}\}$ and apply Corollary 14.12.

14.Y. Let $x_{mn} = 0$ for $m < n$ and let $x_{mn} = (-1)^m/n$ for $m \geq n$.

Section 15

15.A. If $a = 0$, take $\delta(\epsilon) = \epsilon^2$. If $a > 0$, use the estimate

$$|\sqrt{x} - \sqrt{a}| = \frac{|x - a|}{\sqrt{x} + \sqrt{a}} \leq \frac{|x - a|}{\sqrt{a}}.$$

15.B. Apply Example 15.5(b) and Theorem 15.6.

15.C. Apply Exercise 15.B and Theorem 15.6.

15.E. Show that $|f(x) - f(\frac{1}{2})| = |x - \frac{1}{2}|$.

15.F. Every real number is a limit of a sequence of rational numbers.

15.J. There exist sequences (x_n), (y_n) such that $\lim (h(x_n)) = 1, \lim (h(y_n)) = -1$.

15.K. If $x \leq c \leq y$, then $f(x) \leq f(y)$. Hence $f(x) \leq r(c)$ for all $x \leq c$, and therefore $l(c) \leq r(c)$. Let $A = f(b) - f(a)$; then there are at most n points c for which $j(c) \geq A/n$.

15.L. Show that $f(a + h) - f(a) = f(h) - f(0)$. If f is monotone on $\mathbf{R}$, then it is continuous at some point.

15.M. Show that $f(0) = 0$ and $f(n) = nc$ for $n \in \mathbf{N}$. Also $f(n) + f(-n) = 0$, so $f(n) = nc$ for $n \in \mathbf{Z}$. Since $f(m/n) = mf(1/n)$, it follows on taking $m = n$ that $f(1/n) = c/n$, whence $f(m/n) = c(m/n)$. Now use the continuity of f.

15.N. Either $g(0) = 0$, in which case $g(x) = 0$ for all x in $\mathbf{R}$, or $g(0) = 1$, in which case

$$g(a + h) - g(a) = g(a)\{g(h) - g(0)\}.$$

15.R. $f(1, 1) = (3, 1, -1), f(1, 3) = (5, 1, -3)$.

15.S. A vector (a, b, c) is in the range of f if and only if $a - 2b + c = 0$.

15.V. If $\Delta = 0$, then $f(-b, a) = (0, 0)$. If $\Delta \neq 0$, then the only solution of

$$ax + by = 0, \qquad cx + dy = 0$$

is $(x, y) = (0, 0)$.

15.X. Note that $g(x) = g(y)$, if and only if $g(x - y) = \theta$.

Section 16

16.C. If $f(x_0) > 0$, then $V = \{y \in \mathbf{R} : y > 0\}$ is a neighborhood of $f(x_0)$.

16.F. Let $f(s, t) = 0$ if $st = 0$ and $f(s, t) = 1$ if $st \neq 0$.

16.G, H. These functions cannot be continuous.

16.J. Suppose the coefficient of the highest power is positive. Show that there exist $x_1 < 0 < x_2$ such that $f(x_1) < 0 < f(x_2)$.

16.K. Let $f(x) = x^n$. If $c > 1$, then $f(0) = 0 < c < f(c)$.

16.L. If $f(c) > 0$, there is a neighborhood of c on which f is positive, whence $c \neq \sup N$. Similarly if $f(c) < 0$.

16.M. Since f is strictly increasing, it is easily seen that f is one-one and f^{-1} is strictly increasing. Moreover, if $a < b$, then f maps the open interval (a, b) in a one-one fashion onto the open interval $(f(a), f(b))$, from which it follows that f^{-1} is continuous.

16.N. Yes. Let $a < b$ be fixed and suppose that $f(a) < f(b)$. If c is such that $a < c < b$, then either (i) $f(c) = f(a)$, (ii) $f(c) < f(a)$, or (iii) $f(a) < f(c)$. Case (i) is excluded by hypothesis. If (ii), then there exists a_1 in (c, b) such that $f(a_1) = f(a)$, a contradiction. Hence (iii) must hold. Similarly, $f(c) < f(b)$ and f is strictly increasing.

16.O. Assume that g is continuous and let $c_1 < c_2$ be the two points in I where g attains its supremum. If $0 < c_1$, choose numbers a_1, a_2 such that $0 < a_1 < c_1 < a_2 < c_2$ and let k satisfy $g(a_i) < k < g(c_i)$. Then there exist three numbers b_i such that

$$a_1 < b_1 < c_1 < b_2 < a_2 < b_3 < c_2$$

and where $k = g(b_i)$, a contradiction. Therefore, we must have $c_1 = 0$ and $c_2 = 1$. Now apply the same type of argument to the points where g attains its infimum to obtain a contradiction.

16.Q. The functions in Example 15.5 (a, b, i) are uniformly continuous.

16.S. Yes.

16.U. Show that there exists a number L such that if (x_n) is any sequence in $(0, 1)$ which converges to 0, then $L = \lim (f(x_n))$.

Section 17

17.B. Yes.

17.C. Obtain the function in Example 15.5(h) as the limit of a sequence of continuous functions.

17.D. Yes.

17.E. (a) The convergence is uniform for $0 \le x \le 1$. (b) The convergence is uniform on any closed set not containing $x = 1$. (c) The convergence is uniform for $0 \le x \le 1$ or for $x \ge c$, where $c > 1$.

17.I. (Yes)[3]. Give examples.

17.J. It follows that f is monotone increasing. By hypothesis, f is uniformly continuous. If $\epsilon > 0$, let $0 = x_0 < x_1 < \cdots < x_k = 1$ be such that $f(x_j) - f(x_{j-1}) < \epsilon$ and let $N(x_i)$ be such that if $n \ge N(x_i)$, then $|f(x_j) - f_n(x_j)| < \epsilon$. If $n \ge \sup \{N(x_0), \ldots, N(x_k)\}$, show that $\|f - f_n\| < 3\epsilon$.

17.O. Observe that if $\theta_1 \neq \theta_2$ are two points in the interval $[0, 2\pi]$, then either $\sin \theta_1 \neq \sin \theta_2$ or $\cos \theta_1 \neq \cos \theta_2$. Since the functions

$$\sin (n\theta) \sin (m\theta), \qquad \sin (n\theta) \cos (m\theta), \qquad \cos (n\theta) \cos (m\theta)$$

are given by linear combinations of the functions

$$\sin (n \pm m)\theta, \qquad \cos (n \pm m)\theta,$$

it follows that the collection of trigonometric polynomials satisfies the hypotheses of the Stone-Weierstrass Theorem.

17.R. The function $f(x) = 1/x$ is continuous for $x \neq 0$, but there is no way to extend it to a continuous function on $\mathbf{R}$.

17.T. Use the Heine-Borel Theorem or the Lebesgue Covering Theorem as in the proof of the Uniform Continuity Theorem.

Section 18

18.G. (b) If $\epsilon > 0$, there exists $\delta(\epsilon) > 0$ such that if $c < x < c + \delta(\epsilon)$, $x \in \mathfrak{D}(f)$, then $|f(x) - b| < \epsilon$. (c) If (x_n) is any sequence in $\mathfrak{D}(f)$ such that $c < x_n$ and $c = \lim (x_n)$, then $b = \lim (f(x_n))$.

18.J. (a) If $M > 0$, there exists $m > 0$ such that if $x \geq m$ and $x \in \mathfrak{D}(f)$, then $f(x) \geq M$. (b) If $M < 0$, there exists $\delta > 0$ such that if $0 < |x - c| < \delta$, then $f(x) < M$.

18.L. (a) Let $\varphi(r) = \sup \{f(x) : x > r\}$ and set $L = \lim\limits_{r \to +\infty} \varphi(r)$. Alternatively, if $\epsilon > 0$ there exists $m(\epsilon)$ such that if $x \geq m(\epsilon)$, then $|\sup \{f(x) : x > r\} - L| < \epsilon$.

18.M. Apply Lemma 18.12.

18.N. Consider the function $f(x) = -1/|x|$ for $x \neq 0$ and $f(0) = 0$.

18.P. Consider Example 15.5(h).

18.R. Not necessarily. Consider $f_n(x) = -x^n$ for $x \in \mathbf{I}$.

18.S. Yes.

Section 19

19.D. Observe that $g'(0) = 0$ and that $g'(x) = 2x \sin (1/x) - \cos (1/x)$ for $x \neq 0$.

19.E. Yes.

19.F. Let $\{r_n\}$ be an enumeration of the rational numbers in $\mathbf{I}$ and consider $\sum 2^{-n} |x - r_n|$.

19.H. Yes.

19.K. If a and b are not multiple roots of f, then $f'(a)f'(b) < 0$. The general case can be reduced to this one.

19.M. The function f has n-fold roots at $x = \pm 1$. Hence f' has $(n - 1)$-fold roots at $x = \pm 1$ and a root in the interval $(-1, 1)$, etc.

19.U. (a) Since $f'(a)$ exists, if $\epsilon > 0$, then $f(a \pm h) - f(a) = \pm hf'(a) \pm h\epsilon_{\pm}(h)$, where $|\epsilon_{\pm}(h)| < \epsilon$ for h sufficiently small. Hence $f(a + h) - f(a - h) = 2hf'(a) + h[\epsilon_+(h) + \epsilon_-(h)]$.

19.V. Use the Mean Value Theorem.

19.X. That such examples exist is an immediate consequence of the Weierstrass Approximation Theorem.

Section 20

20.F. The partial derivatives f_ξ, f_η at θ are both 0. By Theorem 20.6, if f is differentiable at θ, then $Df(\theta)$ sends the vector (a, b) into 0. However, this possibility for $Df(\theta)$ does not satisfy equation (20.2).

20.I. By Theorem 20.6, the directional derivative of f at c in the direction of the unit vector $w = (\omega_1, \ldots, \omega_p)$ is given by

$$f_w(c) = f_{\xi_1}(c)\omega_1 + \cdots + f_{\xi_p}(c)\omega_p.$$

By the C.-B.-S. Inequality 7.6, we have

$$f_w(c) \le \{\textstyle\sum |f_{\xi_j}(c)|^2\}^{1/2}.$$

If at least one partial derivative is non-zero, the equality can hold if and only if w is a multiple of the vector $v_c = (f_{\xi_1}(c), \ldots, f_{\xi_p}(c))$.

20.K. If $f(x) \cdot f(x) = 1$ for $x \in D$, then applying Theorem 20.8(b), we obtain $2f(c) \cdot Df(c)(u) = 0$ for all u.

20.L. $Df(\eta_1, \eta_2)(\xi_1, \xi_2) = (2A\eta_1 + B\eta_2)\xi_1 + (B\eta_1 + 2C\eta_2)\xi_2$.

20.O. Consider the function defined just before Theorem 20.7.

20.P. Consider the function $f(\xi, \eta) = \eta^2 \sin(\xi/\eta)$ for $\eta \ne 0$ and $f(\xi, 0) = 0$.

20.R. It follows from Theorem 8.20 that any two points in D can be joined by a polygonal curve lying inside D.

20.U. In fact $f_{\xi\eta}(0, 0) = -1$ and $f_{\eta\xi}(0, 0) = +1$.

Section 21

21.E. Consider $f(x) = x^3$.

21.F. Show that f is not one-one near $x = 0$.

21.G. Reconsider 21.F.

21.H. Apply the Chain Rule 20.9.

21.J. Examine the proof of 21.4.

21.K. Apply Lemma 21.7.

21.P. If $\xi_j = \varphi_j(\eta_1, \eta_2)$, then

$$\frac{\partial \varphi_1}{\partial \eta_1}(\eta_1, \eta_2) = \frac{3\xi_2{}^3 + \eta_1}{\eta_1\eta_2 - 9\xi_1{}^2\xi_2{}^2}.$$

21.R. Observe that $f(t, t) > 0$, $f(t, -t) < 0$ for $t \ne 0$.

21.X. Take a box with dimensions in the ratio $a:b:c$.

21.Y. (a) $1/n^n$.

Section 22

22.D. If $||P|| < \delta$ and if Q is a refinement of P, then $||Q|| < \delta$.

22.F. If $\epsilon > 0$, let $P_\epsilon = (x_0, x_1, \ldots, x_n)$ be a partition of J such that if $P \supseteq P_\epsilon$ and $S(P; f)$ is any corresponding Riemann sum, then $|S(P; f) - \int_a^b f| < \epsilon$.

Let $M \geq ||f||$ and let $\delta = \epsilon/4Mn$. If $Q = (y_0, y_1, \ldots, y_m)$ is a partition with norm $||Q|| < \delta$, let $Q^* = Q \cup P_\epsilon$ so that $Q^* \supseteq P$ and has at most $n - 1$ more points than Q. Show that $S(Q^*;f) - S(Q;f)$ reduces to at most $2(n - 1)$ terms of the form $\pm \{f(\xi) - f(\eta)\}(x_j - y_k)$ with $|x_j - y_k| < \delta$.

22.G. Observe that the displayed inequality asserts that if $S_j(P;f,g), j = 1, 2$, are two Riemann-Stieltjes sums corresponding to the partition P, then $|S_1(P;f,g) - S_2(P;f,g)| < \epsilon$. In proving the sufficiency of this condition, it may be convenient to select ξ_j and η_j such that $f(\xi_j)$ and $f(\eta_j)$ are close to the supremum and the infimum, respectively, of f on the interval $[x_{j-1}, x_j]$.

22.H. Apply Exercise 22.G.

22.X. Let $g_1(0) = 0, g_1(x) = \frac{1}{2}$ for $0 < x < 1$ and $g_1(1) = 1$.

Section 23

23.C. If $m \leq f(x) \leq M$ for $c \leq x \leq d$, then there exists a constant A with $m \leq A \leq M$ such that

$$F(d) - F(c) = \int_c^d f\, dg = A \{g(d) - g(c)\}.$$

23.D. Consider $f(x) = -1$ for $x < 0$ and $f(x) = 1$ for $x \geq 0$, then $F(x) = |x|$.

23.E. Apply the Mean Value Theorem 19.6 to obtain $F(b) - F(a)$ as a Riemann sum for the integral of f.

23.J. If $m \leq f(x) \leq M$ for $x \in J$, then

$$m \int_a^b h \leq \int_a^b fh \leq M \int_a^b h.$$

Now use Bolzano's Theorem 16.4.

23.K. Since $f_n(x) - f_n(c) = \int_c^x f_n'$, we can apply Theorem 22.12 to obtain $f(x) - f(c) = \int_c^x g$ for all $x \in J$. Show that $g = f'$.

23.N. Direct estimation shows that $M_n \leq M(b - a)^{1/n}$. Conversely, $f(x) \geq M - \epsilon$ on some subinterval of J.

23.O. The functions φ, φ^{-1} are one-one and continuous. The partitions of $[c, d]$ are in one-one correspondence with the partitions of $[a, b]$ and the Riemann-Stieltjes sums of $f \circ g$ with respect to $g \circ \varphi$ are in one-one correspondence with the Riemann-Stieltjes sums of f with respect to g.

23.R. Prove that the functions G and H are continuous. The remainder of the proof is as in 23.12.

23.S. Apply Theorem 23.5 to (23.15) with $h(t) = (b - t)^{n-1}$.

23.V. The function f is uniformly continuous on $J_1 \times J_2$.

Section 24

24.A. Since f is uniformly continuous, if $\epsilon > 0$, one can divide I into a finite number of subintervals I_j such that if $x, y \in I_j$, then $|f(x) - f(y)| < \epsilon$. Hence G can be enclosed in a finite number of rectangles with total content less than ϵ.

24.F. Apply Theorem 7.11.

24.G. Since f is uniformly continuous, if the partition P is sufficiently fine and if $M \geq \|g\|$, then

$$\sum f(\xi_k)g(\eta_k)A(J_k) = \epsilon M A(J) + S(P; fg).$$

24.H. If x is a boundary point of $D \cup B$, then every neighborhood V of x contains a point in $D \cup B$ and a point in $\mathcal{C}(D \cup B) \subseteq \mathcal{C}(D)$. Since B is the boundary of D, it follows that V contains a point of D. Hence x is in B. Consider Example 24.2(g).

24.P. Apply Taylor's Theorem 23.13 to the function F on I to $\mathbf{R}$ defined by $F(t) = f(x + t(y - x))$. Then $F'(t) = Df(x + t(y - x))(y - x)$, etc.

Section 25

25.D. (a), (b), (d) are convergent.

25.E. (a) is convergent for $p, q > -1$. (b) is convergent for $p + q > -1$.

25.F. (a) and (c) are absolutely convergent. (b) is divergent.

25.G. (a) The integral is absolutely convergent if $q > p + 1$. (b) The integral is convergent if $q > 0$ and absolutely convergent if $q > 1$.

25.K. If $0 \leq t \leq \beta$, then $x^t e^{-x} \leq x^\beta e^{-x}$.

25.L. Apply Dirichlet's Test 25.15.

25.M. (a), (c), (e) converge uniformly for all t.

25.P. $\sqrt{\pi}$.

25.Q. $F(t) = (\sqrt{\pi}/2)e^{-t^2/4}$.

25.R. $G(t) = (\sqrt{\pi}/2)e^{-2t}$.

Section 26

26.C. Group the terms in the series $\sum_{n=1}^{\infty} (-1)^n$ to produce convergence to -1 and to 0.

26.G. Consider $\sum ((-1)^n n^{-1/2})$. However, consider also the case where $a_n \geq 0$.

26.H. If $a, b \geq 0$, then $2(ab)^{1/2} \leq a + b$.

26.I. Show that $b_1 + b_2 + \cdots + b_n > a_1(1 + 1/2 + \cdots + 1/n)$.

26.J. Use Exercise 26.F(a).

26.K. Show that $a_1 + a_2 + \cdots + a_{2^n}$ is bounded below by $\frac{1}{2}\{a_1 + 2a_2 + \cdots + 2^n a_{2^n}\}$ and above by $a_1 + 2a_2 + \cdots + 2^{n-1}a_{2^{n-1}} + a_{2^n}$.

26.O. Consider the partial sums s_k with $n/2 \leq k \leq n$ and apply the Cauchy Criterion.

26.Q. If $m > n$, then $s_{mn} = +1$; if $m = n$, then $s_{mn} = 0$; if $m < n$, then $s_{mn} = -1$.

26.S. Note that $2mn \leq m^2 + n^2$.

Section 27

27.A. (c) If $\sum (a_n)$ is absolutely convergent, then $\sum (b_n)$ is too. If $a_n = 0$ except when $\sin(n)$ is near ± 1, we can obtain a counter-example. (d) Consider $a_n = [n(\log n)^2]^{-1}$.

27.D. (a) and (e) are divergent. (b) is convergent.

27.E. (b), (c), and (e) are divergent.

27.I. (a) is convergent. (b) is divergent.

27.J. (a) is convergent. (c) is divergent.

27.R. Apply Dirichlet's Test.

Section 28

28.A. (a) and (c) converge uniformly for all x. (b) converges for $x \neq 0$ and uniformly for x in the complement of any neighborhood of $x = 0$. (d) converges for $x > 1$ and uniformly for $x \geq a$, where $a > 1$.

28.C. If the series is uniformly convergent, then

$$|c_n \sin nx + \cdots + c_{2n} \sin 2nx| < \epsilon,$$

provided n is sufficiently large. Now restrict attention to x in an interval such that $\sin kx > \frac{1}{2}$ for $n \leq k \leq 2n$.

28.H. (a) ∞, (c) $1/e$, (f) 1.

28.L. Apply the Uniqueness Theorem 28.17.

28.N. Show that if $n \in \mathbf{N}$, then there exists a polynomial P_n such that if $x \neq 0$, then $f^{(n)}(x) = e^{-1/x^2} P_n(1/x)$.

28.T. The series $A(x) = \sum (a_n x^n)$, $B(x) = \sum (b_n x^n)$, and $C(x) = \sum (c_n x^n)$ converge to continuous functions on I. By the Multiplication Theorem 28.8, $C(x) = A(x)B(x)$ for $0 \leq x < 1$, and by continuity $C(1) = A(1)B(1)$.

28.U. The sequence of partial sums is increasing on the interval [0, 1].

28.V. If $\epsilon > 0$, then $|a_n| \leq \epsilon p_n$ for $n > N$. Break the sum $\sum (a_n x^n)$ into a sum over $n = 1, \ldots, N$ and a sum over $n > N$.

Index